Geometric Formulas

Right circular cone

Volume
$$V = \tfrac{1}{3}\pi r^2 h$$
Lateral surface area
$$S = \pi r \ell$$
Total surface area
$$T = \pi r(\ell + r)$$

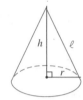

Triangle

Area
$$A = \tfrac{1}{2}bh$$
Perimeter
$$P = a + b + c$$
$$\angle A + \angle B + \angle C = 180°$$

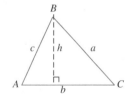

Parallelepiped

Volume
$$V = \ell w h$$
Surface area
$$S = 2(\ell w + \ell h + wh)$$

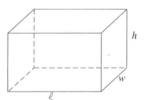

Sphere

Volume
$$V = \tfrac{4}{3}\pi r^3$$
Surface area
$$S = 4\pi r^2$$

FOURTH EDITION

Elementary Algebra

FOURTH EDITION

Elementary Algebra

Daniel L. Auvil
Kent State University

Charles Poluga
Kent State University

▲ **ADDISON-WESLEY PUBLISHING COMPANY**
Reading, Massachusetts ∘ Menlo Park, California
New York ∘ Don Mills, Ontario ∘ Wokingham, England
Amsterdam ∘ Bonn ∘ Sydney ∘ Singapore ∘ Tokyo
Madrid ∘ San Juan ∘ Milan ∘ Paris

Sponsoring Editor	Bill Poole
Managing Editor	Karen Guardino
Production Supervisor	Jack Casteel
Design	Sally Steele
Editorial and Production Services	Michael Bass & Associates
Copy Editor	Elliot Simon
Illustrator	G&S Typesetters, Inc.
Art Consultant	Loretta Bailey
Manufacturing Supervisor	Roy Logan
Cover Design	Peter Blaiwas

PHOTO CREDITS

David S. Strickler/Strix Pix 1, 61; Steve Skjold 123, 325; AP/Wide World Photos 173, 217, 271, 357, 407

Library of Congress Cataloging-in-Publication Data

Auvil, Daniel L.
    Elementary algebra / Daniel L. Auvil. — 4th ed.
      p. cm.
    Includes index.
    ISBN 0-201-14985-0
    1. Algebra. I. Title.
QA152.2.A86 1992
512.9—dc20
                                      91-28106
                                          CIP

4 5 6 7 8 9 10 DO 959493

Preface

The fourth edition of *Elementary Algebra* was written with the NCTM (National Council of Teachers of Mathematics) *Standards* in mind. The book can be used as a traditional text or as a worktext. However you choose to use this book, you can rely on the following features to provide support for you and your students.

Pedagogical Features

Chapter Introductions   Each chapter begins with a motivational photo and a caption that describes an applied problem that will be solved later in the chapter.

Try Problem Indicators   A unique feature, these margin indicators direct the reader from the examples to comparable exercises in the problem sets. They provide students with immediate reinforcements of concepts.

Problem Solving Boxes   These applied examples help students move from words to math and learn to use algebra in daily life.

Floaters   A running commentary, in color, explains the steps of an example.

Cautions   Occasional informative statements, with supporting examples, help students avoid common mistakes.

Historical Footnotes   Historical material expressed in brief passages lets students in on the people and dates behind the algebraic formulas.

Two-Color Format   A second color is used to highlight important parts of the text.

Chapter Summaries   Key terms and key rules are summarized at the end of each chapter.

Problems

Learning Through Writing   Placed at the beginning of each problem set, these exercises encourage students to explain key terms, key rules, and key steps in solving a problem.

Problem Sets   These exercises, graded from simple to challenging, are written in pairs to facilitate assigning either the odd or the even problems. Exercises corresponding to the Try Problem Indicators are in color. Answers to all of the odd problems are found at the end of the text.

Calculator Problems   Included with many problem sets is an example, solved using a calculator, along with several problems designed to give students practice using their own calculators.

Chapter Review Problems   These are selections of problems touching all the major concepts of each chapter. The problems are keyed to the appropriate chapter section. Answers to all chapter review problems are in the back of the book.

Chapter Tests   These sample tests allow students to measure their readiness to take an actual classroom test over the chapter. Answers to all chapter test problems are in the back of the book.

Final Exam   A sample final exam is provided at the end of the text. Answers to the final exam are in the back of the book.

Supplements

The supplements for *Elementary Algebra* include:

INSTRUCTOR'S SOLUTIONS MANUAL—contains detailed solutions to all even-numbered exercises.

STUDENT'S SOLUTIONS MANUAL—contains detailed solutions to all odd-numbered exercises.

PRINTED TEST BANK—provides five forms of a chapter test for each chapter in the text, with answers, plus three forms of a final examination, with answers.

OMNITEST (IBM)—is an algorithm-driven system with full editing capabilities that provides both open-ended and multiple-choice questions for every section of the text. It is easy to create up to 99 variations of a customized text, with just a few key strokes. Tests can be created for either individual or multiple sections or chapters.

Acknowledgments

We would like to express our sincere appreciation to those whose comments and suggestions were invaluable in writing this book:

Susan A. Baim, Miami University at Hamilton
Debbie Cochener, Austin Peay State University
Sharon J. Edgmon, Weill Institute of Bakersfield College
Robert A. Grasser, Oakland Community College
E. Lee Hansen, Santa Rosa Junior College
Eleanor Kendrick, San Jose City College
Mike Kurta, Lorain Community College

Rudi Maglio, Oakton Community College
Lawrence P. Mahar, Jr., North Texas State University
Lucy H. McAvery, Southern Illinois University at Edwardsville
Myrna L. Mitchell, Pima County Community College
Karla Neal, Louisiana State University
Donald Perry, Lee College
Sharon Sledge, San Jacinto College-Central
Judith Staver, Florida Community College at Jacksonville
Carol Urban, College of DuPage
Sue S. Watkins, Lorain Community College

Canton, Ohio   D.L.A.
Ashtabula, Ohio   C.P.

Index of Applications

Index of Applications (continued)

Contents

CHAPTER 6

Linear Equations and Inequalities in Two Variables   271

CHAPTER 7

Linear Systems   325

CHAPTER 8

Roots and Radicals   357

CHAPTER 9

More Quadratic Equations   407

FOURTH EDITION
Elementary Algebra

Real Numbers and Their Properties

We use positive numbers to represent temperatures above zero degrees and negative numbers to represent temperatures below zero degrees. For example, the low temperatures on New Year's Day for the past five years in a particular town might be represented by the numbers 2°, −6°, 3°, 0°, and −9°. In Section 1.7 you will see how to use operations on real numbers to find the average of these temperatures.

1

numerator : tử số
Denominator : mẫu số
fraction bar : dấu gữa ngang 2 số
discuss : (dis'kʌʃən) v.t : bàn luận, tranh luận, thảo luận.
Simplest : không bị cấu thành mợ, đơn giản, giản di.
Factor ('fæktɚ) n. thừa số, yếu tố phần tử, động lực.

...es, Constants, and Fractions

...s and Constants

...aking algebra for the first time you are probably wondering what the ...is between arithmetic and algebra. In arithmetic, all of the quantities ...m are known. In algebra, one or more of the quantities are unknown.

...tic Problem

...m of 3 and 5 is 8.

...= 8

Algebra Problem

The sum of a number and 2 is 6.

$x + 2 = 6$

Since one of the numbers in the algebra problem just given is unknown, we use the letter x to represent that unknown number until its value can be determined. A **variable** is a symbol, usually a letter such as x, y, or z, that represents an unknown quantity. A **constant,** such as 3, 5, or 8, is a symbol that represents a known quantity.

We shall use the variables a and b to represent numbers in order to define the symbols for addition, subtraction, multiplication, and division.

Our present custom of using letters of the alphabet as variables was introduced by the French mathematician François Viète (1540–1603) and later refined by his countryman René Descartes (1596–1650).

FUNDAMENTAL OPERATIONS

Addition: The **sum** of a and b is written $a + b$.
Subtraction: The **difference** of a and b is written $a - b$.
Multiplication: The **product** of a and b is written $a \times b$, $a \cdot b$, $a(b)$, $(a)b$, $(a)(b)$, or ab.
Division: The **quotient** of a and b is written $a \div b$, a/b, or $b\overline{)a}$.

...n algebra we usually use a dot for multiplication instead of the symbol $\times$, to ...void confusion with the variable x.

...ractions

...ome quantities cannot be described as whole numbers. For example, if ...pizzas are divided equally among 3 persons, the portion each person receives ...is the **fraction** 2/3. The top number in a fraction is called the **numerator,** and the bottom number is called the **denominator.**

Numerator →

Denominator →

$$\frac{2}{3}$$ ← *Fraction bar*

...olution. (sə'luʃn) (n) : dử tan, dung ... né dung giải, dung dịch, ...ách giải quyết

...ultiply : ('mʌltiplai) : nhóm, làm bội lên.

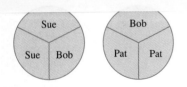

Before we can discuss the simplest form of a fraction, we need to define the term *factor*. In the multiplication $2 \cdot 3 = 6$, the numbers 2 and 3 are called **factors** (or **divisors**) of 6.

$$2 \cdot 3 = 6$$

Factors   Product

Other factors of 6 are 1 and 6. The **greatest common factor** (**GCF**) of two numbers is the largest number that is a factor of both numbers.

EXAMPLE 1   Find the greatest common factor of 12 and 16.

Solution   The factors of 12 are 1, 2, 3, 4, 6, and 12. The factors of 16 are 1, 2, 4, 8, and 16. The factors common to 12 and 16 are 1, 2, and 4. Therefore the greatest common factor of 12 and 16 is 4.   ■

Try Problem 5 >

A fraction is in **lowest terms** when the numerator and the denominator have no common factor except 1. For example, 2/3 is in lowest terms since 2 and 3 have no common factor except 1. To write a fraction in lowest terms, use the following two steps.

WRITING A FRACTION IN LOWEST TERMS

1. Find the greatest common factor of the numerator and the denominator.
2. Divide both the numerator and the denominator by the greatest common factor.

EXAMPLE 2   Write 12/16 in lowest terms.

Solution   In Example 1 we found that the greatest common factor of 12 and 16 is 4. Therefore divide numerator and denominator by 4.

Try Problem 11 >

$$\frac{12}{16} = \frac{12 \div 4}{16 \div 4} = \frac{3}{4}$$ ■

EXAMPLE 3   Write 15/30 in lowest terms.

Solution   Divide numerator and denominator by the greatest common factor of 15 and 30 (which is 15).

Try Problem 15 >

$$\frac{15}{30} = \frac{15 \div 15}{30 \div 15} = \frac{1}{2}$$ ■

To **multiply** two fractions, multiply their numerators and multiply their denominators. We can write this rule in symbols as follows.

MULTIPLYING FRACTIONS

$$\frac{a}{b} \cdot \frac{c}{d} = \frac{a \cdot c}{b \cdot d}$$

EXAMPLE 4   Find the product of 3/10 and 4/9.

Solution

$$\frac{3}{10} \cdot \frac{4}{9} = \frac{3 \cdot 4}{10 \cdot 9} \qquad \textit{Multiply numerators, multiply denominators}$$

$$= \frac{12}{90}$$

$$= \frac{12 \div 6}{90 \div 6} \qquad \textit{Divide out the GCF, 6}$$

Try Problem 21 >
$$= \frac{2}{15}$$

You may find it easier to divide out the greatest common factor in Example 4 *before* you multiply. This will allow you to work with smaller numbers, as shown here:

$$\frac{3}{10} \cdot \frac{4}{9} = \frac{\overset{1}{\cancel{3}}}{10} \cdot \frac{4}{\underset{3}{\cancel{9}}} \qquad \textit{Divide both 3 and 9 by 3}$$

$$= \frac{\overset{1}{\cancel{3}}}{\underset{5}{\cancel{10}}} \cdot \frac{\overset{2}{\cancel{4}}}{\underset{3}{\cancel{9}}} \qquad \textit{Divide both 4 and 10 by 2}$$

$$= \frac{1 \cdot 2}{5 \cdot 3} \qquad \textit{Multiply}$$

$$= \frac{2}{15}$$

Dividing out common factors in this manner is called **canceling. We can cancel only when multiplying fractions.** We cannot cancel when adding, subtracting, or dividing fractions.

…eatest
…mmon ('komən) adj chung, thường
…g, thông dụng
…atest common factor (GCF)
… số chung lớn nhất.
…st: cái nhỏ, thấp kém.
…st common denominator:
… số chung nhỏ nhất (LCD)

MULTIPLYING FRACTIONS (nhân phân số)

$\frac{a}{b} \cdot \frac{c}{d} = \frac{a.c}{b.d}$ sau đó ra kết quả có thể tìm GCF để ra kết quả nhỏ nhất.

$\frac{3}{10} \cdot \frac{4}{9} = \frac{3.4}{10.9} = \frac{12}{90} = \frac{12 \div 6}{90 \div 6} = \frac{2}{15}$.

DIVIDING FRACTIONS

$\frac{a}{b} \div \frac{c}{d} = \frac{a}{b} \cdot \frac{d}{c}$ (chia phân số)

…o fractions are **reciprocals** of each other if their product is 1. For ex-… 2/3 and 3/2 are reciprocals since

$$\ldots \cdot \frac{3}{2} = 1.$$

…4 and 1/4 are reciprocals of each other. In general,

$$\ldots\text{e reciprocal of } \frac{a}{b} \text{ is } \frac{b}{a}.$$

…o **divide** one fraction by another, multiply the first fraction by the recipro-… the second; that is, invert the second fraction and multiply.

…DING FRACTIONS

$$\ldots \div \frac{c}{d} = \frac{a}{b} \cdot \frac{d}{c}$$

…LE 5 Find the quotient of 4/7 and 3/4.

…n Multiply the first fraction by the reciprocal of the second.

$$\ldots \frac{3}{4} = \frac{4}{7} \cdot \frac{4}{3} \quad \textit{Invert 3/4 and multiply}$$

$$= \frac{4 \cdot 4}{7 \cdot 3}$$

$$= \frac{16}{21}$$

We did not cancel the 4's in the first step because the operation was division. ■

Try Problem 31 >

To **add** two fractions having the same denominator, add their numerators and place the sum over the common denominator.

ADDING FRACTIONS

$$\frac{a}{c} + \frac{b}{c} = \frac{a + b}{c}$$

EXAMPLE 6   Find the sum of 9/15 and 1/15.

Solution

$$\frac{9}{15} + \frac{1}{15} = \frac{9 + 1}{15} \qquad \textit{Add the numerators, keep the same denominator}$$

$$= \frac{10}{15}$$

Try Problem 39 >
$$= \frac{2}{3} \qquad \textit{Write in lowest terms} \qquad ■$$

To **subtract** two fractions having the same denominator, subtract their numerators and place the difference over the common denominator.

SUBTRACTING FRACTIONS

$$\frac{a}{c} - \frac{b}{c} = \frac{a - b}{c}$$

EXAMPLE 7   Find the difference of 7/10 and 3/10.

Solution

$$\frac{7}{10} - \frac{3}{10} = \frac{7 - 3}{10} \qquad \textit{Subtract the numerators, keep the same denominator}$$

$$= \frac{4}{10}$$

Try Problem 43 >
$$= \frac{2}{5} \qquad \textit{Write in lowest terms} \qquad ■$$

To add (or subtract) two fractions that do not have the same denominator, first rewrite each fraction so they both have the same denominator. The denominator you should use is the smallest number that can be divided (without remainder) by both of the original denominators. This denominator is called the **least common denominator** (**LCD**). For example, suppose we want to write 3/4 with a denominator of 8.

$$\frac{3}{4} = \frac{?}{8}$$

Since 8 ÷ 4 = 2, multiply 3/4 by 1 (in the form 2/2).

$$\frac{3}{4} = \frac{3}{4} \cdot 1 = \frac{3}{4} \cdot \frac{2}{2} = \frac{6}{8}$$

Notice that multiplying by 1 does not change the value of the fraction 3/4.

ADDING FRACTION.

(cộng phân số)

$\dfrac{a}{c} + \dfrac{b}{c} = \dfrac{a+b}{c}.$ $\dfrac{9}{15} + \dfrac{1}{15} = \dfrac{9+1}{15} = \dfrac{10}{15}$

$= \dfrac{2}{3}$

SUBTRACTING FRACTION

$\dfrac{a}{c} - \dfrac{b}{c} = \dfrac{a-b}{c} = \dfrac{7}{10} - \dfrac{3}{10} = \dfrac{7-3}{10}$

$= \dfrac{4}{10} = \dfrac{2}{5}$

LEAST COMMON denominator. 10 (LCD)

VD: $\dfrac{1}{2} + \dfrac{1}{3}$ $\dfrac{1}{2} = \dfrac{1}{2} \cdot \dfrac{3}{3} = \boxed{\dfrac{3}{6}}$ and

$\dfrac{1}{3} = \dfrac{1}{3} \cdot \dfrac{2}{2} = \boxed{\dfrac{2}{6}}$ $\dfrac{3}{6} + \dfrac{2}{6} = \dfrac{5}{6}$

Chapter 1 / Real Numbers and Their Properties 7

8 Add $1/2 + 1/3$.

The smallest number that can be divided by both 2 and 3 is 6. Write each fraction with denominator 6.

$$\frac{1}{2} = \frac{1}{2} \cdot \frac{3}{3} = \frac{3}{6} \quad \text{and} \quad \frac{1}{3} = \frac{1}{3} \cdot \frac{2}{2} = \frac{2}{6}$$

$$\frac{3}{6} + \frac{2}{6} = \frac{5}{6}$$ ∎

9 Subtract $3/4 - 2/3$.

Solution You cannot cancel the 3's. Instead, write each fraction with denominator 12.

Try Problem 55 >

$$\frac{3}{4} - \frac{2}{3} = \frac{3}{4} \cdot \frac{3}{3} - \frac{2}{3} \cdot \frac{4}{4} = \frac{9}{12} - \frac{8}{12} = \frac{1}{12}$$ ∎

A **mixed number** is the sum of a whole number and a fraction. The mixed number

$$4 + \frac{2}{3}$$

is usually written

$$4\frac{2}{3}.$$

Make sure you don't confuse $4\frac{2}{3}$, which means $4 + \frac{2}{3}$, with $4(\frac{2}{3})$, which means $4 \cdot \frac{2}{3}$.

An **improper fraction** is a fraction whose numerator is greater than (or equal to) its denominator. We can convert a mixed number to an improper fraction as follows:

$$4\frac{2}{3} = 4 + \frac{2}{3} = \frac{4}{1} + \frac{2}{3} = \frac{12}{3} + \frac{2}{3} = \frac{14}{3}.$$

If you study this example closely, you will see a shortcut. Multiply the denominator, 3, by the whole number, 4. Then add the product, 12, to the numerator, 2, and place the sum, 14, over the denominator, 3.

Add

$$4\frac{2}{3} = \frac{14}{3}$$

Multiply

To convert an improper fraction to a mixed number, divide the numerator, 14, by the denominator, 3.

$$3\overline{)14} \begin{array}{r} 4 \\ \underline{12} \\ 2 \end{array}$$

Add the quotient, 4, to the fraction formed by placing the remainder, 2, over the denominator, 3.

In arithmetic, some problems are easier to solve using mixed numbers and others are easier to solve using improper fractions. However, most problems in algebra are easier to solve using improper fractions. Therefore, to prepare ourselves for algebra, we will convert all mixed numbers to improper fractions. (The term *improper fraction* is a misnomer. There is nothing "improper" about an improper fraction.)

EXAMPLE 10   Divide 2 4/7 ÷ 1 1/2.

Solution

$$2\frac{4}{7} \div 1\frac{1}{2} = \frac{18}{7} \div \frac{3}{2} \qquad \textit{Convert to improper fractions}$$

$$= \frac{18}{7} \cdot \frac{2}{3} \qquad \textit{Invert and multiply}$$

$$= \frac{\overset{6}{\cancel{18}}}{7} \cdot \frac{2}{\underset{1}{\cancel{3}}} \qquad \textit{Divide both } 18 \textit{ and } 3 \textit{ by } 3$$

$$= \frac{12}{7} \qquad \textit{Multiply}$$

Try Problem 63 >   Both 12/7 and 1 5/7 are correct answers.   ■

EXAMPLE 11   Subtract 4 − 2 6/7.

Solution   Convert to improper fractions.

$$4 - 2\frac{6}{7} = \frac{4}{1} - \frac{20}{7} = \frac{28}{7} - \frac{20}{7} = \frac{8}{7}$$

Try Problem 67 >   Both 8/7 and 1 1/7 are correct answers.   ■

> PROBLEM SOLVING

EXAMPLE 12   The **average** of n numbers is the sum of the numbers divided by n. For example, the average of the five test scores 87, 93, 79, 81, and 90 is calculated as follows:

$$\text{Average} = \frac{87 + 93 + 79 + 81 + 90}{5} = \frac{430}{5} = 86.$$

If a restaurant served the following amounts of shrimp during its first three weeks of business, find the average amount of shrimp served per week.

Week 1	Week 2	Week 3
3 1/4 cases	2 3/4 cases	4 1/2 cases

Solution   Add the three mixed numbers.

$$3\frac{1}{4} + 2\frac{3}{4} + 4\frac{1}{2} = \frac{13}{4} + \frac{11}{4} + \frac{9}{2} \qquad \textit{Convert to improper fractions}$$

$$= \frac{13}{4} + \frac{11}{4} + \frac{18}{4} \qquad \textit{Write with denominator 4}$$

$$= \frac{42}{4} \qquad \textit{Add numerators}$$

$$= \frac{21}{2} \qquad \textit{Write in lowest terms}$$

Now divide this sum by 3.

$$\frac{21}{2} \div 3 = \frac{21}{2} \div \frac{3}{1} \qquad \textit{Write 3 as 3/1}$$

$$= \frac{21}{2} \cdot \frac{1}{3} \qquad \textit{Invert and multiply}$$

$$= \frac{\overset{7}{\cancel{21}}}{2} \cdot \frac{1}{\underset{1}{\cancel{3}}} \qquad \textit{Divide both 21 and 3 by 3}$$

$$= \frac{7}{2} \qquad \textit{Multiply}$$

Try Problem 77 >   The average amount of shrimp used per week was 7/2, or 3 1/2, cases. ▪

The most common error made by students when working with fractions involves incorrect canceling. Here is a summary of when you can and cannot cancel.

Caution! ■ You can cancel only when the operation is multiplication. You cannot cancel in
■ addition, subtraction, or division.

| *Correct* | *Wrong* | *Wrong* | *Wrong* |

$$\dfrac{\overset{1}{\cancel{2}}}{7}\cdot\dfrac{1}{\cancel{2}}$$ $$\dfrac{\overset{1}{\cancel{3}}}{7}\cancel{+}\dfrac{1}{\cancel{2}}$$ $$\dfrac{\overset{1}{\cancel{3}}-\cancel{1}}{\cancel{10}}$$ $$\dfrac{\overset{1}{\cancel{2}}}{9}\cancel{+}\dfrac{1}{\cancel{2}}$$

1.1 Problem Set

LEARNING THROUGH WRITING

☐ Explain the difference between a *variable* and a *constant.*

☐ Write each operation in words.

a. $5 + 9$ b. $13 - 7$ c. $4 \cdot 6$ d. $\dfrac{18}{3}$

☐ What does the word *factor* mean?

☐ Let a and b represent numbers. Describe the difference between the greatest common factor of a and b and the least common denominator of $1/a$ and $1/b$.

☐ How do you know when a fraction is in lowest terms?

☐ Discuss how to multiply, divide, add, and subtract two fractions.

☐ How do you know when two fractions are reciprocals?

☐ Describe how to (a) convert a mixed number to an improper fraction, (b) convert an improper fraction to a mixed number.

☐ How do you find the average of several numbers?

☐ Explain when you can and cannot cancel.

Find the greatest common factor (GCF) of each pair of numbers.

1. 6, 8   **2.** 6, 15   **3.** 4, 20   **4.** 9, 27
5. 12, 18   **6.** 16, 24   **7.** 2, 21   **8.** 3, 10

Write each fraction in lowest terms.

9. $\dfrac{2}{4}$ **10.** $\dfrac{3}{9}$ **11.** $\dfrac{8}{12}$ **12.** $\dfrac{12}{28}$

13. $\dfrac{15}{20}$ **14.** $\dfrac{14}{21}$ **15.** $\dfrac{30}{54}$ **16.** $\dfrac{42}{48}$

17. $\dfrac{60}{48}$ **18.** $\dfrac{60}{36}$ **19.** $\dfrac{240}{800}$ **20.** $\dfrac{630}{900}$

Find each product or quotient. Write your answer in lowest terms.

21. $\dfrac{3}{8}\cdot\dfrac{4}{9}$ **22.** $\dfrac{8}{9}\cdot\dfrac{3}{4}$ **23.** $\dfrac{1}{2}\cdot\dfrac{1}{2}$ **24.** $\dfrac{1}{3}\cdot\dfrac{1}{3}$

25. $4\cdot\dfrac{3}{40}$ **26.** $5\cdot\dfrac{7}{50}$ **27.** $\dfrac{2}{7}\div\dfrac{3}{5}$ **28.** $\dfrac{2}{11}\div\dfrac{3}{7}$

29. $\dfrac{1}{2} \div 2$ **30.** $\dfrac{1}{4} \div 2$ **31.** $\dfrac{4}{9} \div \dfrac{3}{4}$ **32.** $\dfrac{3}{8} \div \dfrac{2}{3}$

33. $\dfrac{3}{7} \cdot 21$ **34.** $\dfrac{5}{9} \cdot 45$ **35.** $\dfrac{9}{2} \div \dfrac{3}{2}$ **36.** $\dfrac{10}{3} \div \dfrac{5}{3}$

Find each sum or difference. Write your answer in lowest terms.

37. $\dfrac{1}{4} + \dfrac{1}{4}$ **38.** $\dfrac{1}{6} + \dfrac{1}{6}$ **39.** $\dfrac{5}{8} + \dfrac{1}{8}$ **40.** $\dfrac{3}{10} + \dfrac{1}{10}$

41. $\dfrac{5}{7} - \dfrac{3}{7}$ **42.** $\dfrac{4}{5} - \dfrac{1}{5}$ **43.** $\dfrac{13}{20} - \dfrac{7}{20}$ **44.** $\dfrac{25}{28} - \dfrac{19}{28}$

45. $\dfrac{2}{3} + \dfrac{1}{9}$ **46.** $\dfrac{2}{5} + \dfrac{1}{15}$ **47.** $\dfrac{1}{2} + \dfrac{1}{5}$ **48.** $\dfrac{1}{3} + \dfrac{1}{7}$

49. $\dfrac{8}{15} - \dfrac{2}{5}$ **50.** $\dfrac{17}{18} - \dfrac{2}{3}$ **51.** $\dfrac{1}{3} - \dfrac{1}{4}$ **52.** $\dfrac{1}{2} - \dfrac{1}{3}$

53. $\dfrac{1}{6} + \dfrac{5}{9}$ **54.** $\dfrac{1}{4} + \dfrac{5}{6}$ **55.** $\dfrac{5}{6} - \dfrac{3}{4}$ **56.** $\dfrac{8}{9} - \dfrac{5}{6}$

57. $6 - \dfrac{3}{7}$ **58.** $7 - \dfrac{4}{7}$ **59.** $\dfrac{2}{5} + \dfrac{1}{4} + \dfrac{3}{10}$ **60.** $\dfrac{3}{8} + \dfrac{1}{4} + \dfrac{5}{12}$

Perform the indicated operation. Write your answer in lowest terms.

61. $3\dfrac{1}{2} \cdot 2\dfrac{1}{5}$ **62.** $4\dfrac{1}{3} \cdot 1\dfrac{1}{4}$ **63.** $2\dfrac{2}{5} \div 1\dfrac{1}{3}$ **64.** $3\dfrac{3}{4} \div 1\dfrac{2}{3}$

65. $4\dfrac{1}{2} + 2\dfrac{1}{5}$ **66.** $2\dfrac{1}{3} + 5\dfrac{1}{4}$ **67.** $8 - 3\dfrac{2}{3}$ **68.** $9 - 3\dfrac{2}{5}$

Solve each word problem. Write your answer in lowest terms.

69. The employees of an insurance company attempted to raise $25,000 for charity. They raised $22,500. What fraction of their goal was raised?

70. Of 6000 fires in a 1-year period, 2250 were caused by smoking in bed. What fraction of the fires were caused by smoking in bed?

71. A factory worker who earns $12 an hour works an 8 1/4-hour day. Find his total earnings per day.

72. If 1 inch on a map represents 50 miles on land, how many miles on land are represented by 3 3/10 inches on the map?

73. A share of stock was worth $10 1/8 per share on Monday. Three days later it was worth $7 1/2. How much did the stock fall?

74. A bolt of material contained 11 1/2 yards of cloth. After four sales, the bolt contained 2 2/3 yards. How much material was sold?

75. How many 2 2/3-ounce wine glasses can be filled from a bottle holding 24 ounces?

76. A board 8 3/4 feet long is to be cut into five equal pieces. Find the length of each piece.

77. While working out for an upcoming meet, a jogger ran 5 1/2 miles on Thursday, 3 2/5 miles on Friday, 7 3/5 miles on Saturday, and 6 miles on Sunday. Find her average distance per day.

78. A hospital delivered quintuplets on Christmas Day. The weights of the five babies were 2 3/4 pounds, 3 pounds, 3 1/2 pounds, 3 1/4 pounds, and 4 pounds. Find their average weight.

79. A dump truck is loaded with 10 tons of gravel. It dumps 2 3/4 tons at the first stop and 3 1/2 tons at the second. How much gravel is left in the truck?

80. A carpenter cuts two pieces of lengths 5 1/2 feet and 6 7/8 feet from an 18-foot board. Find the length of the piece that remains.

81. A recipe for 16 brownies requires 2/3 cup of flour. How much flour is needed to make one dozen brownies?

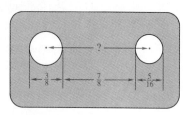

FIGURE 1.1

82. Two holes are to be drilled in a metal plate so that the distance between the holes is 7/8 centimeter. The diameter of (distance across) one hole is 3/8 centimeter, and the diameter of the other is 5/16 centimeter. Find the distance between the centers (see Fig. 1.1).

1.2   Real Numbers and the Number Line

Many rules of algebra are true for certain kinds of numbers but false for others. This section provides a brief overview of the various types of numbers used in algebra.

Normally we refer to a collection of numbers as a *set* of numbers. A **set** is a collection of objects, called **elements.** The elements are listed within braces and separated by commas. For example, the set {*a, b, c*} consists of the three elements *a, b,* and *c.* The most basic set of numbers is the set of **whole numbers.**

DEFINITION OF WHOLE NUMBERS

   {0, 1, 2, 3, 4, 5, . . .}

FIGURE 1.2

The three dots indicate that the pattern continues without end. There is no largest whole number.

We can illustrate the whole numbers by using a **number line** like the one shown in Fig. 1.2. To construct a number line, draw a line and select any point on the line to correspond to 0. Draw a hash mark to indicate the location of this point. Then choose any point to the right of 0 to correspond to 1. Using the distance between 0 and 1 as the unit of measure, locate the remaining whole numbers by drawing additional hash marks.

We can use a whole number to represent a temperature of 3° above zero (also written +3°). To describe a temperature of 3° below zero we write −3°.

If we turn the thermometer to a horizontal position, we have an extension of our original number line (see Fig. 1.3). Numbers to the right of 0 are called **positive numbers.** Numbers to the left of 0 are **negative numbers.** Positive numbers and negative numbers are collectively called **signed numbers,** or **directed numbers. The number 0 is neither positive nor negative.**

Positive and negative numbers were used by the Chinese more than 2000 years ago for bookkeeping purposes. Positive numbers were written in black and negative numbers in red, which gave rise to the expressions "in the black" and "in the red." The symbol + was first used in 1840, and the symbol − in 1849.

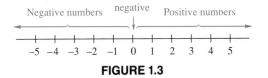

FIGURE 1.3

The set of numbers that correspond to the hash marks in Fig. 1.3 is called the set of **integers.**

DEFINITION OF INTEGERS

$$\{\ldots, -3, -2, -1, 0, 1, 2, 3, \ldots\}$$

Note that **every whole number is also an integer.**

Of course, not every number is an integer. Numbers like 2.5, 4 1/3, and 3/4 are not integers. However, we can write each of these numbers as a quotient of two integers, as follows.

$$2.5 = 2\frac{5}{10} = 2\frac{1}{2} = \frac{5}{2} \qquad \textit{Quotient of 5 and 2}$$

$$4\frac{1}{3} = \frac{13}{3} \qquad \textit{Quotient of 13 and 3}$$

$$\frac{3}{4} \qquad \textit{This is already a quotient of two integers}$$

A number that can be written as a quotient of two integers (with denominator *not* 0) is called a **rational number.**

DEFINITION OF RATIONAL NUMBERS

{quotients of two integers, with denominator not 0}

Since every integer can be written as a quotient of itself and 1, **every integer is also a rational number.** For example,

$$6 = \frac{6}{1}, \qquad -3 = \frac{-3}{1}, \qquad \text{and} \qquad 0 = \frac{0}{1}.$$

The **graph** of a number is the point on the number line that corresponds to the number. We indicate the location of this point by drawing a solid dot. Figure 1.4 presents the graphs of the rational numbers −3, 0, 3/4, 2.5, 4 1/3, and

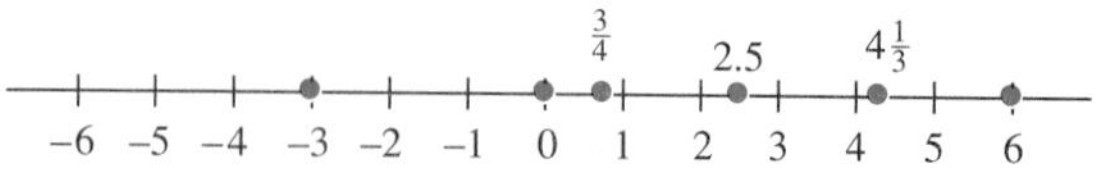

FIGURE 1.4

6. Notice that those points that do not correspond to integers (namely, 3/4, 2.5, and 4 1/3) are labeled by writing the appropriate number above the point. The points that correspond to integers are labeled below the number line.

Although there is an infinite number of rational numbers, there are still many numbers (in fact, infinitely many) that are not rational. For example, the square root of 4 is 2, since $2 \cdot 2 = 4$. The square root of 9 is 3, since $3 \cdot 3 = 9$. Using the symbol $\sqrt{a}$ to mean the **square root of a**, we can write $\sqrt{4} = 2$ and $\sqrt{9} = 3$. But the square root of 2, written $\sqrt{2}$, is not a rational number, since it cannot be written as a quotient of two integers. A number that can be represented on the number line that is not a rational number is called an **irrational number.**

> The ancient Greeks at first believed that every number could be written as a quotient of two integers. They were so disturbed when they could not express $\sqrt{2}$ as a quotient of integers that, for a while, they kept the matter secret.

DEFINITION OF IRRATIONAL NUMBERS

   {numbers represented on the number line that are not rational}

Other examples of irrational numbers are $\sqrt{10}$ and $-\sqrt{5}$. The approximate values of $\sqrt{2}$, $\sqrt{10}$, and $-\sqrt{5}$ follow. (The symbol $\approx$ means "approximately equals.")

$$\sqrt{2} \approx 1.41 \qquad \sqrt{10} \approx 3.16 \qquad -\sqrt{5} \approx -2.24$$

We can use these values to graph the three numbers on the number line (see Fig. 1.5). We will discuss irrational numbers in more detail later in the text.

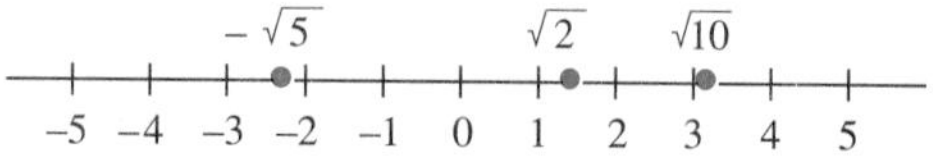

FIGURE 1.5

If we combine the set of rational numbers and the set of irrational numbers, we obtain the set of *real numbers*. A **real number** is any number that can be represented on the number line.

DEFINITION OF REAL NUMBERS

   {numbers that can be represented on the number line}

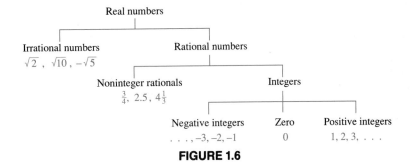

FIGURE 1.6

All of the numbers we have discussed up to this point—whole numbers, integers, rational numbers, and irrational numbers—are also real numbers. An example of a number that is not a real number is the square root of a negative number, such as $\sqrt{-4}$. We will discuss these numbers in Chapter 9. Figure 1.6 shows the relationship between the various types of real numbers.

EXAMPLE 1   Consider the following set of numbers.

$$\left\{-6, 3, \sqrt{3}, 0, -4\frac{1}{3}, \sqrt{4}, 2.8, \frac{3}{8}, -\sqrt{7}\right\}$$

a. The whole numbers are 3, 0, and $\sqrt{4}$ (since $\sqrt{4} = 2$).
b. The integers are $-6, 3, 0,$ and $\sqrt{4}$.
c. The rational numbers are $-6, 3, 0, -4\ 1/3, \sqrt{4}, 2.8,$ and 3/8.
d. The irrational numbers are $\sqrt{3}$ and $-\sqrt{7}$.
e. All of the numbers are real numbers.

Try Problem 35 >

(đổi nhau)

Opposite of a Number

Since the numbers 3 and -3 are the same distance from 0 but on opposite sides of 0, we call 3 and -3 **opposites** of each other.

EXAMPLE 2

a. The opposite of 5 is -5.
b. The opposite of -8 is 8.
c. 0 is its own opposite.

Try Problem 37 >

Note that the symbol $-$ has three different, though related, meanings. First, it denotes subtraction.

$5 - 2$ means "5 subtract 2"

Second, it denotes a negative number.

-4 means "negative 4"

Third, it denotes the opposite of a number.

−4 means "the opposite of 4"

We rely on the context to tell us which meaning is intended.

Since the minus sign before a number denotes the opposite of that number, then −(−3) denotes the opposite of −3. But the opposite of −3 is 3. That is,

−(−3) = the opposite of −3 = 3.

This suggests the following rule.

DOUBLE-NEGATIVE RULE

For any real number a,

$$-(-a) = a.$$

EXAMPLE 3   Simplify.

a. −(−8) = 8   *Double-negative rule*
b. −(−(−2)) = −(2)   *Since* −(−2) = 2
          = −2

Try Problem 53 >

1.2 Problem Set

Use positive and negative numbers to represent the following quantities.

1. A temperature of 18° above zero, a temperature of 4° below zero

2. Three golf stokes over par, two golf strokes under par

3. A rise of 1 3/8, a fall of 3 1/8 in the price of a stock

4. An altitude of 250 feet above sea level, an altitude of 75 feet below sea level

5. A gain of 6 yards on a football play, a loss of 3 yards

6. A profit of $80, a loss of $15

True or false.

7. −78 is a whole number.

8. 29 is an integer.

9. 0 is an integer.

10. 0 is a whole number.

11. 0 is a positive integer.

12. 0 is a negative integer.

13. 2/3 is a rational number.

14. −0.5 is an irrational number.

15. 6 1/4 is an irrational number.

16. $\sqrt{17}$ is a rational number.

17. Every negative integer is a rational number.

18. Every positive integer is a rational number.

19. Every whole number is an integer.

20. Every integer is a rational number.

21. There are rational numbers that are not integers.

22. There are integers that are not whole numbers.

23. No rational number is an irrational number.

24. No irrational number is a rational number.

25. Some rational numbers are negative.

26. Some irrational numbers are negative.

27. Every irrational number is a real number.

28. Every rational number is a real number.

Give three examples of numbers that satisfy the given conditions.

29. An integer but not a whole number

30. A rational number but not an integer

31. A real number but not a rational number

32. A real number but not an irrational number

33. A rational number but not a positive integer

34. An irrational number but not a negative number

For each set of numbers, identify the elements of the set that are

a. *whole numbers.*

b. *integers.*) 18, − 10, 0

c. *rational numbers.* $\frac{5}{7}$, 0.35, −3$\frac{1}{6}$

d. *irrational numbers.* $\sqrt{6}$, $\sqrt{9}$, −$\sqrt{2}$

e. *real numbers.*

35. $\left\{ \dfrac{5}{7}, 18, \sqrt{6}, 0.35, -10, 0, \sqrt{9}, -3\dfrac{1}{6}, -\sqrt{2} \right\}$

36. $\left\{ -19, -1.79, 23, \sqrt{10}, 0, \dfrac{2}{7}, 4\dfrac{2}{3}, -\sqrt{3}, \sqrt{1} \right\}$

State the opposite of each number.

37. 2   − 2

38. 4   − 4

39. −63

40. −89

41. $-\dfrac{5}{6}$ + $\dfrac{5}{6}$

42. $-\dfrac{3}{8}$ $\dfrac{3}{8}$

43. 0.125

44. 0.707

45. $-9\dfrac{1}{4}$ 9 $\dfrac{1}{4}$

46. $-5\dfrac{1}{3}$ 5 $\dfrac{1}{3}$

47. 0

48. −1

49. $\sqrt{3}$

50. $\sqrt{11}$

51. $-\sqrt{15}$

52. $-\sqrt{6}$

Simplify.

53. −(−5)

54. −(−9)

55. $-\left(-4\dfrac{2}{5} \right)$

56. $-\left(-3\dfrac{4}{7} \right)$

57. −(−8.6)

58. −(−2.4)

59. −(−(−17))

60. −(−(−13))

61. Graph each of the following rational numbers on a number line. Be sure to label each point.

$$3, \dfrac{1}{4}, 4.5, -1, -\dfrac{7}{3}$$

62. Graph each of the following rational numbers on a number line. Be sure to label each point.

$$4, 1\dfrac{3}{4}, 0.5, -2, -\dfrac{10}{3}$$

63. If x is a negative number, is $-x$ a negative number or a positive number?

64. If x is a negative number, is $-(-x)$ a negative number or a positive number?

▦ CALCULATOR PROBLEMS

To find the opposite of 6.8 on your calculator, press

| Clear | 6 | · | 8 | +/− | −6.8 |

Find the opposite of each number.

65. 1   **66.** 7.2   **67.** 0.375   **68.** −5

To find a decimal approximation of $\sqrt{2}$ *on your calculator, press*

| Clear | 2 | $\sqrt{x}$ | 1.4142136 |

The number 1.4142136 *is an approximate value of* $\sqrt{2}$. *To the nearest hundredth,* $\sqrt{2} = 1.41$. *Graph each irrational number on a number line. Be sure to label each point.*

69. $\sqrt{3}$ **70.** $\sqrt{5}$ **71.** $-\sqrt{7}$ **72.** $-\sqrt{22}$

73. Try to find $\sqrt{-4}$ on your calculator.

1.3   Symbols of Inequality and Absolute Value

(bất đẳng thức,
bất phương trình)   (Trị số tuyệt đối)

We can use the number line to define two useful concepts in mathematics—inequality and absolute value.

Inequality

The English mathematician Robert Recorde (1510–1558) was the first to use the symbol = to denote equality. Referring to the two line segments that make up the symbol, he said, "No two things can be more equal."

As we have seen, the symbol for equality is =, and it is written between two quantities that are equal. For example,

$3 + 5 = 8$ means   "3 plus 5 equals 8."

The symbol ≠ means "is not equal to." For example,

$3 + 5 \neq 9$.

If two numbers are not equal, then one number must be less than the other. The symbol < means "is less than." For example,

$4 < 7$ means   "4 is less than 7."

Instead of saying, "4 is less than 7," we could say, "7 is greater than 4," written $7 > 4$.

$4 < 7$ or $7 > 4$

One way to keep the symbols < and > straight is to remember that **the inequality symbol always points to the smaller number.**

We can use the number line (Fig. 1.7) to define the concept of inequality more precisely. Note that lesser numbers are to the left and greater numbers are to the right. For example, 2 is less than 4, written $2 < 4$, since 2 lies to the left of 4. On the other hand, −1 is greater than −5, written $-1 > -5$, since −1

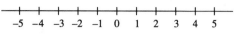

FIGURE 1.7

lies to the right of -5. (Remember, a temperature of $-1°$ is higher than a temperature of $-5°$.)

DEFINITION OF INEQUALITY

The real number a **is less than** the real number b, written $a < b$, if a lies to the left of b on the number line.

EXAMPLE 1   Insert $<$ or $>$ to make a true statement.

a. 3.09   3.8   b. 1   0
c. -2 2   d. $-1/2$ $-3/4$

Solution   Each of the numbers is graphed on the number line.

a. $3.09 < 3.8$, since 3.09 lies to the left of 3.8.
b. $1 > 0$, since 1 lies to the right of 0.
c. $-2 < 2$, since -2 lies to the left of 2.

Try Problem 1 >   d. $-1/2 > -3/4$ since $-1/2$ lies to the right of $-3/4$.   ■

If either $a < b$ or $a = b$, we can write $a \le b$. For example,

$7 \le 8$ means   "7 is less than or equal to 8."

In this case, $7 < 8$. We could also write $7 \le 7$, since $7 = 7$. We *cannot* write $7 \le 6$, since neither $7 < 6$ nor $7 = 6$ is true. In a similar fashion, the symbol $\ge$ means "is greater than or equal to."

EXAMPLE 2   To be eligible to vote, your age, a, must be at least 18 years. Write this statement as an inequality.

Solution   To be at least 18, either your age, a, must be 18 (written $a = 18$) or your age, a, must be greater than 18 (written $a > 18$). Combining these statements, we have

$a \ge 18$ yr.

Try Problem 27 >   Both $a \ge 18$ yr and 18 yr $\le a$ are correct answers.   ■

	SYMBOLS OF EQUALITY AND INEQUALITY	
Symbol	*Meaning*	*Example*
$=$	is equal to	$1 + 2 = 3$
$\neq$	is not equal to	$-5 \neq 5$
$<$	is less than	$\dfrac{1}{3} < \dfrac{1}{2}$
$>$	is greater than	$100 > 99$
$\leq$	is less than or equal to	$-8 \leq -7$
$\geq$	is greater than or equal to	$0 \geq 0$

Double Inequalities

To denote that a number is between two other numbers, we combine two separate inequalities to form one *double inequality*. For example, since 5 is between 1 and 6, we can combine the two inequalities

$1 < 5$ and $5 < 6$

to form the **double inequality** $1 < 5 < 6$.

$1 < 5 < 6$ means   "1 is less than 5 and 5 is less than 6."

You can also write that 5 is between 1 and 6 by writing $6 > 5 > 1$.

$6 > 5 > 1$ means   "6 is greater than 5 and 5 is greater than 1."

Here is another example of a double inequality.

$-3 \leq -1 < 1$ means   "-3 is less than or equal to -1 and
                                        -1 is less than 1."

Caution! ■ Never write a double inequality so that the two inequality symbols point in opposite directions.

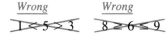

Wrong   *Wrong*
~~$1 < 5 > 3$~~   ~~$8 \geq 6 \leq 9$~~

Notice that 5 is *not* between 1 and 3, and 6 is *not* between 8 and 9.

PROBLEM SOLVING

EXAMPLE 3   A company that manufactures roller bearings must make the bearings so that the diameter, d, is more than 2 centimeters but no more than 2.1 centimeters. Write a double inequality that describes the range of values for d.

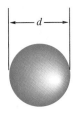

Solution   The diameter, d, must be more than 2 centimeters, written $d > 2$ cm. This can also be written 2 cm $< d$. Also, the diameter, d, must be no more than 2.1 centimeters; that is, d must be 2.1 cm or less. This is written $d \leq 2.1$ cm. Combine these two inequalities to form the double inequality

$$2 \text{ cm} < d \leq 2.1 \text{ cm}.$$

Try Problem 39 >   Another correct answer is 2.1 cm $\geq d > 2$ cm.

Absolute Value

Every nonzero number on the number line can be characterized by two important properties: a *direction* from 0 and a *distance* from 0. The direction from 0 is given by the $+$ or $-$ sign in front of the number. The distance from 0 is called the *absolute value* of the number.

The term *absolute value* is derived from the Latin word *absolvere*, meaning "to free from," as in "to free from its sign." The absolute value symbol | | was first used by the German mathematician Karl Weierstrass (1815–1897).

DEFINITION OF ABSOLUTE VALUE

The **absolute value** of a real number x is denoted $|x|$ and is given by

$$|x| = \text{the distance between } x \text{ and } 0.$$

$$|-5| = 5 \qquad |5| = 5$$

FIGURE 1.8

The numbers 5 and -5 are not equal, but they are the same distance from 0 (Fig. 1.8). We say that 5 and -5 are "equal in absolute value but opposite in sign." Here are some other examples of absolute value.

Number	Absolute Value of the Number
4	$|4| = 4$
-4	$|-4| = 4$
0	$|0| = 0$
$-\dfrac{2}{3}$	$\left|-\dfrac{2}{3}\right| = \dfrac{2}{3}$

Since absolute value measures distance, **the absolute value of a number is either a positive number or 0.** However, a negative sign outside the absolute value symbol is not affected by the absolute value symbol.

EXAMPLE 4   Simplify.

a. $-|3|$ b. $-|-3|$ c. $|9 - 2|$

Solution

a. $-|3| = -3$ *Find the absolute value of 3, then take the opposite*
b. $-|-3| = -3$ *Find the absolute value of -3, then take the opposite*

Try Problem 59 >   c. $|9 - 2| = |7| = 7$ *Subtract, then apply $|\ |$*

EXAMPLE 5   Insert $=$, $<$, or $>$ to make a true statement.

a. $|-8|\ \ |8|$ b. $|-6|\ \ |2|$ c. $|-5|\ \ |9|$

Solution

a. $|-8| = |8|$, since both $|-8|$ and $|8|$ equal 8.
b. $|-6| > |2|$, since $|-6| = 6$ and $|2| = 2$.

Try Problem 75 >   c. $|-5| < |9|$, since $|-5| = 5$ and $|9| = 9$.

1.3 Problem Set

LEARNING THROUGH WRITING

☐ Explain how to determine which of two different real numbers is larger.

☐ Write each inequality in words.
   a. $4 < 9$ b. $x \geq 17$ c. $-8 < y < 0$

☐ Do you think there is a smallest positive real number? Why or why not?

☐ What is meant by the absolute value of a real number?

Insert $<$ or $>$ to make a true statement.

1. 5 3

2. 4 1

3. 7.07 7.1

4. 0.1 1

5. -7 0

6. 15 -9

7. -4 -2

8. -2.08 -2.2

9. 0.3 -0.6

10. $\sqrt{2}$ 1

11. $-1\dfrac{3}{5}$ $-1\dfrac{2}{5}$

12. -100 -99

13. $\dfrac{3}{4}$ $\dfrac{5}{7}$

14. $-\dfrac{3}{4}$ $-\dfrac{5}{7}$

Write the following word statements using the symbols $=$, $\neq$, $<$, $>$, $\leq$, and $\geq$.

15. x is equal to -17.

16. y is not equal to 42.

17. z is less than 8.

18. z is greater than 4.

19. r is greater than or equal to -6.

20. r is less than or equal to -5.

21. p is at most 7.

22. p is no less than 13.

23. x is a positive number.

24. *x* is a negative number.

25. *y* is a nonnegative number.

26. *y* is a nonpositive number.

27. To drink, your age, *a*, must be at least 21 years.

28. To run for president of the United States, your age, *a*, must be at least 35 years.

29. To fight as a middleweight, a boxer's weight, *w*, can be no more than 160 pounds.

30. To fight as a welterweight, a boxer's weight, *w*, can be no more than 147 pounds.

Write the following word statements using a double inequality.

31. 4 is less than *x* and *x* is less than 9.

32. 8 is greater than *x* and *x* is greater than 2.

33. 12 is greater than or equal to *y* and *y* is greater than −1.

34. −15 is less than *y* and *y* is less than or equal to 5.

35. *z* is between −3 and 6.

36. *z* is between −12 and −7.

37. *p* is less than 10 but no less than 3.

38. *p* is more than 1 but no more than 5.

39. A weather reporter forecasts that the temperature, *t*, on Christmas Day will range from a morning low of −8° to an afternoon high of 19°.

40. To enlist in the U.S. Army, your height, *h*, must be a minimum of 60 inches and a maximum of 80 inches.

41. A turnpike has a minimum speed of 35 mph and a maximum speed of 55 mph. If *d* represents the distance you can legally travel on this turnpike in 3 hours, write a double inequality that describes the range of values for *d*.

42. A car with a fuel capacity of 15 gallons gets 22 mpg in the city and 33 mpg on the highway. If *d* is the distance the car can travel on a full tank, write a double inequality that describes the range of values for *d*.

43. Organizers of a banquet for 40 persons estimate the total cost of the banquet to be anywhere from $450 to $600. If everyone is to share the cost of the banquet equally, and *C* is the cost per person, write a double inequality that describes the values for *C*.

44. In a particular region it costs anywhere from $9 to $17 per foot to drill a well. To hit water the well must be anywhere from 130 feet to 150 feet deep. If *C* is the total cost of drilling the well, write a double inequality that describes the range of values for *C*.

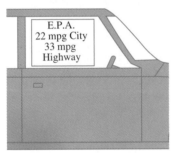

E.P.A.
22 mpg City
33 mpg Highway

Find the absolute value of each number.

45. 6

46. 9

47. −6

48. −9

49. −1

50. 0

51. $-\dfrac{3}{4}$

52. $-\dfrac{4}{5}$

53. 7.2

54. −9.3

55. $-\sqrt{2}$

56. $\sqrt{3}$

Simplify.

57. −|10|

58. −|15|

59. −|−10|

60. −|−15|

61. |8 − 3|

62. |7 − 5|

63. −|8 − 3|

64. −|7 − 5|

65. |−9| − |2|

66. |4| − |−1|

67. |−6| − |−4|

68. |−8| − |−2|

Insert =, <, or > to make a true statement.

69. |8.1| |5.96|

70. |4.88| |6.2|

71. |−25| |0|

72. |0| |−1|

73. |1| |−1|

74. |−20| |20|

75. |3| |−9|

76. |7| |−2|

77. |−14| |18|

78. |−16| |12|

79. $\left|-\dfrac{1}{2}\right|$ $\left|-\dfrac{3}{4}\right|$

80. $\left|-\dfrac{1}{3}\right|$ $\left|-\dfrac{4}{5}\right|$

81. Name two numbers whose absolute value is 8.

82. Name two numbers whose absolute value is 13.

83. Name two numbers that are 6 units from -2 on the number line.

84. Name two numbers that are 4 units from 1 on the number line.

True or false. If false, explain why.

85. $|a| = a$

86. If $a = b$, then $|a| = |b|$.

87. If $a < b$, then $|a| < |b|$.

88. If $|a| = |b|$, then $a = b$.

<table>
<tr><td>**1.4**</td><td>**Addition of Real Numbers**</td></tr>
</table>

Before we can use algebra to solve problems, we must learn how to perform operations on positive and negative numbers. In the next four sections we learn how to add, subtract, multiply, and divide real numbers. We begin with addition.

The best way to illustrate addition of real numbers is with the number line. Arrows pointing to the right will represent positive numbers, and arrows pointing to the left will represent negative numbers.

EXAMPLE 1   A football team gains 3 yards on its first play from scrimmage and 2 yards on its next play. Find the total yardage gained on the two plays.

Try Problem 1 >

Solution   The total yardage is given by the sum of 3 and 2, which is $3 + 2 = 5$. This sum is illustrated in Fig. 1.9. ∎

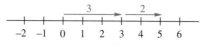

FIGURE 1.9

EXAMPLE 2   Find the total yardage on two football plays if the first play results in a loss of 3 yards and the second play results in a loss of 2 yards.

Try Problem 3 >

Solution   The total yardage is the sum of -3 and -2, which is $-3 + (-2) = -5$ (see Fig. 1.10). ∎

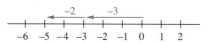

FIGURE 1.10

If you study Examples 1 and 2 closely, you will see that you can add the numbers without the aid of a number line. **To add two numbers having the same sign, add the absolute values and prefix the common sign.**

EXAMPLE 3 Find the sum of -7 and -10.

Solution The numbers have the same sign, so add the absolute values.

$$|-7| + |-10| = 7 + 10 = 17$$

Now prefix the common sign, which is $-$.

Try Problem 5 > $-7 + (-10) = -17$ ■

Caution! To avoid confusion, always use parentheses to separate the symbols $+$, $-$, $\cdot$, and $\div$.

Correct	*Wrong*
$-7 + (-10)$	~~$-7 + -10$~~

EXAMPLE 4 If a loss of 4 yards on a football play is followed by a gain of 5 yards, find the total yardage.

Solution The total yardage is the sum of -4 and 5, which is $-4 + 5 = 1$
Try Problem 7 > (see Fig. 1.11). ■

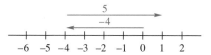

FIGURE 1.11

EXAMPLE 5 If a gain of 4 yards is followed by a loss of 5 yards, find the total yardage.

Try Problem 9 > **Solution** The sum of 4 and -5 is $4 + (-5) = -1$, as shown in Fig. 1.12. ■

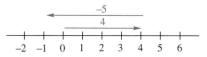

FIGURE 1.12

In Examples 4 and 5 we were adding numbers with different signs. **To add two numbers having different signs, subtract the smaller absolute value from the larger. Then prefix the sign of the number having the larger absolute value.**

EXAMPLE 6   Find the sum of -8 and 2.

Solution   The numbers have different signs, so subtract the smaller absolute value from the larger.

$$|-8| - |2| = 8 - 2 = 6$$

Since -8 has a larger absolute value than 2, the answer is negative.

Try Problem 11 > $-8 + 2 = -6$ ■

EXAMPLE 7   Find the sum of 9 and -4.

Solution   The numbers have different signs, so subtract the smaller absolute value from the larger.

$$|9| - |-4| = 9 - 4 = 5$$

Since 9 has a larger absolute value than -4, the answer is positive.

Try Problem 13 > $9 + (-4) = 5$ ■

These examples illustrate the rules for adding real numbers. In actual practice, you should mentally perform the operations involving absolute values whenever possible.

EXAMPLE 8   Add all combinations of positive and negative 3 and 5.

Solution
   a. $3 + 5 = 8$ *Same sign, sum is positive*
   b. $-3 + (-5) = -8$ *Same sign, sum is negative*
   c. $3 + (-5) = -2$ *Different signs, sum is negative*

Try Problem 25 >   d. $-3 + 5 = 2$ *Different signs, sum is positive*   ■

ADDING REAL NUMBERS

Same sign: Add the absolute values. The answer has the same sign as the given numbers.

Different signs: Subtract the smaller absolute value from the larger. The answer has the same sign as the number with the larger absolute value.

The sign rules for adding real numbers apply to fractions and decimals as well as to integers.

EXAMPLE 9   Add 3/4 + (−5/6).

Solution

$$\frac{3}{4} + \left(-\frac{5}{6}\right) = \frac{9}{12} + \left(-\frac{10}{12}\right) \quad \textit{Write with the LCD, 12}$$

Try Problem 43 >

$$= -\frac{1}{12} \qquad \textit{Add}$$ ■

EXAMPLE 10   Add −7.8 + (−3.62).

Solution   First add the absolute values.

┌──── *Line up decimal points*
↓
7.80
+ 3.62
─────
11.42

Then prefix the correct sign.

Try Problem 47 >

$$-7.8 + (-3.62) = -11.42$$ ■

P R O B L E M   S O L V I N G

EXAMPLE 11   A fullback carried the ball six times, with the following results: 7-yard gain, 3-yard loss, 6-yard gain, 4-yard gain, 1-yard loss, 2-yard gain. Find the total yardage.

Solution   Add the numbers, treating the gains as positive and the losses as negative.

$$7 + (-3) + 6 + 4 + (-1) + 2$$
$$= (7 + 6 + 4 + 2) + [(-3) + (-1)] \quad \textit{Group the positives, group the}$$
$$\textit{negatives}$$
$$= 19 + [-4] \qquad\qquad\qquad \textit{Find the sum of each group}$$
$$= 15 \qquad\qquad\qquad\qquad \textit{Add the two sums}$$

Try Problem 67 >   The fullback had a total yardage of 15 yards. ■

1.4 Problem Set

LEARNING THROUGH WRITING

☐ Write each operation in words.
  a. 5 + (−7)   b. −13 + 19   c. −1 + (−20)

☐ Explain how to add two real numbers.

Find each sum. You may want to draw a few on the number line.

1. 4 + 2   **2.** 1 + 3   **3.** −2 + (−5)   **4.** −1 + (−4)

5. −6 + (−9)   **6.** −8 + (−7)   **7.** −3 + 7   **8.** −4 + 6

9. 1 + (−5)   **10.** 3 + (−4)   **11.** −9 + 5   **12.** −6 + 2

13. 10 + (−3)   **14.** 12 + (−8)   **15.** −8 + (−6)   **16.** −5 + (−7)

17. 18 + (−5)   **18.** 19 + (−4)   **19.** 2 + (−17)   **20.** 3 + (−15)

21. −14 + 13   **22.** −16 + 15   **23.** 11 + (−7)   **24.** 13 + (−2)

Add all combinations of positive and negative values for each pair of numbers.

25. 2 and 6   **26.** 185 and 98   **27.** 24.1 and 9.2   **28.** $4\frac{1}{2}$ and $2\frac{3}{5}$

Find the sums.

29. 1 + (−1)   **30.** −4 + 4   **31.** −8 + 0   **32.** 0 + (−6)

33. −156 + 156   **34.** 132 + (−132)   **35.** 0 + (−93)   **36.** −200 + 0

37. $-\frac{2}{7} + \left(-\frac{3}{7}\right)$ **38.** $-\frac{2}{5} + \left(-\frac{1}{5}\right)$ **39.** $-\frac{1}{3} + \frac{5}{6}$ **40.** $-\frac{1}{5} + \frac{9}{10}$

41. $-\frac{4}{5} + \frac{4}{5}$ **42.** $-\frac{3}{8} + \frac{3}{8}$ **43.** $\frac{2}{3} + \left(-\frac{3}{4}\right)$ **44.** $\frac{7}{9} + \left(-\frac{5}{6}\right)$

45. 6.8 + (−1.5)   **46.** 5.9 + (−3.2)   **47.** −8.3 + (−5.94)   **48.** −7.6 + (−4.83)

49. 4.7 + (−4.7)   **50.** 8.9 + (−8.9)   **51.** −4.1 + 3.62   **52.** −2.3 + 1.72

53. 1 + 5 + (−4) + (−2)   **54.** 4 + 5 + (−2) + (−7)   **55.** 4 + (−6) + 8 + (−10)

56. 3 + (−5) + 8 + (−12)   **57.** 18 + (−3) + (−3) + (−3)   **58.** 19 + (−5) + (−5) + (−5)

59. −27 + 17 + 10 + 31   **60.** −30 + 14 + 16 + 28

Solve each word problem.

61. What number must be added to 6 to obtain −4?

62. What number must be added to −2 to obtain −10?

63. The sum of what number and −5 is 3?

64. The sum of what number and 8 is −1?

65. The temperature is −8°. If it rises 21°, what is the new temperature?

66. Dave's checking account has a balance of $−5. If he makes a $17 deposit, what is the new balance?

67. Sharon played nine holes of golf, with the following results: +2, par, +1, −2, −3, −2, par, −1, +3. Find her final score in relation to par.

68. From an elevation of −457 feet, a party of spelunkers (cave explorers) ascends 110 feet, descends 68 feet, ascends 95 feet, and descends 23 feet. Find its final elevation.

69. The Dow Jones industrial average posted the following results over a five-day trading period: up 3.67, down 4.19, up 1.12, down 0.92, up 6.43. Find the net change in the Dow.

70. Ken bet six horse races at a nearby track with the following results: won $16.20, won $8.60, lost $14, lost $2, won $3.20, lost $6. Find his net winnings.

▦ CALCULATOR PROBLEMS

To find −9 + 4 *on your calculator, press*

| Clear | 9 | +/− | + | 4 | = | −5 |

Therefore −9 + 4 = −5. *Find each sum on your calculator.*

71. −94 + 38   **72.** 213 + (−146)   **73.** −882 + (−579)

1.5 Subtraction of Real Numbers

We could use the number line to illustrate subtraction of real numbers. However, there is a better way. We convert each subtraction problem to an addition problem, and then use the rules for addition.

Consider the following two problems.

$$6 - 2 = 4 \qquad 6 + (-2) = 4$$

Note that subtracting 2 is equivalent to adding the opposite of 2. This observation leads to the following definition.

DEFINITION OF SUBTRACTION

For any real numbers a and b,

$$a - b = a + (-b).$$

This definition says that **to subtract b from a, add the opposite of b to a.** In other words, change the sign of b and add.

EXAMPLE 1   Find the difference of 3 and 5.

Solution   Change the subtraction problem $3 - 5$ to an addition problem.

No change
Change subtraction to addition
Opposite of 5

Try Problem 1 > $3 - 5 = 3 + (-5) = -2$ ∎

EXAMPLE 2   Find the difference of -10 and 4.

Solution   Change the subtraction problem $-10 - 4$ to an addition problem.

No change
Change subtraction to addition
Opposite of 4

Try Problem 3 > $-10 - 4 = -10 + (-4) = -14$ ∎

EXAMPLE 3   Find the difference of 8 and -7.

Solution   Change the subtraction problem $8 - (-7)$ to an addition problem.

No change
Change subtraction to addition
Opposite of -7

Try Problem 5 > $8 - (-7) = 8 + 7 = 15$ ∎

EXAMPLE 4 Subtract all combinations of positive and negative 6 and 1.

Solution
a. $6 - 1 = 6 + (-1) = 5$ *To subtract 1, add −1*
b. $-6 - 1 = -6 + (-1) = -7$ *To subtract 1, add −1*
c. $6 - (-1) = 6 + 1 = 7$ *To subtract −1, add 1*

Try Problem 45 > d. $-6 - (-1) = -6 + 1 = -5$ *To subtract −1, add 1* ∎

TO SUBTRACT REAL NUMBERS

1. Change the subtraction to an addition.
2. Change the sign of the second number.
3. Add using the rules for addition.

EXAMPLE 5 Subtract 1 3/4 − 11.

Solution

$$1\frac{3}{4} - 11 = \frac{7}{4} - \frac{11}{1}$$ *Convert to improper fractions*

$$= \frac{7}{4} - \frac{44}{4}$$ *Write with the same denominator*

$$= \frac{7}{4} + \left(-\frac{44}{4}\right)$$ *Change to addition, change the sign of the second number*

$$= -\frac{37}{4}$$ *Add*

Try Problem 55 > Both −37/4 and −9 1/4 are correct answers. ∎

EXAMPLE 6 Subtract 5.61 − (−2.3).

Solution
$$5.61 - (-2.3) = 5.61 + 2.3$$ *Change to addition, change the sign of the second number*

Try Problem 61 > $$= 7.91$$ *Add* ∎

P R O B L E M   S O L V I N G

EXAMPLE 7 Find the difference in elevation between Pikes Peak at 14,110 feet above sea level and Death Valley at 280 feet below sea level.

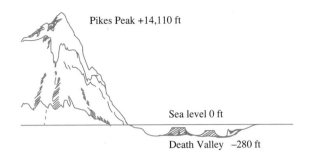

Pikes Peak +14,110 ft

Sea level 0 ft

Death Valley   −280 ft

Solution   Treat the elevation above sea level as a positive number and the elevation below sea level as a negative number. Then the difference in elevation between +14,110 feet and −280 feet is calculated as follows.

$$14{,}110 - (-280) = 14{,}110 + 280 \quad \textit{Change to addition}$$
$$= 14{,}390 \qquad \textit{Add}$$

Try Problem 77 >   The difference in elevation is 14,390 feet.

1.5 Problem Set

LEARNING THROUGH WRITING

☐ Explain how to subtract two real numbers.

☐ Write each operation in words.
   a. $4 - 9$ b. $-16 - 10$ c. $-7 - (-8)$

Find each difference.

1. $3 - 7$	**2.** $2 - 6$	**3.** $-5 - 4$	**4.** $-8 - 5$
5. $9 - (-6)$	**6.** $7 - (-3)$	**7.** $4 - 8$	**8.** $6 - 13$
9. $-3 - 3$	**10.** $-2 - 2$	**11.** $6 - (-1)$	**12.** $8 - (-4)$
13. $-12 - 3$	**14.** $-14 - 2$	**15.** $10 - 15$	**16.** $15 - 25$
17. $11 - (-12)$	**18.** $13 - (-14)$	**19.** $-8 - (-2)$	**20.** $-6 - (-3)$
21. $-9 - 8$	**22.** $-4 - 6$	**23.** $16 - 0$	**24.** $18 - 0$
25. $-1 - (-7)$	**26.** $-1 - (-9)$	**27.** $-15 - (-6)$	**28.** $-19 - (-5)$
29. $0 - 5$	**30.** $0 - 8$	**31.** $0 - (-10)$	**32.** $0 - (-12)$
33. $93 - 49$	**34.** $85 - 37$	**35.** $70 - (-70)$	**36.** $60 - (-60)$
37. $17 - 189$	**38.** $16 - 191$	**39.** $110 - 110$	**40.** $99 - 99$
41. $-52 - 0$	**42.** $-73 - 0$	**43.** $-200 - (-200)$	**44.** $-150 - (-150)$

Subtract all combinations of positive and negative values for each pair of numbers.

45. 432 and 167   **46.** $\dfrac{3}{7}$ and $\dfrac{4}{7}$ **47.** $5\dfrac{1}{2}$ and $3\dfrac{3}{4}$ **48.** 18.3 and 6.06

Find each difference.

49. $\dfrac{1}{3} - \dfrac{1}{2}$ **50.** $\dfrac{1}{4} - \dfrac{1}{3}$ **51.** $\dfrac{1}{3} - \dfrac{5}{9}$ **52.** $\dfrac{1}{2} - \dfrac{5}{8}$

53. $-\dfrac{3}{4} - \left(-\dfrac{5}{6}\right)$ **54.** $-\dfrac{2}{9} - \left(-\dfrac{5}{6}\right)$ **55.** $1\dfrac{3}{5} - 6$ **56.** $1\dfrac{2}{7} - 4$

57. $-5.7 - 3.1$ **58.** $-8.6 - 4.3$ **59.** $4.99 - 8.3$ **60.** $3.74 - 7.5$

61. $6.84 - (-5.2)$ **62.** $7.45 - (-6.1)$ **63.** $-1.9 - (-2.3)$ **64.** $-2.4 - (-5.1)$

Write two subtraction problems that are suggested by each addition problem. For example, $2 + 3 = 5$ suggests $5 - 2 = 3$ and $5 - 3 = 2$.

65. $-2 + 7 = 5$ **66.** $-8 + 5 = -3$ **67.** $-1 + (-3) = -4$ **68.** $9 + (-2) = 7$

Solve each word problem.

69. Subtract 8 from 2.

70. Subtract 4 from -9.

71. Subtract -13 from 6.

72. Subtract -9 from -11.

73. Find the difference of -23 and 14.

74. Find the difference of 18 and -35.

75. The temperature is $-2°$. If it falls $9°$, what is the new temperature?

76. The temperature is $3°$. If it falls $13°$, what is the new temperature?

77. Find the difference in elevation between Mt. Whitney at 14,490 feet above sea level and Death Valley at 280 feet below sea level.

78. Ted completed a round of golf with a score of 1 stroke under par. Andy's score was 6 strokes under par. Find the difference between Ted's score and Andy's score.

79. Sally's checking account is overdrawn $8.36. If she writes a check for $7.67, what will her balance be if the check clears the bank?

80. Larry's credit card balance is $\$-43.32$. If he charges a purchase of $15.95, what is his new balance?

▦ CALCULATOR PROBLEMS

To find $2 - (-6)$ on your calculator, press

| Clear | 2 | − | 6 | +/− | = | 8 |

Therefore $2 - (-6) = 8$. Find each difference on your calculator.

81. $63 - 91$ **82.** $-247 - 138$ **83.** $-559 - (-712)$

1.6   Multiplication of Real Numbers

We already know that the product of two positive numbers is a positive number. Also, the product of any real number and 0 is 0.

> **MULTIPLICATION PROPERTY OF 0**
>
> If a is any real number, then
> $$a \cdot 0 = 0 \quad \text{and} \quad 0 \cdot a = 0.$$

Now let's see what happens when we multiply a negative number and a positive number. Consider the following products.

Numbers decrease by 1 ⟶   ⟵*Numbers decrease by 5*

$$3 \cdot 5 = 15$$
$$2 \cdot 5 = 10$$
$$1 \cdot 5 = 5$$
$$0 \cdot 5 = 0$$
$$-1 \cdot 5 = ?$$
$$-2 \cdot 5 = ?$$

If we continue this pattern, then $-1 \cdot 5 = -5$ and $-2 \cdot 5 = -10$. This suggests the following rule: **The product of a negative number and a positive number is a negative number.**

EXAMPLE 1   Find the product of -4 and 7.

Solution   The product of a negative number and a positive number is a negative number.

Try Problem 3 > $(-4)7 = -28$ ∎

EXAMPLE 2   Find the product of 6 and -5.

Solution   The product of a positive number and a negative number is a negative number.

Try Problem 5 > $6(-5) = -30$ ∎

Now we use the fact that a positive times a negative is a negative to illustrate what happens when we multiply two negatives.

Numbers decrease by 1 ⟶   ⟵*Numbers increase by 5*

$$3(-5) = -15$$
$$2(-5) = -10$$
$$1(-5) = -5$$
$$0(-5) = 0$$
$$-1(-5) = ?$$
$$-2(-5) = ?$$

If we continue this pattern, then $-1(-5) = 5$ and $-2(-5) = 10$. This suggests the following rule: **The product of two negative numbers is a positive number.**

EXAMPLE 3   Find the product of -9 and -5.

Solution   The product of two negative numbers is a positive number.

Try Problem 9 > $-9(-5) = 45$ ∎

Caution! ■
■
■
■
■
■

The correct use of parentheses is very important when operating with real numbers. Compare the following two examples.

Subtraction	*Multiplication*
$-2 - 3 = -2 + (-3) = -5$	$-2(-3) = 6$

EXAMPLE 4   Find each product.

a. $(-18)(-1) = 18$ *Product of two negatives*
b. $5(-5) = -25$ *Product of a positive and a negative*
c. $(-6)1 = -6$ *Product of a negative and a positive*

Try Problem 17 >   d. $0(-9) = 0$ *Product of 0 and a number*   ■

MULTIPLYING REAL NUMBERS

Multiply the absolute values. If the numbers have the same sign, the product is positive; if they have different signs, the product is negative.

EXAMPLE 5   Multiply all combinations of positive and negative 3 and 4.

Solution

a. $3(4) = 12$ *Same sign, product is positive*
b. $-3(-4) = 12$ *Same sign, product is positive*
c. $3(-4) = -12$ *Different signs, product is negative*

Try Problem 27 >   d. $(-3)4 = -12$ *Different signs, product is negative*   ■

EXAMPLE 6   Multiply $(-2/5)(-3/7)$.

Solution

$$\left(-\frac{2}{5}\right)\left(-\frac{3}{7}\right) = +\frac{2 \cdot 3}{5 \cdot 7} \quad \text{\textit{Same sign, product is positive}}$$

Try Problem 31 >
$$= \frac{6}{35}$$ ■

EXAMPLE 7   Multiply $(-6.45)2.3$.

Solution   Multiply the absolute values.

$$
\begin{array}{rl}
6.45 & \textit{2 decimal places} \\
\times\ 2.3 & \textit{1 decimal place} \\
\hline
1935 & \\
1290 & \\
\hline
14.835 & \textit{3 decimal places}
\end{array}
$$

The numbers have different signs, so the product is negative.

Try Problem 47 > $(-6.45)2.3 = -14.835$ ■

EXAMPLE 8   Find each product.

a. $(-1)(-1)(-1) = (1)(-1) = -1$
b. $(-3)(2)(-5) = (-6)(-5) = 30$
c. $(-4)(-2)(-6)(-3) = (8)(18) = 144$

Try Problem 55 >   d. $10(-8)(-2)(-2) = (-80)(4) = -320$ ■

Example 8 illustrates the following rule: **When a collection of factors contains an even number of negative factors, the product will be positive; when it contains an odd number of negative factors, the product will be negative.**

Since reciprocals multiply to 1, we can use the rules for multiplication to find the reciprocal of a negative number.

EXAMPLE 9

a. The reciprocal of -2 is $-1/2$, since $(-2)(-1/2) = 1$.
b. The reciprocal of $-3/4$ is $-4/3$, since $(-3/4)(-4/3) = 1$.

Try Problem 63 >   c. The reciprocal of -1 is -1, since $(-1)(-1) = 1$.   ■

PROBLEM   SOLVING

EXAMPLE 10   Let's agree that if someone handles money, a gain will be represented by a positive number and a loss by a negative number. Also, time in the future will be represented by a positive number and time in the past by a negative number. Use products of real numbers to illustrate the increase or decrease in the person's wealth.

Solution   If a man gains five dollars a day, then three days in the future he will be fifteen dollars richer.

$(+5)(+3) = +15$

If he loses five dollars a day, then three days in the future he will be fifteen dollars poorer.

$(-5)(+3) = -15$

If he gains five dollars a day, then three days ago he was fifteen dollars poorer.

$(+5)(-3) = -15$

If he loses five dollars a day, then three days ago he was fifteen dollars richer.

Try Problem 73 > $(-5)(-3) = +15$ ■

1.6   Problem Set

LEARNING THROUGH WRITING   ☐ Explain how to multiply two real numbers.

☐ Write each operation in words.
   a. $-8(4)$ b. $6(-15)$ c. $(-2)(-1)$

Find the products and observe the pattern.

1. $3 \cdot 10 =$	**2.** $3(-10) =$
$2 \cdot 10 =$	$2(-10) =$
$1 \cdot 10 =$	$1(-10) =$
$0 \cdot 10 =$	$0(-10) =$
$-1 \cdot 10 =$	$-1(-10) =$
$-2 \cdot 10 =$	$-2(-10) =$

Find each product.

3. $(-8)2$ **4.** $(-7)4$ **5.** $5(-4)$ **6.** $6(-3)$

7. $6 \cdot 7$ **8.** $8 \cdot 9$ **9.** $-2(-3)$ **10.** $-5(-8)$

11. $-1(-1)$ **12.** $(-1)1$ **13.** $16(-1)$ **14.** $(-14)(-1)$

15. $-23 \cdot 0$ **16.** $-12 \cdot 0$ **17.** $6(-6)$ **18.** $8(-8)$

19. $(-9)1$ **20.** $4(-1)$ **21.** $(-12)(-12)$ **22.** $(-10)(-10)$

23. $(-15)(-4)$ **24.** $(-5)(-12)$ **25.** $0(-6)$ **26.** $0(-2)$

Multiply all combinations of positive and negative values for each pair of numbers.

27. 6 and 8   **28.** 17 and 190   **29.** 168 and 4.2   **30.** $5\frac{1}{2}$ and $3\frac{2}{3}$

Find the products.

31. $\left(-\dfrac{3}{4}\right)\left(-\dfrac{5}{7}\right)$ **32.** $\left(-\dfrac{3}{5}\right)\left(-\dfrac{4}{7}\right)$ **33.** $\left(-\dfrac{2}{9}\right)\dfrac{5}{2}$ **34.** $\left(-\dfrac{3}{8}\right)\dfrac{5}{3}$

35. $10\left(-\dfrac{1}{2}\right)$ **36.** $12\left(-\dfrac{1}{2}\right)$ **37.** $3\left(-\dfrac{1}{3}\right)$ **38.** $4\left(-\dfrac{1}{4}\right)$

39. $\left(-\dfrac{1}{6}\right)(-6)$ **40.** $\left(-\dfrac{1}{8}\right)(-8)$ **41.** $(-1.1)(-1.1)$ **42.** $(-2.2)(-2.2)$

43. $13.9(-6.7)$ **44.** $15.2(-4.8)$ **45.** $(-0.08)(-0.02)$ **46.** $(-0.09)(-0.03)$

47. $(-7.35)4.3$ **48.** $(-8.65)2.7$ **49.** $(-2)(-5)(-7)$ **50.** $(-3)(-2)(-6)$

51. $(-4)(4)(-4)$ **52.** $(-5)(5)(-5)$ **53.** $(-1)(-4)(-2)(-3)$ **54.** $(-2)(-1)(-3)(-5)$

55. $10(-6)(-2)(-5)$ **56.** $20(-4)(-3)(-2)$ **57.** $9(-2)(0)(7)(-8)$ **58.** $6(-7)(8)(0)(-3)$

Find the reciprocal of each number. Write your answer in simplest form.

59. 5   **60.** $\dfrac{1}{4}$ **61.** $-\dfrac{1}{6}$ **62.** -3

63. $-\dfrac{2}{3}$ **64.** $\dfrac{6}{5}$ **65.** 1   **66.** -1

67. -0.1 **68.** 0.2 **69.** $2\dfrac{3}{7}$ **70.** $-5\dfrac{2}{7}$

Solve each word problem.

71. A quarterback is sacked for a four-yard loss on each of three consecutive plays. Find the total yardage for the three plays.

73. A dieter loses 2 pounds per week for six consecutive weeks. Write the dieter's weight change as a signed number.

75. A small business has a $500 line of credit at each of five different banks. If it has borrowed its limit at all five banks, write its balance as a signed number.

72. A golfer shoots two strokes under par each day of a four-day tournament. What was the golfer's score in relation to par at the end of the tournament?

74. A gambler loses $6 per race on nine consecutive races. Write the gambler's profit as a signed number.

76. The Dow Jones industrial average declines 2.85 points on each of two consecutive days of trading. Find the total change in the Dow.

 ## CALCULATOR PROBLEMS

To find $7(-3)$ *on your calculator, press*

| Clear | 7 | × | 3 | +/− | = | −21 |

Therefore $7(-3) = -21$. *Find each product on your calculator.*

77. $19(-14)$ **78.** $(-28)35$ **79.** $(-182)(-653)$

To find the reciprocal of 8 *on your calculator, press*

| Clear | 8 | 1/x | 0.125 |

Therefore the reciprocal of 8 *is* 0.125, *or* 1/8. *Find the reciprocal of each number on your calculator.*

80. 16   **81.** -2.5 **82.** $3\dfrac{7}{8}$

1.7   Division of Real Numbers

We can use the rules for multiplying real numbers to develop rules for dividing real numbers. First let's divide two numbers having the same sign.

EXAMPLE 1   Find the quotient of 6 and 2.

Try Problem 3 >   Solution $\dfrac{6}{2} = 3$, since $2 \cdot 3 = 6$.   ■

EXAMPLE 2   Find the quotient of -6 and -2.

Try Problem 7 >   Solution $\dfrac{-6}{-2} = 3$, since $-2 \cdot 3 = -6$.   ■

Examples 1 and 2 suggest the following rule: **The quotient of two numbers having the same sign is a positive number.** Now let's divide two numbers having different signs.

EXAMPLE 3   Find the quotient of -6 and 2.

Try Problem 9 >   Solution $\dfrac{-6}{2} = -3$, since $2 \cdot (-3) = -6$.   ∎

EXAMPLE 4   Find the quotient of 6 and -2.

Try Problem 11 >   Solution $\dfrac{6}{-2} = -3$, since $-2 \cdot (-3) = 6$.   ∎

Examples 3 and 4 suggest the following rule: **The quotient of two numbers having different signs is a negative number.**

EXAMPLE 5   Find each quotient.

a. $\dfrac{-25}{-1} = 25$ *Same sign, quotient is positive*

b. $\dfrac{-14}{-14} = 1$ *Same sign, quotient is positive*

c. $\dfrac{-45}{1} = -45$ *Different signs, quotient is negative*

Try Problem 25 >   d. $\dfrac{12}{-12} = -1$ *Different signs, quotient is negative*   ∎

DIVIDING REAL NUMBERS

Divide the absolute values. If the numbers have the same sign, the quotient is positive; if they have different signs, the quotient is negative.

EXAMPLE 6   Divide all combinations of positive and negative 12 and 3.

Solution

a. $\dfrac{12}{3} = 4$ *Same sign, quotient is positive*

b. $\dfrac{-12}{-3} = 4$ *Same sign, quotient is positive*

c. $\dfrac{-12}{3} = -4$ *Different signs, quotient is negative*

Try Problem 31 >   d. $\dfrac{12}{-3} = -4$ *Different signs, quotient is negative*   ∎

Before we illustrate division of fractions, consider the following three fractions.

$$-\frac{6}{2} \qquad \frac{-6}{2} \qquad \frac{6}{-2}$$

Since each of these fractions is equal to -3, the fractions must be equal to each other.

SIGNS OF A FRACTION

If $b \neq 0$, then

$$-\frac{a}{b} = \frac{-a}{b} = \frac{a}{-b}.$$

The form

$$\frac{a}{-b}$$

is seldom used. For example, we usually write

$$-\frac{3}{4} \quad \text{or} \quad \frac{-3}{4} \quad \text{instead of} \quad \frac{3}{-4}.$$

Here are two other fractions to consider.

$$\frac{-6}{-2} \qquad \frac{6}{2}$$

Since each of these fractions is equal to 3, the fractions must be equal to each other.

SIGNS OF A FRACTION

If $b \neq 0$, then

$$\frac{-a}{-b} = \frac{a}{b}.$$

EXAMPLE 7   Simplify each fraction.

a. $\dfrac{-3}{-5} = \dfrac{3}{5}$

b. $-\dfrac{-4}{9} = \dfrac{-4}{-9} = \dfrac{4}{9}$

c. $-\dfrac{6}{-12} = \dfrac{-6}{-12} = \dfrac{6}{12} = \dfrac{1}{2}$

Try Problem 43 >   d. $-\dfrac{-15}{-20} = -\dfrac{15}{20} = -\dfrac{3}{4}$ ■

EXAMPLE 8   Divide $\dfrac{-18}{5} \div \left(\dfrac{9}{-4} \right)$.

Solution

$$\dfrac{-18}{5} \div \left(\dfrac{9}{-4} \right) = -\dfrac{18}{5} \div \left(-\dfrac{9}{4} \right) \qquad \textit{Reposition negative signs}$$

$$= -\dfrac{18}{5} \cdot \left(-\dfrac{4}{9} \right) \qquad \textit{Invert and multiply}$$

$$= -\dfrac{\overset{2}{\cancel{18}}}{5} \cdot \left(-\dfrac{4}{\underset{1}{\cancel{9}}} \right) \qquad \textit{Divide both 18 and 9 by 9}$$

Try Problem 51 >
$$= \dfrac{8}{5} \qquad \textit{Same sign, product is positive} \qquad ■$$

EXAMPLE 9   Divide $350.35 \div (-24.5)$.

Solution   Divide the absolute values.

```
           14.3
  24.5,)350.3̣5
        245
        105 3
         98 0
          7 3 5
          7 3 5
              0
```

The numbers have different signs, so the quotient is negative.

Try Problem 59 >
$$350.35 \div (-24.5) = -14.3 \qquad ■$$

When we defined a rational number we stated that the denominator could not be 0. We shall now see why. Consider the quotient 0/6:

If $\dfrac{0}{6} = x,$ then $6 \cdot x = 0.$

The only value of x that makes $6 \cdot x = 0$ a true statement is 0. Therefore $0/6 = 0$. Now consider the quotient 6/0:

If $\dfrac{6}{0} = x,$ then $0 \cdot x = 6.$

But 0 times any number is 0, not 6. So there is no value of x that makes $0 \cdot x = 6$ a true statement. Therefore we say that 6/0 is undefined. In general, **division by 0 is undefined.**

DIVISION INVOLVING 0

If $a \neq 0$, then $0/a = 0$, and $a/0$ is undefined.

P R O B L E M   S O L V I N G

EXAMPLE 10   For the past five years, the low temperatures on New Year's Day in Wintertown were 2°, −6°, 3°, 0°, and −9°. Find the average of these temperatures.

Solution   Add the numbers and divide by 5.

$$\text{Average} = \frac{2 + (-6) + 3 + 0 + (-9)}{5} = \frac{-10}{5} = -2$$

Try Problem 79 >   The average low temperature was −2°.

1.7   **Problem Set**

LEARNING THROUGH WRITING   ☐ Explain how to divide two real numbers.

☐ Write each operation in words.

a. $-14 \div 7$ b. $\dfrac{-30}{-5}$ c. $6\overline{)24}$

Find the quotients and observe the pattern.

1. $15 \div 5 =$ **2.** $15 \div (-5) =$
   $10 \div 5 =$ $10 \div (-5) =$
   $5 \div 5 =$ $5 \div (-5) =$
   $0 \div 5 =$ $0 \div (-5) =$
   $-5 \div 5 =$ $-5 \div (-5) =$
   $-10 \div 5 =$ $-10 \div (-5) =$

Find each quotient.

3. $\dfrac{10}{2}$ **4.** $\dfrac{12}{2}$ **5.** $\dfrac{12}{-3}$ **6.** $\dfrac{15}{-3}$

7. $\dfrac{-15}{-5}$ **8.** $\dfrac{-8}{-4}$ **9.** $\dfrac{-20}{5}$ **10.** $\dfrac{-12}{6}$

11. $\dfrac{34}{-17}$ **12.** $\dfrac{39}{-13}$ **13.** $\dfrac{-27}{-9}$ **14.** $\dfrac{-32}{-8}$

15. $\dfrac{-25}{-5}$ **16.** $\dfrac{-21}{-7}$ **17.** $\dfrac{-6}{1}$ **18.** $\dfrac{-9}{1}$

19. $\dfrac{-18}{18}$ **20.** $\dfrac{19}{-19}$ **21.** $\dfrac{-280}{7}$ **22.** $\dfrac{-350}{7}$

23. $\dfrac{1}{-1}$ **24.** $\dfrac{-1}{1}$ **25.** $\dfrac{-56}{-1}$ **26.** $\dfrac{-72}{-1}$

27. $\dfrac{180}{-20}$ **28.** $\dfrac{240}{-30}$ **29.** $\dfrac{-23}{-23}$ **30.** $\dfrac{-27}{-27}$

Divide all combinations of positive and negative values for each pair of numbers.

31. 16 and 2   **32.** 246 and 12   **33.** 6 and $\dfrac{2}{3}$ **34.** 86 and 3.44

Simplify each fraction.

35. $\dfrac{-2}{-5}$ **36.** $\dfrac{-4}{-7}$ **37.** $\dfrac{-12}{30}$ **38.** $\dfrac{-8}{20}$

39. $-\dfrac{-3}{8}$ **40.** $-\dfrac{-2}{9}$ **41.** $\dfrac{10}{-25}$ **42.** $\dfrac{14}{-35}$

43. $-\dfrac{4}{-16}$ **44.** $-\dfrac{6}{-18}$ **45.** $-\dfrac{-21}{-28}$ **46.** $-\dfrac{-9}{-15}$

Find each quotient.

47. $\dfrac{-3}{8} \div \dfrac{2}{5}$ **48.** $\dfrac{-5}{9} \div \dfrac{2}{3}$ **49.** $\dfrac{1}{2} \div (-2)$ **50.** $\dfrac{1}{3} \div (-3)$

51. $\dfrac{-15}{4} \div \left(\dfrac{5}{-6}\right)$ **52.** $\dfrac{-24}{5} \div \left(\dfrac{8}{-3}\right)$ **53.** $-18 \div \left(\dfrac{9}{-10}\right)$ **54.** $-12 \div \left(\dfrac{6}{-8}\right)$

55. $-21.44 \div 6.7$ **56.** $-44.52 \div 5.3$ **57.** $-10.8 \div (-0.72)$ **58.** $-9.5 \div (-0.38)$

59. $328.02 \div (-21.3)$ **60.** $861.84 \div (-32.4)$

Determine whether each quotient is 0 or is undefined.

61. $\dfrac{0}{5}$ **62.** $\dfrac{0}{-9}$ **63.** $\dfrac{-4}{0}$ **64.** $\dfrac{6}{0}$

65. $0 \div 13$ **66.** $0 \div (-7)$ **67.** $-1 \div 0$ **68.** $10 \div 0$

Write two division problems that are suggested by each multiplication problem. For example, $2 \cdot 3 = 6$ suggests $6 \div 2 = 3$ and $6 \div 3 = 2$.

69. $4(-6) = -24$ **70.** $(-3)6 = -18$ **71.** $(-5)(-8) = 40$ **72.** $(-2)(-15) = 30$

Solve each word problem.

73. Divide 6 by -12.

74. Divide -6 by -18.

75. Find the quotient of -10 and 0.

76. Find the quotient of 0 and 15.

77. The temperature fell 21° over a seven-hour period. Find the average change per hour.

78. The Dow Jones industrial average lost 5 points in one five-hour period. Find the average change per hour.

79. A halfback carried the ball six times, with the following results: 3-yard loss, 2-yard gain, 1-yard gain, no gain, 9-yard loss, 3-yard loss. Find the average gain per carry.

80. Sandy's charge card balances over one four-day period were $\$-12$, $\$-17$, $\$0$, and $\$-23$. Find the average balance for the four days.

81. Explain why 0 divided by 4 is 0.

82. Explain why 9 divided by 0 is undefined.

🖩 CALCULATOR PROBLEMS

To find the quotient $-8 \div 0$ *on your calculator, press*

Clear	8	+/−	÷	0	=	Error

Your calculator registered an error because division by 0 is undefined. Try to find each quotient on your calculator.

83. $0 \div (-4)$ **84.** $-5 \div 0$ **85.** $-271.86 \div 19.7$

1.8 Exponents and Order of Operations

Exponents

Multiplication problems involving repeated factors, such as

$$2 \cdot 2 \cdot 2 \quad \text{and} \quad x \cdot x \cdot x \cdot x,$$

occur often in algebra. Therefore mathematicians developed an abbreviated way of writing them. For example, since 2 appears as a factor three times in $2 \cdot 2 \cdot 2$, we abbreviate this product as 2^3. The number 2 is called the **base** and the number 3 is called the **exponent.** The product $x \cdot x \cdot x \cdot x$ is abbreviated x^4. In this case x is the base and 4 is the exponent.

Exponential notation (in the form employed today) was first used by the French mathematician and philosopher René Descartes (1596–1650) in his book *La Géométrie.*

EXPONENTIAL NOTATION

If a is a real number and n is a positive integer, then

$$a^n = \underbrace{a \cdot a \cdot a \cdot \cdots \cdot a.}_{n \text{ factors of } a}$$

EXAMPLE 1   Evaluate.

a. $5^2 = 5 \cdot 5 = 25$ *Read 5^2 as "5 squared"*

b. $10^3 = 10 \cdot 10 \cdot 10 = 1000$ *Read 10^3 as "10 cubed"*

c. $\left(\dfrac{2}{3}\right)^4 = \dfrac{2}{3} \cdot \dfrac{2}{3} \cdot \dfrac{2}{3} \cdot \dfrac{2}{3} = \dfrac{16}{81}$ *Read $(2/3)^4$ as "2/3 to the fourth power"*

Try Problem 1>   d. $8^1 = 8$ *Read 8^1 as "8 to the first power"*   ∎

EXAMPLE 2   Evaluate.

a. $(-3)^2 = (-3)(-3) = 9$ *Base is -3*
b. $-3^2 = -(3 \cdot 3) = -9$ *Base is 3*
c. $(-2)^3 = (-2)(-2)(-2) = -8$ *Base is -2*
d. $-2^3 = -(2 \cdot 2 \cdot 2) = -8$ *Base is 2*

Try Problem 9 >

Caution! ■

The base in -4^2 is 4, *not* -4. Therefore to evaluate -4^2, square the 4 and *then* apply the negative sign.

Correct	*Wrong*
$-4^2 = -16$	~~$-4^2 = 16$~~

Order of Operations

Many problems involve more than one arithmetic operation. For example, to evaluate

$$2 + 3 \cdot 4,$$

do we add first and get 20, or do we multiply first and get 14? To avoid this confusion, mathematicians have agreed on the following order of operations.

ORDER OF OPERATIONS

Perform all operations in the following numerical order.

1. Do all operations above and below fraction bars separately.
2. Do all operations in parentheses ( ) and brackets [ ], applying the innermost grouping symbols first.
3. Apply all exponents.
4. Do all multiplications and divisions, from left to right.
5. Do all additions and subtractions, from left to right.

The following examples illustrate how to apply the rules for order of operations.

EXAMPLE 3   Evaluate.

a. $2 + 3 \cdot 4$ b. $(2 + 3) \cdot 4$

Solution
a. $2 + 3 \cdot 4 = 2 + 12$ *Multiply before adding*
$\qquad\qquad = 14$ *Add*
b. $(2 + 3) \cdot 4 = 5 \cdot 4$ *Apply ( ) before multiplying*
Try Problem 25 > $\qquad\qquad = 20$ *Multiply*   ■

EXAMPLE 4   Evaluate $14 \div 7 \cdot 2$.

Solution

Try Problem 29 >

$$14 \div 7 \cdot 2 = 2 \cdot 2 \qquad \textit{Divide, since} \div \textit{is on the left}$$
$$= 4 \qquad \textit{Multiply}$$ ■

EXAMPLE 5   Evaluate $13 - 2^3 + 2^2$.

Solution

Try Problem 37 >

$$13 - 2^3 + 2^2 = 13 - 8 + 4 \qquad \textit{Apply exponents}$$
$$= 5 + 4 \qquad \textit{Subtract, since} - \textit{is on the left}$$
$$= 9 \qquad \textit{Add}$$ ■

EXAMPLE 6   Evaluate $6 + 4[2(-7 + 5) - 1]$.

Solution

Try Problem 51 >

$$6 + 4[2(-7 + 5) - 1]$$
$$= 6 + 4[2(-2) - 1] \qquad \textit{Apply innermost ( )}$$
$$= 6 + 4[-4 - 1] \qquad \textit{Multiply before subtracting}$$
$$= 6 + 4[-5] \qquad \textit{Apply [ ]}$$
$$= 6 + (-20) \qquad \textit{Multiply before adding}$$
$$= -14 \qquad \textit{Add}$$ ■

EXAMPLE 7   Evaluate $\dfrac{4(-7) + (-1)5}{-2 - 1}$.

Solution   Do all operations above and below the fraction bar separately.

Try Problem 61 >

$$\frac{4(-7) + (-1)5}{-2 - 1} = \frac{-28 + (-5)}{-2 + (-1)} \qquad \begin{array}{l}\textit{Multiply in numerator, change} \\ \textit{subtraction to addition in denominator}\end{array}$$
$$= \frac{-33}{-3} \qquad \textit{Add in numerator, add in denominator}$$
$$= 11 \qquad \textit{Divide}$$ ■

Often we must apply the order of operations when evaluating an *algebraic expression*. An **algebraic expression,** or simply an **expression,** is a meaningful collection of constants, variables, and operations. Here are three examples of algebraic expressions.

$$3x + 6 \qquad 2x - 4y + 7 \qquad z^2 + 6z - 10$$

An algebraic expression takes on different values as its variable(s) take on different values.

EXAMPLE 8   Evaluate $3x + 6$ at $x = 4$.

Solution

$$3x + 6 = 3(4) + 6 \quad \textit{Replace x with 4}$$
$$= 12 + 6 \quad \textit{Multiply before adding}$$
$$= 18 \quad \textit{Add}$$

Try Problem 67 >

EXAMPLE 9   Evaluate $2x - 4y + 7$ at $x = 3$ and $y = -2$.

Solution

$$2x - 4y + 7 = 2(3) - 4(-2) + 7 \quad \textit{Replace x with 3 and y with -2}$$
$$= 6 - (-8) + 7 \quad \textit{Multiply before adding or subtracting}$$
$$= 6 + 8 + 7 \quad \textit{Change subtraction to addition}$$
$$= 21 \quad \textit{Add in any order}$$

Try Problem 69 >

PROBLEM SOLVING

EXAMPLE 10   A furniture store sold two rugs at a loss of $27 per rug, three paintings at a loss of $13 per painting, and seven lamps at a profit of $32 per lamp. Determine the net amount of the 12 sales.

Solution   Treat the profits as positive numbers and the losses as negative numbers. Then total the profits and losses.

$$2(-27) + 3(-13) + 7(32) = -54 + (-39) + 224 \quad \textit{Multiply before adding}$$
$$= 131 \quad \textit{Add in any order}$$

Try Problem 83 >   The net amount was $131.

1.8 Problem Set

LEARNING THROUGH WRITING

☐ Write each operation in words.
  a. 4^2 b. $(-6)^3$ c. 12^{10}

☐ Explain the difference between $3 \cdot 2$ and 3^2.

☐ Explain the difference between $(-5)^2$ and -5^2.

☐ Discuss the difference between the *base* and the *exponent*.

☐ Define the term *algebraic expression*.

☐ State the order of operations.

Evaluate.

1. 8^2

2. 4^3

3. 10^4

4. 2^5

5. $(-5)^2$

6. $(-4)^2$

7. -5^2

8. -4^2

9. $(-5)^3$ **10.** $(-4)^3$ **11.** -5^3 **12.** -4^3

13. $\left(\dfrac{3}{4}\right)^4$ **14.** $\left(\dfrac{2}{5}\right)^4$ **15.** $\left(-\dfrac{1}{2}\right)^2$ **16.** $\left(-\dfrac{1}{3}\right)^2$

17. -2^4 **18.** -3^4 **19.** $(-1)^6$ **20.** -1^8

Evaluate.

21. $2 \cdot 5^2$ **22.** $2 \cdot 4^2$ **23.** $12 - 3^2$

24. $30 - 5^2$ **25.** $5 + 2 \cdot 3$ **26.** $6 + 4 \cdot 2$

27. $18 - 5 + 3$ **28.** $19 - 8 + 3$ **29.** $16 \div 8 \cdot 2$

30. $12 \div 6 \cdot 2$ **31.** $3 + 12 \div 3 + 3$ **32.** $4 + 18 \div 2 + 4$

33. $6 - 3 + 4^2 - 2$ **34.** $8 - 5 + 3^2 - 1$ **35.** $100 \div 10 \cdot 10 \div 100$

36. $100 \cdot 10 \div 10 \cdot 10$ **37.** $15 - 2^2 + 2^3$ **38.** $30 - 3^2 + 3^3$

39. $3 + [7 + 3(2 + 5)]$ **40.** $7 + [4 + 2(3 + 4)]$ **41.** $3(2[10 - 2(4 - 2)])$

42. $3(2[12 - 4(8 - 6)])$ **43.** $\dfrac{2}{5} + \dfrac{3}{5} \cdot 20$ **44.** $\dfrac{4}{7} + \dfrac{3}{7} \cdot 14$

45. $(-2)(-4) + 5(-3)$ **46.** $(-3)(-6) + 7(-4)$ **47.** $1 - 8 - 3 - 5$

48. $2 - 9 - 5 - 4$ **49.** $4 + 3[1 - 2(-5)]$ **50.** $6 + 2[5 - 3(-4)]$

51. $2 + [4(-5 + 3) - 2]$ **52.** $5 + [6(-8 + 7) - 3]$ **53.** $-4^2 + 7(3[4 - 5 \cdot 2])$

54. $-6^2 + 2(4[6 - 7 \cdot 2])$ **55.** $\left(-\dfrac{1}{2}\right)^2 \div \left(\dfrac{1}{2} - \dfrac{1}{3}\right)$ **56.** $\left(-\dfrac{1}{3}\right)^2 \div \left(\dfrac{1}{3} - \dfrac{1}{4}\right)$

57. $\left|\dfrac{-50}{6 - 11}\right|$ **58.** $\left|\dfrac{-100}{2 - 12}\right|$ **59.** $\dfrac{2(-12) + 4}{|-5 + 1|}$

60. $\dfrac{3(-8) + 4}{|-6 + 1|}$ **61.** $\dfrac{5(-2) + (-1)4}{-6 - 1}$ **62.** $\dfrac{4(-1) + (-2)3}{-1 - 1}$

63. $\dfrac{2 \cdot 3^2 - 3 \cdot 4^2}{2^2 + 1^2}$ **64.** $\dfrac{2 \cdot 4^2 - 2 \cdot 5^2}{2^2 - 1^2}$ **65.** $\dfrac{8[3 \cdot 5 - 4(3 \cdot 2 - 5)]}{4[5(1 + 6) - 4^2 + 9]}$

66. $\dfrac{3[2 \cdot 7 - 5(3 \cdot 4 - 11)]}{6[8(1 + 4) - 6^2 + 8]}$

Evaluate each algebraic expression at $x = 2$, $y = -3$, and $z = 5$.

67. $2x + 5$ **68.** $3x + 4$ **69.** $3x - 5y + 8$ **70.** $4|x + 3y - 6|$

71. $8x^2 - y^2 + 1$ **72.** $|x - y| + |y - x|$ **73.** $(-2y)(9x - 5z)^2$ **74.** $x(6y + 7z)(4x - z)$

75. $\dfrac{-x^2 + 5x - 8}{|z - y^2|}$ **76.** $\dfrac{4z - (x - y)^2}{2z}$

Solve each word problem.

77. Allen's bank balance is $16 when he writes four checks for $5 each. What will his balance be when the checks clear?

78. The temperature is 9°. If it falls at the rate of 2° per hour for six hours, what will the new temperature be?

79. Dava, who weighed 125 pounds, went on a diet and lost 13 pounds. If she later gained 2 pounds, how much does she weigh now?

80. A bus was loaded with 32 people. At the first stop 5 people got off. At the second stop 2 people got on. How many people are on the bus now?

81. A gambler began with $50, tripled it, and then lost $120. How much money does the gambler have now?

82. Bruce owned 200 shares of stock when the stock split, doubling his shares. If he then sold 325 shares, how many shares does he own now?

83. A car dealer sold two cars at a loss of $50 per car, three cars at a loss of $35 per car, and ten cars at a profit of $200 per car. Determine the net amount of the 15 sales.

84. A clothing store sold three blouses at a loss of $2 per blouse, four skirts at a loss of $3 per skirt, and six dresses at a profit of $30 per dress. Determine the net amount of the 13 sales.

CALCULATOR PROBLEMS

To evaluate 6^2 on your calculator, press

| Clear | 6 | x^2 | 36 |

To evaluate 2^3 on your calculator, press

| Clear | 2 | y^x | 3 | = | 8 |

Evaluate each of the following.

85. 7^2 **86.** 1.1^3 **87.** 2^{20}

Your calculator should follow the order of operations. To check, calculate $2 + 3 \cdot 4$ as follows:

| Clear | 2 | + | 3 | × | 4 | = | 14 |

If your calculator multiplied first (as it should), the display will read 14. If it added first, the display will read 20. Now try these problems on your calculator.

88. $24 \div 3 \cdot 2$ **89.** $4 + 12 \div 2 + 2$ **90.** $19 - 2^2 + 2^3$

1.9   Properties of Addition and Multiplication

In this section we state the basic properties of addition and multiplication of real numbers. As we state each property, keep in mind that a, b, and c represent real numbers.

> **COMMUTATIVE PROPERTIES**
> $$a + b = b + a$$
> $$ab = ba$$

The commutative properties state that we can add or multiply two numbers in either order and the answer will be the same.

EXAMPLE 1   Use a commutative property to complete each statement.

a. $-8 + 6 = ?$ b. $3(-7) = ?$

Solution

Try Problem 1 >

a. $-8 + 6 = 6 + (-8)$ *Change the order*

b. $3(-7) = (-7)3$ *Change the order*   ■

Caution! ■   Neither subtraction nor division is a commutative operation.

■
■
■
■
■
■
■

Subtraction	*Division*
$5 - 2 = 2 - 5$	$6 \div 3 = 3 \div 6$
$3 = -3$ *False*	$2 = \dfrac{1}{2}$ *False*

The next two properties state that we can change the grouping (or association) when adding or multiplying and the answer will be the same.

ASSOCIATIVE PROPERTIES

$$a + (b + c) = (a + b) + c$$
$$a(bc) = (ab)c$$

EXAMPLE 2   Use an associative property to complete each statement.

a. $4 + (5 + x) = ?$ b. $\dfrac{1}{2}(2y) = ?$

Solution

a. $4 + (5 + x) = (4 + 5) + x$ *Change the grouping*

Try Problem 11 >

b. $\dfrac{1}{2}(2y) = \left(\dfrac{1}{2} \cdot 2\right)y$ *Change the grouping*   ■

Caution! ■   Neither subtraction nor division is an associative operation.

■
■
■
■
■
■
■

Subtraction	*Division*
$3 - (2 - 1) = (3 - 2) - 1$	$8 \div (4 \div 2) = (8 \div 4) \div 2$
$3 - 1 = 1 - 1$	$8 \div 2 = 2 \div 2$
$2 = 0$ *False*	$4 = 1$ *False*

Taken together, the commutative and associative properties allow us to rearrange sums in several ways. For example,

$$(1 + 2) + 3 = 3 + 3 = 6,$$
$$1 + (2 + 3) = 1 + 5 = 6,$$
$$2 + (1 + 3) = 2 + 4 = 6.$$

For this reason, we do not have to write parentheses in the expression $1 + 2 + 3$. We also do not have to write parentheses when computing products like $2 \cdot 3 \cdot 5$.

When a number is added to 0, the identity of the number is unchanged. Therefore 0 is called the **identity element for addition.** Since multiplication by 1 leaves the identity of a number unchanged, 1 is called the **identity element for multiplication.**

IDENTITY PROPERTIES

$$a + 0 = a \quad \text{and} \quad 0 + a = a$$
$$a \cdot 1 = a \quad \text{and} \quad 1 \cdot a = a$$

EXAMPLE 3   Use an identity property to complete each statement.

a. $9 + 0 = ?$ b. $1(-10) = ?$

Solution

a. $9 + 0 = 9$ *0 preserves identities under addition*

Try Problem 13 >   b. $1(-10) = -10$ *1 preserves identities under multiplication*   ■

The next two properties tell us what number we must add to a given number to produce 0, and what number we must multiply a given number by to produce 1.

INVERSE PROPERTIES

For each real number a there is a unique real number called the **opposite** of a, written $-a$, such that

$$a + (-a) = 0 \quad \text{and} \quad -a + a = 0.$$

For each real number a (except 0) there is a unique real number called the **reciprocal** of a, written $1/a$, such that

$$a \cdot \frac{1}{a} = 1 \quad \text{and} \quad \frac{1}{a} \cdot a = 1.$$

EXAMPLE 4   Use an inverse property to complete each statement.

a. $7 + (-7) = ?$ b. $(-4)\left(-\dfrac{1}{4}\right) = ?$

Solution

a. $7 + (-7) = 0$ *Opposites add to 0*

Try Problem 19 >   b. $(-4)\left(-\dfrac{1}{4}\right) = 1$ *Reciprocals multiply to 1*   ■

The final property relates addition and multiplication. To illustrate this property, consider the following two statements.

$$2(3 + 4) = 2(7) = 14$$
$$2 \cdot 3 + 2 \cdot 4 = 6 + 8 = 14$$

Since both $2(3 + 4)$ and $2 \cdot 3 + 2 \cdot 4$ equal 14, they must be equal to each other. That is,

$$2(3 + 4) = 2 \cdot 3 + 2 \cdot 4.$$

We say that "multiplication distributes over addition."

$$\overset{\frown}{2(3 + 4)} = 2(3) + 2(4)$$

DISTRIBUTIVE PROPERTY

$$a(b + c) = ab + ac$$

The British mathematicians Augustus DeMorgan (1806–1871), Duncan Gregory (1813–1844), and George Peacock (1791–1858) were the first to notice the presence of a structure to algebra such as the commutative, associative, and distributive properties.

Since multiplication is commutative, we can also distribute from the right.

$$\overset{\frown}{(b + c)}a = ba + ca$$

And since subtraction can be written in terms of addition, we can distribute multiplication over subtraction.

$$a(b - c) \quad ab - ac \quad \text{and} \quad (b - c)a = ba - ca$$

Finally, we can distribute over three or more numbers.

$$a(b + c + d) = ab + ac + ad$$

EXAMPLE 5   Use the distributive property to complete each statement.

a. $2(3 + x) = ?$ b. $(9 + 4)5 = ?$
c. $6(2y - 7) = ?$ d. $-1(x + y + 3) = ?$

Solution

a. $2(3 + x) = 2 \cdot 3 + 2 \cdot x$ *Distributive property*
b. $(9 + 4)5 = 9 \cdot 5 + 4 \cdot 5$ *Distribute from the right*
c. $6(2y - 7) = 6(2y) - 6(7)$ *Distribute over subtraction*
d. $-1(x + y + 3) = (-1)x + (-1)y + (-1)3$ *Distribute over three*

Try Problem 25 >   *numbers*   ∎

We will now see how these properties can be used to simplify algebraic expressions.

EXAMPLE 6   Simplify $\frac{2}{3}\left(\frac{3}{2}x\right)$.

Solution

$$\frac{2}{3}\left(\frac{3}{2}x\right) = \left(\frac{2}{3}\cdot\frac{3}{2}\right)x \quad \textit{Associative property}$$
$$= 1x \qquad\qquad \textit{Inverse property}$$
$$= x \qquad\qquad \textit{Identity property}$$

Try Problem 35 >

■

EXAMPLE 7   Simplify $-4 + (x + 4)$.

Solution

$$-4 + (x + 4) = -4 + (4 + x) \quad \textit{Commutative property}$$
$$= (-4 + 4) + x \quad \textit{Associative property}$$
$$= 0 + x \qquad\quad \textit{Inverse property}$$
$$= x \qquad\qquad \textit{Identity property}$$

Try Problem 37 >

■

EXAMPLE 8   Simplify $6(4x - 5)$.

Solution

$$6(4x - 5) = 6(4x) - 6(5) \quad \textit{Distributive property}$$
$$= (6\cdot 4)x - 6(5) \quad \textit{Associative property}$$
$$= 24x - 30 \qquad\quad \textit{Multiply}$$

Try Problem 45 >

■

EXAMPLE 9   Simplify $y - 3 - 4$.

Solution

$$y - 3 - 4 = y + (-3) + (-4) \quad \textit{Change to addition}$$
$$= y + (-7) \qquad\qquad \textit{Add } -3 \textit{ and } -4$$
$$= y - 7 \qquad\qquad\quad \textit{Change to subtraction}$$

Try Problem 61 >

■

EXAMPLE 10   Simplify $-2(3x + 4)$.

Solution

$$-2(3x + 4) = -2(3x) + (-2)4 \quad \textit{Distributive property}$$
$$= (-2\cdot 3)x + (-2)4 \quad \textit{Associative property}$$
$$= -6x + (-8) \qquad\quad \textit{Multiply}$$
$$= -6x - 8 \qquad\qquad \textit{Change to subtraction}$$

Try Problem 73 >

■

In order to solve the next example, note that

$$-5 = -1 \cdot 5 \qquad \text{and} \qquad -x = -1 \cdot x.$$

EXAMPLE 11   Simplify $-(y - 5)$.

Solution

$$
\begin{aligned}
-(y - 5) &= -1 \cdot (y - 5) &&\textit{Since } -x = -1 \cdot x \\
&= (-1)y - (-1)5 &&\textit{Distributive property} \\
&= -y - (-5) &&-1 \textit{ times } y, \textit{ and } -1 \textit{ times } 5 \\
&= -y + 5 &&\textit{Change to addition}
\end{aligned}
$$

Try Problem 77 >

Caution! ■   In the expression $-(x + 8)$, make sure you distribute -1 over both x and 8. This has the effect of changing the sign of both x and 8.

Wrong	*Correct*
$-(x + 8) = -x + 8$	$-(x + 8) = -x - 8$

EXAMPLE 12   Simplify $\dfrac{-12x}{3}$.

Solution

$$
\begin{aligned}
\frac{-12x}{3} &= \frac{-12}{3} \cdot \frac{x}{1} &&\textit{Multiplication of fractions} \\
&= -4 \cdot x &&\textit{Divide } -12 \textit{ by } 3 \textit{ and divide } x \textit{ by } 1 \\
&= -4x
\end{aligned}
$$

Try Problem 85 >

1.9 Problem Set

LEARNING THROUGH WRITING

☐ Write each expression in words.
  a. $(5 + 3) + 6$ b. $2(9x)$ c. $4(y - 7)$

☐ State the following properties of addition in words.
  a. Commutative   b. Associative
  c. Identity   d. Inverse

☐ State the following properties of multiplication in words.
  a. Commutative   b. Associative
  c. Identity   d. Inverse

☐ State the distributive property in words.

Use a commutative property to complete each statement.

1. $-2 + 6 = ?$ 2. $3 + (-4) = ?$ 3. $5(-7) = ?$ 4. $-2 \cdot 8 = ?$
5. $3 + x = ?$ 6. $y \cdot 6 = ?$

Use an associative property to complete each statement.

7. $(1 + 2) + (-5) = ?$ **8.** $(-3 + 1) + 6 = ?$ **9.** $(-3 \cdot 4)5 = ?$ **10.** $[2(-4)]7 = ?$

11. $\dfrac{1}{3}(3y) = ?$ **12.** $5 + (9 + x) = ?$

Use an identity property to complete each statement.

13. $5 + 0 = ?$ **14.** $1 \cdot 15 = ?$ **15.** $0 + x = ?$ **16.** $x + 0 = ?$

17. $1 \cdot y = ?$ **18.** $y \cdot 1 = ?$

Use an inverse property to complete each statement.

19. $2 + (-2) = ?$ **20.** $(-5)\left(-\dfrac{1}{5}\right) = ?$ **21.** $-8.2 + 8.2 = ?$ **22.** $4.3 + (-4.3) = ?$

23. $\dfrac{3}{8} \cdot \dfrac{8}{3} = ?$ **24.** $\dfrac{5}{9} \cdot \dfrac{9}{5} = ?$

Use the distributive property to complete each statement.

25. $3(5 + x) = ?$ **26.** $4(1 + x) = ?$ **27.** $(2 + 4)7 = ?$ **28.** $(6 + 3)5 = ?$

29. $2(8y - 1) = ?$ **30.** $3(9y - 2) = ?$ **31.** $-1(x + y - 6) = ?$ **32.** $-1(x - y + 7) = ?$

Use the properties of addition and multiplication to simplify each expression.

33. $2(5x)$ **34.** $(x + 5) + 3$ **35.** $\dfrac{3}{4}\left(\dfrac{4}{3}x\right)$ **36.** $\dfrac{2}{5}\left(\dfrac{5}{2}x\right)$

37. $-8 + (x + 8)$ **38.** $(3 + x) + (-3)$ **39.** $(7x)\dfrac{1}{7}$ **40.** $(8x)\dfrac{1}{8}$

41. $4(x + 1)$ **42.** $5(x + 2)$ **43.** $6(2y + 4)$ **44.** $7(3y + 1)$

45. $8(3x - 4)$ **46.** $9(2x - 3)$ **47.** $16\left(\dfrac{3t}{2} - \dfrac{5}{8}\right)$ **48.** $18\left(\dfrac{3t}{2} - \dfrac{5}{9}\right)$

49. $2(2x + 3y - 4)$ **50.** $3(3x + 5y - 1)$ **51.** $(x + 7) + (-3)$ **52.** $-3 + (x + 6)$

53. $x + (-x + 5)$ **54.** $x + (-x + 4)$ **55.** $(x + 1) + (-x)$ **56.** $(x + 9) + (-x)$

57. $x + 5 - 1$ **58.** $x + 7 - 2$ **59.** $x - 8 + 8$ **60.** $x + 3 - 3$

61. $y - 2 - 3$ **62.** $y - 1 - 7$ **63.** $4 + y - 5$ **64.** $5 + y - 8$

65. $-2(3x)$ **66.** $-3(5x)$ **67.** $5(-4x)$ **68.** $4\left(-\dfrac{1}{2}y\right)$

69. $\left(-\dfrac{3}{5}y\right)10$ **70.** $\left(-\dfrac{3}{4}y\right)12$ **71.** $-\dfrac{1}{2}(-2r)$ **72.** $-\dfrac{4}{9}\left(-\dfrac{9}{4}r\right)$

73. $-3(2x + 5)$ **74.** $-2(4x + 3)$ **75.** $5(-4x + 1)$ **76.** $-15(-x - 2)$

77. $-(y - 7)$ **78.** $-(y - 9)$ **79.** $-(8y + 12)$ **80.** $-(7y + 11)$

81. $-(-a - 3b + 5c)$ **82.** $-(-a + 4b - 7c)$ **83.** $-4\left(\dfrac{x}{2} - \dfrac{y}{4} + 3\right)$ **84.** $6\left(-\dfrac{2}{3}z - \dfrac{1}{3}\right)$

85. $\dfrac{-15x}{3}$ **86.** $\dfrac{-18x}{6}$ **87.** $\dfrac{8x}{-4}$ **88.** $\dfrac{-7x}{7}$

89. $\dfrac{-3y}{-3}$ **90.** $\dfrac{-y}{-1}$

Construct a specific example to illustrate each statement.

91. Subtraction is not commutative.

92. Division is not commutative.

93. Subtraction is not associative.

94. Division is not associative.

C H A P T E R 1 S U M M A R Y

Key Terms

Absolute value, p. 21
Algebraic expression, p. 45
Average, p. 9
Base, p. 43
Constant, p. 2
Denominator, p. 2
Double inequality, p. 20
Exponent, p. 43

Exponential notation, p. 43
Factor, p. 3
Greatest common factor (GCF), p. 3
Identity element for addition, p. 50
Identity element for multiplication, p. 50
Improper fraction, p. 7
Inequality, p. 18

Least common denominator (LCD), p. 6
Mixed number, p. 7
Numerator, p. 2
Opposite, p. 15
Reciprocal, p. 5
Set, p. 12
Variable, p. 2

Key Rules

Operations on Fractions
Assume no denominator is 0.

Addition: $\dfrac{a}{c} + \dfrac{b}{c} = \dfrac{a+b}{c}$

Subtraction: $\dfrac{a}{c} - \dfrac{b}{c} = \dfrac{a-b}{c}$

Multiplication: $\dfrac{a}{b} \cdot \dfrac{c}{d} = \dfrac{ac}{bd}$

Division: $\dfrac{a}{b} \div \dfrac{c}{d} = \dfrac{a}{b} \cdot \dfrac{d}{c} = \dfrac{ad}{bc}$

Sets of Numbers
Real numbers: {numbers that can be represented on the number line}
Whole numbers: {0, 1, 2, 3, . . .}
Integers: {. . . , $-3, -2, -1, 0, 1, 2, 3, . . .$}
Rational numbers: {quotients of two integers, with denominator not 0}
Irrational numbers: {numbers represented on the number line that are not rational}

Double-Negative Rule
For any real number a, $-(-a) = a$.

Symbols of Equality and Inequality
= is equal to
$\neq$ is not equal to
< is less than
> is greater than
$\leq$ is less than or equal to
$\geq$ is greater than or equal to

Operations on Real Numbers
Addition
   Same sign: Add the absolute values. The answer has the same sign as the given numbers.
   Different signs: Subtract the smaller absolute value from the larger. The answer has the same sign as the number with the larger absolute value.
Subtraction: To subtract b from a, add the opposite of b to a. In symbols,

$$a - b = a + (-b).$$

Multiplication and Division: Multiply (divide) the absolute values. If the numbers have the same sign, the answer is positive; if they have different signs, the answer is negative.

Multiplication Property of 0
If a is any real number, then

$$a \cdot 0 = 0 \quad \text{and} \quad 0 \cdot a = 0.$$

Signs of a Fraction
If $b \neq 0$, then

$$-\frac{a}{b} = \frac{-a}{b} = \frac{a}{-b} \quad \text{and} \quad \frac{-a}{-b} = \frac{a}{b}.$$

Division Involving 0
If $a \neq 0$, then

$$\frac{0}{a} = 0 \quad \text{and} \quad \frac{a}{0} \text{ is undefined.}$$

Order of Operations

Perform all operations in the following numerical order.

1. Do all operations above and below fraction bars separately.
2. Do all operations in parentheses ( ) and brackets [ ], applying the innermost grouping symbols first.
3. Apply all exponents.
4. Do all multiplications and divisions, from left to right.
5. Do all additions and subtractions, from left to right.

Properties of Addition and Multiplication

Assume a, b, and c are real numbers.

Property	Addition	Multiplication
Commutative	$a + b = b + a$	$ab = ba$
Associative	$a + (b + c) =$ $(a + b) + c$	$a(bc) = (ab)c$
Identity	$a + 0 = 0 + a = a$	$a \cdot 1 = 1 \cdot a = a$
Inverse	$-a + a =$ $a + (-a) = 0$	$a \cdot \dfrac{1}{a} = \dfrac{1}{a} \cdot a = 1$
Distributive	$a(b + c) = ab + ac$	

C H A P T E R 1 ⟩ R E V I E W   P R O B L E M S

[1.1] *Write each fraction in lowest terms.*

1. $\dfrac{12}{18}$

2. $\dfrac{70}{350}$

Perform the indicated operation. Write your answer in lowest terms.

3. $\dfrac{2}{5} \cdot \dfrac{6}{5}$

4. $\dfrac{3}{8} \cdot \dfrac{4}{15}$

5. $\dfrac{9}{4} \div \dfrac{3}{4}$

6. $3\dfrac{3}{5} \div 1\dfrac{1}{2}$

7. $\dfrac{1}{6} + \dfrac{1}{6}$

8. $\dfrac{4}{5} + \dfrac{1}{10}$

9. $\dfrac{3}{4} - \dfrac{1}{6}$

10. $6\dfrac{2}{5} - 4\dfrac{4}{5}$

11. How high is a stack of 12 sheets of plywood if each sheet is 5/8 of an inch thick?

12. A truck is loaded with 20 cubic yards of concrete. It unloads 7 1/2 cubic yards at the first stop, and 5 3/4 cubic yards at the second. How many cubic yards are left on the truck?

[1.2] *State the opposite of each number.*

13. $-7 = 7$

14. $\dfrac{3}{5}$

Simplify.

15. $-(-6)$

16. $-(-(-23))$

17. Graph each number on a number line: 5, 2 1/4, -4, $-5/3$

Consider the following set of numbers:

$$\left\{ 6.2,\ -3,\ 14,\ \sqrt{16},\ -\dfrac{9}{2},\ 0,\ \sqrt{7},\ 3\dfrac{2}{7} \right\}$$

Identify the elements of this set that are

18. Whole numbers

19. Integers

20. Rational numbers

21. Irrational numbers

22. Positive integers

23. Real numbers

[1.3] *Insert < or > to make a true statement.*

24. $-75 \quad -50$

25. $\dfrac{4}{9} \quad \dfrac{7}{16}$

Write the following word statements using the symbols =, ≠, <, >, ≤, and ≥.

26. x is equal to -6.

27. y is not equal to 9.

28. p is at least 4.

Write the following word statements using a double inequality.

29. -1 is less than x and x is less than 1.

30. r is more than -2 but no more than 5.

31. A dimmer switch can control the wattage, w, of a light so that it ranges from a low of 0 watts to a high of 150 watts.

Find the absolute value of each number.

32. 4

33. -13

Simplify.

34. $-|-12|$

35. $|-8| - |-3|$

Insert =, <, or > to make a true statement.

36. $|-6| \quad |4|$

37. $|-9| \quad |9|$

[1.4] *Find each sum.* (tổng)

38. $7 + (-4) + 0$

39. $-10 + 2 + 3$

40. $-1 + (-6) + 9$

41. $-3.92 + 8.4$ ✕

42. $-\dfrac{4}{7} + \left(-\dfrac{1}{7}\right)$

43. $-\dfrac{3}{4} + \dfrac{3}{8}$

44. The temperature is $-4°$. If it rises $3°$ one day and $10°$ the next day, what is the new temperature?

[1.5] *Find each difference.* (làm tính TRỪ)

45. $4 - 9$

46. $-5 - 5$

47. $8 - (-3)$

48. $-1.8 - (-4.62)$

49. $1\dfrac{2}{5} - 6$

50. $\dfrac{5}{6} - \left(-\dfrac{4}{9}\right)$

51. The lowest recorded temperature in the United States is $-80°$ at Prospect Creek, Alaska. The lowest recorded temperature on earth is $-127°$ at Vostok, Antarctica. ✕ Find the difference in the two temperatures.

[1.6] *Find each product.* (làm tính nhân)

52. $5(-1)$

53. $(-3)(-7)4$

54. $(-1)(-4)(-6)2$

55. $\left(-\dfrac{1}{3}\right)6$

56. $(-9.25)3.7$

57. $\left(-\dfrac{5}{8}\right)\left(-\dfrac{2}{5}\right)$

Find the reciprocal of each number. Write your answer in simplest form.
(Trao đổi, đảo ngược)

58. 3

59. $-2\dfrac{2}{5}$

60. The Dow Jones industrial average declines 1.35 points on each of four consecutive days. Find the total change in the Dow.

[1.7] *Find each quotient.* (làm Tính chia)

61. $\dfrac{-15}{-1}$

62. $\dfrac{30}{-3}$

63. $\dfrac{-28}{-7}$

64. $\dfrac{-9}{9}$

65. $-\dfrac{5}{8} \div \dfrac{4}{5}$

66. $-10.4 \div (-0.52)$

Simplify each fraction. (làm đơn giản lại)

67. $-\dfrac{4}{-9}$

68. $-\dfrac{-6}{-12}$

Determine whether each quotient is 0 or is undefined.

69. $0 \div (-10)$

70. $-11 \div 0$

71. A tailback carried the football three times, with the following results: 1-yard gain, 5-yard loss, 2-yard loss. Find the average gain per carry.

[1.8] *Evaluate.* (ước lg định giá)

72. 10^3

73. -3^4

74. $\left(-\dfrac{1}{4}\right)^2$

75. -1^2

(Tính)

Evaluate using the order of operations.

76. $20 - 2^2 + 2^3$

77. $2(4[15 - 5(5 - 3)])$

78. $4 + [3(-7 + 4) - 1]$

79. $\dfrac{8(-2) + (-1)4}{|-4 - 1|}$

80. $5\left(1 + \dfrac{1}{5}\right) \div \left(\dfrac{2}{5}\right)^2$

81. $\dfrac{-1^2[5 - 2(1 - 3)^2]^2}{6 \cdot 4 \div 2^2 + 6}$

82. Evaluate $5x - 2y - z$ when $x = -4$, $y = 1$, and $z = -3$.

83. Thirteen people got on an empty elevator on the first floor. At the first stop, 4 people got off. At the second stop, 3 people got off. At the third stop, 1 person got on. How many people are now on the elevator?

[1.9] *Use the given property to complete each statement.*

84. Commutative property: $x \cdot y = $?
$= y \cdot x$

85. Associative property: $(y + 6) + 8 = $?

86. Identity property: $m + 0 = $?

87. Inverse property: $\dfrac{2}{3} \cdot \dfrac{3}{2} = $?

88. Distributive property: $5(4x + 7) = $?

Use the properties of addition and multiplication to simplify each expression.

89. $-5 + (x + 5)$

90. $-\dfrac{3}{5}\left(-\dfrac{5}{3}x\right)$

91. $12\left(\dfrac{3}{4}y - \dfrac{2}{3}\right)$

92. $y - 7 - 8$

93. $\dfrac{z}{-1}$

94. $\dfrac{-2z}{-2}$

95. $\left(-\dfrac{1}{5}y\right)10$

96. $-2(3x + 4y - 1)$

97. $-(-t - 6)$

C H A P T E R 1 TEST

1. State the opposite of $-3/4$.

2. Find the reciprocal of -5.

Evaluate.

3. 4^3

4. -5^2

Perform the indicated operations. Write your answer in simplest form.

5. $-9 + (-3)$

6. $-4 - (-10)$

7. $2.6 - 7.3$

8. $(-4)(-5)(-1)$

9. $\dfrac{-32}{-8}$

10. $-\dfrac{4}{5} + \dfrac{1}{5}$

11. $\dfrac{7}{8}\left(-\dfrac{5}{7}\right)$

12. $8.5 \div (-2.5)$

13. $\dfrac{7}{-7}$

14. $\dfrac{-13}{0}$

15. $-4\dfrac{2}{3} \div 3\dfrac{1}{2}$

16. $-\dfrac{1}{6} - \dfrac{7}{9}$

Insert, =, <, or > to make a true statement.

17. $-|-4|$ __ $|4|$

18. $|3 - 9|$ __ $|9 - 3|$

Write the following word statements using the symbols <, >, ≤, and ≥.

19. x is greater than -7.

20. y is less than 14 but no less than 11.

Evaluate.

21. $3 \cdot 5^2 + 8(-4)$

22. $3(5[12 - 2(7 - 4)])$

23. $\dfrac{(-6)4 + 5(-2)}{-1 - 1}$

24. $\dfrac{5 \cdot 3^2 - 2 \cdot 10^2}{3^2 - 2^2}$

Simplify each expression.

25. $x - 8 + 4$

26. $12\left(-\dfrac{1}{4}r\right)$

27. $-\dfrac{-10}{15}$

28. $6\left(\dfrac{2}{3}z - \dfrac{1}{2}\right)$

29. $\dfrac{-4m}{-4}$

30. $-(-t + 1)$

31. Evaluate $|x| + 3|y - 2z|$ when $x = 4$, $y = -5$, and $z = -1$.

32. Find the average of the numbers 2 1/8, 3 3/8, and 4 5/8.

33. Graph each number on a number line: 4, 2.5, -3, $-4/3$.

Use the given property to complete each statement.

34. Commutative property: $3 + x = $?

35. Identity property: $1 \cdot y = $?

36. Associative property: $4(5m) = $?

37. Distributive property: $7(x + y) = $?

38. Inverse property: $-9 + 9 = $?

Linear Equations and Inequalities

A department store may mark down an item in order to sell it quickly and make room for a new model. In Section 2.6 you will see how to use a linear equation to determine the original price of a large-screen television set that has been marked down 15% to $3638.

2.1   Simplifying Expressions

In this section we continue our discussion of simplifying algebraic expressions by using the properties of addition and multiplication. We need to know how to simplify expressions in order to solve equations later in the chapter.

Just as **factors** are expressions that are related by multiplication, **terms** are expressions that are related by addition.

$$\underset{3\ factors}{a \cdot b \cdot c} \qquad \underset{3\ terms}{a + b + c}$$

Therefore the expression $3x - 5y + 2$, which also can be written $3x + (-5y) + 2$, contains the three terms $3x$, $-5y$, and 2.

Expression	Terms
$x + 7$	$x, 7$
$3x^2 - x - 6$	$3x^2, -x, -6$
$x^2 + 2xy + y^2$	$x^2, 2xy, y^2$
$-\dfrac{2z}{5} - \dfrac{3}{5}$	$-\dfrac{2z}{5}, -\dfrac{3}{5}$

The numerical factor in a term is called the *numerical coefficient*, or simply the **coefficient,** of the term.

Term	Coefficient	
$5x^2$	5	
$-10xy^2z^3$	-10	
p	1	*Since $p = 1 \cdot p$*
$-p$	-1	*Since $-p = -1 \cdot p$*
$\dfrac{3r}{4}$	$\dfrac{3}{4}$	*Since $\dfrac{3r}{4} = \dfrac{3}{4} \cdot r$*

Terms that have the same variables with the same exponents are called **like terms.**

Like Terms	Unlike Terms	
$3x, 2x$	$3x, 2y$	*Different variables*
$7y^2, 4y^2, y^2$	$5y^2, 5y$	*Different exponents*
$9p, -p$	$9p, -1$	*Different variables*
$-10rs, 8rs$	r^2s, rs^2	*Different exponents*

We can use the distributive property to add or subtract like terms. This is called *combining like terms.*

EXAMPLE 1   Combine like terms: $3x + 2x$.

Solution

$$3x + 2x = (3 + 2)x \quad \textit{Distributive property}$$
$$= 5x \quad \textit{Add the coefficients}$$

Try Problem 31 >

■

EXAMPLE 2   Combine like terms: $7y^2 + 4y^2 + y^2$.

Solution

$$7y^2 + 4y^2 + y^2 = 7y^2 + 4y^2 + 1y^2 \quad \textit{Since } y^2 = 1 \cdot y^2$$
$$= (7 + 4 + 1)y^2 \quad \textit{Distributive property}$$
$$= 12y^2 \quad \textit{Add the coefficients}$$

Try Problem 37 >

■

EXAMPLE 3   Combine like terms: $9p - p$.

Solution

$$9p - p = 9p - 1p \quad \textit{Since } p = 1 \cdot p$$
$$= (9 - 1)p \quad \textit{Distributive property}$$
$$= 8p \quad \textit{Subtract the coefficients}$$

Try Problem 39 >

■

EXAMPLE 4   Combine like terms: $-10rs + 8rs$.

Solution

$$-10rs + 8rs = (-10 + 8)rs \quad \textit{Distributive property}$$
$$= -2rs \quad \textit{Add the coefficients}$$

Try Problem 43 >

■

These examples illustrate that **we combine like terms simply by adding or subtracting their coefficients.** That is, $3x + 2x = 5x$ in the same way that $3¢ + 2¢ = 5¢$.

Caution! ■
■
■
■
■
■
■

We cannot combine unlike terms. That is, we cannot simplify $3x + 2y$ any more than we can simplify 3 cars + 2 cows.

Cannot Simplify	*Cannot Simplify*	*Cannot Simplify*	*Cannot Simplify*
$3x + 2y$	$5y^2 + 5y$	$9p - 1$	$r^2s + rs^2$

EXAMPLE 5   Combine like terms.

a. $6x - 13x = -7x$ *Since* $6 - 13 = -7$
b. $-5y^2 - y^2 = -6y^2$ *Since* $-5 - 1 = -6$
c. $-z^3 + 2z^3 = 1z^3 = z^3$ *Since* $-1 + 2 = 1$
d. $4p + (-4p) = 0p = 0$ *Since* $4 + (-4) = 0$

Try Problem 53 >

■

Sometimes an algebraic expression contains several terms. We must identify the like terms so we know which terms can be combined.

EXAMPLE 6   Combine like terms: $4m + 13 + 7m$.

Solution   The like terms are $4m$ and $7m$.

$$4m + 13 + 7m = 4m + 7m + 13 \quad \textit{Rearrange terms}$$
$$= 11m + 13 \quad \textit{Add } 4m \textit{ and } 7m$$

Try Problem 59 >

Since addition is commutative, both $11m + 13$ and $13 + 11m$ are correct answers. Usually we write the variable term first, however, as in $11m + 13$. ■

EXAMPLE 7   Combine like terms: $6p + 9 - 2p - 15$.

Solution $6p$ and $-2p$ are like terms, and 9 and -15 are like terms.

$$6p + 9 - 2p - 15 = 6p - 2p + 9 - 15 \quad \textit{Rearrange terms}$$
$$= 4p - 6 \quad \textit{Combine like terms}$$

Try Problem 63 >

Once we identify the like terms in an expression, it is not necessary to rearrange the terms. We simply combine like terms mentally as we go along.

EXAMPLE 8   Combine like terms: $-8r^2 - 3r - 4r^2 + r + 9$.

Solution $-8r^2$ and $-4r^2$ are like terms, and $-3r$ and r are like terms.

$$-8r^2 - 3r - 4r^2 + r + 9 = -12r^2 - 3r + r + 9 \quad \begin{array}{l}\textit{Combine } -8r^2 \\ \textit{and } -4r^2\end{array}$$
$$= -12r^2 - 2r + 9 \quad \begin{array}{l}\textit{Combine } -3r \\ \textit{and } r\end{array}$$

Try Problem 69 >

Sometimes we must use the distributive property to remove parentheses before we can combine like terms.

EXAMPLE 9   Simplify $9 + 2(x + 4)$.

Solution   By the order of operations, we multiply before adding. Therefore do not add 9 and 2. Instead, multiply 2 and $x + 4$.

$$9 + 2(x + 4) = 9 + 2(x) + 2(4) \quad \textit{Distributive property}$$
$$= 9 + 2x + 8 \quad \textit{Find each product}$$
$$= 2x + 17 \quad \textit{Add 9 and 8}$$

Try Problem 71 >

EXAMPLE 10   Simplify $13y - 3(6y - 4)$.

Solution
$$13y - 3(6y - 4) = 13y - 3(6y) - 3(-4) \quad \textit{Distribute } -3$$
$$= 13y - 18y + 12 \quad \textit{Find each product}$$
$$= -5y + 12 \quad \textit{Add } 13y \textit{ and } -18y$$

Try Problem 75 >

EXAMPLE 11   Simplify $-3(4x - y) - (x + 5y)$.

Solution

$$-3(4x - y) - (x + 5y)$$

$\quad = -3(4x - y) - 1(x + 5y)$ *Since $x + 5y = 1 \cdot (x + 5y)$*

$\quad = -3(4x) - 3(-y) - 1(x) - 1(5y)$ *Distribute -3, distribute -1*

$\quad = -12x + 3y - x - 5y$ *Find each product*

$\quad = -13x - 2y$ *Combine like terms*   ∎

Try Problem 83 >

EXAMPLE 12   Simplify $8 + 2(a - 1) + 5(-2a) - (-3a)4$.

Solution

$$8 + 2(a - 1) + 5(-2a) - (-3a)4$$

$\quad = 8 + 2a - 2 - 10a + 12a$ *Multiply before adding or subtracting*

$\quad = 4a + 6$ *Combine like terms*   ∎

Try Problem 91 >

2.1 Problem Set

LEARNING THROUGH WRITING

☐ Explain the difference between *terms* and *factors*.

☐ What is meant by the *coefficient* of a term?

☐ What are *like terms?*

☐ How are like terms added?

State the terms of each algebraic expression.

1. $x + 3$ **2.** $7x + 6$ **3.** $-3x + 4y - 10$ **4.** $4x^2 - x - 15$

5. $x^2 + 5xy - y^2$ **6.** $x^2 - 2xy + y^2$

State the coefficient of each term.

7. $4x$ **8.** $-9x$ **9.** $6y^2$ **10.** $8y^2$

11. $-15xy^3z$ **12.** $20x^3yz$ **13.** r **14.** $-t$

15. $\dfrac{2z}{3}$ **16.** -5.8 **17.** 2.9 **18.** $-\dfrac{x}{5}$

Determine whether the given terms are like terms or unlike terms.

19. $5x, 4x$ **20.** $2x, 6x$ **21.** $3x, 8y$ **22.** $7y, 9x$

23. $15y^2, y$ **24.** $6y, 6y^2$ **25.** $-p, 7p$ **26.** $p, 1$

27. $-11r^3s, 9r^3s$ **28.** $-14rs^2, 8rs^2$ **29.** $-20r^2s, -30sr^2$ **30.** $10r^3s, 50sr^3$

Simplify each expression by combining like terms.

31. $5x + 4x$ **32.** $2x + 6x$ **33.** $17z + 24z - 1$ **34.** $4y + 3y + 7$

35. $8m + 11m + 13m$ **36.** $6m + 12m + 18m$ **37.** $2y^2 + 10y^2 + y^2$ **38.** $3y^2 + 15y^2 + y^2$

39. $7p - p$ **40.** $5p - p$ **41.** $9p^2 - p^2 + p$ **42.** $6p^2 - p^2 - p$

43. $-11rs + 9rs$ **44.** $-14rs + 8rs$ **45.** $5m - 10m$ **46.** $2m - 7m$

47. $4x - 3 - 3x$ **48.** $6x - 5 - 5x$ **49.** $-4y^2 - y^2$ **50.** $-6y^2 - y^2$

51. $-6r + 6r - 1$ **52.** $8r + (-8r) - 1$ **53.** $-3z^3 + 4z^3$ **54.** $-2z^3 + 3z^3$

55. $2t^3 + 5t^2 + 5t^3$ **56.** $4t^3 + 3t^2 + 3t^3$ **57.** $-2y - 4 + 4 + 2y$ **58.** $-3y + 6 - 6 + 3y$

59. $8m + 15 + 3m$ **60.** $2m + 17 + 5m$ **61.** $-3r + 9 + 8r - 9$ **62.** $-2r - 7 + 6r + 7$

63. $6p + 4 - 2p - 19$ **64.** $9p + 8 - 3p - 21$ **65.** $-t - 5 - 4t - 5$ **66.** $-t - 4 - 7t - 4$

67. $15y - 13x - 2y + 2x$ **68.** $14x - 12y - 5x + 5y$

Simplify each expression.

69. $-9r^2 + 4r - r^2 - 2r + 6$ **70.** $-6r^2 - 8r + 9 - r^2 + 3r$ **71.** $8 + 2(x + 3)$

72. $9 + 3(x + 2)$ **73.** $6y - (y + 5)$ **74.** $8y - (y + 1)$

75. $15y - 4(5y - 2)$ **76.** $12y - 5(4y - 3)$ **77.** $5(2x - 1) - 3(-x + 7)$

78. $4(3x - 2) - 2(-x + 7)$ **79.** $7(x - 4) - (x - 6)$ **80.** $3(x - 5) - (x + 8)$

81. $3(a - 2b) - 7(3a - b)$ **82.** $5(2a - b) - 2(4a - 2b)$ **83.** $-2(3x - 4y) - (x + 8y)$

84. $-3(5x - 2y) - (x + 6y)$ **85.** $-(11x + 9y) - (x - 14y)$ **86.** $-(-x + 4y) - (19x + 15y)$

87. $5 + 5(p + 1) - 6(2p)$ **88.** $6 + 4(p + 2) - 2(5p)$ **89.** $4 + 2(m - 13) + 3(-3m)$

90. $3 + 2(m - 12) + 4(-4m)$ **91.** $2 + 4(a - 1) + 3(-5a) - (-2a)4$

92. $5 + 2(a - 3) + 3(-6a) - (-4a)7$ **93.** $3 + 6[k + 2(k + 1)]$

94. $7 + 4[k + 5(k + 2)]$ **95.** $12 - 2[m - 3(2m - 5)]$

96. $13 - 3[m - 2(3m - 4)]$ **97.** $1 + 4[6x - (5x + 4) - x]$

98. $2 + 5[3x - (2x + 6) - x]$

2.2   The Addition Property of Equality

One of the most powerful problem-solving tools in algebra is the *equation*. An **equation** is a statement that two algebraic expressions are equal. Here are some examples of equations.

$$x + 2 = 6 \qquad 3y = 15 \qquad 4(m - 1) = 2m + 7$$

We label the parts of an equation as follows:

$$\underbrace{x + 2}_{} = 6$$

Left side ⟶   ↑   ⟵Right side
        Equality symbol

Since the equation $x + 2 = 6$ is true when x is 4, we call 4 a **solution** of the equation. We also say that 4 *satisfies* the equation.

EXAMPLE 1   Determine whether -4 is a solution of the equation $3m + 5 = 17$.

Solution

$$3m + 5 = 17 \quad \textit{Original equation}$$
$$3(-4) + 5 = 17 \quad \textit{Replace m with } -4$$
$$-12 + 5 = 17 \quad \textit{Multiply before adding}$$
$$-7 = 17 \quad \textit{False}$$

Try Problem 3 >   The number -4 is not a solution of the equation.   ■

EXAMPLE 2   Determine whether 5 is a solution of the equation $2(t - 9) = 3t - 23$.

Solution

$$2(t - 9) = 3t - 23 \quad \textit{Original equation}$$
$$2(5 - 9) = 3(5) - 23 \quad \textit{Replace t with 5}$$
$$2(-4) = 15 - 23 \quad \textit{Order of operations}$$
$$-8 = -8 \quad \textit{True}$$

Try Problem 7 >   The number 5 is a solution of the equation.   ■

To **solve** an equation means to find its solutions. Some equations, like $x + 2 = 6$, are easy to solve just by looking at them. However, to solve more complicated equations, we need a systematic method. To develop such a method, consider the following two equations.

$$x - 2 = 5 \quad \textit{Solution is 7}$$
$$x = 7 \quad \textit{Solution is 7}$$

Since both equations have the same solution, they are called **equivalent equations.** Notice that the solution is more obvious in the equation $x = 7$ than in the equation $x - 2 = 5$. This is because the variable is isolated on one side of the equation. Therefore, to solve an equation, we will write a sequence of equivalent equations until we reach an equation of the form

$x =$ a number.

One of the properties we need to isolate x on one side of the equation is the **addition property of equality.**

ADDITION PROPERTY OF EQUALITY

Let A, B, and C be algebraic expressions.

If $A = B$,   then $A + C = B + C$.

The addition property states that we can add the same quantity to both sides of an equation and the result is an equivalent equation.

We can think of an equation as a balance scale with equal weights on both sides (see Fig. 2.1). If we add the same quantity C to both sides of the scale, we maintain the balance (see Fig. 2.2). When solving an equation we must make certain that we maintain the balance of the equation at all times.

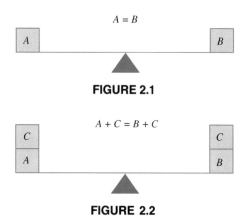

FIGURE 2.1

FIGURE 2.2

EXAMPLE 3   Solve $x - 2 = 5$.

Solution   To isolate x, add the opposite of -2, namely 2, to both sides of the equation.

$$
\begin{array}{ll}
x - 2 = 5 & \textit{Original equation} \\
x - 2 + 2 = 5 + 2 & \textit{Add 2 to both sides} \\
x = 7 & \textit{Simplify each side}
\end{array}
$$

The solution is 7, which you can check as follows.

$$
\begin{array}{lll}
\textit{Check:} & x - 2 = 5 & \textit{Original equation} \\
& 7 - 2 = 5 & \textit{Replace x with 7} \\
& 5 = 5 & \textit{True}
\end{array}
$$

Try Problem 9 >

Since subtracting C is the same as adding $-C$, the balance of an equation is also maintained when we subtract the same quantity from both sides.

EXAMPLE 4   Solve $y + 9 = 6$.

Solution   To isolate y, subtract 9 from both sides of the equation.

$$
\begin{array}{ll}
y + 9 = 6 & \textit{Original equation} \\
y + 9 - 9 = 6 - 9 & \textit{Subtract 9 from both sides} \\
y = -3 & \textit{Simplify each side}
\end{array}
$$

Try Problem 11 >   The solution is -3. Check in the original equation.

The Dutch mathematician Albert Girard (1595–1632) and the French mathematician René Descartes (1596–1650) were the first to admit that the solution of an equation could be a negative number.

Sometimes it is easier to isolate the variable on the right side of the equation.

EXAMPLE 5   Solve $1/3 = 1/3 + z$.

Solution

$$\frac{1}{3} = \frac{1}{3} + z \qquad \textit{Original equation}$$

$$\frac{1}{3} - \frac{1}{3} = \frac{1}{3} + z - \frac{1}{3} \qquad \textit{Subtract 1/3 from both sides}$$

$$0 = z \qquad \textit{Simplify each side}$$

Try Problem 23 >   The solution is 0. Check in the original equation.   ■

Often we must add or subtract a variable expression on both sides of an equation in order to solve the equation.

EXAMPLE 6   Solve $-3m = -15 - 4m$.

Solution

$$-3m = -15 - 4m \qquad \textit{Original equation}$$

$$-3m + 4m = -15 - 4m + 4m \qquad \textit{Add 4m to both sides}$$

$$m = -15 \qquad \textit{Simplify each side}$$

Try Problem 33 >   The solution is -15. Check in the original equation.   ■

Here are some examples of equations and the best way to solve them.

Equation	*To Solve*
$x + 8 = 6$	Subtract 8 from both sides
$1 = y - 4$	Add 4 to both sides
$-5k = -6k + 9$	Add $6k$ to both sides
$2p + 10 = 3p$	Subtract $2p$ from both sides

Before you add or subtract any expression on both sides of an equation, make sure you simplify each side of the equation.

EXAMPLE 7   Solve $-7p + 15p - 8 + 3 = 5p - 6 + 4p$.

Solution   Begin by simplifying each side.

$$-7p + 15p - 8 + 3 = 5p - 6 + 4p \qquad \textit{Original equation}$$

$$8p - 5 = 9p - 6 \qquad \textit{Combine like terms}$$

In this equation, it is easier to isolate p on the right side.

$$8p - 5 - 8p = 9p - 6 - 8p \qquad \textit{Subtract 8p from both sides}$$
$$-5 = p - 6 \qquad \textit{Simplify each side}$$
$$-5 + 6 = p - 6 + 6 \qquad \textit{Add 6 to both sides}$$
$$1 = p \qquad \textit{Simplify each side}$$

Try Problem 49 >   The solution is 1. Check in the original equation.   ∎

EXAMPLE 8   Solve $6 - 3(5r - 4) = 7r - (23r + 8)$.

Solution   Begin by simplifying each side.

$$6 - 3(5r - 4) = 7r - (23r + 8) \qquad \textit{Original equation}$$
$$6 - 15r + 12 = 7r - 23r - 8 \qquad \textit{Distributive property}$$
$$-15r + 18 = -16r - 8 \qquad \textit{Combine like terms}$$
$$-15r + 18 + 16r = -16r - 8 + 16r \qquad \textit{Add 16r to both sides}$$
$$r + 18 = -8 \qquad \textit{Simplify each side}$$
$$r + 18 - 18 = -8 - 18 \qquad \textit{Subtract 18 from both sides}$$
$$r = -26 \qquad \textit{Simplify each side}$$

Try Problem 63 >   The solution is -26. Check in the original equation.   ∎

2.2 Problem Set

LEARNING THROUGH WRITING

☐ What is an *equation?*

☐ What is a *solution* of an equation?

☐ What does it mean to *solve* an equation?

☐ What are *equivalent equations?*

☐ State the *addition property of equality* in words.

Determine whether the given number is a solution of the given equation.

1. $2y - 5 = 1; 3$

2. $3y + 7 = 13; 2$

3. $4m + 9 = 11; -5$

4. $5m - 4 = -11; -3$

5. $3p - 5p - 2 = 0; -1$

6. $4p - 6p - 10 = 0; -5$

7. $6(t - 5) = 3t - 24; 2$

8. $8(t - 6) = 2t - 24; 4$

Solve each equation and check your solution.

9. $x - 3 = 4$

10. $x - 3 = -12$

11. $y + 7 = 3$

12. $y + 8 = 5$

13. $k - 5 = -11$

14. $k - 3 = 10$

15. $61 + p = 104$

16. $51 + p = 82$

17. $7.8 + m = -5.3$

18. $6.7 + m = -4.9$

19. $-19 = t - 19$

20. $-26 = t - 26$

21. $r + 23 = 0$

22. $r - 17 = 0$

23. $\dfrac{1}{2} = \dfrac{1}{2} + z$

24. $\dfrac{1}{4} = \dfrac{1}{4} + z$

25. $k - \dfrac{1}{2} = -\dfrac{5}{2}$

26. $k - \dfrac{1}{3} = -\dfrac{4}{3}$

Solve each equation and check your solution.

27. $5x = 4x + 6$

28. $7x = 6x + 5$

29. $8y - 2 = 9y$

30. $2y - 4 = 3y$

31. $15 - 7k = -6k$

32. $18 - 9k = -8k$

33. $-2m = -10 - 3m$

34. $-4m = -12 - 5m$

35. $2t + 3 = t - 8$

36. $3t + 2 = 2t - 6$

37. $5p + 7 = 6p - 4$

38. $6p + 5 = 7p - 1$

39. $-14 - 10r = -9r - 1$

40. $-11 - 13r = -12r - 4$

41. $5.4 - 2.7z = 9.9 - 3.7z$

42. $3.2 - 4.3z = 8.7 - 5.3z$

43. $\dfrac{4}{3}x + \dfrac{2}{5} = \dfrac{1}{3}x + \dfrac{9}{5}$

44. $\dfrac{3}{2}x + \dfrac{1}{4} = \dfrac{1}{2}x + \dfrac{7}{4}$

Simplify each side of the equation. Then solve the equation and check your solution.

45. $6x + 3 - 2x - 3x = 4 + 8$

46. $8x + 5 - 2x - 5x = 3 + 9$

47. $5y - 9 + y = 3y - 7 + 2y$

48. $7y - 4 + y = 5y - 3 + 2y$

49. $-4p + 6p + 2 - 8 = 2p - 13 + p$

50. $-5p + 9p - 8 + 1 = 2p - 11 + 3p$

51. $-12 - 3 - 9z - 1 + 4z = -3z - 4 - 3z$

52. $-16 - 2 - 6z - 7 + 3z = -2z - 5 - 2z$

53. $3(2m - 4) - 5m = 3 + 9$

54. $2(5m - 6) - 9m = 7 + 5$

55. $4(t + 2) = 3t - 6$

56. $5(t + 3) = 4t - 7$

57. $-8(k + 3) = 14 - 7k$

58. $-10(k + 2) = 17 - 9k$

59. $2y - (y - 5) = -8 - 4$

60. $2y - (y - 4) = -5 - 8$

61. $5(3 - 2x) + 3(7 + 2x) = 9 - 5x$

62. $4(2 - 3x) + 3(5 + 2x) = 6 - 7x$

63. $9 - 4(3r - 6) = 10r - (23r + 1)$

64. $12 - 5(4r - 2) = 8r - (29r + 6)$

65. $12\left(\dfrac{x}{6} + \dfrac{2}{3}\right) = 7x - 6x + 8$

66. $18\left(\dfrac{x}{9} + \dfrac{5}{6}\right) = 9x - 8x + 15$

67. $\dfrac{2}{3} + \dfrac{3z}{8} = \dfrac{2}{9} - \dfrac{5z}{8}$

68. $\dfrac{2}{3} + \dfrac{2z}{9} = \dfrac{1}{6} - \dfrac{7z}{9}$

2.3 ## The Multiplication Property of Equality

We know from Section 2.2 that we isolate x on one side of the equation $x - 2 = 5$ by adding 2 to both sides. To isolate x on one side of the equation $2x = 8$, we multiply both sides by 1/2.

> **MULTIPLICATION PROPERTY OF EQUALITY**
>
> Let A, B, and C ($C \neq 0$) be algebraic expressions.
>
> If $A = B$, then $AC = BC$.

The **multiplication property of equality** states that we can multiply both sides of an equation by the same nonzero quantity and the result is an equivalent equation.

EXAMPLE 1 Solve $2x = 8$.

Solution To isolate x, multiply both sides of the equation by the reciprocal of 2, namely 1/2.

$$2x = 8 \qquad \textit{Original equation}$$

$$\frac{1}{2} \cdot 2x = \frac{1}{2} \cdot 8 \qquad \textit{Multiply both sides by 1/2}$$

$$x = 4 \qquad \textit{Simplify each side}$$

Try Problem 1 >   The solution is 4. Check in the original equation.   ■

Since dividing by C is the same as multiplying by $1/C$, we can also divide both sides of an equation by the same nonzero number, and the result is an equivalent equation.

EXAMPLE 2 Solve $-5y = 35$.

Solution To isolate y, divide both sides of the equation by the coefficient of y, namely -5.

$$-5y = 35 \qquad \textit{Original equation}$$

$$\frac{-5y}{-5} = \frac{35}{-5} \qquad \textit{Divide both sides by } -5$$

$$y = -7 \qquad \textit{Simplify each side}$$

Try Problem 5 >   The solution is -7. Check in the original equation.   ■

EXAMPLE 3 Solve $\dfrac{3}{4}p = 12$.

Solution Multiply both sides by the reciprocal of 3/4, namely 4/3.

$$\frac{3}{4}p = 12 \qquad \textit{Original equation}$$

$$\frac{4}{3} \cdot \frac{3}{4}p = \frac{4}{3} \cdot 12 \qquad \textit{Multiply both sides by 4/3}$$

$$1p = \frac{4}{\cancel{3}_{1}} \cdot \frac{\cancel{12}^{4}}{1} \qquad \textit{Simplify each side}$$

$$p = 16$$

Try Problem 11 >   The solution is 16. Check in the original equation.   ■

If an equation contains a fraction, it is usually easier to isolate a variable by multiplying both sides by the reciprocal of the coefficient of the variable. Here are some examples of equations and the best way to solve them. The complete solutions are shown in Examples 4 through 7.

Equation	*To Solve*
$-3x = 0$	Divide both sides by -3
$\dfrac{m}{6} = -4$	Multiply both sides by 6
$-\dfrac{7}{3} = -3k$	Multiply both sides by $-1/3$
$-z = \dfrac{4}{5}$	Multiply both sides by -1

EXAMPLE 4   Solve $-3x = 0$.

Solution

$$-3x = 0 \qquad \text{\textit{Original equation}}$$
$$\frac{-3x}{-3} = \frac{0}{-3} \qquad \text{\textit{Divide both sides by} } -3$$
$$x = 0 \qquad \text{\textit{Simplify each side}}$$

Try Problem 17 >   The solution is 0. Check in the original equation.   ■

EXAMPLE 5   Solve $\dfrac{m}{6} = -4$.

Solution

$$\frac{m}{6} = -4 \qquad \text{\textit{Original equation}}$$
$$\frac{1}{6}m = -4 \qquad \text{\textit{Since} } \frac{m}{6} = \frac{1}{6} \cdot \frac{m}{1} = \frac{1}{6}m$$
$$6\left(\frac{1}{6}m\right) = 6(-4) \qquad \text{\textit{Multiply both sides by} 6}$$
$$m = -24 \qquad \text{\textit{Simplify each side}}$$

Try Problem 19 >   The solution is -24. Check in the original equation.   ■

EXAMPLE 6   Solve $-7/3 = -3k$.

Solution

$$-\frac{7}{3} = -3k \qquad \text{\textit{Original equation}}$$
$$\left(-\frac{1}{3}\right)\left(-\frac{7}{3}\right) = \left(-\frac{1}{3}\right)(-3k) \qquad \text{\textit{Multiply both sides by} } -\frac{1}{3}$$
$$\frac{7}{9} = k \qquad \text{\textit{Simplify each side}}$$

Try Problem 23 >   The solution is 7/9. Check in the original equation.   ■

EXAMPLE 7   Solve $-z = \dfrac{4}{5}$.

Solution

$$-z = \frac{4}{5} \qquad \text{\textit{Original equation}}$$

$$(-1)(-z) = (-1)\frac{4}{5} \qquad \text{\textit{Multiply both sides by}} -1$$

$$z = -\frac{4}{5} \qquad \text{\textit{Simplify each side}}$$

Try Problem 27 >   The solution is $-4/5$. Check in the original equation.   ∎

Before you multiply or divide both sides of an equation by a number, make sure you simplify each side of the equation.

EXAMPLE 8   Solve $3(5y + 1) - (7y + 3) = -2 - 2$.

Solution   Begin by simplifying each side.

$$
\begin{aligned}
3(5y + 1) - (7y + 3) &= -2 - 2 \qquad &\text{\textit{Original equation}} \\
15y + 3 - 7y - 3 &= -2 - 2 \qquad &\text{\textit{Distributive property}} \\
8y &= -4 \qquad &\text{\textit{Combine like terms}} \\
\frac{8y}{8} &= \frac{-4}{8} \qquad &\text{\textit{Divide both sides by 8}} \\
y &= -\frac{1}{2} \qquad &\text{\textit{Simplify each side}}
\end{aligned}
$$

Try Problem 53 >   The solution is $-1/2$. Check in the original equation.   ∎

2.3 Problem Set

LEARNING THROUGH WRITING

☐ State the *multiplication property of equality* in words.

☐ In solving an equation, when is it better to multiply and when is it better to divide?

Solve each equation and check your solution.

1. $3x = 6$
2. $6x = -6$
3. $12y = 3$
4. $12y = 4$
5. $-4y = 20$
6. $-21 = -7m$
7. $-m = 4$
8. $-m = -5$

9. $-3z = -2$ **10.** $-4z = 3$ **11.** $\dfrac{2}{3}p = 6$ **12.** $\dfrac{3}{2}p = 6$

13. $\dfrac{5}{2}p = 3$ **14.** $\dfrac{4}{5}p = 3$ **15.** $-24 = -\dfrac{3}{4}r$ **16.** $-20 = -\dfrac{2}{5}r$

17. $-2x = 0$ **18.** $4x = 0$ **19.** $\dfrac{m}{8} = -2$ **20.** $\dfrac{m}{5} = -3$

21. $7y = \dfrac{7}{9}$ **22.** $8y = \dfrac{8}{9}$ **23.** $-\dfrac{5}{3} = 3k$ **24.** $-\dfrac{7}{2} = 2k$

25. $\dfrac{2}{7}x = 0$ **26.** $-\dfrac{4}{5}x = 0$ **27.** $-z = \dfrac{3}{8}$ **28.** $-z = -\dfrac{5}{8}$

29. $\dfrac{5}{4}y = -\dfrac{5}{12}$ **30.** $\dfrac{7}{3}y = \dfrac{7}{12}$ **31.** $-\dfrac{r}{2} = \dfrac{4}{5}$ **32.** $-\dfrac{r}{3} = -\dfrac{2}{5}$

33. $5.6t = -44.8$ **34.** $-3.1m = 6.2$ **35.** $-1.08z = -7.02$ **36.** $0.25x = -1.8$

Simplify each side of the equation. Then solve the equation and check your solution.

37. $5x - 2x + 6x = 4 + 12 + 2$
38. $7x - 3x + 4x = 8 + 1 + 15$
39. $-3 + 4r - 7r + 3 = 2 - 5$
40. $-5 + 6r - 9r + 5 = 4 - 7$
41. $3m + 8 - 3m = -10m + m + 5m$
42. $2m + 10 - 2m = -12m + m + 6m$
43. $-8k + 12k - 2k = -2 - 3 - 9$
44. $-9k + 13k - 2k = -2 - 5 - 11$
45. $-9p - 9p - 7 + 7 = 12 + 6$
46. $-8p - 8p - 4 + 4 = 11 + 5$
47. $3z - 3z + z - 2z = -8 + 3$
48. $5z - 5z + 2z - 3z = -9 + 2$
49. $15r - 8r - 8r = r - 6r + 5r$
50. $17r - 9r - 9r = r - 4r + 3r$
51. $2(x - 3) + 6 = 12 + 8$
52. $3(x - 2) + 6 = 14 + 16$
53. $4(3y + 1) - (8y + 4) = -1 - 1$
54. $5(2y + 1) - (4y + 5) = -2 - 2$
55. $-3(6 - 2k) + 2(k + 9) = -15 - 9$
56. $-2(6 - 2k) + 3(k + 4) = -17 - 4$
57. $5(m + 4) - 5m = -2m - 3(m - 1) - 3$
58. $4(m + 3) - 4m = -m - 2(m - 1) - 2$
59. $6.28k - 2.08k = 18.3 + 2.7$
60. $5.49k - 1.09k = 17.2 + 9.2$

61. $4\left(\dfrac{x}{2} - \dfrac{3}{4}\right) + 3 = 32 - 7 - 1$
62. $6\left(\dfrac{x}{3} - \dfrac{5}{6}\right) + 5 = 45 - 6 - 3$

63. $\dfrac{2}{3}p + \dfrac{2}{3}p = \dfrac{2}{3} + \dfrac{1}{2}$
64. $\dfrac{3}{5}p + \dfrac{3}{5}p = \dfrac{4}{5} + \dfrac{1}{10}$

2.4   Solving Linear Equations

All of the equations we solved in Sections 2.2 and 2.3 were *first-degree equations*. They are called **first-degree** (or **linear**) **equations** because the variable in the equation is raised to the first power.

> **DEFINITION OF A LINEAR EQUATION**
>
> A **linear equation,** or **first-degree equation,** in the variable x is an equation that can be expressed in the form
>
> $$ax + b = 0,$$
>
> where a and b are constants and $a \neq 0$.

Consider the equation

$$3x - 5 = 13.$$

The order of operations on the left side of the equation states that we multiply 3 and x and then subtract 5. To isolate x, we must undo these operations on x, in reverse order. Since the last operation is subtraction, we begin by adding 5 to both sides of the equation. Once this is done, we divide both sides of the equation by 3.

EXAMPLE 1   Solve $3x - 5 = 13$.

Solution

$$3x - 5 = 13 \qquad \textit{Original equation}$$
$$3x - 5 + 5 = 13 + 5 \qquad \textit{Add 5 to both sides}$$
$$3x = 18 \qquad \textit{Simplify each side}$$
$$\frac{3x}{3} = \frac{18}{3} \qquad \textit{Divide both sides by 3}$$
$$x = 6 \qquad \textit{Simplify each side}$$

Try Problem 1 >   The solution is 6. Check in the original equation.   ∎

As you become more proficient in solving equations, you will find yourself doing some of the steps in your head. For example, you might solve the equation in Example 1 as follows.

$$3x - 5 = 13 \qquad \textit{Original equation}$$
$$3x = 18 \qquad \textit{Add 5 to both sides}$$
$$x = 6 \qquad \textit{Divide both sides by 3}$$

EXAMPLE 2   Solve $20 - 2y = 34$.

Solution

$$20 - 2y = 34 \qquad \textit{Original equation}$$
$$20 - 2y - 20 = 34 - 20 \qquad \textit{Subtract 20 from both sides}$$
$$-2y = 14 \qquad \textit{Simplify each side}$$
$$\frac{-2y}{-2} = \frac{14}{-2} \qquad \textit{Divide both sides by } -2$$
$$y = -7 \qquad \textit{Simplify each side}$$

Try Problem 15 >   The solution is -7. Check in the original equation.   ■

EXAMPLE 3   Solve $\dfrac{9}{5}r - \dfrac{7}{5}r + 6 = 26$.

Solution

$$\frac{9}{5}r - \frac{7}{5}r + 6 = 26 \qquad \textit{Original equation}$$

$$\frac{2}{5}r + 6 = 26 \qquad \textit{Combine like terms}$$

$$\frac{2}{5}r + 6 - 6 = 26 - 6 \qquad \textit{Subtract 6 from both sides}$$

$$\frac{2}{5}r = 20 \qquad \textit{Simplify each side}$$

$$\frac{5}{2} \cdot \frac{2}{5}r = \frac{5}{2} \cdot 20 \qquad \textit{Multiply both sides by 5/2}$$

$$r = 50 \qquad \textit{Simplify each side}$$

Try Problem 25 >   The solution is 50. Check in the original equation.   ■

If like terms appear on opposite sides of an equation, bring them together on the same side so that you can combine them.

EXAMPLE 4   Solve $8z + 1 = -4z - 23$.

Solution   Add $4z$ to both sides to get the variable terms on the left side.

$$8z + 1 = -4z - 23 \qquad \textit{Original equation}$$
$$8z + 1 + 4z = -4z - 23 + 4z \qquad \textit{Add 4z to both sides}$$
$$12z + 1 = -23 \qquad \textit{Simplify each side}$$

Subtract 1 from both sides to get the constant terms on the right side.

$$12z + 1 - 1 = -23 - 1 \qquad \textit{Subtract 1 from both sides}$$
$$12z = -24 \qquad \textit{Simplify each side}$$
$$\frac{12z}{12} = \frac{-24}{12} \qquad \textit{Divide both sides by 12}$$
$$z = -2 \qquad \textit{Simplify each side}$$

Try Problem 29 >   The solution is -2. Check in the original equation.   ■

If an equation involves parentheses, use the distributive property to remove the parentheses.

EXAMPLE 5   Solve $m - (3m - 4) = -16$.

Solution

$$
\begin{array}{ll}
m - (3m - 4) = -16 & \textit{Original equation} \\
m - 3m + 4 = -16 & \textit{Distributive property} \\
-2m + 4 = -16 & \textit{Combine like terms} \\
-2m + 4 - 4 = -16 - 4 & \textit{Subtract 4 from both sides} \\
-2m = -20 & \textit{Simplify each side} \\
\dfrac{-2m}{-2} = \dfrac{-20}{-2} & \textit{Divide both sides by } -2 \\
m = 10 & \textit{Simplify each side}
\end{array}
$$

Try Problem 43 >   The solution is 10. Check in the original equation.   ■

TO SOLVE A LINEAR EQUATION

1. Use the distributive property to remove parentheses.
2. Simplify each side by combining like terms.
3. Use the addition property of equality to collect all variable terms on one side of the equation and all constant terms on the other side.
4. Use the multiplication property of equality to write the variable term with a coefficient of 1.
5. Check your solution in the original equation.

EXAMPLE 6   Solve $4 - (2p + 3) = 7p + 2(p + 6)$.

Solution

Step 1   *Use the distributive property to remove parentheses.*

$$
\begin{array}{ll}
4 - (2p + 3) = 7p + 2(p + 6) & \textit{Original equation} \\
4 - 2p - 3 = 7p + 2p + 12 & \textit{Distributive property}
\end{array}
$$

Step 2   *Simplify each side by combining like terms.*

$$
-2p + 1 = 9p + 12 \qquad \textit{Simplify each side}
$$

Step 3   *Collect all variable terms on one side and all constant terms on the other side.* We decide to collect variable terms on the right side.

$$
\begin{array}{ll}
-2p + 1 + 2p = 9p + 12 + 2p & \textit{Add 2p to both sides} \\
1 = 11p + 12 & \textit{Simplify each side} \\
1 - 12 = 11p + 12 - 12 & \textit{Subtract 12 from both sides} \\
-11 = 11p & \textit{Simplify each side}
\end{array}
$$

Step 4   *Write the variable term with a coefficient of* 1.

$$\frac{-11}{11} = \frac{11p}{11} \qquad \text{\textit{Divide both sides by} 11}$$

$$-1 = p \qquad \text{\textit{Simplify each side}}$$

Step 5   *Check in the original equation.*

$$4 - (2p + 3) = 7p + 2(p + 6) \qquad \text{\textit{Original equation}}$$

$$4 - [2(-1) + 3] = 7(-1) + 2(-1 + 6) \quad \text{\textit{Replace p with} } -1$$

Use the order of operations to simplify each side.

$$4 - [-2 + 3] = -7 + 2(5)$$

$$4 - 1 = -7 + 10$$

Try Problem 51 > $\qquad\qquad\qquad\qquad 3 = 3 \qquad\qquad\qquad \text{\textit{True}} \qquad\qquad\blacksquare$

2.4   Problem Set

LEARNING THROUGH WRITING

☐ Describe the steps in solving a linear equation.

☐ Define a *linear equation* in the variable y.

Solve each equation.

1. $5x - 3 = 12$

2. $4x - 7 = 13$

3. $2p + 5 = -13$

4. $4p + 3 = -21$

5. $2t + 11 = 11$

6. $2t + 15 = 15$

7. $4.2r - 1.7 = -12.2$

8. $2.5r - 4.9 = -14.4$

9. $-\dfrac{3}{2}m + 5 = -19$

10. $-\dfrac{2}{3}m + 3 = -17$

11. $-7k + 8 = 34$

12. $-6k + 5 = 36$

13. $6 - x = 12$

14. $8 - x = 16$

15. $15 - 2y = 25$

16. $16 - 3y = 28$

17. $-19 - 4p = -3$

18. $-13 - 2p = -3$

Solve each equation.

19. $2x + 5 = 9 + 4$

20. $2x + 8 = 5 + 9$

21. $5y + 3y = -24$

22. $4y + 3y = -21$

23. $8p - 9p = -10 - 1$

24. $7p - 8p = -12 - 3$

25. $\dfrac{11}{3}r - \dfrac{7}{3}r + 3 = 15$

26. $\dfrac{11}{5}r - \dfrac{7}{5}r + 2 = 22$

27. $x - 6x + 4 = 20 - 21$

28. $x - 5x + 7 = 29 - 30$

29. $9z + 1 = -6z - 29$

30. $5z + 1 = -6z - 21$

31. $-p + 14 = p + 9$

32. $-p + 10 = p + 3$

33. $r + 7 = 2r - 6$

34. $r + 4 = 2r - 1$

35. $7t - 4 = t - 4$

36. $6t - 5 = t - 5$

Solve each equation.

37. $5(x - 1) = 3x - 7$

38. $3(x - 2) = x - 10$

39. $3y - 2(y + 1) = 5(y + 2)$

40. $4y - 3(y + 1) = 6(y + 7)$

41. $3(k + 5) + 4(k + 5) = 21$

42. $2(k + 6) + 5(k + 3) = 20$

43. $m - (4m - 5) = -19$

44. $m - (6m - 5) = -25$

45. $8 - (w - 4) = 3w + 9$

46. $5 - (w - 1) = 4w + 4$

47. $15 - 3(a + 6) = 9 - (4a + 5)$

48. $12 - 3(a + 6) = 8 - (4a + 5)$

49. $t - 2(3t - 2) = -t - 16$

50. $t - 2(4t - 3) = -2t - 9$

51. $7 - (3p + 2) = 2p + 5(p + 7)$

52. $4 - (4p + 1) = 5p + 3(p + 9)$

53. $6.1k - 4.3(2k - 5) = 2(1.5 + k) - 10.3$

54. $7.2k - 5.4(2k - 6) = 3(1.5 + k) - 8.4$

55. $-\dfrac{1}{3}(6x + 3) - 1 = \dfrac{1}{2}(4x - 10)$

56. $-\dfrac{1}{4}(8x + 4) - 1 = \dfrac{1}{2}(6x - 10)$

57. $-2[8y - 5(2y - 3)] = 3y - 8$

58. $-3[9y - 2(5y - 6)] = 2y - 9$

59. $5 + 3[1 + 2(2m - 3)] = 6(m + 5)$

60. $6 + 2[1 + 3(2m - 4)] = 4(m + 9)$

2.5   Formulas (công thức)

A **formula** is an equation that relates two or more variable quantities. For example, the equation

$$P = 2\ell + 2w$$

relates the perimeter, P, the length, ℓ, and the width, w, of a rectangle. Therefore this equation is a formula.

Many formulas in mathematics are geometric in nature. Some of the more commonly used geometric formulas are given in Table 2.1. As you study the table, keep in mind that the **perimeter,** P, of a plane figure is the distance

TABLE 2.1   Perimeters and Areas of Common Figures

Figure	Diagram	Perimeter	Area
Square		$P = 4s$	$A = s^2$
Rectangle		$P = 2\ell + 2w$	$A = \ell w$
Triangle		$P = a + b + c$	$A = \dfrac{1}{2} bh$
Trapezoid		$P = a + b + c + B$	$A = \dfrac{h}{2}(B + b)$

around the figure. The **area,** *A,* of a plane figure is the amount of space inside the figure.

Since perimeter measures distance, perimeter is measured in units such as inches, feet, yards, miles, meters, centimeters, and kilometers.

EXAMPLE 1   Find the length of a rectangle with perimeter 70 feet and width 15 feet.

Solution

Step 1   *Write down the formula that fits the problem.*

$$P = 2\ell + 2w$$

Step 2   *Substitute the known values.*

$70 = 2\ell + 2(15)$ *Replace P with 70 and w with 15*

Step 3   *Solve to find the unknown value,* ℓ*.*

$70 = 2\ell + 30$ *Multiply 2 and 15*
$40 = 2\ell$ *Subtract 30 from both sides*
$20 = \ell$ *Divide both sides by 2*

Step 4   *Attach the appropriate units of measure.*

$$\ell = 20 \text{ ft}$$

Try Problem 3 >   The length of the rectangle is 20 feet.   ■

Here is a summary of the steps for using a formula to solve a problem.

USING A FORMULA TO SOLVE A PROBLEM

1. Write down the formula that fits the problem.
2. Substitute the known values into the formula.
3. Solve to find the unknown value.
4. Attach the appropriate units of measure.

The amount of space inside a square that is 1 foot by 1 foot is called 1 **square foot** (Fig. 2.3). Therefore area is measured in units such as square inches, square feet, and square yards.

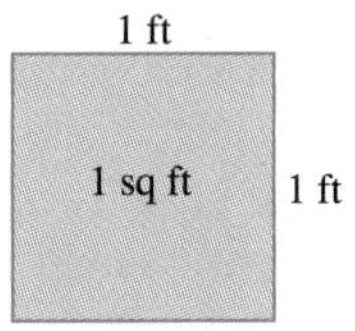

1 ft

1 sq ft   1 ft

FIGURE 2.3

The symbol π is the Greek letter pi, the first letter in the Greek word for perimeter. Calculations in 1 Kings 7:23 of the Bible indicate that 3 was used as the value of π. The Rhind Papyrus, dated around 1650 B.C., contains an estimate for π of 3.1604. The Greek mathematician Archimedes (287–212 B.C.) estimated π as 3.14. In the late 1800s the Indiana state legislature tried to pass a law fixing the value of π as some terminating decimal. They abandoned the idea after being ridiculed in the press. In 1989 the value of π was calculated, via computer, to more than a billion decimal places. To ten decimal places, the value of π is 3.1415926536.

TABLE 2.2   Circumference and Area of a Circle

Figure	Diagram	Circumference	Area
Circle	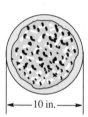	$C = \pi d = 2\pi r$	$A = \pi r^2$

Another plane figure that occupies a prominent position in mathematics is the *circle* (Table 2.2). The **diameter,** *d,* of a circle is the distance across the circle (through the center of the circle). The **radius,** *r,* of a circle is one-half the diameter. The **circumference,** *C,* of a circle is the distance around the circle. We find the circumference of a circle by multiplying the diameter by the irrational number π, which has an approximate value of 3.14.

EXAMPLE 2   Find the area of a circular pizza that is 10 inches in diameter (see Fig. 2.4).

←——10 in.——→

FIGURE 2.4

Solution

$A = \pi r^2$ (d T hint pron) *Write down the formula that fits the problem*

Since the diameter is $d = 10$ in., the radius is $r = 10/2 = 5$ in.

$A = 3.14(5^2)$ *Substitute the known values, using 3.14 for π*
$A = 3.14(25) = 78.5$ *Solve to find A*
$A = 78.5$ sq in.   *Attach the appropriate units*

Try Problem 9 >   The area is 78.5 square inches.   ■

The **volume,** *V,* of a solid is the amount of space contained in the solid. The amount of space contained in a cube that is 1 yard by 1 yard by 1 yard is called 1 **cubic yard** (Fig. 2.5). Therefore volume is measured in units such as cubic inches, cubic feet, and cubic yards. See Table 2.3 for formulas for the volumes of some common solids.

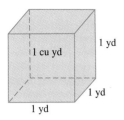

FIGURE 2.5

TABLE 2.3   Volumes of Common Solids

Figure	Diagram	Volume
Parallelepiped	h ℓ w	$V = \ell wh$
Cylinder	h r	$V = \pi r^2 h$
Cone	h r	$V = \dfrac{1}{3}\pi r^2 h$
Sphere	r	$V = \dfrac{4}{3}\pi r^3$

EXAMPLE 3   How much water will a rectangular aquarium that is 21 inches long, 11 inches wide, and 8 inches high hold? (See Fig. 2.6.)

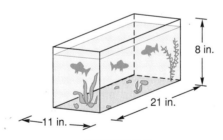

8 in.

21 in.

11 in.

FIGURE 2.6

Solution

$V = \ell wh$ *Write down the formula that fits the problem*

$V = 21 \cdot 11 \cdot 8$ *Substitute the known values*

$V = 1848$ cu in.   *Solve for V and attach the appropriate units*

Try Problem 17 >   The aquarium will hold 1848 cubic inches of water.   ■

To calculate simple interest, I, we use the formula

$I = Prt,$

where P is the principal (amount invested or borrowed), r is the interest rate in decimal form, and t is the time in years.

EXAMPLE 4 How much should be invested at 8% for 2 years to accumulate $120 in simple interest?

Solution

$$I = Prt \qquad \textit{Write down the formula that fits the problem}$$
$$120 = P(0.08)(2) \qquad \textit{Substitute the known values, using } r = 8\% = 0.08$$
$$120 = P(0.16)$$
$$\left. \frac{120}{0.16} = \frac{P(0.16)}{0.16} \right\} \textit{Solve to find P}$$
$$\$750 = P \qquad \textit{Attach the appropriate units}$$

Try Problem 23 > The amount invested should be $750. ∎

Caution! ∎ Make sure you convert the interest rate, r, to decimal form before you substitute for r in the formula $I = Prt$.

Example: $P = \$100$, $r = 12\%$, $t = 3$ yr, find I.

Correct
$$I = Prt$$
$$I = (100)(0.12)(3) = \$36$$

Wrong
$$I = Prt$$
$$I = (100)(12)(3) = \$3600$$

The formula that relates distance, d, rate (speed), r, and time, t, is

$$d = rt.$$

EXAMPLE 5 An ostrich is capable of maintaining a speed of 50 miles per hour for 30 minutes. Under these conditions, how far would the ostrich run?

Solution

$$d = rt \qquad \textit{Write down the formula that fits the problem}$$

Since rate is given in miles per hour, we must convert 30 minutes to hours: 30 minutes = 30/60 = 1/2 hr.

$$d = 50 \cdot \frac{1}{2} \qquad \textit{Substitute the known values}$$
$$d = 25 \text{ mi} \qquad \textit{Solve to find d and attach the appropriate units}$$

Try Problem 27 > The ostrich would run 25 miles. ∎

Caution! ∎ Make sure the units of measure are consistent before you substitute values into the formula $d = rt$. For instance, if rate is in miles per hour, then time must be in hours.

Example: $r = 60$ mph, $t = 15$ min, find d.

Correct
$$d = rt$$
$$d = 60 \cdot \frac{1}{4} = 15 \text{ mi}$$

Wrong
$$d = rt$$
$$d = 60 \cdot 15 = 900 \text{ mi}$$

Solving for a Specified Variable

Since d is isolated on one side of the equation $d = rt,$ we say that the formula is *solved for d*. Sometimes it is more convenient if such a formula is solved for one of the other variables. For example, suppose we want to calculate the time it would take to travel a distance of 495 miles at a rate of (a) 45 mph, (b) 50 mph, and (c) 55 mph. Since we are looking for time in each case, it would be more convenient if the formula were solved for t.

EXAMPLE 6   Solve $d = rt$ for t. Then find t when $d = 495$ miles and

a. $r = 45$ mph.   b. $r = 50$ mph.   c. $r = 55$ mph.

Solution   To solve for t we must isolate t on one side of the equation.

$$d = rt \qquad \textit{Original equation}$$

$$\frac{d}{r} = \frac{rt}{r} \qquad \textit{Divide both sides by r}$$

$$\frac{d}{r} = t \qquad \textit{Simplify the right side}$$

We can also write the answer as $t = d/r.$ If $d = 495$ miles, then

a. when $r = 45$ mph, $t = \dfrac{d}{r} = \dfrac{495}{45} = 11$ hr.

b. when $r = 50$ mph, $t = \dfrac{d}{r} = \dfrac{495}{50} = 9.9$ hr.

Try Problem 33 >   c. when $r = 55$ mph, $t = \dfrac{d}{r} = \dfrac{495}{55} = 9$ hr.   ■

EXAMPLE 7   Solve $P = 2\ell + 2w$ for ℓ.

Solution   To solve for ℓ we must isolate ℓ on one side of the equation.

$$P = 2\ell + 2w \qquad\qquad \textit{Original equation}$$

$$P - 2w = 2\ell + 2w - 2w \qquad \textit{Subtract 2w from both sides}$$

$$P - 2w = 2\ell \qquad\qquad \textit{Simplify the right side}$$

$$\frac{P - 2w}{2} \qquad \frac{2\ell}{2} \qquad\qquad \textit{Divide both sides by 2}$$

$$\frac{P - 2w}{2} = \ell \qquad\qquad \textit{Simplify the right side}$$

Try Problem 39 >   We can also write the answer as $\ell = (P - 2w)/2.$ ■

Caution! ■   Here are two correct ways and one wrong way to write the answer to Example 7.

Correct	*Correct*	*Wrong*
$\ell = \dfrac{P - 2w}{2}$	$\ell = \dfrac{P}{2} - w$	$\ell = P - w$

The Celsius and Fahrenheit temperature scales were named after their
respective inventors, the Swedish
astronomer Anders Celsius (1701–
1744) and the German physicist
Gabriel Fahrenheit (1686–1736).

The formula that relates Celsius temperature, C, and Fahrenheit temperature, F, is

$$C = \frac{5}{9}(F - 32).$$ ✳

EXAMPLE 8   Solve $C = \dfrac{5}{9}(F - 32)$ for F.

Solution   To clear the fraction, multiply both sides by the reciprocal of 5/9.

$$\frac{9}{5} \cdot C = \frac{9}{5} \cdot \frac{5}{9}(F - 32) \qquad \textit{Multiply both sides by 9/5}$$

$$\frac{9}{5}C = F - 32 \qquad\qquad \textit{Simplify the right side}$$

$$\frac{9}{5}C + 32 = F - 32 + 32 \qquad \textit{Add 32 to both sides}$$

$$\frac{9}{5}C + 32 = F \qquad\qquad \textit{Simplify the right side}$$

Try Problem 53>   We can also write the answer as $F = \dfrac{9}{5}C + 32$.   ■

2.5 Problem Set

LEARNING THROUGH WRITING

☐ What is a *formula?*

☐ Discuss the steps in using a formula to solve an applied problem.

☐ Discuss the number π.

☐ Name each plane figure.

☐ Name each solid.

☐ What does it mean to *solve a formula* for one of its variables?

☐ Compare and contrast the terms *perimeter, area,* and *volume*. Include situations where each might be used and appropriate units of measure for each.

☐ Compare and contrast the terms *radius, diameter,* and *circumference*. Include situations where each might be used and appropriate units for each.

Use the formula $P = 2\ell + 2w$ and the known values to find the unknown value.

1. $\ell = 6$ yd, $w = 5$ yd
2. $\ell = 7$ yd, $w = 4$ yd
3. $P = 82$ ft, $w = 16$ ft
4. $P = 56$ ft, $\ell = 15$ ft

Use the formula $A = \ell w$ and the known values to find the unknown value.

5. $\ell = 4$ m, $w = 3$ m
6. $\ell = 5$ m, $w = 2$ m
7. $A = 36$ sq cm, $\ell = 8$ cm
8. $A = 76$ sq cm, $w = 8$ cm

Use the formula $A = \pi r^2$ and the known values to find the unknown value.

9. $\pi = 3.14$, $r = 10$ in.
10. $\pi = 3.14$, $r = 9$ in.
11. $\pi = 3.14$, $r = \dfrac{1}{2}$mi
12. $\pi = 3.14$, $r = 2.5$ mi

Use the formula $C = \pi d$ and the known values to find the unknown value.

13. $\pi = 3.14$, $d = 5$ ft
14. $\pi = 3.14$, $d = 4$ ft
15. $C = 15.7$ km, $\pi = 3.14$
16. $C = 18.84$ km, $\pi = 3.14$

Use the formula $V = \ell w h$ and the known values to find the unknown value.

17. $\ell = 22$ in., $w = 9$ in., $h = 5$ in.
18. $\ell = 15$ in., $w = 6$ in., $h = 7$ in.
19. $V = 600$ cu ft, $\ell = 25$ ft, $h = 2$ ft
20. $V = 900$ cu ft, $\ell = 20$ ft, $h = 3$ ft

Use the formula $I = Prt$ and the known values to find the unknown value.

21. $P = \$375$, $r = 12\%$, $t = 1$ yr
22. $P = \$560$, $r = 15\%$, $t = 1$ yr
23. $I = \$306$, $r = 9\%$, $t = 4$ yr
24. $I = \$81$, $r = 6\%$, $t = 3$ yr

Use the formula $d = rt$ and the known values to find the unknown value.

25. $r = 25$ mph, $t = 3$ hr
26. $r = 45$ mph, $t = 2$ hr
27. $r = 60$ mph, $t = 20$ min
28. $r = 12$ mph, $t = 45$ min

Use the formula $A = \dfrac{1}{2} bh$ and the known values to find the unknown value.

29. $b = 13$ cm, $h = 8$ cm
30. $b = 19$ cm, $h = 6$ cm
31. $A = 50$ sq yd, $h = 5$ yd
32. $A = 28$ sq yd, $h = 7$ yd

33. Solve $d = rt$ for t. Then find t when $d = 420$ miles and
    a. $r = 30$ mph.   b. $r = 35$ mph.   c. $r = 40$ mph.

34. Solve $d = rt$ for r. Then find r when $d = 380$ miles and
    a. $t = 5$ hr.   b. $t = 8$ hr.   c. $t = 10$ hr.

Solve each formula for the specified variable.

35. $A = \ell w$ for ℓ
36. $C = \pi d$ for d
37. $I = Prt$ for r

38. $V = \ell w h$ for ℓ
39. $P = 2\ell + 2w$ for w
40. $P = 2\ell + 2w$ for ℓ

41. $I = P + Prt$ for t
42. $I = P + Prt$ for r
43. $A = \dfrac{1}{2}bh$ for h

44. $V = \dfrac{1}{3}Bh$ for B
45. $s = \dfrac{1}{2}(a + b + c)$ for a
46. $s = \dfrac{1}{2}(a + b + c)$ for c

47. $A = \dfrac{h}{2}(B + b)$ for b
48. $A = \dfrac{h}{2}(B + b)$ for B
49. $c^2 = a^2 + b^2$ for a^2

50. $c^2 = a^2 + b^2$ for b^2
51. $V = \dfrac{1}{3}\pi r^2 h$ for r^2
52. $V = \dfrac{4}{3}\pi r^3$ for r^3

53. Solve $C = \dfrac{5}{9}(F - 32)$ for F. Then find F when
    a. $C = 75°$.   b. $C = 0°$.   c. $C = -20°$.

54. Solve $F = \dfrac{9}{5}C + 32$ for C. Then find C when
    a. $F = 212°$.   b. $F = 32°$.   c. $F = -13°$.

Solve the following word problems using the formulas given in this section. Use $\pi = 3.14$.

55. An MX missile can travel 4700 miles in 30 minutes. Find its speed, in miles per hour.

56. The British Airways Supersonic Flagship Concorde can travel 270 miles in 12 minutes. Find its speed, in miles per hour.

57. You see lightning 4 seconds before you hear the thunder. If the speed of sound is 1100 feet per second, how far away is the lightning?

58. You see fireworks 2 seconds before you hear them. If the speed of sound is 1100 feet per second, how far away are the fireworks?

59. A pizza shop sells two small circular pizzas for the same price as one large circular pizza. The small pizzas are 8 inches in diameter, and the large pizza is 12 inches in diameter. Which is the better buy?

60. Which of the two cake pans pictured in Fig. 2.7 has the greater volume?

61. How much grain is contained in a conical pile that is 9 feet high with base 8 feet in diameter? See Fig. 2.8.

62. How much water will a spherical water tank whose diameter is 30 feet hold? See Fig. 2.9.

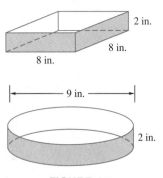

FIGURE 2.7

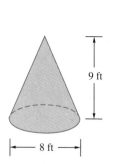

FIGURE 2.8

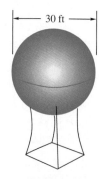

FIGURE 2.9

63. An oval track is to be constructed by putting two semicircles on each of the shorter ends of a rectangle that is 55 yards by 130 yards (see Fig. 2.10). Find the length of the track.

64. A baseball infield is a square with 90 feet between the bases (Fig. 2.11). Find the total distance around the bases.

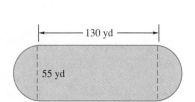

FIGURE 2.10

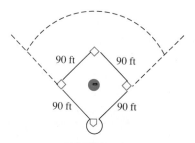

FIGURE 2.11

65. If carpeting a room costs $15 per square yard, how much will it cost to carpet the room in Fig. 2.12. (Hint: 1 square yard = 9 square feet.)

66. If sodding a lawn costs $3 per square yard, how much will it cost to sod the shaded lawn in Fig. 2.13. (Hint: 1 square yard = 9 square feet.)

67. Find the area of the shaded region in Fig. 2.14.

68. Find the area of the shaded region in Fig. 2.15.

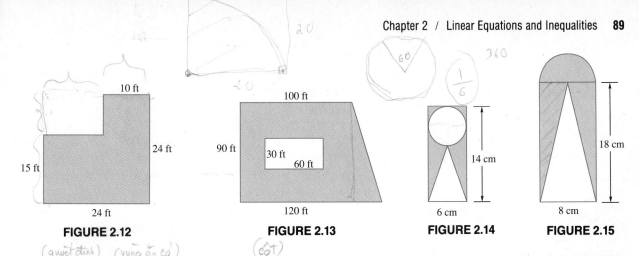

FIGURE 2.12   **FIGURE 2.13**   **FIGURE 2.14**   **FIGURE 2.15**

69. Determine the grazing area of a horse that is tied with a 20-foot rope to a stake at one corner of a barn that is 20 feet by 20 feet.

70. Determine the grazing area of the horse in Problem 69 if the rope is tied to a stake halfway along one side of the barn.

📟 CALCULATOR PROBLEMS

To find π on your calculator, press

| Clear | | π | 3.141592654 |

The exact value of π is actually a nonterminating, nonrepeating decimal. Therefore the number 3.141592654 *is only an approximate value of* π.

71. To the nearest thousandth, find the circumference of a circle whose radius is 17.8 centimeters.

72. To the nearest thousandth, find the area of a circle whose diameter is 9.3 meters.

2.6   Translating Words into Algebra

Mathematics is a language in much the same way that English is a language. In English we use words, together with the rules of grammar, to communicate ideas. In mathematics we use symbols, together with mathematical laws, to solve problems.

Before we can use the laws of mathematics to solve problems that are expressed in words, we must be able to translate the problems from words into algebra. Here are some examples of how to translate a word phrase into an algebraic expression.

Word Phrase	*Algebraic Expression*
Addition	
The sum of a number and 5	$x + 5$
Two more than a number	$y + 2$
A number increased by 10	$z + 10$
A number plus 7	$n + 7$
Nine added to a number	$p + 9$
Subtraction	
The difference of a number and 4	$x - 4$
Six less than a number	$y - 6$
A number decreased by 12	$z - 12$
Three minus a number	$3 - r$
Eight subtracted from a number	$t - 8$
Multiplication	
The product of a number and 6	$6x$
Twice a number	$2y$
A number multiplied by 5	$5z$
Seven times a number	$7k$
Three-fourths of a number	$\frac{3}{4}m$ or $\frac{3m}{4}$
Eight percent of a number	$0.08t$
Division	
The quotient of a number and 9	$\frac{x}{9}$
A number divided by 4	$\frac{y}{4}$
One-half a number	$\frac{z}{2}$ or $\frac{1}{2}z$

(Thương số, tỉ số)

(phép tính)

Caution! ▪ Subtraction and division are *not* commutative operations, and we must be care-
▪ ful to write them in the correct order.
▪
▪
▪
▪ | | *Correct* | *Wrong* |
▪ |---|---|---|
▪ | Five less than a number | $x - 5$ | ~~5 − x~~ |
▪ | The quotient of a number and 10 | $\frac{x}{10}$ | ~~$\frac{10}{x}$~~ |
▪

EXAMPLE 1

Try Problem 1 >

a. The sum of three times a number and 8 is $3x + 8$.
b. Three times the sum of a number and 8 is $3(x + 8)$. ▪

EXAMPLE 2

a. The number of hours in t days is $24t$ hours.
b. The number of calories in $z + 5$ waffles at 225 calories per waffle is $225(z + 5)$ calories.
c. The value of x nickels and y dimes is $5x + 10y$ cents.
d. The simple interest on m dollars invested for 1 year at 6% is $0.06m$ dollars.

Try Problem 15 >

biến số

When two or more quantities in a problem are related, we usually represent the most basic quantity by a single variable. Then we represent the other quantities in the problem as algebraic expressions in terms of that variable. One example of quantities that are related are *consecutive integers*. **Consecutive** – *liên tiếp* **integers** (such as 9 and 10, or 31 and 32) are integers that differ by 1. On the other hand, *consecutive even integers* (such as 4 and 6) are even integers that differ by 2. *Consecutive odd integers* (such as 5 and 7) are odd integers that differ by 2.

số nguyên

EXAMPLE 3   Write algebraic expressions that represent two consecutive integers.

(biểu diễn)

Solution   If we represent the smaller integer by x, then the larger integer would be $x + 1$. Another solution would be to represent the larger integer by x; then the smaller integer would be $x - 1$.

(giải đáp)

Try Problem 25 >

EXAMPLE 4   Write algebraic expressions that represent three consecutive even integers.

Solution   If we represent the smallest integer by x, the middle integer would be $x + 2$, and the largest integer would be $x + 4$.

Try Problem 27 >

EXAMPLE 5   Write algebraic expressions that represent the number of students and the number of nonstudents attending a school play if the total attendance was 600 people.

Solution   If z represents the number of students attending, then $600 - z$ represents the number of nonstudents attending.

Try Problem 35 >

EXAMPLE 6   Write an algebraic expression that represents the following statement: Six times the difference of a number and 4 is added to the number. Then simplify the expression.

Solution

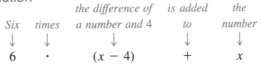

Six	times	the difference of a number and 4	is added to	the number
↓	↓	↓	↓	↓
6	·	$(x - 4)$	+	x

Now simplify the expression.

Try Problem 37 >

$$6(x - 4) + x \quad \text{\textit{Original expression}}$$
$$= 6x - 24 + x \quad \text{\textit{Distributive property}}$$
$$= 7x - 24 \quad \text{\textit{Add 6x and x}}$$

We will now see how to translate a word problem into an algebraic equation. Then by solving the equation, we can find the unknown quantity asked for in the problem.

Word problems have been of interest to mathematicians for thousands of years. The following problem is from the Rhind papyrus, dated about 1650 B.C.: A number added to 1/7 of the number is 19. What is the number?

EXAMPLE 7 Three more than twice a number is 19. Find the number.

Solution Represent the unknown number by x. Then translate the word problem into an algebraic equation.

Three	more than	twice	a number	is	19
↓	↓	↓	↓	↓	↓
3	+	2 ·	x	=	19

Now solve the equation to find the unknown number x.

$$3 + 2x = 19 \quad \text{\textit{Original equation}}$$
$$2x = 16 \quad \text{\textit{Subtract 3 from both sides}}$$
$$x = 8 \quad \text{\textit{Divide both sides by 2}}$$

Try Problem 47 >

The number is 8. Check in the words of the original problem as follows: Three more than twice 8 is 19.

Caution!

Always check the solution to a word problem in the words of the original *problem*, not in the original *equation*. You may have made a mistake when you wrote the equation.

EXAMPLE 8 Six times the sum of a number and 1 is 9 less than the number. Find the number.

Solution Let y represent the number. Then translate the word problem into an algebraic equation.

Six	times	the sum of a number and 1	is	9 less than the number
↓	↓	↓	↓	↓
6	·	$(y + 1)$	=	$y - 9$

Now solve the equation to find y.

$$6(y + 1) = y - 9 \quad \textit{Original equation}$$
$$6y + 6 = y - 9 \quad \textit{Distributive property}$$
$$5y + 6 = -9 \quad \textit{Subtract y from both sides}$$
$$5y = -15 \quad \textit{Subtract 6 from both sides}$$
$$y = -3 \quad \textit{Divide both sides by 5}$$

Try Problem 57 >   The number is -3. Check in the words of the original problem.   ■

PROBLEM SOLVING

EXAMPLE 9   The *cost* of an item is the amount a business pays for the item. The *price* of an item is the amount a business charges its customers for the item. A 50% *markup* means that the price of an item is determined by adding 50% of the cost of the item to the cost. For example, if a video store pays $8 for a compact disk and marks it up 50%, then the price at which the store sells the disk is $12.

$$\$8 + 50\% \text{ of } \$8 = 8 + 0.50(8) = 8 + 4 = \$12$$

A 10% *markdown* means that the price of an item is determined by subtracting 10% of the original price of the item from the original price. For example, if a necklace normally priced at $50 is marked down 10%, the new price is $45.

$$\$50 - 10\% \text{ of } \$50 = 50 - 0.10(50) = 50 - 5 = \$45$$

Suppose a department store is having a 15% markdown sale. What was the original price of a rear-projection television set whose sale price is $3638?

Solution   Let $p =$ the original price.

Original price	*minus*	*markdown*	*equals*	*sale price*
↓	↓	↓	↓	↓
p	$-$	15% of p	$=$	3638

Solve the equation to find p.

$$p - 0.15p = 3638 \quad \textit{Since 15\% of p is } 0.15p$$
$$1.00p - 0.15p = 3638 \quad \textit{Since } p = 1.00p$$
$$0.85p = 3638 \quad \textit{Since } 1.00 - 0.15 = 0.85$$
$$\frac{0.85p}{0.85} = \frac{3638}{0.85} \quad \textit{Divide both sides by 0.85}$$
$$p = 4280$$

The original price of the television set was \$4280. Check in the words of the original problem.

Try Problem 59 >

\$4280	*Original price*	\$4280	*Original price*
× 0.15	*Markdown rate*	− 642	*Markdown*
\$ 642	*Markdown*	\$3638	*Sale price*

2.6 Problem Set

LEARNING THROUGH WRITING

☐ Write each algebraic expression in words.

   a. $10 - 3x$ b. $\dfrac{x}{2} - 9 = 15$ c. $4(x + 7) + 2x$

☐ Define *consecutive integers, consecutive even integers,* and *consecutive odd integers.*

Write each word phrase as an algebraic expression.

1. The sum of twice a number and 5
2. The difference of four times a number and 3
3. Twice the sum of a number and 5
4. Four times the difference of a number and 3
5. The difference of one-third of a number and 1
6. The sum of one-half of a number and 7
7. Six times the square of a number
8. Nine times the cube of a number
9. The opposite of eight times a number
10. The reciprocal of five times a number
11. The quotient of a number and 2 decreased by 1/2
12. The quotient of a number and 3 decreased by 1/3
13. The number of seconds in t minutes
14. The cost of renting a racquetball court for t hours at \$9.50 per hour
15. The number of calories in $z + 6$ doughnuts at 175 calories per doughnut
16. The distance traveled in t hours at 53 mph
17. The value of x nickels and y quarters
18. The value of x dimes and y quarters
19. The simple interest on m dollars invested for 1 year at 11%
20. The simple interest on m dollars invested for 1 year at 7%
21. The amount of pure acid in $40 - p$ liters of a 5% acid solution
22. The amount of pure antifreeze in $25 - p$ liters of a 45% antifreeze solution
23. The length of each piece if a 60-foot log is cut into x equal pieces
24. The amount given to each heir if an estate of \$65,000 is divided equally among x heirs

For each problem, choose a variable to represent one of the quantities. Then represent the other quantities in the problem as algebraic expressions in terms of that variable.

25. Three consecutive integers
26. Four consecutive integers
27. Four consecutive even integers
28. Three consecutive odd integers
29. The number of calories in lite beer and in regular beer if lite beer has 2/3 the calories of regular beer
30. The salary of the president and of the chief executive officer if the president's salary is 3/4 the chief executive officer's salary
31. Sue's age now and Sue's age in 6 years
32. John's age now and John's age 7 years ago

33. Mel's age now and 5 years ago, and Doug's age now and 5 years ago given that Doug is currently twice as old as Mel

34. Julie's age now and in 9 years, and Kelly's age now and in 9 years given that Kelly is currently 3 times as old as Julie

35. The amount invested in each of two accounts if a total of $500 is invested

36. Kathy's mileage and her husband's mileage if they were the only drivers of a car whose odometer reads 40,000 miles

Write each sentence or word phrase as an algebraic expression. Then simplify the expression.

37. Two times the sum of a number and 8 is added to the number.

38. Three times the sum of a number and 5 is subtracted from the number.

39. Four times the difference of a number and 7 is subtracted from the sum of the number and 1.

40. Five times the difference of a number and 9 is added to the sum of the number and 3.

41. Six less than three times the sum of two consecutive odd integers

42. Nine less than twice the sum of two consecutive even integers

43. Eight percent of a number is subtracted from the number.

44. Twelve percent of a number is added to the number.

Solve each word problem.

45. Stephanie studied ten hours longer for the bar exam than did Betsy. Lisa studied twice as long as Stephanie. Write an algebraic expression that represents the total time studied by the three women. Then simplify the expression.

46. A cash register contains two fewer dimes than nickels and three times as many quarters as nickels. Write an algebraic expression that represents
a. the total number of coins in the cash register.
b. the total value of the coins in the cash register.
Then simplify each expression.

Choose a variable to represent the unknown quantity. Then translate the problem into an algebraic equation. Finally, solve the equation to find the unknown quantity.

47. Seven more than twice a number is 29. Find the number.

48. Eight less than three times a number is 13. Find the number.

49. Three-fifths of a number is 45. Find the number.

50. Three-eighths of a number is 48. Find the number.

51. If 38% of a number is 20.9, find the number.

52. If 42% of a number is 27.3, find the number.

53. Three times a number is 10 more than twice the number. Find the number.

54. Five times a number is 12 more than four times the number. Find the number.

55. Four times a number minus 7 is 1 less than the number. Find the number.

56. Three times a number minus 9 is 3 less than the number. Find the number.

57. Nine times the sum of a number and 4 is 4 less than the number. Find the number.

58. Seven times the sum of a number and 5 is 7 less than the number. Find the number.

59. An appliance store has a 30% markup. That means the selling price of an item is determined by adding 30% of the cost of the item to the cost. What was the cost of a toaster oven that is priced at $49.40?

60. A furniture store is having a 20% markdown sale. That means the sale price is determined by subtracting 20% of the original price from the original price. What was the original price of a sofa whose sale price is $650?

61. The population of a town decreases 7% to 5115. Find the original population.

62. The price of a snow blower plus a 5% tax is $462. Find the price of the snow blower itself.

63. It costs $2.65 per month to rent a telephone. You can buy a new phone for $25.44. In how many months will the cost of renting equal the price of a new phone?

64. Suppose you spend $4.75 per week at a coin laundry. A new washer and dryer costs $536.75. In how many weeks will the cost of the coin laundry equal the price of a new washer and dryer?

65. Algebra is a generalized form of arithmetic. The following example illustrates the difference between arithmetic and algebra.

Arithmetic Solution	Puzzle	Algebraic Solution
7	Think of a number	x
$7 + 5 = 12$	Add 5	$x + 5$
$2 \cdot 12 = 24$	Multiply by 2	$2(x + 5) = 2x + 10$
$24 - 4 = 20$	Subtract 4	$2x + 10 - 4 = 2x + 6$
$3 \cdot 20 = 60$	Multiply by 3	$3(2x + 6) = 6x + 18$
$\dfrac{60}{6} = 10$	Divide by 6	$\dfrac{6x + 18}{6} = \dfrac{6x}{6} + \dfrac{18}{6} = x + 3$
$10 - 7 = 3$	Subtract your original number, and the result is 3	$x + 3 - x = 3$

Using this example as a model, write an arithmetic and an algebraic solution to the following puzzle: Think of a number. Add 7. Multiply by 3. Subtract 9. Multiply by 2. Divide by 6. Subtract your original number. The result is 4.

2.7 Number, Age, and Geometry Problems

Before you begin to solve any word problem, you should read the problem carefully. You may need to do so several times in order to determine the information that is given in the problem and the question that is being asked. Then use the following steps to solve the problem.

TO SOLVE A WORD PROBLEM

1. Write down the unknown quantities, and represent one of them by a variable, say x. Then write the other unknown quantities in terms of x.
2. Use the information given in the problem to write an equation involving x. Sometimes a chart or a diagram is helpful in keeping track of the unknown quantities and in writing the equation.
3. Solve the equation to find the value of x. Then use this value to find the values of the other unknown quantities.
4. Check your solution in the words of the original problem.

Number Problems

EXAMPLE 1   One number is twice another. The sum of the two numbers is 24. Find the numbers.

Solution
Step 1   *Write down the unknown quantities and represent one of them by x. Then write the other unknown quantity in terms of x.*

x = first number
$2x$ = second number

Step 2   *Write an equation involving x.*

First		*second*		
number	*plus*	*number*	*is*	24
↓	↓	↓	↓	↓
x	$+$	$2x$	$=$	24

Step 3   *Solve the equation to find x. Then use the value of x to find 2x, the other unknown quantity.*

$$x + 2x = 24 \quad \text{\textit{Original equation}}$$
$$3x = 24 \quad \text{\textit{Combine like terms}}$$
$$x = 8 \quad \text{\textit{Divide both sides by}} \ 3$$

The first number is 8. The second number is $2x = 2(8) = 16$.

Step 4   *Check in the words of the original problem.* Sixteen is twice 8, and the sum of 16 and 8 is 24.   ■

Try Problem 1 >

EXAMPLE 2   If the smaller of two consecutive integers is doubled, the result is 6 more than the larger. Find the integers.

Solution
x = smaller integer
$x + 1$ = larger integer

If the smaller	*the*		*more*	*the*
is doubled,	*result is*	6	*than*	*larger*
↓	↓	↓	↓	↓
$2x$	$=$	6	$+$	$(x + 1)$

Solve the equation.

$$2x = 6 + x + 1 \quad \text{\textit{Original equation}}$$
$$2x = 7 + x \quad \text{\textit{Combine like terms}}$$
$$x = 7 \quad \text{\textit{Subtract x from both sides}}$$

The smaller integer is 7. The larger integer is $x + 1 = 7 + 1 = 8$. To check, note that 7 and 8 are consecutive integers, and twice 7 is 14, which is 6 more than 8.   ■

Try Problem 5 >

Age Problems

EXAMPLE 3   Paula is twice as old as her sister. Six years ago she was four times as old as her sister. Find their present ages.

Solution

$x =$ sister's present age
$2x =$ Paula's present age

A chart is helpful in organizing the information and writing the equation.

	Age Now	Age 6 Years Ago
Sister	x	$x - 6$
Paula	$2x$	$2x - 6$

$$
\begin{array}{ccccc}
\textit{Paula's age} & & & & \textit{sister's age} \\
\textit{6 years ago} & \textit{is} & \textit{four} & \textit{times} & \textit{6 years ago} \\
\downarrow & \downarrow & \downarrow & \downarrow & \downarrow \\
2x - 6 & = & 4 & \cdot & (x - 6)
\end{array}
$$

Solve the equation.

$$
\begin{aligned}
2x - 6 &= 4x - 24 \qquad \textit{Distributive property} \\
-6 &= 2x - 24 \qquad \textit{Subtract 2x from both sides} \\
18 &= 2x \qquad\qquad \textit{Add 24 to both sides} \\
9 &= x \qquad\qquad\;\; \textit{Divide both sides by 2}
\end{aligned}
$$

Paula's sister is 9 years old. Paula is $2x = 2(9) = 18$ years old. To check, note that Paula's age, 18, is twice her sister's age, 9. Also, six years ago Paula was 12 and her sister was 3, and 12 is 4 times 3.   ■

Try Problem 13 >

Geometry Problems

EXAMPLE 4   The length of a rectangle is 4 meters less than three times the width. If the perimeter is 32 meters, find the width and length.

Solution

$x =$ width of rectangle
$3x - 4 =$ length of rectangle

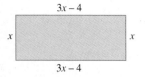

Twice the width	plus	twice the length	is	the perimeter
↓	↓	↓	↓	↓
$2 \cdot x$	$+$	$2 \cdot (3x - 4)$	$=$	32

Solve the equation.

$$
\begin{aligned}
2x + 6x - 8 &= 32 \quad && \textit{Distributive property} \\
8x - 8 &= 32 \quad && \textit{Combine like terms} \\
8x &= 40 \quad && \textit{Add 8 to both sides} \\
x &= 5 \quad && \textit{Divide both sides by 8}
\end{aligned}
$$

The width is 5 meters. The length is $3x - 4 = 3(5) - 4 = 11$ meters. Check in the words of the original problem.   ■

Try Problem 17 >

In the next example we use the fact that the sum of the angles of any triangle is 180°.

EXAMPLE 5   The second angle in a triangle is 12° less than the first angle. The third angle is four times the second angle. Find the measure of each angle.

Solution

$$
\begin{aligned}
x &= \text{first angle} \\
x - 12 &= \text{second angle} \\
4(x - 12) &= \text{third angle}
\end{aligned}
$$

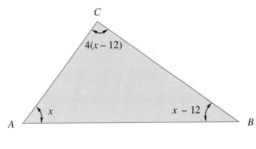

$\angle A$	$+$	$\angle B$	$+$	$\angle C$	$=$	$180°$
↓	↓	↓	↓	↓	↓	↓
x	$+$	$(x - 12)$	$+$	$4(x - 12)$	$=$	180

Solve the equation.

$$
\begin{aligned}
x + x - 12 + 4x - 48 &= 180 \quad && \textit{Distributive property} \\
6x - 60 &= 180 \quad && \textit{Combine like terms} \\
6x &= 240 \quad && \textit{Add 60 to both sides} \\
x &= 40 \quad && \textit{Divide both sides by 6}
\end{aligned}
$$

The first angle is 40°. The second angle is $x - 12 = 40 - 12 = 28°$. The third angle is $4(x - 12) = 4(40 - 12) = 112°$. Check in the words of the original problem.   ■

Try Problem 25 >

2.7 Problem Set

LEARNING THROUGH WRITING

☐ Describe the steps in solving a word problem.

☐ What can be said about the three angles of a triangle?

Solve the following number problems.

1. One number is twice another. The sum of the two numbers is 33. Find the numbers.

2. One number is three times another. The sum of the two numbers is 36. Find the numbers.

3. Two consecutive even integers have a sum of 54. Find the integers.

4. Two consecutive odd integers have a sum of 56. Find the integers.

5. If the smaller of two consecutive integers is tripled, the result is 9 more than the larger. Find the integers.

6. If the smaller of two consecutive integers is doubled, the result is 8 more than the larger. Find the integers.

7. The difference of two positive numbers is 7/20. If one number is 3/5 of the other, find the numbers.

8. The difference of two positive numbers is 3/14. If one number is 5/7 of the other, find the numbers.

Solve the following age problems.

9. Sean is 4 years older than Stacy. In 5 years the sum of their ages will be 38. Find their present ages.

10. Kim is 6 years older than Terry. In 8 years the sum of their ages will be 54. Find their present ages.

11. Nancy is 9 years older than Lisa. In 2 years she will be four times as old as Lisa. Find their present ages.

12. Dave is 10 years older than Mark. In 3 years he will be three times as old as Mark. Find their present ages.

13. Steve is twice as old as his brother. Seven years ago he was three times as old as his brother. Find their present ages.

14. Jill is twice as old as her sister. Four years ago she was three times as old as her sister. Find their present ages.

15. Chris is one-third his mother's age. In 8 years, Chris will be the same age as his mother was 16 years ago. Find the present ages of Chris and his mother.

16. Jennifer is one-fourth her father's age. In 12 years, Jennifer will be the same age her father was 15 years ago. Find the present ages of Jennifer and her father.

Solve the following geometry problems.

17. The length of a rectangle is 5 meters less than three times the width. If the perimeter is 54 meters, find the width and length.

18. The length of a rectangle is 6 meters less than three times the width. If the perimeter is 76 meters, find the width and length.

19. A tennis court for singles play is 24 feet longer than twice the width (see Fig. 2.16). If the perimeter is 210 feet, find the width and length.

20. A tennis court for doubles play is 6 feet longer than twice the width (see Fig. 2.16). If the perimeter is 228 feet, find the width and length.

FIGURE 2.16

21. A vacant lot forms a perfect square. Find the length of one side of the lot if the perimeter is 392 feet.

22. An oil painting forms a perfect square. Find the length of one side of the painting if the perimeter is 68 inches.

23. The longest side of a triangle is twice the shortest side. The middle side is 2 feet more than the shortest side. The perimeter is 86 feet. Find the length of each side.

24. The longest side of a triangle is three times the shortest side. The middle side is 3 feet more than the shortest side. The perimeter is 128 feet. Find the length of each side.

25. The second angle in a triangle is 12° less than the first angle. The third angle is twice the second angle. Find the measure of each angle.

26. The second angle in a triangle is 15° less than the first angle. The third angle is three times the second angle. Find the measure of each angle.

Solve the following word problems.

27. Eric plans to cut a 16-foot board into three pieces so that the second piece is 2 feet longer than the first piece, and the third piece is 3 feet longer than the second. Find the length of each piece.

28. Helen has $50 to spend on gifts for her three grandchildren. She spends $5 more on the middle grandchild than on the youngest, and $7 more on the oldest than on the middle grandchild. How much did she spend on each grandchild?

29. Richard laid shingles for four days. Each day he laid two more bundles than the previous day. If he laid 92 bundles in all, how many did he lay on the first day?

30. Sally must read 720 pages in four days. Each day she wants to read 20 pages less than the previous day. How many pages should she read the first day?

31. The cost of renting a car is $25 per day plus 18¢ per mile. How many miles can you drive in one day for a total cost of $70?

32. The cost of renting a car is $35 per day plus 16¢ per mile. How many miles can you drive in one day for a total cost of $91?

2.8   Money, Interest, Mixture, and Motion Problems

In this section we solve different types of word problems than we solved in the previous section. Still, we use the same four steps as previously.

Money Problems

In a money problem we must keep track of the value of the various unknown quantities.

Quantity	Value
3 nickels	$5 \cdot 3 = 15$ cents
8 dimes	$10 \cdot 8 = 80$ cents
x quarters	$25 \cdot x = 25x$ cents

EXAMPLE 1   A coin changer holding only nickels and dimes contains 3 more dimes than nickels. The total value of the coins in the changer is $4.80. How many nickels and how many dimes are in the changer?

Solution

Step 1   *Write down the unknown quantities. Call one x, and write the other in terms of x.*

$$x = \text{number of nickels}$$
$$x + 3 = \text{number of dimes}$$

Step 2   *Write an equation involving x. A chart is helpful here.*

	Number	Value (in cents)
Nickels	x	$5x$
Dimes	$x + 3$	$10(x + 3)$

Value is value of each coin times number of coins

Value of nickels	plus	value of dimes	is	total value
↓	↓	↓	↓	↓
$5x$	$+$	$10(x + 3)$	$=$	480

Step 3   *Solve to find x and x + 3.*

$$5x + 10x + 30 = 480 \qquad \textit{Distributive property}$$
$$15x + 30 = 480 \qquad \textit{Combine like terms}$$
$$15x = 450 \qquad \textit{Subtract 30 from both sides}$$
$$x = 30 \qquad \textit{Divide both sides by 15}$$

The changer contains 30 nickels and $x + 3 = 30 + 3 = 33$ dimes.

Step 4   *Check in the words of the original problem.* Thirty nickels are worth $1.50. Thirty-three dimes are worth $3.30. Therefore the total value is $4.80, and there are 3 more dimes than nickels.   ■

Try Problem 1 >

Caution! ■ Make sure the units are consistent when you write your equation. Here are two correct ways and two incorrect ways to write the equation for Example 1.

Correct	*Wrong*
$5x + 10(x + 3) = 480$	$5x + 10(x + 3) = 4.80$
$0.05x + 0.10(x + 3) = 4.80$	$0.05x + 0.10(x + 3) = 480$

EXAMPLE 2   Jessica's day job pays $7 per hour; her night job pays $4.50 per hour. She worked a total of 46 hours one week and earned a total of $297. How many hours did she work at each job?

Solution

$$x = \text{number of hours worked at day job}$$
$$46 - x = \text{number of hours worked at night job}$$

	Hours Worked	Money Earned
Day job	x	$7x$
Night job	$46 - x$	$4.50(46 - x)$

Money earned is earnings per hour times number of hours

Money earned at day job	plus	money earned at night job	equals	total money earned
↓	↓	↓	↓	↓
$7x$	$+$	$4.50(46 - x)$	$=$	297

Solve the equation.

$$7x + 207 - 4.5x = 297 \quad \text{\textit{Distributive property}}$$
$$2.5x + 207 = 297 \quad \text{\textit{Combine like terms}}$$
$$2.5x = 90 \quad \text{\textit{Subtract 207 from both sides}}$$
$$x = 36 \quad \text{\textit{Divide both sides by 2.5}}$$

Try Problem 7 >

Jessica worked 36 hours at her day job, and she worked $46 - x = 46 - 36 = 10$ hours at her night job. Check in the words of the original problem. ∎

Interest Problems

To solve a simple-interest problem we use the formula

$$I = Prt,$$

where I is the interest, P is the principal, r is the interest rate (in decimal form), and t is the time (in years). For example, the simple interest, I, on $500 invested at 8% for 1 year is

$$I = (500)(0.08)(1) = \$40.$$

EXAMPLE 3   Laura invested her graduation money in two separate accounts. She invested part of it in a low-risk account paying 9% interest, and twice that amount in a higher-risk account paying 12% interest. The total first-year interest from the two investments was $132. How much did she invest at each rate?

Solution

$$x = \text{amount invested at 9\%}$$
$$2x = \text{amount invested at 12\%}$$

	Amount Invested	Interest Earned
9% investment	x	$0.09x$
12% investment	$2x$	$0.12(2x)$

Since $I = Prt$ and $t = 1$

	Interest on 9% investment	*plus*	*interest on 12% investment*	*equals*	*total interest*
	↓	↓	↓	↓	↓
	$0.09x$	$+$	$0.12(2x)$	$=$	132

Solve the equation.

$$0.09x + 0.24x = 132 \quad \text{\textit{Multiply} 0.12 \textit{and} 2x}$$
$$0.33x = 132 \quad \text{\textit{Combine like terms}}$$
$$x = 400 \quad \text{\textit{Divide both sides by} 0.33}$$

Try Problem 9 >

Laura invested $400 at 9% and $2x = 2(400) = \$800$ at 12%. Check in the words of the original problem. ∎

Mixture Problems
(7×6ח ושח)

An alloy is a metal that is a mixture of two or more metals. For example, a 40% gold alloy is 40% gold and 60% some other metal. Thus 50 grams of a 40% gold alloy contains $0.40(50) = 20$ grams of gold. If we mix together a 40% gold alloy and a 70% gold alloy, the result is an alloy containing some percentage of gold between 40% and 70%.

EXAMPLE 4   A jeweler has an alloy that is 70% gold. She wants to melt some of it with 30 grams of an alloy that is 40% gold to produce an alloy that is 50% gold. How much of the 70% alloy should she use?

Solution
$$x = \text{amount of 70\% alloy needed}$$
$$x + 30 = \text{amount of 50\% alloy that results}$$

	Grams of Alloy	Grams of Gold
40% alloy	30	0.40(30)
70% alloy	x	$0.70x$
50% alloy	$x + 30$	$0.50(x + 30)$

Grams of gold is % of gold in alloy times number of grams of alloy

Since no gold is gained or lost during melting, we can write the following equation.

	Gold in 40% alloy	*plus*	*gold in 70% alloy*	*equals*	*gold in 50% alloy*
	↓	↓	↓	↓	↓
	$0.40(30)$	$+$	$0.70x$	$=$	$0.50(x + 30)$

Solve the equation.

$$12 + 0.7x = 0.5x + 15 \quad \textit{Simplify each side}$$
$$12 + 0.2x = 15 \quad \textit{Subtract } 0.5x \textit{ from both sides}$$
$$0.2x = 3 \quad \textit{Subtract } 12 \textit{ from both sides}$$
$$x = 15 \quad \textit{Divide both sides by } 0.2$$

Try Problem 17 >

The jeweler should use 15 grams of 70% alloy. Check in the words of the original problem.   ■

Motion Problems

To solve motion problems we use the formula

$$d = rt,$$

where d is distance, r is rate, and t is time.

EXAMPLE 5   A salesman leaves home on a business trip driving 35 mph. Sixty minutes later his wife finds the briefcase he left behind and starts after him at 55 mph. How long does it take her to catch him?

Solution

$$x = \text{number of hours wife travels}$$
$$x + 1 = \text{number of hours husband travels}$$

	Rate	Time	Distance
Wife	55	x	$55x$
Husband	35	$x + 1$	$35(x + 1)$

$\Big]$ *Since* $d = rt$

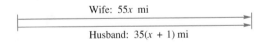

Wife: $55x$ mi

Husband: $35(x + 1)$ mi

Since both travel the same distance, we can write the following equation.

Distance wife travels	*equals*	*distance husband travels*
↓	↓	↓
$55x$	$=$	$35(x + 1)$

Solve the equation.

$$55x = 35x + 35 \quad \textit{Distributive property}$$
$$20x = 35 \quad \textit{Subtract } 35x \textit{ from both sides}$$
$$x = 1.75 \quad \textit{Divide both sides by } 20$$

Try Problem 25 >

It takes the wife 1.75 hours to catch her husband. Check in the words of the original problem.   ∎

Caution! ∎

Make sure the units of measure are consistent when you write the equation for Example 5. Since rates are in miles per hour, time should be in hours (not minutes).

Correct	*Wrong*
$55x = 35(x + 1)$	~~$55x = 35(x + 60)$~~

EXAMPLE 6   Two trains 276 miles apart start toward each other on parallel tracks. One train travels 8 mph faster than the other. If they meet in 3 hours, find the speed of each.

Solution

$$x = \text{speed of slower train}$$
$$x + 8 = \text{speed of faster train}$$

	Rate	Time	Distance
Slower train	x	3	$3x$
Faster train	$x + 8$	3	$3(x + 8)$

Since d = rt

276 mi

Slower train: $3x$ mi   Faster train: $3(x + 8)$ mi

Since the total distance traveled by the two trains is 276 miles, we can write the following equation.

Distance slower train travels	*plus*	*distance faster train travels*	*equals*	*total distance*
↓	↓	↓	↓	↓
$3x$	$+$	$3(x + 8)$	$=$	276

Solve the equation.

$$3x + 3x + 24 = 276 \quad \textit{Distributive property}$$
$$6x + 24 = 276 \quad \textit{Combine like terms}$$
$$6x = 252 \quad \textit{Subtract 24 from both sides}$$
$$x = 42 \quad \textit{Divide both sides by 6}$$

Try Problem 29 >   The speed of the slower train is 42 mph, and the speed of the faster train is $x + 8 = 42 + 8 = 50$ mph. Check in the words of the original problem. ■

2.8 Problem Set

Solve the following money problems.

1. A change purse containing only nickels and dimes has 6 more dimes than nickels. The total value of the collection is $3.60. How many nickels and how many dimes are in the purse?

2. A piggy bank holding only nickels and dimes contains 3 fewer dimes than nickels. The total value of the coins is $5.70. How many nickels and how many dimes are in the bank?

3. Tim has in his pocket nickels, dimes, and quarters worth $7.50. He has 3 fewer dimes than nickels and twice as many quarters as nickels. How many of each kind of coin does he have?

4. A cash register contains nickels, dimes, and quarters worth $6.80. There are 5 more dimes than nickels and three times as many quarters as nickels. How many of each kind of coin are in the register?

5. A collection of 40 nickels and dimes is worth $3.15. How many nickels and how many dimes are there?

6. A collection of 30 dimes and quarters is worth $4.35. How many dimes and how many quarters are there?

	Number	Value
Nickels	x	
Dimes	$40 - x$	

	Number	Value
Dimes	x	
Quarters	$30 - x$	

7. Pam has two part-time jobs. One job pays $5.00 per hour and the other pays $4.50 per hour. She worked a total of 28 hours one week and earned a total of $134. How many hours did she work at each job?

8. Frank's day job pays $6.50 per hour and his night job pays $4.00 per hour. He worked a total of 52 hours one week and earned a total of $298. How many hours did he work at each job?

Solve the following interest problems.

9. Dorothy invested her income tax refund in two separate accounts. She invested part of it at 7% and triple that amount at 11%. The total first-year interest from the two investments was $120. How much did she invest at each rate?

10. Lee received an inheritance. He invested part of it at 6% and four times that amount at 11%. The total first-year interest from the two investments was $1000. How much did he invest at each rate?

11. Scott invests $1260 more at 8% than he invests at 12%. The interest from the two investments is the same. How much did he invest at each rate?

12. Lucy invests $1320 more at 9% than she invests at 12%. The interest from the two investments is the same. How much did she invest at each rate?

13. A stockbroker is given $12,000 to invest in bonds. The broker invests part of the money in a short-term bond fund paying 9 1/2% and the rest in a long-term bond fund paying 14 1/2%. How much was invested at each rate if the interest from the two investments is the same?

14. The administrator of a $27,000 cash estate invests part of the estate in a money market fund paying 8 1/2% and the rest in a certificate of deposit paying 11 1/2%. How much was invested at each rate if the interest from the two investments is the same?

15. A retirement fund invested 5% of its assets in a high-risk fund paying 16%, 30% of its assets in a moderate-risk fund paying 14%, and the rest of its assets in a low-risk fund paying 8%. If the annual interest was $76,500, what was the original value of the retirement fund? (Let x = original value of retirement fund.)

	Amount	Interest
16% investment	0.05x	0.16(0.05x)
14% investment	0.30x	
8% investment	0.65x	

16. A trust fund invested 10% of its assets in a high-risk fund paying 15%, 20% of its assets in a moderate-risk fund paying 12%, and the rest of its assets in a low-risk fund paying 8%. If the annual interest was $38,000, what was the original value of the trust fund? (Let x = original value of trust fund.)

	Amount	Interest
15% investment	0.10x	0.15(0.10x)
12% investment	0.20x	
8% investment	0.70x	

Solve the following mixture problems.

17. How many grams of an alloy that is 90% gold should be melted with 40 grams of an alloy that is 30% gold to produce an alloy that is 50% gold?

19. A chemist wants to mix a 60% acid solution with 20 kilograms of a 45% acid solution to produce a 55% acid solution. How much 60% solution should she use?

21. How many pounds of pure antifreeze should be mixed with 60 pounds of a 45% antifreeze solution to produce a 50% antifreeze solution?

	Pounds of Solution	Pounds of Antifreeze
45% solution	60	
100% solution	x	1.00x
50% solution	$x + 60$	

18. How many grams of an alloy that is 70% silver should be melted with 60 grams of an alloy that is 20% silver to produce an alloy that is 30% silver?

20. A winemaker wants to mix a 10% alcohol wine with 40 kilograms of a 25% alcohol wine to produce a wine cooler that is 15% alcohol. How much 10% alcohol wine should he use?

22. How many pounds of pure salt should be mixed with 5 pounds of a 40% salt solution to produce a 50% salt solution?

	Pounds of Solution	Pounds of Salt
40% solution	5	
100% solution	x	1.00x
50% solution	$x + 5$	

23. A company that processes cattle feed receives an order for 21 tons of feed at $40 per ton. The company has in stock feed priced at $45.50 per ton and feed priced at $38 per ton. How many tons of each should the company mix to fill the order?

24. A tea company receives an order for 70 bushels of tea at $3.20 per bushel. The company has in stock tea priced at $4.40 per bushel and tea priced at $2.80 per bushel. How many bushels of each should the company mix to fill the order?

Solve the following motion problems.

25. A ship steams out of port at 25 mph. Sixty minutes later a second ship leaves the same port and travels the same route at 35 mph. How long does it take the second ship to overtake the first?

27. Two cyclists head in opposite directions on a straight road. One cycles at 10 mph and the other at 15 mph. In how many hours will they be 75 miles apart?

26. An airplane takes off heading east at 190 mph. One hundred twenty minutes later a second airplane takes off from the same airport and heads east at 240 mph. How long does it take the second plane to overtake the first?

28. Two runners in a marathon begin at the same time and run the same straight-road course. One runs at 7 mph and the other at 12 mph. In how many hours will they be 10 miles apart?

```
  7–mph runner            10 mi
|----------------------|<------>|
|-------------------------------|
        12–mph runner
```

29. Two trains 300 miles apart start toward each other on parallel tracks. One train travels 5 mph faster than the other. If they meet in 4 hours, what was the speed of each train?

30. Two cars 190 miles apart start toward each other on the same road. One car travels 5 mph faster than the other. If they meet in 2 hours, what was the speed of each car?

31. One runner finishes a race in 1 hour. A second runner finishes 20 minutes later. If the rate of the faster runner is 2 mph more than the rate of the slower runner, what was the rate of each?

32. One runner finishes a race in 1 hour. A second runner finishes 30 minutes later. If the rate of the faster runner is 4 mph more than the rate of the slower runner, what was the rate of each?

33. How far can a plane fly with the wind at 320 mph and still return against the wind at 280 mph if it has 6 hours' worth of fuel?

34. How far can a canoe club paddle upstream at 3 mph and still return downstream at 5 mph in a total time of 2 hours?

	r	t	d
With wind	320	x	
Against wind	280	$6 - x$	

	r	t	d
Upstream	3	x	
Downstream	5	$2 - x$	

35. How long will it take a runner traveling 11 mph to lap a runner traveling 8 mph on a 1-mile oval track? Assume both runners start from the same point at the same time.

36. How long will it take a car traveling 180 mph to lap a car traveling 160 mph on a 2-mile oval track? Assume both cars start from the same point at the same time.

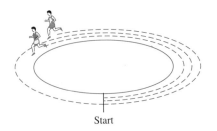

Start

2.9   Solving Linear Inequalities

Recall that an equation is a statement that relates two algebraic expressions with the symbol $=$. All of the following are linear equations.

$$3x - 9 = 8 \qquad 2y - 7 = y + 4 \qquad 6 = 5(p - 1)$$

An **inequality** is a statement that relates two algebraic expressions with one of the symbols $<$, $>$, $\leq$, or $\geq$. All of the following are **linear inequalities.**

$$3x - 9 < 8 \qquad 2y - 7 \geq y + 4 \qquad 6 > 5(p - 1)$$

We solve a linear inequality in much the same way we solve a linear equation. That is, we write a sequence of equivalent inequalities (inequalities with the same solution) until we isolate the variable on one side of the inequality.

To illustrate the properties of inequality, let's start with the true inequality $-3 < 5$ and see what happens when we add a number to both sides.

$$-3 < 5 \qquad \textit{True}$$
$$-3 + 2 \; ? \; 5 + 2 \qquad \textit{Add 2 to both sides}$$
$$-1 < 7 \qquad \textit{True}$$

This suggests that we can add the same quantity to both sides of an inequality and the result is an equivalent inequality.

ADDITION PROPERTY OF INEQUALITY

Let A, B, and C be algebraic expressions.

$$\text{If} \quad A < B, \quad \text{then} \quad A + C < B + C.$$

The **addition property of inequality** is also true when $<$ is replaced by $>$, $\leq$, or $\geq$.

EXAMPLE 1 Solve $x - 1 < 2$. Then graph the solution.

Solution To isolate x, add 1 to both sides of the inequality.

$$x - 1 < 2 \qquad \textit{Original inequality}$$
$$x - 1 + 1 < 2 + 1 \qquad \textit{Add 1 to both sides}$$
$$x < 3 \qquad \textit{Simplify each side}$$

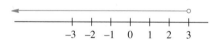

FIGURE 2.17

The solution is all real numbers that are less than 3. A good way to illustrate the solution to an inequality is by graphing. We graph the inequality $x < 3$ by placing an open circle above 3 and drawing an arrow extending from this circle to the left, as shown in Fig. 2.17. The graph is really *on* the number line but is drawn above it to make the diagram easier to read. The circle above 3 is open to show that 3 is not part of the solution.

Try Problem 1 >

Since subtracting C is the same as adding $-C$, we can also subtract the same quantity from both sides of an inequality, and the result is an equivalent inequality.

EXAMPLE 2   Solve $6y + 7 \geq 5y + 8$. Then graph the solution.

Solution

$6y + 7 \geq 5y + 8$	*Original inequality*
$6y + 7 - 5y \geq 5y + 8 - 5y$	*Subtract 5y from both sides*
$y + 7 \geq 8$	*Simplify each side*
$y + 7 - 7 \geq 8 - 7$	*Subtract 7 from both sides*
$y \geq 1$	*Simplify each side*

FIGURE 2.18

Try Problem 11 >

The solution is all real numbers that are greater than or equal to 1. The graph of the solution is shown in Fig. 2.18. The closed circle above 1 indicates that 1 is part of the solution. ∎

The addition property of inequality works in essentially the same way as the addition property of equality. The multiplication property of inequality, however, has one important difference from the multiplication property of equality. To see this difference, consider the true inequality $-3 < 5$. If we multiply both sides by a positive number, the result is a true inequality.

$-3 < 5$	*True*
$2(-3)$? $2(5)$	*Multiply both sides by 2*
$-6 < 10$	*True*

But if we multiply both sides by a negative number, we must reverse the direction of the inequality symbol to keep the statement true.

$-3 < 5$	*True*
$-2(-3)$? $-2(5)$	*Multiply both sides by -2*
$6 > -10$	*True if we reverse the symbol from $<$ to $>$*

These examples suggest the following property of inequality.

MULTIPLICATION PROPERTY OF INEQUALITY

Let A, B, and C be algebraic expressions.

1. If C is positive and $A < B$, then $AC < BC$.
2. If C is negative and $A < B$, then $AC > BC$.

The **multiplication property of inequality** is also true for $>$, $\leq$, and $\geq$.

EXAMPLE 3   Solve $3r \leq 12$. Then graph the solution.

Solution   To isolate r, multiply both sides by the reciprocal of 3, namely 1/3. Since 1/3 is a positive number, do not reverse the direction of the inequality symbol.

$$3r \leq 12 \qquad \textit{Original inequality}$$

$$\frac{1}{3} \cdot 3r \leq \frac{1}{3} \cdot 12 \qquad \textit{Multiply both sides by 1/3, do not reverse} \leq$$

$$r \leq 4 \qquad \textit{Simplify each side}$$

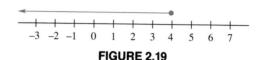

FIGURE 2.19

Try Problem 13 >

The solution is all real numbers less than or equal to 4, as shown in Fig. 2.19.

Since dividing by C is the same as multiplying by $1/C$, we must also reverse the inequality symbol when we divide both sides of an inequality by a negative number.

EXAMPLE 4   Solve $-4t > 8$. Then graph the solution.

Solution   Divide both sides by -4. Since -4 is a negative number, reverse the direction of the inequality symbol.

$$-4t > 8 \qquad \textit{Original inequality}$$

$$\frac{-4t}{-4} < \frac{8}{-4} \qquad \textit{Divide both sides by} -4, \textit{reverse} > \textit{to} <$$

$$t < -2 \qquad \textit{Simplify each side}$$

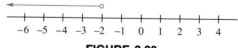

FIGURE 2.20

Try Problem 15 >   The solution is all real numbers less than -2, as shown in Fig. 2.20.

EXAMPLE 5   Solve $-\frac{3}{2}m \leq 12$. Then graph the solution.

Solution   Multiply both sides by the reciprocal of $-3/2$, namely $-2/3$. Since $-2/3$ is a negative number, reverse the direction of the inequality symbol.

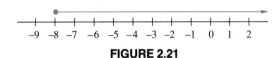

$$-\frac{3}{2}m \le 12 \qquad \textit{Original inequality}$$

$$-\frac{2}{3}\left(-\frac{3}{2}m\right) \ge -\frac{2}{3}(12) \qquad \textit{Multiply both sides by } -2/3, \textit{ reverse } \le \textit{ to } \ge$$

$$m \ge -8 \qquad \textit{Simplify each side}$$

```
 ●
─┼──┼──┼──┼──┼──┼──┼──┼──┼──┼──┼──┼─→
 −9 −8 −7  −6  −5  −4  −3  −2  −1   0   1   2
```

FIGURE 2.21

Try Problem 25 >

The solution is all real numbers greater than or equal to −8, as shown in Fig. 2.21. ∎

TO SOLVE A LINEAR INEQUALITY

1. Use the distributive property to remove parentheses.
2. Simplify each side by combining like terms.
3. Collect all variable terms on one side of the inequality and all constant terms on the other side.
4. Write the variable term with a coefficient of 1. Reverse the inequality symbol if you multiply or divide by a negative number.

EXAMPLE 6   Solve $-9p < 23 - (8p + 27)$. Then graph the solution.

Solution
Step 1   *Use the distributive property to remove parentheses.*

$$-9p < 23 - 8p - 27$$

Step 2   *Simplify each side by combining like terms.*

$$-9p < -8p - 4$$

Step 3   *Collect all variable terms on one side and all constant terms on the other side.*

$$-9p + 8p < -8p - 4 + 8p \qquad \textit{Add 8p to both sides}$$
$$-p < -4 \qquad\qquad\qquad \textit{Simplify each side}$$

Step 4   *Write the variable term with a coefficient of 1.*

$$\frac{-p}{-1} > \frac{-4}{-1} \qquad \textit{Divide by } -1, \textit{ reverse } < \textit{ to } >$$
$$p > 4 \qquad \textit{Simplify each side}$$

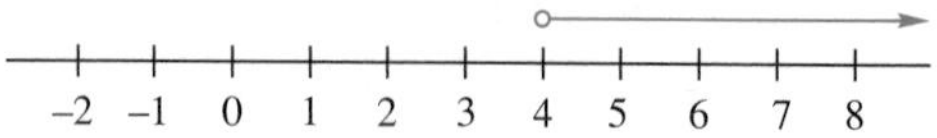

FIGURE 2.22

Try Problem 41 >

The solution is all real numbers greater than 4, as shown in Fig. 2.22. ■

The steps for solving a word problem using an inequality are essentially the same as the steps for solving a word problem using an equation. The primary difference is that in Step 2 we write an inequality instead of an equation.

P R O B L E M   S O L V I N G

EXAMPLE 7   A salesperson can be paid using Plan A or Plan B. In Plan A the salesperson is paid a straight commission of 25% of all sales. In Plan B the salesperson is paid $300 per week plus 10% of all sales. How much does the salesperson need to sell each week to make Plan A better for the salesperson?

Solution
Step 1   *Write down the unknown quantity and call it x.*

x = weekly sales in dollars

Step 2   *Write an inequality involving x.* Since we want to find the values of x that make Plan A better for the salesperson, we write the following inequality.

Salary under Plan A	is greater than	salary under Plan B
↓	↓	↓
$0.25x$	$>$	$0.10x + 300$

Step 3   *Solve the inequality for x.*

$$0.25x > 0.10x + 300 \qquad \text{\textit{Original inequality}}$$
$$0.25x - 0.10x > 0.10x + 300 - 0.10x \qquad \text{\textit{Subtract }} 0.10x \text{ \textit{from both sides}}$$
$$0.15x > 300 \qquad \text{\textit{Simplify each side}}$$
$$\frac{0.15x}{0.15} > \frac{300}{0.15} \qquad \text{\textit{Divide by }} 0.15, \text{\textit{ do not reverse }} >$$
$$x > 2000 \qquad \text{\textit{Simplify each side}}$$

More than $2000 worth of goods each week must be sold to make Plan A better for the salesperson.

Step 4   *Check in the words of the original problem.* If $2000 worth of goods is sold, the salesperson's weekly earnings under both Plan A and Plan B would be $500. If more than $2000 worth of goods is sold, say $2100 worth, the weekly earnings under Plan A would be $525 and the weekly earnings under Plan B would be $510.   ■

Try Problem 77 >

Double Inequalities

Recall that the double inequality

$$1 < x < 5$$

means that x is between 1 and 5. The graph of this inequality is shown in Fig. 2.23.

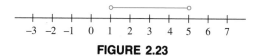

FIGURE 2.23

We solve a double inequality by isolating the variable in the middle.

EXAMPLE 8   Solve $3 < 2r - 5 < 7$. Then graph the solution.

Solution

$$\begin{array}{ll} 3 < 2r - 5 < 7 & \textit{Original inequality} \\ 3 + 5 < 2r - 5 + 5 < 7 + 5 & \textit{Add 5 to each part} \\ 8 < 2r < 12 & \textit{Simplify each part} \\ \dfrac{8}{2} < \dfrac{2r}{2} < \dfrac{12}{2} & \textit{Divide each part by 2, do not reverse} < \\ 4 < r < 6 & \textit{Simplify each part} \end{array}$$

FIGURE 2.24

Try Problem 59 >   The solution is all real numbers between 4 and 6, as shown in Fig. 2.24.   ■

EXAMPLE 9   Solve $-2 \le 4 - 3z < 15$. Then graph the solution.

Solution

$$\begin{array}{ll} -2 \le 4 - 3z < 15 & \textit{Original inequality} \\ -2 - 4 \le 4 - 3z - 4 < 15 - 4 & \textit{Subtract 4 from each part} \\ -6 \le -3z < 11 & \textit{Simplify each part} \\ \dfrac{-6}{-3} \ge \dfrac{-3z}{-3} > \dfrac{11}{-3} & \textit{Divide each part by } -3, \textit{ reverse both} \\ & \textit{inequality symbols} \\ 2 \ge z > -\dfrac{11}{3} & \textit{Simplify each part} \end{array}$$

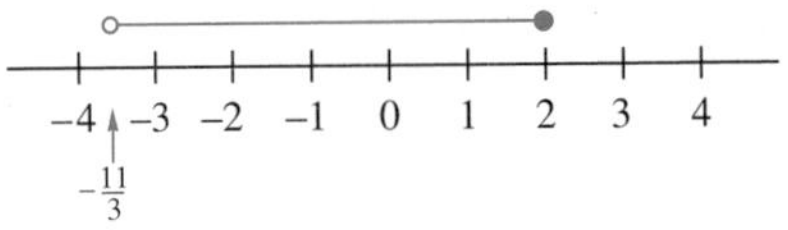

FIGURE 2.25

The solution is all real numbers between $-11/3$ and 2, including 2 but not $-11/3$. The solution can also be written as $-11/3 < z \leq 2$. The graph is shown in Fig. 2.25. ■

Try Problem 61 >

2.9   Problem Set

LEARNING THROUGH WRITING

☐ What is an *inequality?*

☐ How many solutions does the inequality $3x - 5 < 7$ have?

☐ State the *addition property of inequality* in words.

☐ State the *multiplication property of inequality* in words.

Solve each inequality, and graph the solution.

1. $x - 3 < 1$
5. $-10 + t > -9$
9. $7 \geq p + 7$

2. $x - 4 < 1$
6. $-15 + t \leq -12$
10. $11 \geq p + 11$

3. $y + 1 \geq -5$
7. $-9 < x - 7$
11. $8y + 3 \geq 7y + 11$

4. $y + 2 \geq -3$
8. $-6 < x - 5$
12. $5y + 7 \geq 4y + 11$

Solve each inequality, and graph the solution.

13. $4r \leq 20$
17. $-3p < -6$
21. $-y \geq 2$
25. $-\dfrac{4}{5}m \leq 20$

14. $2m \geq -8$
18. $-2p < -6$
22. $-y \geq 4$
26. $-\dfrac{2}{5}m \leq 10$

15. $-5t > 35$
19. $6x > 0$
23. $\dfrac{2}{3}x < 4$
27. $-3z \leq \dfrac{1}{3}$

16. $-6t > 42$
20. $5x < 0$
24. $\dfrac{3}{4}x < 6$
28. $-2z \leq \dfrac{1}{2}$

Solve each inequality, and graph the solution.

29. $2x - 3 < 7$
32. $-7t + 8 < -6$
35. $3y + 9 \leq y + 9$
38. $17 - 6z > 9z - 13$
41. $-8p < 32 - (7p + 33)$
44. $6(t + 1) < 15 - 3(t - 6)$
47. $m - (11m + 10) > 0$
50. $9 - 4(t + 1) > 4t + 7$

30. $5y + 4 > 9$
33. $7x - 4 > 4x + 17$
36. $5y - 2 \geq 3y - 2$
39. $8r - 25 \leq 4r + 23$
42. $-3p < 49 - (2p + 50)$
45. $3p - (5p + 15) < p$
48. $m - (16m + 15) > 0$
51. $4(2x - 1) > 5 - 2(x - 8)$

31. $-2p - 5 \geq 3$
34. $8x - 9 > 3x + 6$
37. $21 - 3z > 7z - 19$
40. $10r - 21 \leq 6r + 23$
43. $4(t + 1) < 12 - 3(t - 2)$
46. $2p - (4p + 18) < p$
49. $8 - 3(t + 2) > 6t + 5$
52. $3(2x - 3) > 9 - 2(x - 1)$

Solve each double inequality, and graph the solution.

53. $2 < x - 1 < 4$

54. $1 < x - 2 < 5$

55. $-6 \le 3y \le 12$

56. $-8 \le 2y \le 10$

57. $5 < -5y \le 15$

58. $8 < -4y \le 12$

59. $1 < 2r - 9 < 3$

60. $1 < 2r - 3 < 5$

61. $-7 \le 5 - 4z < 20$

62. $-5 \le 7 - 3z < 23$

63. $-5 < 6t + 13 < 13$

64. $-6 < 5t + 14 < 14$

65. $-14 \le 1 + \dfrac{5}{3}p \le -9$

66. $-10 \le 2 + \dfrac{4}{3}p \le -6$

67. $-2 < 4 - \dfrac{1}{2}m < 8$

68. $-3 < 6 - \dfrac{1}{3}m < 9$

69. $x + 1 \le 2(x + 3) \le x + 8$

70. $x + 3 \le 2(x + 4) \le x + 10$

Solve each word problem.

71. When three times a number is subtracted from 8, the result is greater than 17. Find all numbers that satisfy this condition.

72. When five times a number is subtracted from 4, the result is less than 29. Find all numbers that satisfy this condition.

73. Three times the difference of a number and 5 is between 6 and 9. Find all such numbers.

74. Four times the difference of a number and 2 is between 8 and 12. Find all such numbers.

75. In designing a building, an architect wants to plan a rectangular conference room whose length is 1.5 times the width. If the perimeter is to be no less than 62.5 feet, what are the possible values for the width of the room?

76. An interior design firm is hired to redesign the executive offices for a large corporation. The firm recommends that the president's office be a rectangle whose length is 5 feet more than the width. If the perimeter is to be no more than 68 feet, what are the possible values for the width?

77. A salesperson can be paid using Plan A or Plan B. In Plan A the salesperson is paid a straight commission of 25% of all sales. In Plan B the salesperson is paid $350 per week plus 5% of all sales. How much does the salesperson need to sell each week to make Plan A better for the salesperson?

78. Ritz Rent-A-Car charges $25 per day plus 22¢ per mile, m, and Royal Rent-A-Car charges $30 per day plus 18¢ per mile, m. For what values of m is Royal the better deal?

79. To earn a C in History, your final average on five tests must be at least 70 and less than 80. Your scores on the first four tests are 74, 81, 68, and 78. What score on the fifth test will give you a C for the course? (Hint: $70 \le$ Final Average < 80)

80. The freezing point of water is 32° F and the boiling point of water is 212° F. Within what range must the temperature stay, in Celsius degrees, to stay between 32° and 212° in Fahrenheit degrees? (Hint: Write $32 < F < 212$, and then use the formula $F = (9/5)C + 32$.)

C H A P T E R   2   S U M M A R Y

Key Terms

Area, p. 80
Circumference, p. 82
Coefficient, p. 62
Consecutive integers, p. 91
Cubic yard, p. 82
Diameter, p. 82
Equation, p. 66
Equivalent equations, p. 67

Factors, p. 62
First-degree equation, p. 75
Formula, p. 80
Inequality, p. 109
Like terms, p. 62
Linear equation, p. 75
Linear inequality, p. 109

Perimeter, p. 80
Radius, p. 82
Solution, p. 66
Solve, p. 67
Square foot, p. 81
Terms, p. 62
Volume, p. 82

Key Rules

Properties of Equality
Addition: If $A = B$, then $A + C = B + C$.
Multiplication: If $A = B$ and $C \neq 0$, then $AC = BC$.

Properties of Inequality
Addition: If $A < B$, then $A + C < B + C$.
Multiplication:
  If $A < B$ and $C > 0$, then $AC < BC$.
  If $A < B$ and $C < 0$, then $AC > BC$.

C H A P T E R 2 R E V I E W P R O B L E M S

[2.1] *State the terms of each algebraic expression.*

1. $2x + 3$

2. $4x^2 - 5y + 1$

State the coefficient of each term.

3. $8x^3$

4. $\dfrac{3y}{5}$

5. $r^2 s$

6. $-z$

Determine whether the given terms are like terms or unlike terms.

7. $6x, -9x$

8. $y^2, 4y^2$

9. $3z^3, 3$

10. $5a^2 b, 7ab^2$

Simplify each expression.

11. $-6mn - 11mn$

12. $-2r^2 + 9r + 3r^2 - 9 - 8$

13. $13 + 7(k + 2)$

14. $4(3x - 2y) - (x + 5y)$

15. $3 + 5(a - 1) + 2(-6a) - (-4a)7$

16. $21 - 2[6t - 4(3t - 1) - t]$

[2.2] *Solve each equation.*

17. $x - 7 = -4$

18. $y + 6 = 2$

19. $z + \dfrac{4}{9} = -\dfrac{2}{9}$

20. $16 - 10p = 11 - 9p$

21. $8m + 9 - 3m = 4m - 2 + 11$

22. $6(2r - 3) - 14 = 6r + 4 + 5r$

23. Determine whether -3 is a solution of $9(x + 4) = 2x + 3$.

[2.3] *Solve each equation.*

24. $-24 = -8y$

25. $-p = 9$

26. $\dfrac{3}{5}z = 30$

27. $-\dfrac{m}{4} = 12$

28. $2t = \dfrac{6}{5}$

29. $7k = 0$

30. $2(4x + 3) - (5x - 9) = -13 - 11$

31. $y + 1.72y = 58.82 - 20.74$

[2.4] *Solve each equation.*

32. $4x - 2 = 10$

33. $-2m + 5 = -11$

34. $-17 - 5k = -12$

35. $-\dfrac{4}{3}y - 8 = -20$

36. $6z - 7z = -9 - 4$

37. $-r + 13 = r + 5$

38. $8p + 13 = 2p + 5$

39. $t - 2(4t - 1) = 3t + 2$

40. $6 - (2y + 3) = 4y + 5(y + 5)$

41. $-2[10x - 7(x + 3)] = 8x - 16$

[2.5] *Use the formula and the known values to find the unknown value.*

42. $P = 2\ell + 2w$, $P = 54$ ft, $\ell = 20$ ft

43. $C = \dfrac{5}{9}(F - 32)$, $C = -15°$

Solve each formula for the specified variable in Problems 44–46.

44. $I = Prt$ for P

45. $s = \dfrac{1}{2}(a + b + c)$ for b

46. $F = \dfrac{9}{5}C + 32$ for C

47. At what speed must you travel to cover 282 miles in 6 hours?

48. A cord of wood just fits into a rectangular box that is 4 feet wide, 8 feet long, and 4 feet high (see Fig. 2.26). Find the volume of the box.

49. Find the area of the shaded region in Fig. 2.27. Use $\pi = 3.14$.

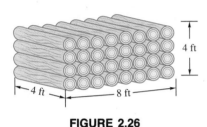

FIGURE 2.26

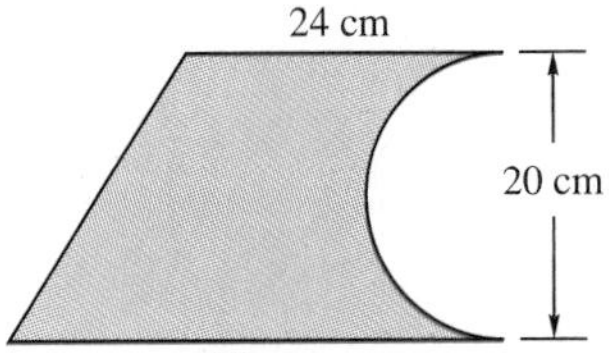

24 cm

20 cm

36 cm

FIGURE 2.27

[2.6] *Write each word phrase as an algebraic expression. Simplify if possible.*

50. The sum of twice a number and 3

51. The distance traveled in x hours at 45 mph

52. The amount of pure gold in y grams of an alloy that is 20% gold

53. Four times the sum of a number and 6 is added to the number x

$4 \times 6 = 24$

54. Ten less than five times the sum of three consecutive odd integers

Represent one quantity by x. Then represent the other quantity in terms of x.

55. Diana's age now and Diana's age 8 years ago

56. The number of students and the number of nonstudents attending a basketball game if the total attendance was 758

Translate each problem into an algebraic equation. Then solve the equation to find the unknown quantity.

57. Five-eighths of a number is 30. Find the number.

58. Eight times the sum of a number and 5 is 9 less than the number. Find the number.

59. The population of a town increases 4% to 2782. Find the original population.

[2.7] *Solve the following word problems.*

60. One number is six times another. The sum of the two numbers is 28. Find the numbers.

61. If the smaller of two consecutive odd integers is doubled, the result is 7 more than the larger. Find the integers.

62. Sandi is 5 years older than Peggy. In 6 years the sum of their ages will be 31. Find their present ages.

63. Derek is twice as old as his brother. Five years ago he was three times as old as his brother. Find their present ages.

64. The length of a rectangle is 2 meters less than four times the width. If the perimeter is 56 meters, find the width and length.

65. The longest side of a triangle is 9 feet more than the middle side. The middle side is twice the shortest side. The perimeter is 59 feet. Find the length of each side.

[2.8] *Solve the following word problems.*

66. A coin purse contains nickels, dimes, and quarters worth $2.25. There are 3 more dimes than nickels, and twice as many quarters as nickels. How many of each kind of coin are in the purse?

68. How many grams of an alloy that is 80% copper should be melted with 20 grams of an alloy that is 30% copper to produce an alloy that is 40% copper?

70. A coffee bean distributor receives an order for 72 pounds of coffee beans at $0.20 per pound. The distributor has on hand beans priced at $0.12 per pound and beans priced at $0.30 per pound. How many pounds of each should the distributor mix to fill the order?

67. *(đầu tư)* George invests $150 more at 8% than he invests at 14%. The interest from the two investments is the same. How much did he invest at each rate? *(tiền lời, lãi xuất)* *(mức lãi xuất)*

69. A jogger leaves the starting point of a cross-country course traveling 6 mph. One hour later, a runner leaves the same point and travels the same course at 11 mph. How long does it take the runner to overtake the jogger?

71. Two ships 150 miles apart start toward each other. One ship travels 10 mph faster than the other. If they meet in 3 hours, what was the speed of each ship?

[2.9] *Solve each inequality, and graph the solution.*

72. $1 \leq r - 9$

74. $-4p \leq 28$

76. $\dfrac{3}{5}t \geq 30$

78. $7 - 2p > p - 2$

80. $11 - (8m + 6) \geq 2 - 3m$

82. $-17 < -3y + 1 \leq 1$

73. $6m > -18$

75. $-x < 0$

77. $4k - 1 < 19$

79. $3(z + 2) \leq 12 - 2(z - 2)$

81. $1 < 2x - 5 < 5$

83. $-2 \leq 2 - \dfrac{k}{4} \leq 3$

Solve each word problem.

84. When four times a number is added to 9, the result is less than 33. Find all numbers that satisfy this condition.

86. Within what range must the temperature stay, in Celsius degrees, to stay between $-4°$ and $23°$ in Fahrenheit degrees? (Hint: Write $-4 < F < 23$, and then use the formula $F = (9/5)C + 32$.)

85. A salesperson can be paid using Plan A or Plan B. In Plan A the salesperson is paid a straight commission of 20% of all sales. In Plan B the salesperson is paid $300 per week plus 5% of all sales. How much does the salesperson need to sell each week to make Plan A better for the salesperson?

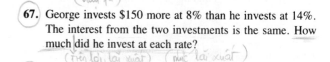

CHAPTER 2   TEST

Simplify each expression.

1. $9p^2 + p - p^2 - 8p - 1$

3. $4 + 2(a - 3) + 5(-2a) - (-6a)3$

2. $3(5x - 4y) - (2x + 6y)$

Solve each equation.

4. $-\dfrac{3}{4}m = 12$

5. $-k + \dfrac{1}{3} = \dfrac{10}{3}$

6. $6x + 1 = 37$

7. $-3 - 2y = -9$

8. $8r + 3 = 5r - 6$

9. $-t + 5 = t + 5$

10. $m - 2(3m - 2) = 4m - 5$

11. $9 + 6(p + 2) = 5p - (p + 1)$

Use the formula and the known values to find the unknown value.

12. $I = Prt$, $I = \$230$, $r = 8\%$, $t = 5$

13. $C = \dfrac{5}{9}(F - 32)$, $F = 50°$

Solve each formula for the specified variable.

14. $P = 2\ell + 2w$ for ℓ

15. $S = \dfrac{1}{3}(n + 1)$ for n

Solve each inequality, and graph the solution.

16. $-4p > 8$

17. $\dfrac{2}{5}r < 10$

18. $6t + 7 \geq 19$

19. $2 - m \leq m + 8$

20. $2(y - 3) > 10 - 4(y - 2)$

21. $-4 < 3x - 1 < 14$

Solve each word problem.

22. Six times a number is 18 more than twice the number. Find the number.

23. Two consecutive integers have a sum of 57. Find the integers.

24. Bryan is 2 years older than Eric. Four years ago the sum of their ages was 36. Find their present ages.

25. The longest side of a triangle is three times the shortest side. The middle side is 9 feet more than the shortest side. If the perimeter is 49 feet, what is the length of each side?

26. A collection of 50 nickels and dimes is worth $3.45. How many of each kind of coin is in the collection?

27. Two trains head in opposite directions, one traveling 35 mph and the other 40 mph. In how many hours will the trains be 525 miles apart?

Exponents and Polynomials

Caffeine is a drug in the sense that it can produce changes in heart rate and body temperature. The half-life of caffeine in the bloodstream is about 6 hours, which means that it takes 6 hours for half of a given amount of caffeine to leave the bloodstream. In Section 3.1 we use a formula involving exponents to measure the caffeine levels in the bloodstream of a person who has consumed a cup of coffee.

3.1   Product and Quotient Rules for Exponents

In Section 1.8 we learned that exponents are a shorthand way of writing repeated factors. In this section we learn rules that allow us to multiply and divide exponential expressions while keeping them in exponential form.

Recall that

$$a^1 = a,$$
$$a^2 = a \cdot a,$$
$$a^3 = a \cdot a \cdot a,$$
$$a^4 = a \cdot a \cdot a \cdot a,$$

and so on. The **base** of a^4 is a, and the **exponent** is 4. The expression a^4 is called a **power of a**.

EXAMPLE 1   State the base and the exponent of each expression.

a. 6^3 b. $(-7)^2$ c. -7^2 d. $3x^4$

Solution

a. Base is 6, exponent is 3
b. Base is -7, exponent is 2
c. Base is 7, exponent is 2

Try Problem 3 >   d. Base is x, exponent is 4   ■

Let's see what happens when we multiply two powers having the same base. Consider the product $a^2 \cdot a^3$.

$$a^2 \cdot a^3 = \underbrace{a \cdot a} \cdot \underbrace{a \cdot a \cdot a} = a^5$$
$$\qquad\quad a^2 \qquad a^3$$

Note that $a^2 \cdot a^3 = a^{2+3} = a^5$. This suggests the following rule.

PRODUCT RULE FOR EXPONENTS

To multiply two powers having the same base, keep the base and add the exponents.

$$a^m \cdot a^n = a^{m+n}$$

EXAMPLE 2   Simplify each expression.

a. $x^4 \cdot x^3 = x^{4+3} = x^7$ *Keep the base, add the exponents*
b. $2^4 \cdot 2^3 = 2^{4+3} = 2^7$ *Keep the base, add the exponents*
c. $5^7 \cdot 5^8 \cdot 5 = 5^{7+8+1} = 5^{16}$ *Keep the base, add the exponents*
d. $x^2 y^6$ *Cannot be simplified, since the bases are different*

Try Problem 19 >

EXAMPLE 3   Simplify each expression.

a. $(3x^2)(5x^6)$ b. $(-4y^7)(7y^3)$

Solution   Use the commutative and associative properties to group the co-efficients and to group the powers of the variable.

a. $(3x^2)(5x^6) = (3 \cdot 5)(x^2 \cdot x^6)$ *Group the coefficients, group the powers of x*

$= 15x^8$ *Multiply*

b. $(-4y^7)(7y^3) = (-4 \cdot 7)(y^7 \cdot y^3)$ *Group the coefficients, group the powers of y*

Try Problem 23 >

$= -28y^{10}$ *Multiply*

Now let's see what happens when we divide two powers having the same base. Consider the quotient a^5/a^2.

$$\frac{a^5}{a^2} = \frac{a \cdot a \cdot a \cdot a \cdot a}{a \cdot a} = a \cdot a \cdot a = a^3$$

Note that $a^5/a^2 = a^{5-2} = a^3$. This suggests the following rule.

QUOTIENT RULE FOR EXPONENTS

To divide two powers having the same base, keep the base and subtract the exponents.

$$\frac{a^m}{a^n} = a^{m-n} \qquad (a \neq 0)$$

EXAMPLE 4   Simplify each expression. Assume $x \neq 0$ and $y \neq 0$.

a. $\dfrac{x^{15}}{x^5} = x^{15-5} = x^{10}$ *Keep the base, subtract the exponents*

b. $\dfrac{4^{15}}{4^5} = 4^{15-5} = 4^{10}$ *Keep the base, subtract the exponents*

c. $\dfrac{6^6}{6} = 6^{6-1} = 6^5$ *Keep the base, subtract the exponents*

Try Problem 31 >   d. $\dfrac{x^9}{y^3}$.   *Cannot be simplified, since the bases are different*

EXAMPLE 5   Simplify each expression. Assume $x \neq 0$ and $y \neq 0$.

a. $\dfrac{10x^7}{2x}$

b. $\dfrac{-28x^{10}y^{12}}{7x^3y^2}$

Solution   Divide the coefficients and the powers of the variables separately.

a. $\dfrac{10x^7}{2x} = \dfrac{10}{2} \cdot \dfrac{x^7}{x}$ *Write as a product of two fractions*

$= 5 \cdot x^{7-1}$ *Divide the coefficients, divide the powers of x*

$= 5x^6$ *Simplify the exponent*

b. $\dfrac{-28x^{10}y^{12}}{7x^3y^2} = \dfrac{-28}{7} \cdot \dfrac{x^{10}}{x^3} \cdot \dfrac{y^{12}}{y^2}$ *Write as a product of three fractions*

$= -4x^{10-3}y^{12-2}$ *Divide the coefficients, divide the powers of the variables*

Try Problem 33 >

$= -4x^7y^{10}$ *Simplify the exponents*   ∎

Suppose we apply the quotient rule when the two exponents are equal. Consider the expression a^2/a^2. If we apply the quotient rule, we have

$$\frac{a^2}{a^2} = a^{2-2} = a^0.$$

But also,

$$\frac{a^2}{a^2} = \frac{a \cdot a}{a \cdot a} = 1.$$

Since $a^2/a^2 = a^0$ and $a^2/a^2 = 1$, then a^0 must equal 1. This suggests the following definition.

DEFINITION OF THE ZERO EXPONENT

Any nonzero number raised to the exponent 0 equals 1.

$$a^0 = 1 \qquad (a \neq 0)$$

The expression 0^0 is undefined.

EXAMPLE 6   Evaluate each expression. Assume $x \neq 0$.

a. $8^0 = 1$
b. $(-8)^0 = 1$
c. $-8^0 = -1$
d. $(3x)^0 = 1$

Try Problem 41 >   e. $3x^0 = 3(1) = 3$ ∎

Now suppose we apply the quotient rule when the exponent in the denominator is larger than the exponent in the numerator. Consider the expression a^2/a^5. If we apply the quotient rule, we have

$$\frac{a^2}{a^5} = a^{2-5} = a^{-3}.$$

But also,

$$\frac{a^2}{a^5} = \frac{a \cdot a}{a \cdot a \cdot a \cdot a \cdot a} = \frac{1}{a \cdot a \cdot a} = \frac{1}{a^3}.$$

Since $a^2/a^5 = a^{-3}$ and $a^2/a^5 = 1/a^3$, then $a^{-3} = 1/a^3$. This suggests the following definition.

DEFINITION OF NEGATIVE EXPONENTS

$$a^{-n} = \frac{1}{a^n} \qquad (a \neq 0)$$

The English mathematician John Wallis (1616–1703) was the first to fully explain the zero exponent and negative exponents.

EXAMPLE 7 Evaluate each expression.

a. $10^{-3} = \dfrac{1}{10^3} = \dfrac{1}{1000}$

b. $5^{-2} = \dfrac{1}{5^2} = \dfrac{1}{25}$

c. $-5^{-2} = -\dfrac{1}{5^2} = -\dfrac{1}{25}$

Try Problem 49 >   d. $3 \cdot 2^{-4} = 3 \cdot \dfrac{1}{2^4} = 3 \cdot \dfrac{1}{16} = \dfrac{3}{16}$ ■

Caution! ■ An exponent acts only on the symbol to its immediate left, unless parentheses indicate otherwise.

Correct	*Wrong*
$-4^0 = -1$	~~$-4^0 = 1$~~
$3y^{-1} = \dfrac{3}{y}$	~~$3y^{-1} = \dfrac{1}{3y}$~~

EXAMPLE 8 Evaluate $(3/4)^{-2}$.

Solution

$$\left(\frac{3}{4}\right)^{-2} = \frac{1}{(3/4)^2} = \frac{1}{9/16} = 1 \div \frac{9}{16} = 1 \cdot \frac{16}{9} = \frac{16}{9}$$

Try Problem 57   Note that $(3/4)^{-2} = 16/9 = (4/3)^2$.   ∎

Example 8 suggests the following shortcut.

NEGATIVE EXPONENT SHORTCUT

$$\left(\frac{a}{b}\right)^{-n} = \left(\frac{b}{a}\right)^{n} \qquad (a \neq 0,\ b \neq 0)$$

EXAMPLE 9   Evaluate.

a. $\left(\dfrac{1}{4}\right)^{-3} = \left(\dfrac{4}{1}\right)^{3} = 4^3 = 64$

Try Problem 59 >   b. $\left(-\dfrac{3}{7}\right)^{-2} = \left(-\dfrac{7}{3}\right)^{2} = \dfrac{49}{9}$ ∎

EXAMPLE 10   Evaluate $\dfrac{1}{5^{-2}}$.

Solution

$$\frac{1}{5^{-2}} = \frac{1}{1/5^2} = \frac{1}{1/25} = 1 \div \frac{1}{25} = 1 \cdot \frac{25}{1} = 25$$

Try Problem 61 >   Note that $\dfrac{1}{5^{-2}} = 25 = 5^2$.   ∎

Example 10 suggests the following shortcut.

NEGATIVE EXPONENT SHORTCUT

$$\frac{1}{a^{-n}} = a^n \qquad (a \neq 0)$$

EXAMPLE 11   Evaluate.

a. $\dfrac{1}{(-6)^{-2}} = (-6)^2 = 36$

Try Problem 63 >   b. $\dfrac{5}{2^{-4}} = \dfrac{5}{1} \cdot \dfrac{1}{2^{-4}} = 5 \cdot 2^4 = 5 \cdot 16 = 80$ ∎

EXAMPLE 12   Evaluate $2^{-1} + 8^{-1}$.

Solution

Try Problem 65 >

$$2^{-1} + 8^{-1} = \frac{1}{2} + \frac{1}{8} = \frac{4}{8} + \frac{1}{8} = \frac{5}{8}$$ ∎

Both the product rule and the quotient rule are true for negative exponents and the zero exponent as well as for positive exponents.

EXAMPLE 13   Simplify each expression. Assume $x \neq 0$.

a. $6^{-3} \cdot 6^{10} = 6^{-3+10} = 6^7$

Try Problem 73 >

b. $x \cdot x^3 \cdot x^{-8} = x^{1+3+(-8)} = x^{-4} = \dfrac{1}{x^4}$ ∎

EXAMPLE 14   Simplify each expression. Assume $a \neq 0$ and $b \neq 0$.

a. $\dfrac{8^2}{8^9} = 8^{2-9} = 8^{-7} = \dfrac{1}{8^7}$

b. $\dfrac{10^{-1}}{10^{-6}} = 10^{-1-(-6)} = 10^{-1+6} = 10^5$

Try Problem 83 >

c. $\dfrac{a^{-2}b^4}{a^3b^{-5}} = a^{-2-3}b^{4-(-5)} = a^{-5}b^9 = \dfrac{1}{a^5} \cdot b^9 = \dfrac{b^9}{a^5}$ ∎

We can also use the product rule and the quotient rule when the exponents are variables.

EXAMPLE 15   Simplify each expression. Assume $x \neq 0$ and $y \neq 0$.

a. $x^{2n+1} \cdot x = x^{(2n+1)+1}$ *Keep the base, add the exponents*

$\qquad\qquad\quad = x^{2n+2}$ *Combine like terms*

b. $\dfrac{y^m}{y^{3m}} = y^{m-3m}$ *Keep the base, subtract the exponents*

$\qquad\quad = y^{-2m}$ *Combine like terms*

Try Problem 91 >

$\qquad\quad = \dfrac{1}{y^{2m}}$ *Write the exponent with a positive coefficient* ∎

P R O B L E M   S O L V I N G

EXAMPLE 16   The quantity, Q, of caffeine that will still be in your bloodstream after t hours is given by the formula

$$Q = A \cdot 2^{-t/6},$$

where A is the amount of caffeine consumed. Suppose you consume 100 milligrams of caffeine (about one cup of coffee). How much caffeine will still be in your bloodstream after each of the following?

a. 0 hours   b. 12 hours

Solution Since the quantity of caffeine consumed is 100 mg, replace A with 100.

$$Q = A \cdot 2^{-t/6} \quad \textit{Original formula}$$
$$Q = 100 \cdot 2^{-t/6} \quad \textit{Replace A with } 100$$

a. After 0 hours:

$$Q = 100 \cdot 2^{-0/6} \quad \textit{Replace t with } 0$$
$$= 100 \cdot 2^0 \quad \textit{Since } -0/6 = 0$$
$$= 100 \cdot 1 \quad \textit{Since } 2^0 = 1$$
$$= 100 \quad \textit{Multiply}$$

Zero hours after drinking 100 mg of caffeine, you still have 100 mg of caffeine in your bloodstream.

b. After 12 hours:

$$Q = 100 \cdot 2^{-12/6} \quad \textit{Replace t with } 12$$
$$= 100 \cdot 2^{-2} \quad \textit{Since } -12/6 = -2$$
$$= 100 \cdot \frac{1}{4} \quad \textit{Since } 2^{-2} = 1/2^2 = 1/4$$
$$= 25 \quad \textit{Multiply}$$

Try Problem 97 >   After 12 hours, 25 mg of caffeine remains in your bloodstream.

3.1 Problem Set

LEARNING THROUGH WRITING

☐ What is the purpose of exponential notation?

☐ State the *product rule for exponents* in words.

☐ State the *quotient rule for exponents* in words.

☐ What is the purpose of the product and quotient rules for exponents?

State the base and the exponent of each expression.

1. 5^4 2. $(-3)^2$ 3. -3^2 4. $(6x)^3$

5. $6x^3$ 6. $-y^7$

Write each expression using exponents.

7. $9 \cdot 9$ 8. $-2 \cdot 2 \cdot 2 \cdot 2$ 9. $(-4x)(-4x)(-4x)$ 10. $8 \cdot y \cdot y \cdot y \cdot y \cdot y$

11. $-t \cdot t \cdot t \cdot t \cdot t \cdot t$ **12.** $(x + 2)(x + 2)$ **13.** $(a^2)(a^2)(a^2)$ **14.** $(ab)(ab)(ab)$

15. $\dfrac{a}{b} \cdot \dfrac{a}{b} \cdot \dfrac{a}{b}$ **16.** $xxy + xyy$

Simplify each expression. Write your answer in exponential form.

17. $a^3 \cdot a^4$ **18.** $x^3 \cdot x^5$ **19.** $3^2 \cdot 3^5$ **20.** $4^3 \cdot 4^5$

21. $y^6 \cdot y^4 \cdot y$ **22.** $9^8 \cdot 9^3 \cdot 9$ **23.** $(3x^4)(2x^5)$ **24.** $(2x^3)(5x^4)$

25. $(-5y^6)(4y^3)$ **26.** $(8y^5)(-3y^7)$ **27.** $(-2p^2)(-p^9)$ **28.** $(-p^6)(-4p^8)$

Simplify each expression. Write your answer in exponential form. Assume no variable is 0.

29. $\dfrac{a^4}{a^2}$ **30.** $\dfrac{x^8}{x^2}$ **31.** $\dfrac{9^{10}}{9^2}$ **32.** $\dfrac{8^4}{8^3}$

33. $\dfrac{18x^8}{3x}$ **34.** $\dfrac{14x^5}{2x}$ **35.** $\dfrac{-16m^9}{-8m^3}$ **36.** $\dfrac{-27m^7}{-9m^2}$

37. $\dfrac{-36x^3y^{20}}{9xy^4}$ **38.** $\dfrac{30x^4y^{16}}{-5xy^4}$ **39.** $\dfrac{a^3}{a^3}$ **40.** $\dfrac{a^3}{a^5}$

Evaluate each expression. Assume $x \neq 0$.

41. 6^0 **42.** 9^0 **43.** $(-6)^0$ **44.** -9^0

45. $\left(\dfrac{3}{4}\right)^0$ **46.** $(5x)^0$ **47.** $-5x^0$ **48.** $4x^0$

Evaluate each expression.

49. 4^{-2} **50.** 10^{-5} **51.** -11^{-2} **52.** -8^{-2}

53. $3 \cdot 2^{-5}$ **54.** $2 \cdot 3^{-4}$ **55.** $(-2)^{-5}$ **56.** $(-3)^{-4}$

57. $\left(\dfrac{2}{5}\right)^{-2}$ **58.** $\left(\dfrac{3}{5}\right)^{-2}$ **59.** $\left(\dfrac{1}{2}\right)^{-3}$ **60.** $\left(-\dfrac{1}{3}\right)^{-3}$

61. $\dfrac{1}{9^{-2}}$ **62.** $\dfrac{1}{(-7)^{-2}}$ **63.** $\dfrac{6}{(-3)^{-4}}$ **64.** $\dfrac{2}{5^{-4}}$

65. $2^{-1} + 4^{-1}$ **66.** $10^0 - 10^{-1}$ **67.** $2 \cdot 3^{-1} + 4 \cdot 6^0$ **68.** $3 \cdot 4^{-1} + 6 \cdot 8^{-1}$

Simplify each expression. Write your answer using positive exponents. Assume no variable is 0.

69. $9^{-3} \cdot 9^7$ **70.** $10^7 \cdot 10^{-3}$ **71.** $5^{-2} \cdot 5^{-4}$ **72.** $6^{-1} \cdot 6^{-9}$

73. $x \cdot x^3 \cdot x^{-6}$ **74.** $x \cdot x^4 \cdot x^{-8}$ **75.** $(3m^{-5})(-5m^9)$ **76.** $(2m^{-3})(-7m^6)$

77. $(-4k^{-3})(-2k^{-1})$ **78.** $(-3k^{-1})(-5k^{-4})$ **79.** $\dfrac{6^4}{6^7}$ **80.** $\dfrac{9^2}{9^5}$

81. $\dfrac{r^{-1}}{r}$ **82.** $\dfrac{r}{r^{-1}}$ **83.** $\dfrac{10^{-2}}{10^{-8}}$ **84.** $\dfrac{10^{-3}}{10^{-9}}$

85. $\dfrac{a^{-3}b^9}{a^4b^{-7}}$ **86.** $\dfrac{a^{-2}b^{11}}{a^5b^{-6}}$ **87.** $\dfrac{4x}{-12x^{-5}y^{-1}}$ **88.** $\dfrac{-5x}{10x^{-4}y^{-3}}$

Simplify each expression. Assume no variable is 0.

89. $x^n \cdot x$ **90.** $x^n \cdot x^2$ **91.** $x^{3n+1} \cdot x^{-1}$ **92.** $y^{3m} \cdot y^{3m+1} \cdot y^{-1}$

93. $\dfrac{x^n}{x^2}$ **94.** $\dfrac{x^n}{x}$ **95.** $\dfrac{z^{5m}}{z^{-m}}$ **96.** $\dfrac{z^{-4m}}{z^{2m}}$

Solve each word problem.

97. The radioactive substance radium-226 decays according to the formula

$$Q = A \cdot 2^{-t/1600},$$

where A represents the original amount and Q is the quantity that remains after t years. If the original amount is 100 grams, find the quantity that remains after each of the following.

a. 0 years   b. 1600 years   c. 3200 years

98. If interest is compounded annually, the value V of a savings account after t years is given by the formula

$$V = P(1 + r)^t,$$

where P is the principal and r is the interest rate in decimal form. A principal of \$2000 is deposited into an account that earns 10% interest compounded annually. Find the value of the account after each of the following.

a. 0 years   b. 1 year   c. 2 years   d. 3 years

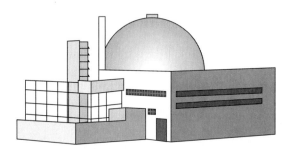

▦ CALCULATOR PROBLEMS

To find 2^{-3} on your calculator, press

Clear	2	y^x	3	$+/-$	=		0.125

Find each power on your calculator.

99. 4^{-2}

100. $(-5)^{-3}$

101. 747^0

102. Find the value of the account in Problem 98 after 20 years.

3.2   Power Rules for Exponents

In Section 3.1 we studied the product and quotient rules for exponents. In this section we study three more rules for exponents. Let's see what happens when we raise a power to another power. Consider the expression $(a^2)^3$.

$$(a^2)^3 = (a^2)(a^2)(a^2) = a^{2+2+2} = a^6$$

Note that $(a^2)^3 = a^{2\cdot3} = a^6$. This suggests the following rule.

POWER-TO-A-POWER RULE

To raise a power to a power, multiply the exponents.

$$(a^m)^n = a^{m \cdot n}$$

EXAMPLE 1   Simplify each expression.

a. $(x^4)^3 = x^{4 \cdot 3} = x^{12}$ *Multiply the exponents*
b. $(7^{-1})^{-8} = 7^8$ *Multiply the exponents*
c. $(5^2)^{-3} = 5^{-6}$ *Multiply the exponents*

Try Problem 1 >

$\qquad\qquad = \dfrac{1}{5^6}$ *Write with a positive exponent*   ■

Caution! ■
■
■
■
■

Note the difference between the power-to-a-power rule and the product rule.

Power-to-a-Power Rule	*Product Rule*
$(x^2)^3 = x^6$	$x^2 \cdot x^3 = x^5$

Now let's see what happens when we raise the product ab to the power 3.

$(ab)^3 = (ab)(ab)(ab)$ *Definition of exponent*
$\qquad = (a \cdot a \cdot a) \cdot (b \cdot b \cdot b)$ *Commutative and associative properties*
$\qquad = a^3 b^3$ *Definition of exponent*

Note that $(ab)^3 = a^3 b^3$. This suggests the following rule.

PRODUCT-TO-A-POWER RULE

To raise a product to a power, raise each factor to the power.

$$(ab)^n = a^n b^n$$

EXAMPLE 2   Simplify each expression.

a. $(5x)^2 = 5^2 x^2$ *Square each factor*
$\qquad\quad = 25x^2$ *Simplify*
b. $(-4pq)^3 = (-4)^3 p^3 q^3$ *Cube each factor*
$\qquad\qquad = -64p^3 q^3$ *Simplify*
c. $2(3rs)^4 = 2 \cdot 3^4 r^4 s^4$ *Product-to-a-power rule*
$\qquad\qquad = 2 \cdot 81 r^4 s^4$ *Since $3^4 = 81$*

Try Problem 7 >

$\qquad\qquad = 162 r^4 s^4$ *Simplify*   ■

EXAMPLE 3   Simplify each expression. Assume $q \neq 0$.

a. $(x^4 y^5)^3 = (x^4)^3 (y^5)^3$ *Product-to-a-power rule*

$\qquad\qquad = x^{12} y^{15}$ *Power-to-a-power rule*

b. $(p^2 q^{-1})^5 = (p^2)^5 (q^{-1})^5$ *Product-to-a-power rule*

$\qquad\qquad = p^{10} q^{-5}$ *Power-to-a-power rule*

$\qquad\qquad = p^{10} \cdot \dfrac{1}{q^5}$ *Write with positive exponents*

Try Problem 13 >

$\qquad\qquad = \dfrac{p^{10}}{q^5}$ *Multiply* ■

Now consider what happens when we raise the quotient a/b to the power 3.

$$\left(\frac{a}{b}\right)^3 = \frac{a}{b} \cdot \frac{a}{b} \cdot \frac{a}{b} = \frac{a \cdot a \cdot a}{b \cdot b \cdot b} = \frac{a^3}{b^3}$$

Note that $(a/b)^3 = a^3/b^3$. This suggests the final rule for exponents.

QUOTIENT-TO-A-POWER RULE

To raise a quotient to a power, raise the numerator and the denominator to the power.

$$\left(\frac{a}{b}\right)^n = \frac{a^n}{b^n} \qquad (b \neq 0)$$

EXAMPLE 4   Simplify each expression. Assume no denominator is 0.

a. $\left(\dfrac{3}{4}\right)^2 = \dfrac{3^2}{4^2}$ *Square the numerator, square the denominator*

$\qquad\qquad = \dfrac{9}{16}$ *Simplify*

b. $\left(\dfrac{x^2}{y^3}\right)^5 = \dfrac{(x^2)^5}{(y^3)^5}$ *Quotient-to-a-power rule*

$\qquad\qquad = \dfrac{x^{10}}{y^{15}}$ *Power-to-a-power rule*

c. $\left(\dfrac{r^{-3}}{s^6}\right)^{-4} = \dfrac{(r^{-3})^{-4}}{(s^6)^{-4}}$ *Quotient-to-a-power rule*

$\qquad\qquad = \dfrac{r^{12}}{s^{-24}}$ *Power-to-a-power rule*

$\qquad\qquad = r^{12} \cdot \dfrac{1}{s^{-24}}$ *Write as a product of two fractions*

Try Problem 27 >

$\qquad\qquad = r^{12} s^{24}$ *Write with positive exponents* ■

In the following examples we use a combination of several rules for exponents to simplify the given expressions.

EXAMPLE 5   Simplify $(a^5a^2)^4$.

Solution

Try Problem 33 >

$$(a^5a^2)^4 = (a^7)^4 \qquad \textit{Product rule}$$
$$= a^{28} \qquad \textit{Power-to-a-power rule}$$ ■

EXAMPLE 6   Simplify $\dfrac{2^8(x^3)^2}{2^{-1}x^7}$. Assume $x \neq 0$.

Solution

$$\frac{2^8(x^3)^2}{2^{-1}x^7} = \frac{2^8x^6}{2^{-1}x^7} \qquad \textit{Power-to-a-power rule}$$

$$= 2^{8-(-1)} \cdot x^{6-7} \qquad \textit{Quotient rule}$$

$$= 2^9 \cdot x^{-1} \qquad \textit{Simplify the exponents}$$

$$= 2^9 \cdot \frac{1}{x} \qquad \textit{Write with positive exponents}$$

Try Problem 39 >

$$= \frac{2^9}{x} \qquad \textit{Multiply}$$ ■

EXAMPLE 7   Simplify $(a^3b^{-1}/c^{-2})^{-3}$. Assume no variable is 0.

Solution

$$\left(\frac{a^3b^{-1}}{c^{-2}}\right)^{-3} = \frac{(a^3)^{-3}(b^{-1})^{-3}}{(c^{-2})^{-3}} \qquad \textit{Quotient-to-a-power rule and product-to-a-power rule}$$

$$= \frac{a^{-9}b^3}{c^6} \qquad \textit{Power-to-a-power rule}$$

$$= a^{-9} \cdot \frac{b^3}{c^6} \qquad \textit{Write as a product of two fractions}$$

$$= \frac{1}{a^9} \cdot \frac{b^3}{c^6} \qquad \textit{Write with positive exponents}$$

Try Problem 51 >

$$= \frac{b^3}{a^9c^6} \qquad \textit{Multiply}$$ ■

EXAMPLE 8   Simplify $6r^5s^4(-2rs^2)^3$.

Solution

$$6r^5s^4(-2rs^2)^3 = 6r^5s^4(-2)^3r^3(s^2)^3 \qquad \textit{Product-to-a-power rule}$$
$$= 6r^5s^4(-8)r^3s^6 \qquad (-2)^3 = -8 \textit{ and power-to-a-power rule}$$
$$= 6 \cdot (-8)r^5r^3s^4s^6 \qquad \textit{Commutative and associative properties}$$

Try Problem 63 >

$$= -48r^8s^{10} \qquad 6(-8) = -48 \textit{ and product rule}$$ ■

The rules for exponents also apply when the exponents are variables.

EXAMPLE 9 Simplify each expression. Assume no variable is 0.

a. $x^{5n} \cdot x^{3n} \cdot x = x^{5n+3n+1}$ *Product rule*
$\qquad\qquad\qquad = x^{8n+1}$ *Combine like terms*

b. $\dfrac{y^{7n}}{y^{-2n}} = y^{7n-(-2n)}$ *Quotient rule*

$\qquad\quad = y^{9n}$ *Combine like terms*

c. $(z^{-6m}z^{4m})^{-2} = (z^{-6m+4m})^{-2}$ *Product rule*
$\qquad\qquad\quad = (z^{-2m})^{-2}$ *Combine like terms*

Try Problem 71 >
$\qquad\qquad\quad = z^{4m}$ *Power-to-a-power rule* ∎

All of the rules for exponents discussed in Sections 3.1 and 3.2 can be summarized as follows.

RULES FOR EXPONENTS

Zero Exponent	$a^0 = 1$	$(a \neq 0)$
Negative Exponents	$a^{-n} = \dfrac{1}{a^n}$	$(a \neq 0)$
Negative Exponent Shortcuts	$\left(\dfrac{a}{b}\right)^{-n} = \left(\dfrac{b}{a}\right)^{n}$	$(a \neq 0,\ b \neq 0)$
	$\dfrac{1}{a^{-n}} = a^n$	$(a \neq 0)$
Product Rule	$a^m \cdot a^n = a^{m+n}$	
Quotient Rule	$\dfrac{a^m}{a^n} = a^{m-n}$	$(a \neq 0)$
Power-to-a-Power Rule	$(a^m)^n = a^{mn}$	
Product-to-a-Power Rule	$(ab)^n = a^n b^n$	
Quotient-to-a-Power Rule	$\left(\dfrac{a}{b}\right)^n = \dfrac{a^n}{b^n}$	$(b \neq 0)$

3.2 Problem Set

LEARNING THROUGH WRITING

☐ State the *power-to-a-power rule for exponents* in words.

☐ State the *product-to-a-power rule for exponents* in words.

☐ State the *quotient-to-a-power rule for exponents* in words.

Simplify each expression. Write your answer with positive exponents. Assume no variable is 0.

1. $(x^3)^2$

2. $(a^3)^4$

3. $(5^{-1})^{-8}$

4. $(3^{-9})^{-1}$

5. $(6^2)^{-5}$

6. $(7^3)^{-3}$

7. $(8x)^2$

8. $(9x)^2$

9. $(-3pq)^3$

10. $(-5pq)^3$

11. $5(2rs)^4$

12. $4(3rs)^4$

13. $(x^3y^6)^2$

14. $(x^5y^4)^3$

15. $(p^3q^{-1})^4$

16. $(p^{-1}q^2)^5$

17. $(7t^{-3})^{-2}$

18. $(6t^{-5})^{-2}$

19. $(-2m^6)^3$

20. $(-3m^7)^3$

21. $(3x)^{-2}$

22. $(2x)^{-3}$

23. $3x^{-2}$

24. $2x^{-3}$

25. $\left(\dfrac{3}{5}\right)^2$

26. $\left(\dfrac{4}{5}\right)^2$

27. $\left(\dfrac{x^3}{y^4}\right)^3$

28. $\left(\dfrac{x^2}{y^6}\right)^3$

29. $\left(\dfrac{a^{-1}}{b^{-1}}\right)^2$

30. $\left(\dfrac{a^{-1}}{b^{-1}}\right)^3$

31. $\left(\dfrac{r^{-2}}{s^5}\right)^{-3}$

32. $\left(\dfrac{r^{-4}}{s^8}\right)^{-2}$

Simplify each expression. Write your answer with positive exponents. Assume no variable is 0.

33. $(a^3a^2)^3$

34. $(a^2a^4)^2$

35. $(x^3)^5(x^2)^2$

36. $(x^3)^4(x^3)^3$

37. $z(z^3)^2(z^2z)^3$

38. $z(z^2)^5(zz^3)^2$

39. $\dfrac{3^7(x^2)^2}{3^{-1}x^5}$

40. $\dfrac{2^9(x^3)^3}{2^{-1}x^{10}}$

41. $\dfrac{y^2 \cdot y^8 \cdot y^5}{(y^3)^2}$

42. $\dfrac{y^3 \cdot y^7 \cdot y^6}{(y^2)^3}$

43. $\dfrac{t^{-4} \cdot t}{t^3 \cdot t^{-1}}$

44. $\dfrac{t^{-5} \cdot t}{t^4 \cdot t^{-1}}$

45. $\dfrac{m^{11}(m^{-3})^4}{(2m^{-4})^2}$

46. $\dfrac{m^{13}(m^{-5})^3}{(3m^{-3})^2}$

47. $\dfrac{(2a^{-2})^5}{a^{-8} \cdot a^0}$

48. $\dfrac{(3a^{-4})^2}{a^{-5} \cdot a^0}$

49. $\dfrac{(r^{-1}s)^2(rs^{-3})^{-4}}{r^2s(rs)^{-1}}$

50. $\dfrac{(r^{-5}s)^2(rs^{-5})^{-3}}{r^3s(rs)^{-1}}$

51. $\left(\dfrac{a^4b^{-2}}{c^{-3}}\right)^{-2}$

52. $\left(\dfrac{a^{-3}b^2}{c^{-1}}\right)^{-4}$

53. $\dfrac{2a^{-1}}{3b^{-2}}$

54. $\dfrac{4a^{-2}}{5b^{-1}}$

55. $\dfrac{(2x^3y^2)^{-2}(2x^{-1}y^4)^3}{(2^{-1}x^2y^{-3})^{-1}}$

56. $\dfrac{(3x^{-4}y)^{-3}(3x^2y^{-5})^2}{(3^{-1}x^{-1}y^3)^{-1}}$

Simplify each expression. Write your answer with positive exponents. Assume no variable is 0.

57. $(-4x^{-2}y^2)^2$

58. $(-5x^3y^{-3})^2$

59. $(2x^2)^3(5x^4)^2$

60. $(3x^3)^2(2x^4)^3$

61. $3a^2b^5(4a^3b)^2$

62. $5a^3b^4(2ab^2)^3$

63. $5r^3s^6(-2rs^3)^3$

64. $2r^5s^3(-3r^4s)^3$

65. $(3p^{-2}q^{-5})^{-2}(3pq^{-2})^5$

66. $(5p^{-2}q^{-5})^{-3}(5p^{-1}q)^6$

67. $-m^2(-m^{-1}m^5)^3(-m^{-2}m^{-3})^2$

68. $-m^4(-m^{-3}m^{-1})^2(-m^7m^{-2})^3$

Use the rules for exponents to simplify each expression. Assume no variable is 0.

69. $x^{3n} \cdot x^{4n} \cdot x^2$

70. $x^{6n} \cdot x^{2n} \cdot x^3$

71. $\dfrac{y^{6n}}{y^{-n}}$

72. $\dfrac{y^{4n}}{y^{-n}}$

73. $(z^{-8m} \cdot z^{5m})^{-2}$

74. $(z^{-6m} \cdot z^{2m})^{-2}$

75. $\left(\dfrac{r^{-2}}{s^4}\right)^{-m}$

76. $\left(\dfrac{r^{-5}}{s^3}\right)^{-m}$

77. $(x^{-n}y^{2n})^3$

78. $(x^{3n}y^{-n})^2$

79. $x^2(x^{m+1})^2$

80. $x^3(x^{m-1})^3$

81. Write 4^7 as a power of 2. (Hint: $4 = 2^2$.)

82. Write 144^{10} as a product of powers of 2 and 3. (Hint: $144 = 2^4 \cdot 3^2$.)

▦ CALCULATOR PROBLEMS

83. Suppose you make yearly payments, each of size p into a retirement fund that earns an interest rate r compounded annually. The value, V, of your fund after t years is given by the formula

$$V = p\left[\frac{(1 + r)^t - 1}{r}\right].$$

Find V if $p = \$900$, $r = 10\%$, and $t = 50$ years. Be sure to express r in decimal form.

84. To calculate the size, p, of your monthly car payment, you can use the formula

$$p = \frac{Ar}{12[1 - (1 + r/12)^{-12t}]},$$

where A is the amount borrowed, r is the interest rate in decimal form, and t is the time in years. Suppose you borrow $\$8000$ at 12% interest for 3 years. Find your monthly payment.

3.3 Scientific Notation: An Application of Exponents

Many numbers in science are very large or very small. For example, the distance from the earth to the sun is about 93,000,000 miles, and the mass of a water molecule is 0.0000000000000000000003 gram. To avoid using so many zeros, scientists write these numbers in *scientific notation*. For example, 93,000,000 written in scientific notation is 9.3×10^7. The number 9.3×10^7 is in scientific notation because it is the product of a number between 1 and 10 and a power of 10.

DEFINITION OF SCIENTIFIC NOTATION

A positive real number is in **scientific notation** when it is written in the form

$$a \times 10^n,$$

where $1 \le a < 10$ and n is an integer.

To see how to write 93,000,000 in the form 9.3×10^7, consider the following examples.

Multiplying by a Positive Power of 10

$9.3 \times 10^1 = 9.3 \times 10 = 93.$ *Decimal point moves* 1 *place to the right*

$9.3 \times 10^2 = 9.3 \times 100 = 930.$ *Decimal point moves* 2 *places to the right*

$9.3 \times 10^3 = 9.3 \times 1000 = 9300.$ *Decimal point moves* 3 *places to the right*

These examples tell us that **to move the decimal point k places to the right, multiply by 10^k.**

EXAMPLE 1   Write 93,000,000 in scientific notation.

Solution   To write the number 93,000,000 in scientific notation, we must write the number as a product of a number between 1 and 10 and a power of 10. Notice that 9.3 is between 1 and 10. To get 93,000,000 from 9.3, the decimal point in 9.3 must be moved 7 places to the right. To do this, multiply 9.3 by 10^7.

Try Problem 1 > $93{,}000{,}000 = 9.3 \times 10^7$ ∎

Note that we use the symbol $\times$ for multiplication to avoid confusing the dot multiplication sign with the decimal point.

EXAMPLE 2   Write each number in scientific notation.

a. $707{,}000{,}000 = 7.07 \times 10^8$
b. $10{,}000 = 1 \times 10^4$, or simply 10^4
Try Problem 7 >   c. $2.8 = 2.8 \times 10^0$, or simply 2.8 ∎

To see how to write 0.00000000000000000000003 in scientific notation, consider the following examples.

Multiplying by a Negative Power of 10

$3 \times 10^{-1} = 3 \times \dfrac{1}{10} = \dfrac{3}{10} = 0.3$ *Decimal point moves 1 place to the left*

$3 \times 10^{-2} = 3 \times \dfrac{1}{10^2} = \dfrac{3}{100} = 0.03$ *Decimal point moves 2 places to the left*

$3 \times 10^{-3} = 3 \times \dfrac{1}{10^3} = \dfrac{3}{1000} = 0.003$ *Decimal point moves 3 places to the left*

These examples tell us that **to move the decimal point k places to the left, multiply by 10^{-k}.**

EXAMPLE 3   Write 0.00000000000000000000003 in scientific notation.

Solution   To write the number 0.00000000000000000000003 in scientific notation, we must write the number as a product of a number between 1 and 10 and a power of 10. Notice that 3 is between 1 and 10. To get 0.00000000000000000000003 from 3, the decimal point in 3 must be moved 23 places to the left. To do this, multiply 3 by 10^{-23}.

Try Problem 9 > $0.00000000000000000000003 = 3 \times 10^{-23}$ ∎

EXAMPLE 4   Write each number in scientific notation.

a. $0.47 = 4.7 \times 10^{-1}$
b. $0.05 = 5 \times 10^{-2}$

Try Problem 13 >

c. $0.00000889 = 8.89 \times 10^{-6}$ ∎

EXAMPLE 5   Write 0.28×10^{-5} in scientific notation.

Solution   The number 0.28×10^{-5} is not in scientific notation because 0.28 is not between 1 and 10. To write this number in scientific notation, proceed as follows.

$$0.28 \times 10^{-5} = \mathbf{2.8 \times 10^{-1}} \times 10^{-5} \quad \textit{Write 0.28 in scientific notation}$$

Try Problem 17 >

$$= 2.8 \times 10^{-1+(-5)} \quad \textit{Product rule for exponents}$$
$$= 2.8 \times 10^{-6} \quad \textit{Simplify the exponent} \quad ∎$$

To convert from scientific notation to standard form, we reverse the process.

EXAMPLE 6   Write each number in standard form.

a. $6 \times 10^{10} = 60{,}000{,}000{,}000$ *10 places to the right*
b. $8.5 \times 10^{-3} = 0.0085$ *3 places to the left*
c. $3.124 \times 10^2 = 312.4$ *2 places to the right*

Try Problem 27 >

d. $1.01 \times 10^{-4} = 0.000101$ *4 places to the left* ∎

We can use the product and quotient rules for exponents to find products and quotients of numbers that are written in scientific notation.

EXAMPLE 7   Multiply $(2 \times 10^9)(3 \times 10^{-4})$.

Solution   Use the commutative and associative properties to group the numbers between 1 and 10 separately from the powers of 10.

$$(2 \times 10^9)(3 \times 10^{-4}) = (2 \times 3)(10^9 \times 10^{-4}) \quad \textit{Group the numbers, group}$$
$$\textit{the powers of 10}$$
$$= 6 \times 10^{9+(-4)} \quad \textit{2} \times \textit{3} = \textit{6 and product}$$
$$\textit{rule for exponents}$$

Try Problem 33 >

$$= 6 \times 10^5 \quad \textit{Simplify the exponent} \quad ∎$$

EXAMPLE 8   Multiply $(3.5 \times 10^7)(5.8 \times 10^2)$.

Solution

$$(3.5 \times 10^7)(5.8 \times 10^2) = (3.5 \times 5.8)(10^7 \times 10^2) \quad \textit{Group the numbers,}$$
$$\textit{group the powers}$$
$$\textit{of 10}$$
$$= 20.3 \times 10^9 \quad \textit{Multiply each group}$$

Since 20.3 is not between 1 and 10, write 20.3 in scientific notation and continue.

Try Problem 37 >

$$= 2.03 \times 10 \times 10^9 \qquad \textit{Since } 20.3 = 2.03 \times 10$$

$$= 2.03 \times 10^{10} \qquad \textit{Since } 10 \times 10^9 = 10^{10} \qquad ■$$

EXAMPLE 9   Perform the indicated operations on $\dfrac{(400{,}000{,}000)(0.0062)}{0.0008}$.

Solution

$$\frac{(400{,}000{,}000)(0.0062)}{0.0008} = \frac{(4 \times 10^8)(6.2 \times 10^{-3})}{8 \times 10^{-4}} \qquad \textit{Write each number in scientific notation}$$

$$= \frac{(4)(6.2)}{8} \times \frac{10^8 10^{-3}}{10^{-4}} \qquad \textit{Group the numbers, group the powers of } 10$$

$$= 3.1 \times 10^{8+(-3)-(-4)} \qquad \textit{Simplify each group}$$

$$= 3.1 \times 10^9 \qquad \textit{Simplify the exponent}$$

Try Problem 49 >

■

PROBLEM SOLVING

EXAMPLE 10   Light travels at a fast but finite speed (approximately 186,000 miles per second). How long does it take the sun's rays to reach the earth, 93,000,000 miles away?

Solution   Recall the formula $d = rt$ (distance = rate · time). Since we are given the distance (93,000,000 miles) and the rate (186,000,000 miles per second), the unknown quantity is time t.

$$t = \frac{d}{r} \qquad \textit{Solve } d = rt \textit{ for } t$$

$$t = \frac{93,000,000}{186,000} \qquad \textit{Substitute the known values}$$

$$t = \frac{9.3 \times 10^7}{1.86 \times 10^5} \qquad \textit{Write each number in scientific notation}$$

$$t = \frac{9.3}{1.86} \times \frac{10^7}{10^5} \qquad \textit{Group the numbers, group the powers of 10}$$

$$t = 5 \times 10^2 \qquad \textit{Simplify each group}$$

Try Problem 61 > It takes the sun's rays 500 seconds, or 8 1/3 minutes, to reach the earth. ▮

3.3 Problem Set

LEARNING THROUGH WRITING

☐ What is the purpose of scientific notation?

☐ Define *scientific notation*.

Write each number in scientific notation.

1. 82,000,000
2. 570,000,000
3. 3,030,000,000
4. 60,600,000
5. 912
6. 3750
7. 100,000
8. 0.0001
9. 0.0005
10. 0.00008
11. 0.74
12. 0.095
13. 0.000000618
14. 0.0000000419
15. 52.8×10^3
16. 71.9×10^{-5}
17. 0.93×10^{-4}
18. 0.46×10^6

Write each number in standard form.

19. 7×10^2
20. 9×10^3
21. 6.4×10^{-5}
22. 5.3×10^{-6}
23. 3.18×10^0
24. 2.91×10^0
25. 5×10^{-4}
26. 8×10^{-2}
27. 2.713×10^2
28. 4.652×10
29. 1×10^{-3}
30. 1×10^4

Arrange the numbers in order from smallest to largest.

31. $1.94 \times 10^{-2}, 1.7 \times 10^4, 5.3, 2.6 \times 10^{-5}$
32. $3.6 \times 10^6, 9.88, 5.1 \times 10^{-1}, 7.4 \times 10^{-3}$

Perform the indicated operations without writing the numbers in standard form. Write your answer in scientific notation.

33. $(2 \times 10^8)(4 \times 10^{-5})$
34. $(3 \times 10^{-9})(1.2 \times 10^4)$
35. $(4 \times 10^3)(2.1 \times 10^{-8})$
36. $(4.21 \times 10^{-6})(2 \times 10^{-3})$
37. $(2.5 \times 10)(5.4 \times 10^7)$
38. $(4.5 \times 10^2)(6.2 \times 10^5)$
39. $\dfrac{6 \times 10^7}{2 \times 10^3}$
40. $\dfrac{8 \times 10^{-4}}{4 \times 10^2}$
41. $\dfrac{7.8 \times 10^{-1}}{3 \times 10^{-6}}$
42. $\dfrac{9.2 \times 10^{-2}}{4 \times 10^{-8}}$
43. $\dfrac{3.5 \times 10^3}{5 \times 10^8}$
44. $\dfrac{4.5 \times 10}{9 \times 10^5}$

Write each problem in scientific notation and then perform the indicated operations. Write your answer in scientific notation.

45. $(3{,}000{,}000)(0.0002)$

46. $(40{,}000{,}000)(0.002)$

47. $\dfrac{0.000088}{200{,}000}$

48. $\dfrac{0.0000096}{30{,}000}$

49. $\dfrac{(300{,}000{,}000)(0.0082)}{0.00006}$

50. $\dfrac{(2{,}000{,}000{,}000)(0.00074)}{0.0004}$

51. $\dfrac{(0.0000036)(2400)}{(1{,}200{,}000)(0.18)}$

52. $\dfrac{(0.000039)(4500)}{(150{,}000)(0.013)}$

Solve the following word problems.

53. Other than the sun, the nearest star to the earth is Proxima Centauri, which is 2.5×10^{13} miles away. Write this number in standard form.

54. In 1939, one U.S. dollar bought 3.38 Hungarian pengös. By 1946, however, inflation in Hungary was so bad (the worst in history) that one U.S. dollar bought 5×10^{20} pengös. Write this last number in standard form.

55. The diameter of a red corpuscle is 0.000075 cm. Write this number in scientific notation.

56. According to chemists, the mass of a hydrogen atom is 0.00000000000000000000000167 gram. Write this number in scientific notation.

57. A *quadrillion* is the number 1 followed by 15 zeros. Write this number in scientific notation.

58. A *googol* is the number 1 followed by 100 zeros. Write this number in scientific notation.

59. A *microsecond* is one millionth of a second. Write this number in scientific notation.

60. A *nanosecond* is one billionth of a second. Write this number in scientific notation.

61. Radio waves travel at the speed of light (approximately 186,000 miles per second). If an astronaut 744,000 miles away sends a radio message, how long will it take to reach the earth?

62. Radio waves travel at the speed of light (approximately 186,000 miles per second). How long would it take a radio message from the earth to reach a spaceship 2,418,000 miles away?

63. A computer can perform 4.5×10^5 calculations in a single second. How many calculations can it perform in 10 hours?

64. Each image in a motion picture is on the screen 6×10^{-2} second. How many images are in a 100-minute motion picture?

CALCULATOR PROBLEMS

To square 2,500,000 on your calculator, press

| Clear | 2,500,000 | x^2 | 6.25 12 |

This means that $(2{,}500{,}000)^2 = 6.25 \times 10^{12}$. Your calculator displays the answer in scientific notation because the answer contains too many digits to be displayed in standard form.

Perform the indicated operations on your calculator.

65. $(150{,}000)^2$

66. $(2{,}000{,}000)(3{,}000{,}000)$

67. $\dfrac{0.000005}{80{,}000}$

You can enter a number into your calculator in scientific notation. For example, since $1{,}300{,}000{,}000{,}000 = 1.3 \times 10^{12}$, *you can enter this number into your calculator by pressing*

| Clear | 1.3 | EE | 12 | 1.3   12 |

68. Suppose that the national debt of the United States in 1984 was $1,300,000,000,000 and that the total number of taxpayers was 80,000,000. Use your calculator to find each taxpayer's share of the debt.

3.4   Addition and Subtraction of Polynomials

A type of algebraic expression that has particular importance in mathematics is a *polynomial*. Before we can define a polynomial, we must first define a *monomial*.

The expression

$$4x^3$$

is called a *monomial*. The number 4 is called the **coefficient** of the monomial, and the exponent 3 is the **degree of the monomial.**

DEFINITION OF A MONOMIAL

A **monomial** in x is an expression of the form

$ax^n,$

where a is any real number and n is any whole number.

Here are some more examples of monomials.

Monomial	Coefficient	Degree
$2y^5$	2	5
$-z$	-1 (Since $-z = -1 \cdot z$)	1 (Since $-z = -z^1$)
4	4	0 (Since $4 = 4 \cdot 1 = 4x^0$)

Since the exponent on the variable in a monomial must be a whole number, the following expressions are not monomials.

Not a Monomial	_Reason_
$3x^{-2}$	-2 is not a whole number
$\dfrac{1}{x}$	$1/x = x^{-1}$, and -1 is not a whole number
$9x^{1/2}$	$1/2$ is not a whole number (we will define fractional exponents in Chapter 8)

We now use the definition of a monomial to define a polynomial.

DEFINITION OF A POLYNOMIAL

A **polynomial** is either a monomial or a finite sum of monomials. The **degree of a polynomial** is the same as the degree of the highest-degree monomial in the polynomial.

Here are some examples of polynomials.

Polynomial	_Reason_	_Degree_
$5x^4$	Is a monomial	4
$3x + 7$	Is a sum of the monomials $3x$ and 7	1
$y^2 + 6y - 9$	Is a sum of the monomials y^2, $6y$, and -9	2

Recall that **terms** are algebraic expressions that are related by addition. Therefore the polynomial $8x^2 - 4x + 10$ has three terms, namely $8x^2$, $-4x$, and 10.

$$8x^2 - 4x + 10$$
$$\nwarrow \uparrow \nearrow$$
$$3 \ terms$$

Therefore a **monomial** is a polynomial with one term. A polynomial with two terms is called a **binomial.** A polynomial with three terms is called a **trinomial.**

Monomials	_Binomials_	_Trinomials_
1	$x + 1$	$x^2 + x - 6$
x	$3y - 5$	$2y^2 + 5y - 3$
$-75z^2$	$t^2 - 9$	$m^4 - 2m^2 + 1$

A polynomial with four or more terms is not given a special name. An example of a polynomial with four terms is

$$2x^3 + 3x^2 - 5x + 8.$$

This polynomial is written in **descending order,** since the exponents on x decrease from left to right. The degree of this polynomial is 3, since $2x^3$ is the highest-degree monomial in the polynomial.

EXAMPLE 1　Write each polynomial in descending order, and state its degree. Identify any monomials, binomials, or trinomials:

　　a. x^3　　　b. $5x + 6 + x^2$　　　c. $-3 + 2y$　　　d. $t^5 - t^7 + 4t^3 - t$

Solution
　　a. x^3 is already written in descending order. The degree is 3, and it is a monomial.
　　b. $x^2 + 5x + 6$ is a trinomial of degree 2.
　　c. $2y - 3$ is a binomial of degree 1.

Try Problem 3 >　　d. $-t^7 + t^5 + 4t^3 - t$ is a polynomial of degree 7.　　　■

　　A monomial may contain more than one variable, in which case the degree of the monomial is the sum of the exponents on the variables.

　　$7x^2y^3$　is a monomial of degree $2 + 3 = 5$.

The degree of a polynomial in more than one variable is the same as the degree of the highest-degree monomial in the polynomial.

　　$5x^3 + x^2y^2 - 9y^3$　is a polynomial of degree $2 + 2 = 4$.

　　A polynomial takes on different values as its variable takes on different values. To evaluate a polynomial in x at a particular value of x, say $x = a$, simply replace each x in the polynomial by a. Then simplify using the order of operations.

EXAMPLE 2　Evaluate $x^2 - 3x + 5$ at $x = -2$.

Solution

$$x^2 - 3x + 5 \qquad \text{\textit{Original polynomial}}$$
$$= (-2)^2 - 3(-2) + 5 \quad \text{\textit{Replace x with} } -2$$
$$= 4 + 6 + 5 \qquad \text{\textit{Simplify using the order of operations}}$$
Try Problem 15 >　　$= 15$　　　■

EXAMPLE 3　Evaluate $2r^3 - r^2 - 6r - 7$ at $r = -1$.

Solution

$$2r^3 - r^2 - 6r - 7 \qquad \text{\textit{Original polynomial}}$$
$$= 2(-1)^3 - (-1)^2 - 6(-1) - 7 \quad \text{\textit{Replace r with} } -1$$
$$= 2(-1) - 1 - 6(-1) - 7 \qquad \text{\textit{Simplify using the order of}}$$
$$= -2 - 1 + 6 - 7 \qquad \text{\textit{operations}}$$
Try Problem 21 >　　$= -4$　　　■

Recall that **like terms** are terms that have the same variables with the same exponents. We use the distributive property to combine like terms.

EXAMPLE 4   Combine like terms.

a. $4x^3 + 6x^3 = (4 + 6)x^3$ *Distributive property*
$= 10x^3$ *Add the coefficients*

b. $8m^4 - 12m^4 = (8 - 12)m^4$ *Distributive property*
$= -4m^4$ *Subtract the coefficients*

c. $-x^2y - 5x^2y + 9x^2y = (-1 - 5 + 9)x^2y$ *Distributive property*

Try Problem 29 >
$= 3x^2y$ *Combine the coefficients* ∎

As Example 4 suggests, **we combine like terms by combining their coefficients.** Once we have mastered combining like terms, it is an easy transition to adding and subtracting polynomials.

ADDING POLYNOMIALS

To add two polynomials, add their like terms.

We can add polynomials in either horizontal form or in vertical form. We illustrate the horizontal form in Example 5 and the vertical form in Example 6.

EXAMPLE 5   Add the polynomials $3x^2 + 6x - 4$ and $4x^2 - 2x + 1$, in horizontal form.

Solution

$(3x^2 + 6x - 4) + (4x^2 - 2x + 1)$ *Write the sum in horizontal form*
$= 3x^2 + 6x - 4 + 4x^2 - 2x + 1$ *Remove parentheses*
$= 3x^2 + 4x^2 + 6x - 2x - 4 + 1$ *Use the commutative and associative properties to rearrange the terms*

Try Problem 41(a) >
$= 7x^2 + 4x - 3$ *Combine like terms* ∎

EXAMPLE 6   Add the polynomials $3x^2 + 6x - 4$ and $4x^2 - 2x + 1$, in vertical form.

Solution   To help line up like terms in the same column, write both polynomials in descending order. Then add the like terms.

$$\begin{array}{r} \text{Line up like terms} \\ 3x^2 + 6x - 4 \\ (+)\; \underline{4x^2 - 2x + 1} \\ 7x^2 + 4x - 3 \end{array}$$

Try Problem 41(b) >
Add like terms ∎

Caution! ■ Make sure you write the addition and subtraction symbols in your answer when
■ you add two polynomials. If you don't, the operation is assumed to be
■ multiplication.
■
■
■ <u>Correct</u>   <u>Wrong</u>
■ $5x + 2$ $5x + 2$
■ $3x + 4$ $3x + 4$
■ $8x + 6$ $8x \quad 6$
■

You should be able to add polynomials both in horizontal form and in vertical form. You should also be able to subtract polynomials using either form.

EXAMPLE 7   Subtract $3x - 2$ from $5x + 4$, in horizontal form.

Solution
$$(5x + 4) - (3x - 2)$$ *Write the difference in horizontal form*
$$= 5x + 4 - 3x + 2$$ *Remove parentheses (change each sign of the second polynomial)*
$$= 5x - 3x + 4 + 2$$ *Rearrange terms*

Try Problem 45(a) >
$$= \quad 2x \quad + \quad 6$$ *Combine like terms*   ■

Example 7 suggests the following rule for subtracting polynomials.

SUBTRACTING POLYNOMIALS

To subtract two polynomials, change the sign of each term in the second polynomial, then add like terms.

EXAMPLE 8   Subtract $3x - 2$ from $5x + 4$, in vertical form.

Solution   Line up like terms in the same column.

$$\text{——— Line up like terms}$$
$$5x + 4$$
$$(-) \quad \underline{3x - 2}$$

Change each sign in the second polynomial. Then add like terms.

$$5x + 4$$
$$(+) \quad \underline{-3x + 2} \quad \textit{All signs changed}$$
Try Problem 45(b) > $$\quad 2x + 6 \quad \textit{Add like terms}$$ ■

EXAMPLE 9   Subtract $3y^3 + 4y^2 + y - 6$ from $5y^3 - y^2 + 6$,

a. in horizontal form.
b. in vertical form.

Solution

a. $(5y^3 - y^2 + 6) - (3y^3 + 4y^2 + y - 6)$ *Write the difference*
$= 5y^3 - y^2 + 6 - 3y^3 - 4y^2 - y + 6$ *Remove parentheses (change each sign of the second polynomial)*

$= 5y^3 - 3y^3 - y^2 - 4y^2 - y + 6 + 6$ *Rearrange terms*

$= \qquad 2y^3 \qquad - \quad 5y^2 \qquad - y + 12$ *Combine like terms*

b.
$$
\begin{array}{r}
5y^3 - \ y^2 + 0y + \ 6 \\
(+) \ \ -3y^3 - 4y^2 - \ \ y + \ 6 \\
\hline
2y^3 - 5y^2 - \ \ y + 12
\end{array}
$$
   Write 0y for the missing power of y
   All signs changed
   Add like terms   ∎

Try Problem 47 >

You can subtract two polynomials in vertical form more quickly if you learn to change each sign of the second polynomial mentally as you combine each pair of like terms.

PROBLEM SOLVING

This formula is due largely to the work of the Italian astronomer and mathematician Galileo Galilei (1564–1643) and the English mathematician and physicist Isaac Newton (1642–1727).

EXAMPLE 10   A stone is thrown upward from the top of a building 64 feet high with an initial velocity of 48 feet per second (Fig. 3.1). The height, h, of the stone after t seconds is given by the formula

$h = -16t^2 + 48t + 64.$

Find the stone's height after 2 seconds.

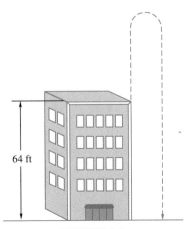

FIGURE 3.1

64 ft

Solution   To find the stone's height after 2 seconds, replace t with 2.

$$h = -16t^2 + 48t + 64 \qquad \textit{Original formula}$$
$$h = -16(2)^2 + 48(2) + 64 \qquad \textit{Replace t with 2}$$
$$h = -16(4) + 96 + 64 \qquad \textit{Simplify using the order of operations}$$
$$h = -64 + 96 + 64$$
$$h = 96$$

Try Problem 79 >   The height of the stone after 2 seconds is 96 feet.

3.4 Problem Set

LEARNING THROUGH WRITING

☐ Define a *monomial*.

☐ What is the *coefficient of a monomial?*

☐ What is the *degree of a monomial?*

☐ Define a *polynomial*.

☐ What is the *degree of a polynomial?*

☐ What are *binomials* and *trinomials?*

☐ How do you write a polynomial in descending order?

☐ How do you evaluate a polynomial at a given number?

☐ How do you add two polynomials?

☐ How do you subtract two polynomials?

Write each polynomial in descending order, and state its degree. Identify any monomials, binomials, or trinomials.

1. x^5
2. $x^7 + 9$
3. $2 + 7x + 3x^2$
4. $-1 + 5y - 6y^3$
5. $-2x^3y^5$
6. $5x^4y^2$
7. $9m + m^2$
8. $r^6 - 10r^3 + 9$
9. $8t^4 + t^6 - t^8 - t^2$
10. $1 + 3t - t^2 - t^3$
11. 4
12. -9

Evaluate each polynomial at the given value of the variable.

13. $2x + 5$ at $x = 6$
14. $3x - 1$ at $x = 5$
15. $x^2 - 5x + 3$ at $x = -2$
16. $x^2 + 6x - 2$ at $x = -1$
17. $4y^2 + y$ at $y = 5.5$
18. $4y^2 - y$ at $y = 7.5$
19. $8t^2 + 6t + 7$ at $t = 0$
20. $-7t^2 + 5t + 8$ at $t = 0$
21. $3r^3 - r^2 - 8r - 9$ at $r = -1$
22. $2r^3 - r^2 - 7r + 9$ at $r = -2$
23. $-z^2 - z + 20$ at $z = 3$
24. $-z^2 - z + 30$ at $z = -4$
25. $5p^3 - p^2 + p - 2$ at $p = \dfrac{3}{5}$
26. $5p^3 - p^2 + p - 3$ at $p = \dfrac{4}{5}$

Combine like terms.

27. $3x^4 + 5x^4$
28. $2x^3 + 7x^3$
29. $6m^3 - 10m^3$
30. $4m^3 - 12m^3$
31. $-y^2 - 8y^2$
32. $-y^2 - 9y^2$
33. $4t^2 + 3t + 7t^2$
34. $5t^3 + 3t^2 + 6t^3$
35. $-x^3y - 4x^3y + 9x^3y$
36. $-xy^2 - 2xy^2 + 8xy^2$
37. $7p^2q^3 + 11p^3q^2 - 2p^2q^3$
38. $9p^3q^4 + 15p^4q^3 - 6p^3q^4$

Add each pair of polynomials (a) in horizontal form, (b) in vertical form.

39. $2x + 5, 3x + 4$

40. $4x + 7, 5x - 2$

41. $4x^2 + 7x - 3, 2x^2 - 5x + 1$

42. $3x^2 - 6x + 1, 6x^2 + 2x - 5$

43. $3x^2 + x^2y^2 - 4y^2, 5x^2 - x^2y^2 + 2y^2$

44. $7x^3 - xy + 3y^3, 2x^3 + xy - 8y^3$

Subtract the second polynomial from the first (a) in horizontal form, (b) in vertical form.

45. $6x + 3, 4x - 1$

46. $8x - 3, 2x + 4$

47. $8y^3 - y^2 + 5, 2y^3 + 6y^2 + y - 5$

48. $7y^3 + y - 8, 3y^3 - 4y^2 + 2y + 8$

49. $x^3 - 8x^2y + 9x, 2x^3 - 5x^2y - 6x + 1$

50. $x^3 + 7xy^2 - y, 4x^3 - 9xy^2 + 2y - 3$

Add each pair of polynomials.

51. $6y^3 - 4y^2 + \quad y - 10$
$\quad\;\; 5y^3 - \quad y^2 + 2y + \quad 4$

52. $7y^3 - \quad y^2 + 4y - 11$
$\quad\;\; 3y^3 + 6y^2 - \quad y + \quad 7$

53. $a^3 - 8a + 5$
$\quad\;\; a^3 \qquad\;\; - 1$

54. $a^3 + 9a^2 - 5$
$\quad\;\; a^3 \qquad\; + 3$

55. $3x^2 - 4xy + \quad 2y^2$
$\quad\;\; 7x^2 + 5xy - 11y^2$

56. $5x^2 + \quad xy + 3y^2$
$\quad\;\; 4x^2 - 10xy - \quad y^2$

Subtract the second polynomial from the first.

57. $10x^2 + 3x + 2$
$\quad\;\; 6x^2 - 2x + 1$

58. $9x^2 + 5x + 4$
$\quad\;\; 3x^2 - 4x + 3$

59. $\quad a^3 + 3a^2 \qquad - 5$
$\quad -a^3 \qquad\;\; - a + 1$

60. $\quad a^3 \qquad + 4a - 5$
$\quad -a^3 + 4a^2 \qquad + 2$

61. $\quad 8x^2 - xy + 6y^3$
$\quad 10x^2 - xy - 6y^3$

62. $7x^3 + xy - 8y^2$
$\quad\;\; 9x^3 + xy + 8y^2$

Perform the indicated additions and subtractions.

63. $(8x^2 + 4x - 7) + (12x^2 - 3x + 10)$

64. $(7x^2 - 2x + 9) + (13x^2 - 6x - 4)$

65. $(y^2 - 2y - 6) - (3y^2 - 5y + 1)$

66. $(y^2 + 4y - 4) - (5y^2 - 2y + 8)$

67. $(a^3 + 4a^2b - 3b^2) - (5a^3 - a^2b + 2b^2)$

68. $(a^2 - 6ab^2 + 2b^3) - (4a^2 + ab^2 - 3b^3)$

69. $(15m^3 + 2m^2 - m + 10) + (m^3 - 7m^2 - 1)$

70. $(12m^3 - m^2 + 4m) + (m^3 - 6m^2 + 2m + 9)$

71. $(7r^3 - 2r^2 + r - 4) - (3r^3 - r^2 + 6r - 2)$

72. $(10r^3 - r^2 + 6r - 1) - (2r^3 + 4r^2 - 2r + 9)$

Solve each word problem.

73. Subtract $x^3 - 3x + 8$ from the sum of $2x^2 + 5x + 7$ and $x^2 - 6x - 9$.

74. Subtract $x^3 - 4x^2 + 6$ from the sum of $x^2 + 3x - 2$ and $5x^2 - 4x + 1$.

75. The sides of a triangle are $3x + 1$, $4x - 5$, and $x + 7$ (Fig. 3.2). Find the perimeter of the triangle.

76. The width of a rectangle is $2x - 3$ and the length is $6x + 7$ (Fig. 3.3). Find the perimeter of the rectangle.

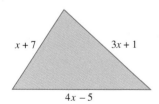

FIGURE 3.2

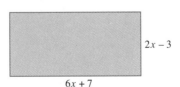

FIGURE 3.3

77. Triangles, rectangles, pentagons, etc. are called *polygons*. The number of diagonals a polygon of n sides has is $0.5n^2 - 1.5n$. Find the number of diagonals for a polygon of (a) 4 sides, and (b) 10 sides.

78. If each of the n teams in a softball league plays every other team twice, then the total number of league games played is $n^2 - n$. Find the total number of league games played in a league consisting of (a) 5 teams, and (b) 10 teams.

79. A toy rocket is shot vertically upward from the top of a building 128 feet high with an initial velocity of 112 feet per second. The height of the rocket at any time t is $-16t^2 + 112t + 128$. Find the rocket's height (a) after 3 seconds, and (b) after 8 seconds.

80. Under ideal conditions, the stopping distance (including reaction time), in feet, of a car traveling r miles per hour is $0.044r^2 + 1.1r$. Find the stopping distance of a car traveling (a) 25 mph, and (b) 50 mph.

3.5 Multiplication of Polynomials

In this section we learn how to multiply polynomials. We begin by multiplying monomials. Recall that we multiply two monomials by using the commutative and associative properties to group the coefficients and to group the powers of the variables.

EXAMPLE 1   Find each product.

Try Problem 3 >

a. $(-2m^3)(7m^5) = (-2 \cdot 7)(m^3 m^5)$ *Group the coefficients, group the powers of m*

$= -14m^8$ *Multiply each group*

b. $(-xy^2)(-5x^2y^4) = [(-1)(-5)](xx^2)(y^2 y^4)$ *Group*

$= 5x^3 y^6$ *Multiply each group* ■

Caution! ■ Note the difference between adding monomials and multiplying monomials.

Adding Monomials	*Multiplying Monomials*
$4x^2 + 3x^2 = 7x^2$	$(4x^2)(3x^2) = 12x^4$

To multiply a monomial by a polynomial with two or more terms, use the distributive property.

EXAMPLE 2   Multiply.

a. $3x(2x^2 + 5) = 3x(2x^2) + 3x(5)$ *Distribute 3x*
$\qquad\qquad\quad = 6x^3 + 15x$ *Multiply the monomials*

b. $-2y^2(3y^2 - 4y - 1)$
$\qquad = -2y^2(3y^2) + (-2y^2)(-4y) + (-2y^2)(-1)$ *Distribute $-2y^2$*
$\qquad = -6y^4 + 8y^3 + 2y^2$ *Multiply the*

Try Problem 15 >   *monomials*   ■

To multiply two binomials, apply the distributive property twice.

EXAMPLE 3   Multiply $(x + 2)(x + 3)$.

Solution   Think of $x + 3$ as a single number, and distribute $x + 3$ from the right.

$(x + 2)(x + 3) = x(x + 3) + 2(x + 3)$ *Distribute $x + 3$*
$\qquad\qquad\qquad = x^2 + 3x + 2x + 6$ *Distribute x, distribute 2*

Try Problem 25 > $= x^2 + 5x + 6$ *Combine like terms*   ■

If you study the second step of Example 3 closely, you will see that each term of the first polynomial is multiplied by each term of the second polynomial. This suggests a rule for multiplying polynomials.

MULTIPLYING POLYNOMIALS

To multiply two polynomials, multiply each term of one polynomial by each term of the other polynomial. Then simplify the result, if possible, by combining like terms.

EXAMPLE 4   Multiply $(3x - 4)(5x + 1)$.

Solution   Multiply each term in $5x + 1$ first by $3x$ and then by -4.

$(3x - 4)(5x + 1) = 3x(5x + 1) - 4(5x + 1)$
$\qquad\qquad\qquad = 15x^2 + 3x - 20x - 4$

Try Problem 31 > $= 15x^2 - 17x - 4$ ■

EXAMPLE 5   Multiply $(3m + 2)(m^2 - 5m + 4)$.

Solution
$(3m + 2)(m^2 - 5m + 4)$
$\qquad = 3m(m^2 - 5m + 4) + 2(m^2 - 5m + 4)$
$\qquad = 3m^3 - 15m^2 + 12m + 2m^2 - 10m + 8$

Try Problem 37 > $= 3m^3 - 13m^2 + 2m + 8$ ■

All of the examples so far have illustrated multiplication of polynomials in horizontal form. We can also multiply two polynomials in vertical form. This form closely resembles multiplication of whole numbers in arithmetic.

EXAMPLE 6   Multiply $(4x^2 + 5x - 3)(x + 2)$, in vertical form.

Solution   Arrange your work as shown.

$$
\begin{array}{r}
4x^2 + 5x - 3 \\
x + 2 \\
\hline
8x^2 + 10x - 6 \quad \leftarrow Multiply\ 4x^2 + 5x - 3\ by\ 2 \\
4x^3 + 5x^2 - 3x \quad \leftarrow Multiply\ 4x^2 + 5x - 3\ by\ x,\ and\ align\ like\ terms \\
\hline
4x^3 + 13x^2 + 7x - 6 \quad \leftarrow Add\ like\ terms
\end{array}
$$

Try Problem 53 >

EXAMPLE 7   Find $(3a - 2b)^3$.

Solution   Since $(3a - 2b)^3 = (3a - 2b)(3a - 2b)(3a - 2b)$, first find $(3a - 2b)(3a - 2b)$.

$$
\begin{array}{r}
3a - 2b \\
3a - 2b \\
\hline
-6ab + 4b^2 \quad \leftarrow Multiply\ 3a - 2b\ by\ -2b \\
9a^2 - 6ab \quad \leftarrow Multiply\ 3a - 2b\ by\ 3a,\ and\ align\ like\ terms \\
\hline
9a^2 - 12ab + 4b^2 \quad \leftarrow Add\ like\ terms
\end{array}
$$

Now multiply this answer by $3a - 2b$.

$$
\begin{array}{r}
9a^2 - 12ab + 4b^2 \\
3a - 2b \\
\hline
-18a^2b + 24ab^2 - 8b^3 \quad \leftarrow Multiply\ 9a^2 - 12ab + 4b^2\ by\ -2b \\
27a^3 - 36a^2b + 12ab^2 \quad \leftarrow Multiply\ 9a^2 - 12ab + 4b^2\ by\ 3a \\
\hline
27a^3 - 54a^2b + 36ab^2 - 8b^3 \quad \leftarrow Add\ like\ terms
\end{array}
$$

Try Problem 67 >

3.5   Problem Set

LEARNING THROUGH WRITING

☐ Describe how to multiply two polynomials.

Find each product of monomials.

1. $(2x^2)(5x^2)$

2. $(3x^3)(6x^3)$

3. $(-3m^4)(4m^5)$

4. $(7m^6)(-5m^2)$

5. $(9a^3)(5b^2)$

6. $(6a^4)(8b^5)$

7. $(2p)(-7q^2)$

8. $(-4p^3)(2q)$

9. $(-r^3s)(-8r^2s^2)$

10. $(-9rs^3)(-r^2s^5)$

11. $(4xy^5)(-2x^2y)(3x^3)$

12. $(5x^3y)(2xy^2)(-3y^6)$

Multiply.

13. $y(y + 5)$

14. $5m(2m - 1)$

15. $5x(2x^2 + 6)$

16. $3x(4x^2 + 8)$

17. $4r(3 - 2r + r^2)$

18. $2r(6 - 7r + r^2)$

19. $-2y^2(4y^2 - 8y - 1)$

20. $-6y^2(3y^2 - 2y - 5)$

21. $-8pq^2(p^2 - 2pq + q^2)$

22. $-4p^2q(p^2 + 2pq - q^2)$

23. $6t^5(t^3 - 8t^2 + 5t)$

24. $4t^6(t^4 + 7t^3 - 3t^2)$

Multiply.

25. $(x + 2)(x + 4)$

26. $(y + 4)(y - 3)$

27. $(t - 3)(t + 3)$

28. $(m - 5)(m + 5)$

29. $(2x + 5)(x + 3)$

30. $(3x + 4)(x + 2)$

31. $(4x - 5)(3x + 2)$

32. $(5x - 6)(4x + 3)$

33. $(3x - 7y)(2x - y)$

34. $(2x - 9y)(4x - y)$

35. $2a(5 + 6a)(3 - 2a)$

36. $-3b(6 + 7b)(2 - 3b)$

Multiply.

37. $(2m + 5)(m^2 - 3m + 4)$

38. $(4m + 3)(m^2 - 2m + 5)$

39. $(x - 3)(2x^2 + x - 1)$

40. $(x - 5)(3x^2 + x - 1)$

41. $(a + 4)(a^3 + 3a - 5)$

42. $(a + 3)(a^3 + 5a - 7)$

43. $(y - 1)(y^3 - 2y^2 + y + 1)$

44. $(y - 1)(y^3 + y^2 - 2y + 1)$

45. $(4p + 3)(5p^3 - 4p^2 + p - 5)$

46. $(6p + 5)(3p^3 - p^2 + 6p + 1)$

47. $(x^2 + 2x - 3)(4x^2 - 5x + 1)$

48. $(x^2 - 3x + 4)(2x^2 + 5x - 1)$

Multiply.

49. $p + 5$
     $\underline{p - 8}$

50. $p + 6$
     $\underline{p - 9}$

51. $2r + 5$
     $\underline{2r - 5}$

52. $3r + 4$
     $\underline{3r - 4}$

53. $2x^2 + 5x - 4$
     $\underline{\qquad x + 3}$

54. $6x^2 - 3x + 7$
     $\underline{\qquad x + 2}$

55. $8p^2 - p + 6$
     $\underline{\qquad 2p^2 - 5}$

56. $9p^2 + p - 4$
     $\underline{\qquad 5p^2 - 3}$

57. $3m^2 - 4m - 7$
     $\underline{\qquad 5m^2 + 2m}$

58. $4m^2 - 3m - 8$
     $\underline{\qquad 2m^2 - 5m}$

59. $x^2 + xy + y^2$
     $\underline{\qquad x - y}$

60. $x^2 - xy + y^2$
     $\underline{\qquad x + y}$

Find each power of a binomial.

61. $(x + 3)^2$

62. $(x - 6)^2$

63. $(4x - 5)^2$

64. $(2x + 5)^2$

65. $(m + 4)^3$

66. $(m - 5)^3$

67. $(5a - 2b)^3$

68. $(3a + 4b)^3$

Solve each word problem.

69. Find an expression for the product of two consecutive even integers if the smaller integer is n.

70. Find an expression for the product of three consecutive odd integers if the smallest integer is n.

71. The width of a rectangle is $2x + 3$, and the length is $7x - 4$ (Fig. 3.4). Write an expression for the area.

72. The base of a triangle is $4x + 6$, and the height is $3x - 1$ (Fig. 3.5). Write an expression for the area.

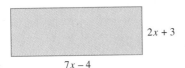

$2x + 3$

$7x - 4$

FIGURE 3.4

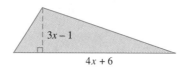

$3x - 1$

$4x + 6$

FIGURE 3.5

73. A concrete walk x feet wide is constructed around a glass enclosure for snakes that is 8 feet by 10 feet (Fig. 3.6). Find an expression for the area of the walk.

74. A piece of metal 12 inches by 12 inches is made into a cake pan by cutting squares x inches by x inches from the corners and turning up the sides (Fig. 3.7). Find an expression for the volume of the pan.

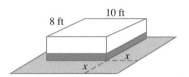

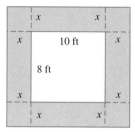

FIGURE 3.6

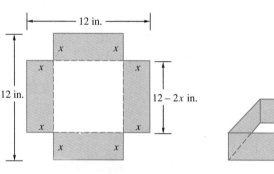

FIGURE 3.7

3.6 Multiplying Binomials

Since the product of two binomials occurs so often in algebra, we give the topic of multiplying binomials special attention.

The FOIL Method

There is a shortcut to finding the product of two binomials. To see this, consider the product of the binomials $x + 3$ and $x + 4$.

$$(x + 3)(x + 4) = x \cdot x + x \cdot 4 + 3 \cdot x + 3 \cdot 4$$
$$= x^2 + 4x + 3x + 12$$
$$= x^2 + 7x + 12$$

Now examine the step just before the answer. The term x^2 is the product of the two *first* terms of the binomials.

First terms $x \cdot x = x^2$

$(x + 3)(x + 4)$

The term $4x$ is the product of the two *outer* terms.

$(x + 3)(x + 4)$

Outer terms $x \cdot 4 = 4x$

The term $3x$ is the product of the two *inner* terms.

$(x + 3)(x + 4)$

Inner terms $3 \cdot x = 3x$

The term 12 is the product of the two *last* terms.

Last terms $3 \cdot 4 = 12$

$(x + 3)(x + 4)$

By remembering the key word **FOIL** (*First, Outer, Inner, Last*), and by adding the outer product $4x$ and the inner product $3x$ mentally, you can perform the multiplication in one step, as follows.

$$(x + 3)(x + 4) = x^2 + 7x + 12 \quad \textit{Add 3x and 4x mentally}$$

We can summarize this method as follows.

THE FOIL METHOD FOR MULTIPLYING TWO BINOMIALS

1. Multiply the two first terms to get the first term of the answer.
2. Multiply the two outer terms. Multiply the two inner terms. Add the two products mentally to get the middle term of the answer.
3. Multiply the two last terms to get the last term of the answer.

We illustrate the FOIL method with several examples.

EXAMPLE 1   Multiply $(x - 2)(x + 5)$.

Solution   Multiply first terms, outer terms, inner terms, and last terms. Add the outer product and the inner product mentally.

Try Problem 3 >

$$(x - 2)(x + 5) = x^2 + 3x - 10 \quad \text{\textit{Add 5x and} } -2x \text{ \textit{mentally}}$$

where the diagram shows x^2, -10, $-2x$, and $5x$.

■

EXAMPLE 2   Multiply $(3x + 4)(2x - 5)$.

Solution

Try Problem 7 >

$$(3x + 4)(2x - 5) = 6x^2 - 7x - 20 \quad \text{\textit{Add} } -15x \text{ \textit{and 8x mentally}}$$

where the diagram shows $6x^2$, -20, $8x$, and $-15x$.

■

EXAMPLE 3   Multiply $(3x - y)(6x - 5y)$.

Solution

Try Problem 15 >

$$(3x - y)(6x - 5y) = 18x^2 - 21xy + 5y^2 \quad \text{\textit{Add} } -15xy \text{ \textit{and} } -6xy$$

where the diagram shows $18x^2$, $5y^2$, $-6xy$, and $-15xy$.

■

The Product of $a + b$ and $a - b$

If we multiply two binomials that are identical except for the sign between the terms, the middle term of the answer will drop out.

$$
\begin{array}{cccc}
F & O & I & L \\
\downarrow & \downarrow & \downarrow & \downarrow
\end{array}
$$

$$(a + b)(a - b) = a^2 - ab + ab - b^2 = a^2 - b^2$$

This is an important product in algebra, so you should memorize the form of the answer.

MULTIPLYING THE SUM AND THE DIFFERENCE OF TWO TERMS

The product of the sum and the difference of two terms is the square of the first term minus the square of the last term.

$$(a + b)(a - b) = a^2 - b^2$$

EXAMPLE 4   Multiply.

a. $(t + 6)(t - 6) = t^2 - 6^2 = t^2 - 36$
b. $(2r + 9s)(2r - 9s) = (2r)^2 - (9s)^2 = 4r^2 - 81s^2$

Try Problem 25 >   c. $(4x + 2.8)(4x - 2.8) = (4x)^2 - (2.8)^2 = 16x^2 - 7.84$ ∎

Square of a Binomial

Another type of product that deserves special attention is the square of a binomial.

$$\begin{array}{cccc} F & O & I & L \\ \downarrow & \downarrow & \downarrow & \downarrow \end{array}$$
$$(a + b)^2 = (a + b)(a + b) = a^2 + ab + ab + b^2 = a^2 + 2ab + b^2$$

$$\begin{array}{cccc} F & O & I & L \\ \downarrow & \downarrow & \downarrow & \downarrow \end{array}$$
$$(a - b)^2 = (a - b)(a - b) = a^2 - ab - ab + b^2 = a^2 - 2ab + b^2$$

You should memorize the following rules for squaring a binomial.

SQUARING A BINOMIAL

The square of a binomial is the square of the first term, plus twice the product of the two terms, plus the square of the last term.

$$(a + b)^2 = a^2 + 2ab + b^2$$
$$(a - b)^2 = a^2 - 2ab + b^2$$

EXAMPLE 5   Find the square of each binomial.

a. $(z - 1)^2 = z^2 - 2(z)(1) + 1^2 = z^2 - 2z + 1$
b. $(3y - 2)^2 = (3y)^2 - 2(3y)(2) + 2^2 = 9y^2 - 12y + 4$

Try Problem 37 >   c. $\left(4k + \dfrac{1}{2}\right)^2 = (4k)^2 + 2(4k)\left(\dfrac{1}{2}\right) + \left(\dfrac{1}{2}\right)^2 = 16k^2 + 4k + \dfrac{1}{4}$ ∎

Caution! ■ You cannot square a binomial simply by squaring the first term and squaring the last term. There is a middle term, which is twice the product of the first and last terms.

Correct   *Wrong*

$(x + 3)^2 = x^2 + 6x + 9$ 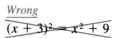

3.6 Problem Set

LEARNING THROUGH WRITING

☐ Describe the FOIL method for multiplying two binomials.

☐ How do you find the product of the sum and the difference of two terms?

☐ How do you square a binomial?

☐ With respect to the box in Fig. 3.8, what does each of the following products represent?
a. $(x + 5)(x + 3)$ b. $(x + 5)(x - 1)$
c. $(x + 5)(x + 3)(x - 1)$

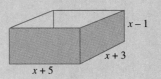

FIGURE 3.8

Use the FOIL method to multiply.

1. $(x + 3)(x + 5)$ **2.** $(x + 2)(x + 6)$ **3.** $(x - 2)(x + 4)$
4. $(x - 3)(x + 5)$ **5.** $(x - 1)(x - 6)$ **6.** $(x - 4)(x - 1)$
7. $(3x + 2)(3x - 5)$ **8.** $(3x + 4)(2x - 3)$ **9.** $(6y - 7)(2y + 3)$
10. $(8y - 5)(4y + 3)$ **11.** $(2r + s)(r + s)$ **12.** $(4r + s)(r + s)$
13. $(4p + q)(p - 7q)$ **14.** $(5p + q)(p - 6q)$ **15.** $(5x - y)(8x - 3y)$
16. $(7x - y)(3x - 5y)$ **17.** $(10a - 3b)(8a + 2b)$ **18.** $(9a - 2b)(4a + 3b)$
19. $(5 - x)(2 + x)$ **20.** $(7 - x)(3 + x)$ **21.** $(m + 5)(m - 5)$
22. $(m + 2)(m - 2)$ **23.** $(2.1x - 1.4)(5.3x + 6.2)$ **24.** $(3.2x + 4.6)(1.5x - 8.8)$

Find the product of each sum and difference of two terms.

25. $(t + 4)(t - 4)$ **26.** $(t + 9)(t - 9)$ **27.** $(p - 8)(p + 8)$
28. $(p - 10)(p + 10)$ **29.** $(6m + 1)(6m - 1)$ **30.** $(4m + 1)(4m - 1)$
31. $(2x - y)(2x + y)$ **32.** $(3x - y)(3x + y)$ **33.** $(3r + 7s)(3r - 7s)$
34. $(5r + 2s)(5r - 2s)$ **35.** $(9x + 3.1)(9x - 3.1)$ **36.** $(7x + 2.6)(7x - 2.6)$

Find the square of each binomial.

37. $(x + 2)^2$ **38.** $(x + 8)^2$ **39.** $(z - 5)^2$ **40.** $(z - 3)^2$
41. $(2y - 3)^2$ **42.** $(2y - 5)^2$ **43.** $(10a + b)^2$ **44.** $(12a + b)^2$
45. $(5x - 9y)^2$ **46.** $(3x - 5y)^2$ **47.** $\left(8k + \dfrac{1}{2}\right)^2$ **48.** $\left(6k + \dfrac{1}{2}\right)^2$

Multiply.

49. $(6y - 5)(3y + 4)$

50. $(7y - 2)(4y + 3)$

51. $(1.1p + 2.5)^2$

52. $(2.4p + 3.5)^2$

53. $\left(3k + \dfrac{2}{3}\right)\left(3k - \dfrac{2}{3}\right)$

54. $\left(4k + \dfrac{3}{5}\right)\left(4k - \dfrac{3}{5}\right)$

55. $(t^2 - 1)(t^2 - 9)$

56. $(t^2 - 1)(t^2 - 4)$

57. $(z^2 - 3)(z^2 + 3)$

58. $(z^2 - 6)(z^2 + 6)$

59. $(5 - x^3)^2$

60. $(10 - x^3)^2$

Simplify.

61. $(x + 1)^2 - (x + 6)(x - 3)$

62. $(x - 1)^2 - (x - 2)(x + 7)$

63. $(z - 6)(z + 6) - (z - 10)^2$

64. $(z + 3)(z - 3) - (z + 4)^2$

65. $(x - y)^2 - (x + y)^2$

66. $(x + y)^2 - (x - y)^2$

3.7 Dividing a Polynomial by a Monomial

We now turn our attention to dividing polynomials. Recall that we divide a monomial by a monomial by dividing the coefficients and dividing the powers of the variables.

EXAMPLE 1 Find each quotient.

Try Problem 1 >

a. $\dfrac{15x^6}{3x^2} = \dfrac{15}{3} \cdot \dfrac{x^6}{x^2} = 5x^{6-2} = 5x^4$

b. $\dfrac{6a^5b^3}{2a^3b^5} = \dfrac{6}{2} \cdot \dfrac{a^5}{a^3} \cdot \dfrac{b^3}{b^5} = 3 \cdot a^2 \cdot \dfrac{1}{b^2} = \dfrac{3a^2}{b^2}$ ∎

To divide a polynomial having two or more terms by a monomial, recall the rule for adding fractions.

$$\frac{a}{c} + \frac{b}{c} = \frac{a + b}{c}$$

If we turn this rule around we have the rule for dividing by a monomial.

DIVIDING BY A MONOMIAL

To divide a polynomial by a monomial, divide each term of the polynomial by the monomial.

$$\frac{a + b}{c} = \frac{a}{c} + \frac{b}{c} \qquad (c \neq 0)$$

EXAMPLE 2   Divide $(3x + 3)/3$.

Solution

$$\frac{3x + 3}{3} = \frac{3x}{3} + \frac{3}{3} \qquad \textit{Divide each term by 3}$$

Try Problem 13 >

$$= x + 1 \qquad \textit{Divide the monomials}$$

EXAMPLE 3   Divide $\dfrac{-16p^3 + 24p^2 + 8p}{-8p}$.

Solution

$$\frac{-16p^3 + 24p^2 + 8p}{-8p} = \frac{-16p^3}{-8p} + \frac{24p^2}{-8p} + \frac{8p}{-8p} \qquad \textit{Divide each term by } -8p$$

Try Problem 21>

$$= 2p^2 - 3p - 1 \qquad \textit{Divide the monomials}$$

EXAMPLE 4   Divide $4r^8s^3 - 14r^6s^2 - 3r^4s + 6r^2$ by $2r^3$.

Solution

$$\frac{4r^8s^3 - 14r^6s^2 - 3r^4s + 6r^2}{2r^3} \qquad \textit{Write the quotient}$$

$$= \frac{4r^8s^3}{2r^3} - \frac{14r^6s^2}{2r^3} - \frac{3r^4s}{2r^3} + \frac{6r^2}{2r^3} \qquad \textit{Divide each term by } 2r^3$$

$$= 2r^5s^3 - 7r^3s^2 - \frac{3}{2}rs + \frac{3}{r} \qquad \textit{Divide the monomials}$$

Try Problem 47 >   Note that the answer is not a polynomial, due to the term $3/r$.

3.7 Problem Set

LEARNING THROUGH WRITING   ☐ How do you divide a polynomial by a monomial?

☐ How do you divide a monomial by a monomial?

Find each quotient.

1. $\dfrac{12x^{10}}{3x^5}$

2. $\dfrac{18x^8}{3x^2}$

3. $\dfrac{-28y^2}{4y}$

4. $\dfrac{-24y^2}{6y}$

5. $\dfrac{10m}{5m^2}$

6. $\dfrac{14m}{2m^2}$

7. $\dfrac{-8r^6s^3}{8r^3}$

8. $\dfrac{-9r^6s^2}{9r^2}$

9. $\dfrac{20a^4b^2}{2a^2b^4}$

10. $\dfrac{25a^7b^4}{5a^4b^7}$

11. $\dfrac{4x^2y^4}{8x^3y}$

12. $\dfrac{2x^3y^6}{6x^4y}$

Divide.

13. $\dfrac{5x + 5}{5}$

14. $\dfrac{7x + 7}{7}$

15. $\dfrac{8x + 8y}{8}$

16. $\dfrac{9x - 9y}{9}$

17. $\dfrac{6x - 4}{-2}$

18. $\dfrac{6x + 9}{-3}$

19. $\dfrac{y^3 - y^2 + y}{y}$

20. $\dfrac{y^5 + y^4 - y^2}{y^2}$

21. $\dfrac{-12p^3 + 18p^2 + 6p}{-6p}$

22. $\dfrac{-16p^3 + 24p^2 + 8p}{-8p}$

23. $\dfrac{6xy^2 - 2x^2y + xy}{xy}$

24. $\dfrac{4x^2y - xy^2 + xy}{xy}$

25. $\dfrac{45a^5b^3 + 75a^3b^5 - 30a^2b^5}{15a^2b^3}$

26. $\dfrac{60a^5b^2 + 40a^3b^3 - 50a^3b^4}{10a^3b^2}$

27. $\dfrac{27m^5 + 2m^3 - 9m^2}{3m^2}$

28. $\dfrac{18m^5 - 5m^3 + 12m^2}{6m^2}$

29. $\dfrac{64x^3 + 3x^2 - 4x}{4x^2}$

30. $\dfrac{25x^3 + 3x^2 - 5x}{5x^2}$

31. $\dfrac{a^2 + 2ab + b^2}{2a}$

32. $\dfrac{a^2 - 2ab + b^2}{2b}$

33. $\dfrac{18k^4 - 6k^3 + 9k^2 - 15k + 2}{3k^2}$

34. $\dfrac{14k^4 - 10k^3 + 16k^2 - 8k + 5}{2k^2}$

Divide each polynomial by 3.

35. $9m^2 + 6m - 12$ **36.** $15m^2 + 6m - 18$ **37.** $21x^5 - 30x^3 - 3$ **38.** $24x^6 - 33x^4 - 3$

39. $3y + 1$ **40.** $6y - 1$ **41.** $z + 9$ **42.** $z + 3$

Divide each polynomial by $4r^3$.

43. $20r^5 - 28r^4$ **44.** $24r^6 + 36r^4$ **45.** $12r^6 + 8r^4 - 4r^3$

46. $16r^7 + 12r^5 - 4r^3$ **47.** $4r^8s^4 - 12r^6s^2 - 2r^4s + 8r^2$ **48.** $8r^9s^5 - 4r^7s^3 - 6r^5s^2 + 20r^2$

True or false.

49. $\dfrac{ab}{b} = a$

50. $\dfrac{ab}{a} = b$

51. $\dfrac{x + 5}{5} = x + 1$

52. $\dfrac{x + 5}{x} = 1 + 5$

Solve each word problem.

53. Show that the average of the three consecutive integers n, $n + 1$, and $n + 2$ is the middle integer.

54. Show that the average of the three consecutive odd integers n, $n + 2$, and $n + 4$ is the middle integer.

3.8   Long Division of Polynomials

In Section 3.7 we learned to divide a polynomial by a monomial. When the divisor is not a monomial, we use a procedure called **long division of polynomials** to find the quotient. This procedure is illustrated in Example 1. As you read through the example, note the similarity between long division of polynomials and long division of whole numbers.

EXAMPLE 1   Divide $3x^2 + 10x + 8$ by $x + 2$.

Solution

Step 1   Write the divisor and the dividend in descending order.

$$x + 2 \overline{)3x^2 + 10x + 8}$$

$\underbrace{}_{Divisor}$ $\underbrace{}_{Dividend}$

Step 2   Divide x into $3x^2$ and get 3x.

$$3x^2/x = 3x$$

$$\begin{array}{r} 3x \\ x + 2 \overline{)3x^2 + 10x + 8} \end{array}$$

Step 3   Multiply 3x by x + 2 and get $3x^2 + 6x$.

Times

$$\begin{array}{r} \boxed{3x} \\ (x + 2)\overline{)3x^2 + 10x + 8} \\ 3x^2 + 6x \end{array}$$

Equals

Step 4   Subtract $3x^2 + 6x$ from $3x^2 + 10x$ and get 4x. Then bring down the next term in the dividend, +8. This gives a new dividend of 4x + 8.

$$\begin{array}{r} 3x \\ x + 2 \overline{)3x^2 + 10x + 8} \\ \underline{3x^2 + 6x } \downarrow \\ 4x + 8 \end{array}$$

Subtract, bring down +8

Step 5   Divide x into 4x and get 4.

$$4x/x = 4$$

$$\begin{array}{r} 3x + 4 \\ x + 2 \overline{)3x^2 + 10x + 8} \\ \underline{3x^2 + 6x } \\ 4x + 8 \end{array}$$

Step 6   Multiply 4 by x + 2 and get 4x + 8.

Times

$$\begin{array}{r} 3x \boxed{+ \ 4} \\ (x + 2)\overline{)3x^2 + 10x + 8} \\ \underline{3x^2 + 6x } \\ 4x + 8 \end{array}$$

Equals $4x + 8$

Step 7 Subtract $4x + 8$ from $4x + 8$ and get the remainder 0.

$$
\begin{array}{r}
3x + 4 \\
x + 2\overline{)3x^2 + 10x + 8} \\
\underline{3x^2 + 6x} \\
4x + 8 \\
\underline{4x + 8} \\
0 \leftarrow \text{\textit{Subtract and get the remainder} } 0
\end{array}
$$

The quotient is $3x + 4$ and the remainder is 0.

Step 8 Check by multiplying the divisor, x + 2, by the quotient, 3x + 4, and adding the product to the remainder, 0. The result should be the dividend, $3x^2 + 10x + 8$.

$$\textit{Divisor} \cdot \textit{quotient} + \textit{remainder} = \textit{dividend}$$
$$\downarrow \qquad \downarrow \qquad \qquad \downarrow \qquad \qquad \downarrow$$
$$(x + 2)(3x + 4) \quad + \quad 0 \quad = 3x^2 + 10x + 8$$

Try Problem 3 $>$
$$3x^2 + 10x + 8 = 3x^2 + 10x + 8 \quad \textit{True} \qquad \blacksquare$$

Caution! When subtracting polynomials, remember to change the sign of each term in the second polynomial and then add.

$$
\begin{array}{cc}
\underline{\textit{Correct}} & \underline{\textit{Wrong}} \\
\begin{array}{r} 4x^2 + 5x \\ (-) \ \underline{4x^2 - 2x} \\ 7x \end{array} &
\begin{array}{r} 4x^2 + 5x \\ (-) \ \underline{4x^2 - 2x} \\ 3x \end{array}
\end{array}
$$

EXAMPLE 2 Divide $\dfrac{6x^3 - x^2 - 7x + 18}{2x + 3}$.

Solution Follow the steps and arrange your work as shown.

$$
\begin{array}{l}
\quad\quad\quad\quad\text{\textit{Step 2}} \quad 6x^3/2x = 3x^2 \\
\quad\quad\quad\quad\quad\text{\textit{Step 5}} \quad -10x^2/2x = -5x \\
\quad\quad\quad\quad\quad\quad\text{\textit{Step 8}} \quad 8x/2x = 4
\end{array}
$$

$$
\begin{array}{r}
3x^2 - 5x + 4 \\
2x + 3\overline{)6x^3 - x^2 - 7x + 18} \\
\underline{6x^3 + 9x^2} \\
-10x^2 - 7x \\
\underline{-10x^2 - 15x} \\
8x + 18 \\
\underline{8x + 12} \\
6
\end{array}
$$

Step 1 Write divisor and dividend in descending order
Step 3 $3x^2$ times $2x + 3$
Step 4 Subtract, bring down next term, $-7x$
Step 6 $-5x$ times $2x + 3$
Step 7 Subtract, bring down next term, $+18$ -
Step 9 4 times $2x + 3$
Step 10 Subtract and get remainder 6

The quotient is $3x^2 - 5x + 4$, and the remainder is 6.

Step **11**   Check as follows.

Divisor · quotient + remainder = dividend

$$\downarrow \qquad\qquad \downarrow \qquad\qquad \downarrow \qquad\qquad \downarrow$$

$$(2x + 3)(3x^2 - 5x + 4) + 6 \quad= 6x^3 - x^2 - 7x + 18$$
$$6x^3 - 10x^2 + 8x + 9x^2 - 15x + 12 + 6 \quad= 6x^3 - x^2 - 7x + 18$$
$$6x^3 - x^2 - 7x + 18 = 6x^3 - x^2 - 7x + 18$$

Try Problem 13 >

True   ■

When we perform long division on two whole numbers, we often put the remainder over the divisor, as in the following example.

$$5\overline{)17} \qquad \text{Answer: } 3\frac{2}{5} = 3 + \frac{2}{5}$$

We can do this because

$$\frac{17}{5} = \frac{15 + 2}{5} = \frac{15}{5} + \frac{2}{5} = 3 + \frac{2}{5}.$$

We use the same form to write the answer to a long division problem involving polynomials. For example, we would write the answer to Example 2 as

$$3x^2 - 5x + 4 + \frac{6}{2x + 3}.$$

Caution! ■   When you write the answer to a long division problem involving polynomials, make sure to write the addition symbol; otherwise, multiplication is assumed.

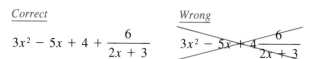

Correct
$$3x^2 - 5x + 4 + \frac{6}{2x + 3}$$

Wrong
$$3x^2 - 5x + 4\frac{6}{2x + 3}$$

EXAMPLE 3   Divide $\dfrac{2m^3 - 9m^2 + 28}{2m - 5}$.

Solution   Write the divisor and the dividend in descending order. Write $0m$ for the missing power of m in the dividend.

$$
\begin{array}{r}
m^2 - 2m - 5 \\
2m - 5 \overline{\smash{)}\; 2m^3 - 9m^2 + 0m + 28} \\
\underline{2m^3 - 5m^2} \\
-4m^2 + 0m \\
\underline{-4m^2 + 10m} \\
-10m + 28 \\
\underline{-10m + 25} \\
3
\end{array}
$$

Try Problem 17 >   The answer is $m^2 - 2m - 5 + \dfrac{3}{2m - 5}$. Check by multiplication.   ■

At first, long division of polynomials may seem a little complicated. However, after you've done a few problems, the procedure becomes very simple since you are repeating the same steps over and over again. These steps can be summarized as follows.

LONG DIVISION OF POLYNOMIALS

1. Write the divisor and the dividend in descending order. Write any missing power with a coefficient of 0.
2. Divide the first term of the divisor into the first term of the dividend. This gives the first term of the quotient.
3. Multiply the term of the quotient obtained in Step 2 by every term of the divisor.
4. Subtract and bring down the next term to get the new dividend.
5. Repeat Steps 2, 3, and 4 with the new dividend. Continue repeating these steps until the degree of the new dividend is less than the degree of the divisor. This last dividend is the remainder.
6. Check by multiplying the divisor by the quotient and adding the remainder. The result should equal the original dividend.

EXAMPLE 4   Divide $\dfrac{x^4 + 2x^3 - 5x + 1}{x^2 - 1}$.

Solution   The dividend is missing the x^2 term, and the divisor is missing the x term. Therefore write these missing powers with a coefficient of 0 and proceed as follows.

$$
\begin{array}{r}
x^2 + 2x + 1 \\
x^2 + 0x - 1 \overline{)\ x^4 + 2x^3 + 0x^2 - 5x + 1} \\
\underline{x^4 + 0x^3 - x^2} \\
2x^3 + x^2 - 5x \\
\underline{2x^3 + 0x^2 - 2x} \\
x^2 - 3x + 1 \\
\underline{x^2 + 0x - 1} \\
-3x + 2
\end{array}
$$

Since the degree of $-3x + 2$ is less than the degree of the divisor, $x^2 - 1$, the division stops. The answer is

$$
x^2 + 2x + 1 + \frac{-3x + 2}{x^2 - 1}.
$$

Try Problem 27 >   Check by multiplication.   ■

3.8 Problem Set

LEARNING THROUGH WRITING

☐ When do we use long division of polynomials?

☐ Describe the steps in long division of polynomials.

Use long division of polynomials to perform each division.

1. $\dfrac{x^2 + 10x + 21}{x + 3}$

2. $\dfrac{x^2 + 8x + 12}{x + 2}$

3. $\dfrac{4x^2 + 11x + 6}{x + 2}$

4. $\dfrac{5x^2 + 17x + 6}{x + 3}$

5. $\dfrac{9x^2 + 6x + 8}{3x - 2}$

6. $\dfrac{9x^2 + 3x + 2}{3x - 1}$

7. $\dfrac{25y^2 - 10y - 13}{5y - 3}$

8. $\dfrac{15y^2 - 2y - 3}{5y - 4}$

9. $\dfrac{2p^2 + 1}{2p + 4}$

10. $\dfrac{2p^2 - 7}{2p - 6}$

11. $\dfrac{1 + 8z^2 - 2z}{1 + 4z}$

12. $\dfrac{1 + 4z^2 - 3z}{1 + 4z}$

13. $\dfrac{8x^3 - 4x^2 - 14x + 21}{2x + 3}$

14. $\dfrac{4x^3 - 6x^2 - 12x + 37}{2x + 4}$

15. $\dfrac{y^3 - 8y + 3}{y + 3}$

16. $\dfrac{y^3 - 15y + 4}{y + 4}$

17. $\dfrac{2m^3 - 11m^2 + 27}{2m - 3}$

18. $\dfrac{4m^3 - 6m^2 + 11}{2m - 1}$

19. $\dfrac{8m^4 - 10m^3 - 19m - 21}{4m + 3}$

20. $\dfrac{16m^4 - 13m^2 + 23m - 15}{4m - 3}$

21. $\dfrac{18p^4 - 3p^3 - 4p^2 + 37p - 5}{6p - 5}$

22. $\dfrac{24p^4 + 8p^3 + 8p^2 - 33p - 5}{6p + 5}$

23. $\dfrac{5x^2 + 9x^4 - 4}{3x + 2}$

24. $\dfrac{6x^2 + 27x^4 - 1}{3x - 1}$

Divide.

25. $\dfrac{x^4 + 6x^3 - 3x^2 - 16x + 12}{x^2 + x - 2}$

26. $\dfrac{x^4 + 5x^3 - 3x^2 - 19x + 8}{x^2 + 2x - 1}$

27. $\dfrac{x^4 + 4x^3 - 7x + 1}{x^2 - 1}$

28. $\dfrac{x^4 + 5x^3 + 7x - 9}{x^2 + 1}$

29. $\dfrac{x^3 - 7x^2 + 4x^5 - 8x^4 - 10x - 3}{2x^2 + 3 - x}$

30. $\dfrac{4x^4 - x^3 - 3x^2 + 6x^5 + 6x - 1}{2x^2 + 1 - 2x}$

31. $(4x^3 - 5x) \div (2x - 1)$

32. $(9x^3 + 5x) \div (3x - 1)$

33. $(m^3 + 27) \div (m + 3)$

34. $(p^4 - 1) \div (p^2 + 1)$

35. $(1 - 4y + 3y^2) \div (3y - 6)$

36. $(4y^2 - 3 - 5y) \div (4y - 8)$

True or false.

37. $\dfrac{a + b}{c} = \dfrac{a}{c} + \dfrac{b}{c}$

38. $\dfrac{a - b}{c} = \dfrac{a}{c} - \dfrac{b}{c}$

39. $\dfrac{c}{a + b} = \dfrac{c}{a} + \dfrac{c}{b}$

40. $\dfrac{c}{a - b} = \dfrac{c}{a} - \dfrac{c}{b}$

Key Terms

Base, p. 124

Binomial, p. 145

Coefficient, p. 144

Degree of a monomial, p. 144

Degree of a polynomial, p. 144

Descending order, p. 146

Exponent, p. 124

FOIL, p. 157

Like terms, p. 147

Long division of polynomials, p. 163

Monomial, p. 144

Polynomial, p. 145

Power of *a*, p. 124

Scientific notation, p. 128

Term, p. 145

Trinomial, p. 145

Key Rules

Rules for Exponents

Zero exponent: $a^0 = 1$ $(a \neq 0)$

Negative exponents: $a^{-n} = \dfrac{1}{a^n}$ $(a \neq 0)$

Negative exponent shortcuts: $\left(\dfrac{a}{b}\right)^{-n} = \left(\dfrac{b}{a}\right)^n$ $(a \neq 0, \ b \neq 0)$

$\dfrac{1}{a^{-n}} = a^n$ $(a \neq 0)$

Product rule: $a^m \cdot a^n = a^{m+n}$

Quotient rule: $\dfrac{a^m}{a^n} = a^{m-n}$ $(a \neq 0)$

Power-to-a-power rule: $(a^m)^n = a^{mn}$

Product-to-a-power rule: $(ab)^n = a^n b^n$

Quotient-to-a-power rule: $\left(\dfrac{a}{b}\right)^n = \dfrac{a^n}{b^n}$ $(b \neq 0)$

Multiplying the Sum and Difference of Two Terms

$(a + b)(a - b) = a^2 - b^2$

Squaring a Binomial

$(a + b)^2 = a^2 + 2ab + b^2$

$(a - b)^2 = a^2 - 2ab + b^2$

[3.1] *State the base and the exponent of each expression.*

1. 9^4

2. -4^2

3. $(7x)^3$

Write each expression using exponents.

4. $6 \cdot x \cdot x \cdot x \cdot x \cdot x$

5. $(y + 5)(y + 5)(y + 5)$

Evaluate each expression.

6. -5^0

7. 3^{-2}

8. -2^{-4}

9. $\dfrac{1}{10^{-3}}$

10. $\left(\dfrac{4}{5}\right)^{-2}$

11. $\left(-\dfrac{1}{3}\right)^{-3}$

12. $12 \cdot 6^{-1}$

13. $8^0 - 8^{-1}$

Simplify each expression. Write your answer using positive exponents. Assume no variable is 0.

14. $y^3 \cdot y^5 \cdot y$

15. $5^2 \cdot 5^{-10}$

16. $(-3x^{-4})(7x^5)$

17. $\dfrac{4^9}{4^3}$

18. $\dfrac{t^2}{t^8}$

19. $\dfrac{-48r^{10}s^{11}}{8rs^3}$

20. $\dfrac{6^{-1}m^{-5}}{6^{-8}m^9}$

21. $\dfrac{p^{3n+1}}{p^2}$

[3.2] *Simplify each expression. Write your answer with positive exponents. Assume no variable is 0.*

22. $(x^{-2})^{-5}$

23. $(-4m^4m^2)^3$

24. $\left(\dfrac{x^4}{y^3}\right)^2$

25. $\dfrac{t^{-6} \cdot t \cdot t^0}{t^3 \cdot t^{-1}}$

26. $\dfrac{p^{10}(p^{-4})^3}{(3p^{-3})^2}$

27. $\left(\dfrac{a^{-2}}{b^{-3}c^4}\right)^{-5}$

28. $4r^4s^7(-2rs^2)^3$

29. $(7p^{-1}q)^{-1}(7pq^{-3})^3$

30. $(z^{-7n} \cdot z^{2n})^{-2}$

[3.3] *Write each number in scientific notation.*

31. 47,000,000

32. 0.000003

33. 908×10^{-5}

Write each number in standard form.

34. 5.19×10^5

35. 6.062×10^{-4}

36. 1×10^{-2}

Perform the indicated operations without writing the numbers in standard form. Write your answer in scientific notation.

37. $(4.1 \times 10^{-4})(2 \times 10^9)$

38. $\dfrac{1.5 \times 10^3}{5 \times 10^{10}}$

Write each problem in scientific notation, and then perform the indicated operations. Write your answer in scientific notation.

39. $(0.00000007)(40,000)$

40. $\dfrac{(300,000)(0.0008)}{0.002}$

41. The human brain contains about 10^{10} cells. If 10^5 cells die each day, how long will it take all of the cells to die?

[3.4] *Write each polynomial in descending order, and state its degree. Identify any monomials, binomials, or trinomials.*

42. $8 + 3x$

43. $6 - 5y^2 + y^4$

44. $9z^3$

45. $m^3 - m^5 + 1 + m$

46. Evaluate $2r^3 - r^2 + 9r + 8$ at $r = -2$.

Add each pair of polynomials.

47. $6x^2 + 8x - 9$
      $\underline{2x^2 - 3x + 5}$

48. $7x^2 + 3xy + y^2$
      $\underline{x^2 - 3xy + y^2}$

Subtract the second polynomial from the first.

49. $5y^2 - 4y + 1$
      $\underline{3y^2 + 4y - 6}$

50. $a^3 - 7a - 8$
      $\underline{-a^3 + 2a^2 + 3}$

Perform the indicated additions and subtractions.

51. $(13m^3 - 2m^2 + m) + (m^3 - 6m^2 - m + 1)$

52. $(a^2 - 8ab + 3b^2) - (5a^2 + 7ab - 3b^2)$

53. $(p^4 - p^2 + 4p + 9) - (-3p^3 + p^2 - 5p - 8)$

54. The cost of producing x vacuum cleaners is $0.5x^2 + 10x + 250$ dollars. Find the cost of producing (a) 10 cleaners, and (b) 20 cleaners.

[3.5] *Find each product.*

55. $(2xy)(-3y^7)(5x^2y^3)$

56. $-m^3(m^2 - 4m + 7)$

57. $2p^2q(p^2 - 2pq + 3q^2)$

58. $(3y + 7)(4y - 5)$

59. $-6n(m - n)(m + n)$

60. $(x - 2)(4x^2 - x + 3)$

61. $(3a + 1)(a^3 - 7a + 2)$

62. $(5p - 4)(2p^3 + 5p^2 + 4p + 3)$

63. $(2k - 1)^3$

Multiply.

64. $6m^2 - m + 7$
      $\underline{ 2m^2 + 3m}$

65. $3x^2 - 5x + 2$
      $\underline{ x^2 + 4x - 1}$

66. Write an expression for the total surface area (four sides, top, and bottom) of the rectangular box shown in Fig. 3.9.

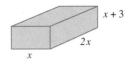

FIGURE 3.9

[3.6] *Find each product.*

67. $(4x + 3)(2x - 5)$

68. $(8a - 5b)(a + 3b)$

69. $(m + 7)^2$

70. $(3t + 10)(3t - 10)$

71. $(r^2 + 5)^2$

72. $(6x - 2y)^2$

73. Simplify $(x + y)(x - y) - (x - y)^2$.

[3.7] *Perform each division.*

74. $\dfrac{-48m}{6m^3}$

75. $\dfrac{-10x^2y^6}{10x^3y^3}$

76. $\dfrac{15r^2 + 25r - 5}{5}$

77. $\dfrac{12a^3b^3 - 6a^2b^2 + 18ab}{6a^2}$

78. Divide $8p^4 - 12p^3 + 2p^2 + 4p$ by $-4p$.

[3.8] *Perform each division.*

79. $\dfrac{x^2 + 9x + 20}{x + 4}$

80. $\dfrac{2y^3 - 9y^2 + 10y + 3}{y - 3}$

81. $\dfrac{8m^3 + 8m^2 - 1}{2m + 1}$

82. $\dfrac{3p^4 - 4p^3 + 6p^2 + p - 15}{3p - 4}$

83. $\dfrac{6x^4 + 4x^3 - x^2 + 11x + 9}{2x + 2x^2 - 1}$

84. $(k^3 - 8) \div (k - 2)$

C H A P T E R 3	T E S T

1. Write 6.3×10^6 in standard form. *(tiêu chuẩn)*

2. Write 0.0000712 in scientific notation. *(ký hiệu khoa học)*

Evaluate each expression. *(biểu thức)*

3. $\dfrac{1}{6^{-1}} =$

4. $\left(\dfrac{3}{7}\right)^{-2}$

5. $2^0 + 2^{-3}$

6. Add.
$$5x^2 - 9x + 4$$
$$2x^2 + 4x - 3$$

7. Subtract.
$$2a^3 + 6a^2 - 4a - 5$$
$$a^3 - 3a^2 + a - 5$$

8. Evaluate $3x^2 - 6x + 7$ at $x = -2$. *(Thui đáp số, tử số, đáp số bài toán chia)*

Find each product or quotient. Write your answer in scientific notation. *(tich số, kết quả bài toán nhân)*

9. $(5 \times 10^{-8})(9 \times 10^{11})$

10. $\dfrac{8.4 \times 10^7}{4 \times 10^3}$

(đồng giản rút gọn)

(giả thử)

Simplify each expression. Write your answer using positive exponents. Assume no denominator is 0.

11. $5xy(-2x^2)^3$

12. $(-4x^{-2})(5x^6)$

13. $\dfrac{36a^{10}b^{12}}{9a^5b^4}$

14. $\dfrac{3^9t^{-2}}{3^3t^8}$

15. $\dfrac{p^3(p^{-5})^2}{p^0(2p^{-1})^3}$

Perform the indicated operations.

16. $4p^2(p^2 - 3p + 6)$

17. $(x - 3y)^2$

18. $(p - 3)(p + 3)$

19. $(4t - 5)(3t + 7)$

20. $(2a + 1)(2a^2 - 3a + 4)$

21. $(3m^3 + 5m^2 - 1) - (m^3 - 4m^2 + m - 9)$

22. $\dfrac{12x^3 + 8x^2 - 4x}{4x}$

23. $\dfrac{6r^4 - 18r^3 + 2r^2 + 6r}{6r^2}$

24. $\dfrac{p^2 + 8p + 15}{p + 5}$

25. $\dfrac{4m^3 + 2m^2 - 20}{2m - 3}$

Factoring and Quadratic Equations

If you pull the bottom of a 25-foot ladder 7 feet away from the side of a building, how far will the top of the ladder slide down the side of the building? The answer is not 7 feet. In Section 4.8 we will answer this question by first writing a quadratic equation and then solving the equation by factoring.

4.1 The Greatest Common Factor

In this chapter we learn to perform an operation called *factoring*. Factoring is the reverse of multiplying. For example, we can multiply 6 and 5 to get 30.

$$6 \cdot 5 = 30$$

On the other hand, we can **factor** 30 by writing 30 as the product of 6 and 5.

$$30 = 6 \cdot 5$$

Factors

The integers 6 and 5 are called *factors*, or *divisors*, of 30. We can factor 30 still further.

$$30 = 6 \cdot 5$$
$$30 = 2 \cdot 3 \cdot 5$$

The integers 2, 3, and 5 are called *prime numbers* since they cannot be factored into the product of two other positive integers.

DEFINITION OF A PRIME NUMBER

A positive integer (except 1) whose only factors (divisors) are 1 and itself is called a **prime number,** or simply a **prime.**

During the third century B.C., the Greek mathematician Euclid proved in his monumental work *Elements* that there is an infinite number of primes.

The first ten prime numbers follow.

2, 3, 5, 7, 11, 13, 17, 19, 23, 29

When a number is written as a product of prime numbers, the number is said to be in **prime factored form.** The prime factored forms of whole numbers from 2 through 100 are listed on the inside back cover.

EXAMPLE 1   Write 50 in prime factored form.

Solution   Divide 50 by the first prime, 2.

$$50 = 2 \cdot 25 \qquad \textit{Divide 50 by 2}$$

We cannot divide 25 by the first prime, 2, or by the second prime, 3, so we divide 25 by the third prime, 5.

Try Problem 1 >

$$50 = 2 \cdot 5 \cdot 5 \qquad \textit{Divide 25 by 5}$$
$$50 = 2 \cdot 5^2 \qquad \textit{Write using exponents}$$

DIVISIBILITY TESTS

Here are some shortcuts that tell you whether a whole number is divisible by 2, 3, or 5.

1. A number is *divisible by* 2 if it ends in 0, 2, 4, 6, or 8.
2. A number is *divisible by* 3 if the sum of its digits is divisible by 3. (For example, 261 is divisible by 3, since $2 + 6 + 1 = 9$ is divisible by 3.)
3. A number is *divisible by* 5 if it ends in 0 or 5.

There are divisibility tests for other prime numbers, but we will just use trial and error when testing those divisors.

EXAMPLE 2   Write 180 in prime factored form.

Solution

$$180 = 2 \cdot 90 \qquad \textit{Divide 180 by 2}$$

$$180 = 2 \cdot 2 \cdot 45 \qquad \textit{Divide 90 by 2}$$

$$180 = 2 \cdot 2 \cdot 3 \cdot 15 \qquad \textit{Divide 45 by 3}$$

$$180 = 2 \cdot 2 \cdot 3 \cdot 3 \cdot 5 \qquad \textit{Divide 15 by 3}$$

Try Problem 3 > $\qquad 180 = 2^2 \cdot 3^2 \cdot 5 \qquad \textit{Write using exponents}$ ■

The largest number that is a factor of two or more integers is called the **greatest common factor** (**GCF**) of the integers. For example, the factors of 4 are 1, 2, and 4. (The numbers -1, -2, and -4 are also factors of 4; but when asked to list the factors of an integer we usually just list the positive factors.) The factors of 6 are 1, 2, 3, and 6. The factors common to 4 and 6 are 1 and 2. Therefore the greatest common factor of 4 and 6 is 2.

The next example shows how to find the greatest common factor when it is not obvious from a simple inspection of the integers.

EXAMPLE 3   Find the greatest common factor of 36 and 60.

Solution   Write each number in prime factored form.

$$36 = 2^2 \cdot 3^2$$
$$60 = 2^2 \cdot 3 \cdot 5$$

Take the *lowest* power of each prime factor. The lowest power of 2 is 2^2. The lowest power of 3 is 3^1. Since 5 does not appear in the factorization of 36, it will not appear in the GCF (its lowest power is 5^0, or 1). Multiply the powers 2^2 and 3^1 to obtain the GCF.

Try Problem 11 >

$$GCF = 2^2 \cdot 3 = 12$$ ∎

EXAMPLE 4   Find the greatest common factor of 10, 14, and 21.

Solution   Write each number in prime factored form.

$$10 = 2 \cdot 5$$
$$14 = 2 \cdot 7$$
$$21 = 3 \cdot 7$$

There is no prime factor common to all three numbers. Therefore the GCF is 1.

Try Problem 13 >

∎

TO FIND THE GREATEST COMMON FACTOR (GCF)

1. Write each number in prime factored form.
2. Take the lowest power of each prime factor. If a particular factor does not appear in all of the factorizations, it will not appear in the GCF.
3. Multiply the powers taken in Step 2. If there are none, the GCF is 1.

We can use the same steps to find the greatest common factor of a collection of algebraic terms.

EXAMPLE 5   Find the greatest common factor of $18x^{13}y^4$, $45x^{15}y^3$, and $27x^8y^7$.

Solution

Step 1   *Write each term in prime factored form.*

$$18x^{13}y^4 = 2 \cdot 3^2 \cdot x^{13} \cdot y^4$$
$$45x^{15}y^3 = 3^2 \cdot 5 \cdot x^{15} \cdot y^3$$
$$27x^8y^7 = 3^3 \cdot x^8 \cdot y^7$$

Step 2   *Take the lowest power of each factor.* The lowest power of 3 is 3^2, the lowest power of x is x^8, and the lowest power of y is y^3. Since 2 and 5 do not appear in all of the factorizations, neither 2 nor 5 will appear in the GCF.
Step 3   *Multiply the powers taken in Step 2.*

Try Problem 23 >

$$GCF = 3^2 \cdot x^8 \cdot y^3 = 9x^8y^3$$ ∎

As we have seen, to factor a number means to write the number as a product of two or more simpler numbers. To **factor** a polynomial means to write the polynomial as a product of two or more simpler polynomials. One way of factoring a polynomial is to *factor out* the greatest common factor from the polynomial.

EXAMPLE 6   Factor $5m + 15$.

Solution   The greatest common factor of the terms $5m$ and 15 is 5. Using the distributive property, we can factor out the GCF.

$$5m + 15 = \mathbf{5} \cdot m + \mathbf{5} \cdot 3 \quad \textit{The GCF is 5}$$
$$= 5(m + 3) \quad \textit{Factor out the GCF}$$

Therefore $5m + 15$ in factored form is $5(m + 3)$. You can check this answer by multiplying 5 and $m + 3$.

Try Problem 29 >

> **TO FACTOR OUT THE GREATEST COMMON FACTOR (GCF)**
>
> 1. Find the GCF of the terms of the polynomial.
> 2. Use the distributive property to factor out the GCF.
> 3. Check your answer by multiplication.

EXAMPLE 7   Factor $8x^2 + 12x$.

Solution
$$8x^2 + 12x = \mathbf{4x} \cdot 2x + \mathbf{4x} \cdot 3 \quad \textit{The GCF is 4x}$$
$$= 4x(2x + 3) \quad \textit{Factor out the GCF}$$

Try Problem 33 >   Check by multiplication.

When factoring a polynomial of two or more terms, we usually do not factor the monomials. That's why we wrote the answer to Example 7 as $4x(2x + 3)$ rather than $2 \cdot 2 \cdot x(2x + 3)$.

EXAMPLE 8   Factor $k^5 + k^3$.

Solution
$$k^5 + k^3 = \mathbf{k^3} \cdot k^2 + \mathbf{k^3} \cdot 1 \quad \textit{The GCF is } k^3$$
$$= k^3(k^2 + 1) \quad \textit{Factor out the GCF}$$

Try Problem 35 >   Check by multiplication.

Caution!   Just as some numbers are prime, so are some polynomials prime. A polynomial is a **prime polynomial** when it cannot be written as the product of two simpler polynomials with integer coefficients.

$x - 5$ is a prime polynomial
$2p + 3$ is a prime polynomial

Sometimes we want to change the signs of the terms of a polynomial. We can do this by factoring out -1 from the polynomial.

EXAMPLE 9   Factor out -1 from the polynomial $-2a^2 - 8a + 5$.

Solution

$$
\begin{aligned}
-2a^2 &- 8a + 5 \\
&= (-1)(2a^2) + (-1)(8a) + (-1)(-5) &&\textit{Write each term with the} \\
& &&\textit{factor } -1 \\
&= (-1)[2a^2 + 8a + (-5)] &&\textit{Factor out } -1 \\
&= -(2a^2 + 8a - 5) &&\textit{Simplify}
\end{aligned}
$$

Try Problem 45 >   Check by multiplication.   ■

EXAMPLE 10   Factor $18x^5y^2 - 30x^4y^3 + 24x^3y^4$.

Solution

$$
\begin{aligned}
18x^5y^2 &- 30x^4y^3 + 24x^3y^4 &&\textit{Original polynomial} \\
&= 6x^3y^2(3x^2) - 6x^3y^2(5xy) + 6x^3y\,(4y^2) &&\textit{The GCF is } 6x^3y^2 \\
&= 6x^3y^2(3x^2 - 5xy + 4y^2) &&\textit{Factor out the GCF}
\end{aligned}
$$

Try Problem 55 >   Check by multiplication.   ■

Sometimes the greatest common factor is a binomial. For example, the greatest common factor may be $a + b$, or $2x + 5$.

EXAMPLE 11   Factor $(a + b)x + (a + b)y$.

Solution

$$
\begin{aligned}
(a + b)\; &+ (a + b)y &&\textit{The GCF is } a + b \\
&= (a + b)(x + y) &&\textit{Factor out the GCF}
\end{aligned}
$$

Try Problem 63 >   Check by multiplication.   ■

EXAMPLE 12   Factor $x(x + 3) - 2(x + 3)$.

Solution

$$
\begin{aligned}
x(x + 3) &- 2(x + 3) &&\textit{The GCF is } x + 3 \\
&= (x + 3)(x - 2) &&\textit{Factor out the GCF}
\end{aligned}
$$

Try Problem 65 >   Check by multiplication.   ■

EXAMPLE 13   Factor $(p - 6) + (p - 6)^2$.

Solution

$$
\begin{aligned}
(p - 6) &+ (p - 6)^2 &&\textit{Original polynomial} \\
&= (p - 6)1 + (p - 6)(p - 6) &&\textit{The GCF is } p - 6 \\
&= (p - 6)[1 + (p - 6)] &&\textit{Factor out the GCF} \\
&= (p - 6)(p - 5) &&\textit{Simplify}
\end{aligned}
$$

Try Problem 71 >   Check by multiplication.   ■

4.1 Problem Set

Write each number in prime factored form.

1. 12

2. 18

3. 126

4. 84

5. 37

6. 43

7. 2520

8. 3780

Find the greatest common factor of each collection of numbers.

9. 4, 12

10. 9, 18

11. 36, 90

12. 60, 72

13. 8, 10, 15

14. 6, 9, 10

15. 336, 252, 420

16. 504, 378, 630

Find the greatest common factor of each collection of terms.

17. $7p$, 35

18. $5p$, 55

19. $3x^3$, $5x^6$

20. $2x^2$, $7x^7$

21. $-50x^3$, $75x^5$, $25x^{15}$

22. $27x^2$, $-18x^5$, $9x^{10}$

23. $24x^{15}y^8$, $28x^7y^8$, $36x^{10}y^6$

24. $45x^{12}y^9$, $63x^8y^5$, $72x^6y^{15}$

25. $x(3a - 4)$, $y(3a - 4)$

26. $x(2a + 5)$, $y(2a + 5)$

27. $m + 5$, $(m + 5)^2$

28. $(m - 7)^2$, $m - 7$

Factor out the greatest common factor.

29. $2m + 6$

30. $14x - 7$

31. $6ab - 15ac$

32. $8ab + 14ac$

33. $12x^2 + 20x$

34. $12x^2 - 18x$

35. $k^3 + k$

36. $5y^6 + 8y^5$

37. $36m^{12} - 24m^8$

38. $72m^{15} + 54m^{10}$

39. $3p + 8$

40. $2p - 9$

Factor out -1 from each polynomial.

41. $-x - 2y$

42. $b - a$

43. $r + s - t$

44. $-8m - n + 5$

45. $-4a^2 - 9a + 10$

46. $-6a^2 + 2a - 9$

Factor out the greatest common factor, including -1 if the highest-degree term has a negative coefficient.

47. $3x^2 + 6x + 9$

48. $5x^2 + 10x + 25$

49. $144r^2 + 125rs - 24s^2$

50. $100r^2 - 75r^2s^2 + 36s^2$

51. $-12y^3 + 18y^2 - 6y$

52. $-8y^3 - 12y^2 + 4y$

53. $8z^{75} - 32z^{50} - 16z^{25}$

54. $6z^{90} - 36z^{30} - 12z^{15}$

55. $24x^5y^2 - 36x^3y^3 + 48x^2y^5$

56. $48x^6y^2 - 32x^3y^3 + 80x^2y^6$

57. $30r^8s^5t^3 + 72r^5s^7t - 18r^6s^9$

58. $24r^9s^4t^2 + 40r^5s^7t - 56r^6s^8$

59. $2a^2bc + 5ab^2c + 9abc^2$

60. $3a^3b^2c^2 + 5a^2b^3c^2 + 7a^2b^2c^3$

61. $-22m^{53}p + 55m^{37}p^2 - 33m^{24}p^3 + 11m^{17}p^4$

62. $-13m^{71}p^2 - 39m^{67}p^3 + 26m^{42}p^4 + 52m^{38}p^5$

Factor out the greatest common factor.

63. $(a + 2b)x + (a + 2b)y$

64. $(a - 3b)x + (a - 3b)y$

65. $x(x + 8) - 3(x + 8)$

66. $x(x + 5) - 4(x + 5)$

67. $x(y^2 + 9) - 2(y^2 + 9)$

68. $x(y^2 + 4) + 7(y^2 + 4)$

69. $(4r - 5s)x + (4r - 5s)$

70. $(3r - 2s)x + (3r - 2s)$

71. $(p - 7) + (p - 7)^2$

72. $(p + 6) + (p + 6)^2$

73. $r(r + 1) + (r + 1)$

74. $r(r - 1) - (r - 1)$

Solve each word problem.

75. The total surface area of a right circular cone (Fig. 4.1) with radius r and lateral height ℓ is $\pi r \ell + \pi r^2$. Write this expression in factored form.

76. The total surface area of a right circular cylinder (Fig. 4.2) with radius r and height h is $2\pi r^2 + 2\pi rh$. Write this expression in factored form.

FIGURE 4.1

FIGURE 4.2

4.2 Factoring by Grouping

If a polynomial has four or more terms, sometimes we can find a common factor by grouping the terms. This procedure is called *factoring by grouping*.

EXAMPLE 1   Factor $xy + 4y + 3x + 12$.

Solution   Note that there is no factor (except 1) common to all four terms. However, we can factor y from the first two terms and 3 from the last two terms.

$$xy + 4y + 3x + 12 = y(x + 4) + 3(x + 4) \qquad \textit{Factor out y, factor out 3}$$
$$= (x + 4)(y + 3) \qquad \textit{Factor out the exposed common binomial factor,} \ x + 4$$

Try Problem 3 >   Check by multiplication.   ∎

In Example 1 we could have grouped the first and third terms and the second and fourth terms. The result would have been the same.

$$xy + 4y + 3x + 12 = xy + 3x + 4y + 12 \qquad \textit{Commutative property}$$
$$= x(y + 3) + 4(y + 3) \qquad \textit{Factor out x, factor out 4}$$
$$= (y + 3)(x + 4) \qquad \textit{Factor out y + 3}$$

Since multiplication is commutative, this answer is the same as $(x + 4)(y + 3)$.

> **TO FACTOR BY GROUPING**
>
> 1. Factor a common factor from the first two terms, and factor a common factor from the last two terms.
> 2. Factor out the common binomial factor exposed in Step 1.
> 3. Check by multiplication.

EXAMPLE 2   Factor $t^3 - 5t^2 + 4t - 20$.

Solution

Step 1   Factor t^2 from the first two terms and 4 from the last two terms.

$$t^3 - 5t^2 + 4t - 20 = t^2(t - 5) + 4(t - 5) \quad \textit{Factor out } t^2, \textit{ factor out } 4$$

Step 2   Factor out the common binomial factor, $t - 5$.

$$= (t - 5)(t^2 + 4) \quad \textit{Factor out } t - 5$$

Step 3   Check by multiplication.

Try Problem 9 >

$$(t - 5)(t^2 + 4) = t^3 - 5t^2 + 4t - 20$$

Consider the polynomial

$$2m^2 + 12m - 3m - 18.$$

We could combine the middle terms, $12m$ and $-3m$, to get the trinomial $2m^2 + 9m - 18$. However, in Section 4.4 we shall learn how to factor a trinomial like this by writing the trinomial as a polynomial in four terms and then factoring by grouping. Therefore we shall practice factoring this type of polynomial by grouping.

EXAMPLE 3   Factor $2m^2 + 12m - 3m - 18$.

Solution

$$\begin{aligned} 2m^2 &+ 12m - 3m - 18 \\ &= 2m(m + 6) - 3(m + 6) \quad \textit{Factor out } 2m, \textit{ factor out } -3 \\ &= (m + 6)(2m - 3) \quad \textit{Factor out } m + 6 \end{aligned}$$

Note that we factored out -3 (*not* 3) from the last two terms. Check by multiplication.

Try Problem 13 >

EXAMPLE 4   Factor $k^3 + 8k^2 + k + 8$.

Solution
$$k^3 + 8k^2 + k + 8$$
$$= k^2(k + 8) + 1(k + 8) \quad \textit{Factor out } k^2, \textit{factor out } 1$$
$$= (k + 8)(k^2 + 1) \quad \textit{Factor out } k + 8$$

Try Problem 21 >   Check by multiplication.   ■

Sometimes we must factor out -1 in order to expose a common factor in the polynomial. This changes the sign of every term inside the parentheses.

EXAMPLE 5   Factor $25x^2 - 5x - 5x + 1$.

Solution
$$25x^2 - 5x - 5x + 1 = 5x(5x - 1) - 1(5x - 1) \quad \textit{Factor out } 5x,$$
$$\textit{factor out } -1$$
$$= (5x - 1)(5x - 1) \quad \textit{Factor out } 5x - 1$$
$$= (5x - 1)^2 \quad \textit{Write with an}$$
$$\textit{exponent}$$

Try Problem 29 >   Check by multiplication.   ■

Sometimes all four terms of a polynomial contain a common factor. **Always factor out the greatest common factor before attempting any other type of factoring.**

EXAMPLE 6   Write $4ab + 20b + 8a + 40$ in prime factored form.

Solution
$$4ab + 20b + 8a + 40 = 4(ab + 5b + 2a + 10) \quad \textit{Factor out the}$$
$$\textit{GCF, } 4$$
$$= 4[b(a + 5) + 2(a + 5)] \quad \textit{Factor out } b, \textit{factor}$$
$$\textit{out } 2$$
$$= 4[(a + 5)(b + 2)] \quad \textit{Factor out } a + 5$$
$$= 4(a + 5)(b + 2) \quad \textit{Write without}$$
$$\textit{brackets}$$

Try Problem 39 >   Check by multiplication.   ■

Factoring by grouping works on many polynomials with four terms, but it will not work on every such polynomial.

4.2 Problem Set

LEARNING THROUGH WRITING   ☐ Describe the steps in factoring by grouping.

☐ When might you try to use factoring by grouping?

Factor by grouping.

1. $ax + ay + bx + by$

2. $ax - ay + bx - by$

3. $xy + 3y + 2x + 6$

4. $xy + 2y + 3x + 6$

5. $rs - 8r + 2s - 16$

6. $rs - 6r + 3s - 18$

7. $3x^2 + 3xy + 2x + 2y$

8. $5x^2 + 5xy + 4x + 4y$

9. $t^3 - 6t^2 + 6t - 36$

10. $p^3 + 5p^2 + 4p + 20$

11. $x^2 - x + 7x - 7$

12. $x^2 - x + 9x - 9$

13. $4m^2 + 8m - 3m - 6$

14. $5m^2 + 15m - 2m - 6$

15. $2y^2 - 9y - 4y + 18$

16. $3y^2 - 7y - 6y + 14$

17. $10r^2 + 6rs + 5rs + 3s^2$

18. $20r^2 + 8rs + 5rs + 2s^2$

19. $6x^2 - 14ax + 15ax - 35a^2$

20. $10x^2 - 8ax + 15ax - 12a^2$

21. $k^3 + 5k^2 + k + 5$

22. $k^3 + 7k^2 + k + 7$

23. $t^2 + 2t + t + 2$

24. $t^2 + 3t + t + 3$

25. $p^2 - 8p - p + 8$

26. $p^2 - 6p - p + 6$

27. $m^2 + m + m + 1$

28. $m^2 - m + m - 1$

29. $16x^2 - 4x - 4x + 1$

30. $4x^2 - 2x - 2x + 1$

31. $x^2y - ax - xy + a$

32. $x^2y + bx - xy - b$

33. $12p^2 - 4pq - 3pq + q^2$

34. $10p^2 - 5pq - 2pq + q^2$

35. $25k^3 - 75k^2 - 6k + 18$

36. $15k^3 - 90k^2 - 2k + 12$

Write in prime factored form.

37. $2ax - 2ay + 2bx - 2by$

38. $8ax + 8ay + 8bx + 8by$

39. $5ab + 20b + 10a + 40$

40. $3ab + 18b + 9a + 54$

41. $36p^3 - 72p^2 + 48p - 96$

42. $24p^3 - 72p^2 + 60p - 180$

43. $9r^4s + 63r^3s^2 - 2r^3s^2 - 14r^2s^3$

44. $7r^4s + 42r^3s^2 - 3r^3s^2 - 18r^2s^3$

45. $4xy^2 - 4y^2 - 4xy + 4y$

46. $6xy^2 + 6y^2 - 6xy - 6y$

47. $x^2 - xy + x + 3x - 3y + 3$

48. $x^2 + xy - x + 6x + 6y - 6$

Solve each word problem.

49. The expression $P(1 + r) + P(1 + r)r$ represents the value of a savings account after 2 years if the interest is compounded annually. P is the principal (initial investment) and r is the interest rate, in decimal form. Factor this expression.

50. The expression $P(1 + r)^2 + P(1 + r)^2r$ represents the value of a savings account after 3 years if the interest is compounded annually. P is the principal (initial investment) and r is the interest rate, in decimal form. Factor this expression.

4.3 Factoring $x^2 + bx + c$

In this section we learn to factor trinomials of the form $ax^2 + bx + c$ with $a = 1$. In the trinomial $ax^2 + bx + c$, the number a is called the **leading coefficient,** the number b is called the **middle coefficient,** and the number c is called the **constant term.**

Recall the FOIL method for multiplying two binomials.

$$
\begin{array}{cccc}
F & O & I & L \\
\downarrow & \downarrow & \downarrow & \downarrow
\end{array}
$$

$$(x + 2)(x + 3) = x^2 + 3x + 2x + 6 = x^2 + 5x + 6$$

In Example 1 we learn how to write the trinomial $x^2 + 5x + 6$ as the product of the two binomials $x + 2$ and $x + 3$.

EXAMPLE 1   Factor $x^2 + 5x + 6$.

Solution   If the trinomial $x^2 + 5x + 6$ is to be written as the product of two binomials, then the product of the two first terms of the binomials must be x^2. Therefore the first term of each binomial must be x.

$$
\overset{\displaystyle x^2}{\overbrace{\qquad\qquad}}
$$

$$x^2 + 5x + 6 = (x\qquad)(x\qquad)$$

Trinomial   Two binomials

Since the last term of the trinomial is 6, the product of the two last terms of the binomials must be 6. Therefore list all pairs of integers whose product is 6.

$$6 = 1 \cdot 6$$
$$6 = 2 \cdot 3$$
$$6 = (-1)(-6)$$
$$6 = (-2)(-3)$$

The four ways to factor 6 suggest four possible ways to factor $x^2 + 5x + 6$.

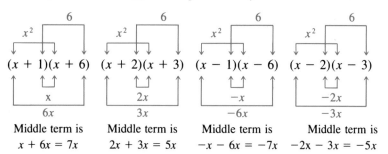

Middle term is	Middle term is	Middle term is	Middle term is
$x + 6x = 7x$	$2x + 3x = 5x$	$-x - 6x = -7x$	$-2x - 3x = -5x$

Of the four possible factorizations, the only one that yields the correct middle term is the second one. Therefore the correct factorization is

$$x^2 + 5x + 6 = (x + 2)(x + 3).$$

Since multiplication is commutative, we can also write our answer as

$$x^2 + 5x + 6 = (x + 3)(x + 2).$$

Try Problem 1 >   We can check this factorization by multiplying $x + 2$ and $x + 3$.   ∎

TO FACTOR A TRINOMIAL OF THE FORM $x^2 + bx + c$

1. List all pairs of integers whose product is c.
2. Find the pair of integers listed in Step 1, say m and n, whose sum is b.
3. Factor the trinomial as follows.

   $$x^2 + bx + c = (x + m)(x + n)$$

4. Check by multiplication.

EXAMPLE 2   Factor $x^2 - 7x + 10$.

Solution   We need a pair of integers whose product is 10 and whose sum is -7.

Step 1   List all pairs of integers whose product is 10.

↓

Product
$1 \cdot 10$
$2 \cdot 5$
$-1(-10)$
$-2(-5)$

Step 2   Find the pair whose sum is -7.

↓

Sum
$1 + 10 = 11$
$2 + 5 = 7$
$-1 + (-10) = -11$
$-2 + (-5) = -7$

The integers -2 and -5 have a product of 10 and a sum of -7.

Step 3   Factor the trinomial as follows.

$$x^2 - 7x + 10 = [x + (-2)][x + (-5)]$$
$$= (x - 2)(x - 5)$$

Step 4   Check by multiplication.

Try Problem 5 >

$$(x - 2)(x - 5) = x^2 - 7x + 10$$

If a trinomial is not already in descending order, write the trinomial in descending order before attempting to factor it.

EXAMPLE 3   Factor $m + m^2 - 12$.

Solution   Write the trinomial in descending order as $m^2 + m - 12$. Then find a pair of integers whose product is -12 and whose sum is 1.

Product	Sum
$1(-12)$	$1 + (-12) = -11$
$2(-6)$	$2 + (-6) = -4$
$3(-4)$	$3 + (-4) = -1$
$-1 \cdot 12$	$-1 + 12 = 11$
$-2 \cdot 6$	$-2 + 6 = 4$
$-3 \cdot 4$	$-3 + 4 = 1$

Therefore

$$m + m^2 - 12 = m^2 + m - 12 = (m - 3)(m + 4).$$

Try Problem 11 >   Check by multiplication. ■

EXAMPLE 4   Factor $p^2 - 3p + 4$.

Solution

Product	Sum
$1 \cdot 4$	$1 + 4 = 5$
$2 \cdot 2$	$2 + 2 = 4$
$-1(-4)$	$-1 + (-4) = -5$
$-2(-2)$	$-2 + (-2) = -4$

Try Problem 15 >   There is no pair of integers whose product is 4 and whose sum is -3. Therefore $p^2 - 3p + 4$ is a prime polynomial. ■

Some of the possibilities in Examples 1 through 4 could have been eliminated immediately. We illustrate how to do this in Examples 5, 6, and 7.

EXAMPLE 5   Factor $x^2 - 9x + 8$.

Solution   The last term is positive, so the factors of 8 must have the same sign. Since the sum of the factors must be -9, both factors must be negative.

Product	Sum	
$-1(-8)$	$-1 + (-8) = -9$	*Stop*
$-2(-4)$		

Try Problem 19 >   Therefore $x^2 - 9x + 8 = (x - 1)(x - 8)$. Check by multiplication. ■

In Example 5 note that we stopped as soon as we found a pair of integers whose product was 8 and whose sum was -9. We stopped because **a poly-**

nomial has one and only one prime factored form. Therefore once we find a prime factored form, we are wasting our time looking for another—there are no others. (Note: We can change the appearance of a prime factored form by factoring out 1 or -1. However, since 1 is not a prime, this is not considered to be a *different* prime factored form.)

EXAMPLE 6   Factor $y^2 - 13y - 30$.

Solution   The last term is negative, so the factors of -30 must have different signs. Since the sum of the factors must be -13, consider only those factors whose sum is negative.

Product	Sum	
$1(-30)$	-29	
$2(-15)$	-13	*Stop*
$3(-10)$		
$5(-6)$		

Try Problem 23 >   Therefore $y^2 - 13y - 30 = (y + 2)(y - 15)$. Check by multiplication.   ■

We can use the same steps to factor a trinomial in two variables.

EXAMPLE 7   Factor $x^2 + 2xy - 15y^2$.

Solution   The last term is negative, so the factors of -15 must have different signs. Since the sum of the factors must be 2, consider only those factors whose sum is positive.

Product	Sum	
$-1 \cdot 15$	14	
$-3 \cdot 5$	2	*Stop*

Try Problem 29 >   Therefore $x^2 + 2xy - 15y^2 = (x - 3y)(x + 5y)$. Check by multiplication.   ■

Caution! ■   When factoring a polynomial in two variables, remember to include both variables in the binomial factors.

Correct	*Wrong*
$x^2 + 7xy + 12y^2$	$x^2 + 7xy + 12y^2$
$= (x + 3y)(x + 4y)$	$= (x + 3)(x + 4)$

When the leading coefficient of the trinomial is -1, begin by factoring out -1 from the trinomial.

EXAMPLE 8   Factor $-x^2 + 11x - 18$.

Solution
$$-x^2 + 11x - 18 = -(x^2 - 11x + 18) \quad \text{\textit{Factor out} } -1$$
$$= -(x - 2)(x - 9) \quad \text{\textit{Factor the trinomial}}$$

Try Problem 37 >   Check by multiplication.   ■

If the terms of a trinomial contain a common factor, factor out the greatest common factor before attempting any other type of factoring.

EXAMPLE 9   Write $5r^4 - 55r^3 + 50r^2$ in prime factored form.

Solution
$$5r^4 - 55r^3 + 50r^2 = 5r^2(r^2 - 11r + 10) \quad \text{\textit{Factor out the GCF}}$$
$$= 5r^2(r - 1)(r - 10) \quad \text{\textit{Factor the trinomial}}$$

Try Problem 49 >   Check by multiplication.   ■

4.3   Problem Set

LEARNING THROUGH WRITING

□ Consider the trinomial $ax^2 + bx + c$. What is a called? What is b called? What is c called?

□ Describe the steps in factoring $x^2 + bx + c$.

□ Discuss shortcuts you can use when factoring $x^2 + bx + c$.

Factor each trinomial.

1. $x^2 + 8x + 15$
2. $x^2 + 7x + 10$
3. $x^2 + 4x + 4$
4. $x^2 + 6x + 9$
5. $x^2 - 5x + 6$
6. $x^2 - 8x + 15$
7. $y^2 - 5y + 4$
8. $y^2 - 7y + 6$
9. $y^2 - 15y + 54$
10. $y^2 - 12y + 32$
11. $4m + m^2 - 12$
12. $3m + m^2 - 18$
13. $m^2 - m - 12$
14. $m^2 - 7m - 18$
15. $p^2 + 5p - 4$
16. $p^2 + 10p - 9$
17. $z^2 - 23z - 24$
18. $z^2 - 35z - 36$
19. $x^2 - 15x + 14$
20. $x^2 - 16x + 15$
21. $t^2 + 14t - 51$
22. $t^2 + 16t - 57$
23. $y^2 - 8y - 20$
24. $y^2 - 18y - 40$

Factor each trinomial.

25. $x^2 + 12xy + 35y^2$
26. $x^2 - 9xy + 18y^2$
27. $m^2 - 10mn + 25n^2$
28. $m^2 + 10mn + 25n^2$
29. $x^2 + 3xy - 28y^2$
30. $x^2 + xy - 20y^2$
31. $r^2 - 5rs - 6s^2$
32. $r^2 - 3rs - 4s^2$
33. $z^2 + 6zk - 18k^2$
34. $z^2 + 8zk - 24k^2$
35. $p^2 + 36q^2 - 13pq$
36. $p^2 + 36q^2 - 15pq$

Factor out -1. Then factor the trinomial.

37. $-x^2 + 11x - 10$
38. $-y^2 - 6y + 55$
39. $45 + 4z - z^2$
40. $35 + 2z - z^2$
41. $-r^2 - 11rs - 30s^2$
42. $-r^2 - 11rs - 28s^2$

Write in prime factored form.

43. $4x^2 + 16x + 16$
44. $4x^2 + 24x + 36$
45. $a^4 + 2a^3 + a^2$

46. $a^4 - 2a^3 + a^2$

47. $m^3 + 6m^2 - 27m$

48. $m^3 + 6m^2 - 16m$

49. $5r^4 - 60r^3 + 55r^2$

50. $5r^4 - 70r^3 + 65r^2$

51. $-10p^3q - 50p^2q^2 + 360pq^3$

52. $-10p^3q - 90p^2q^2 + 360pq^3$

53. $6a^2x^5 - 48a^2x^4 - 72a^2x^3$

54. $8a^2x^5 - 56a^2x^4 - 96a^2x^3$

Factor each polynomial.

55. $t^4 + 5t^2 + 6$

56. $t^4 + 7t^2 + 10$

57. $k^6 + 3k^3 - 10$

58. $k^6 - 2k^3 - 15$

59. $x^4 + 4x^2y^2 + 3y^4$

60. $x^4 + 6x^2y^2 + 5y^4$

Solve each word problem.

61. What polynomial has $(2x - 3)(x + 5)$ as its prime factored form?

62. The prime factored form of $2x^2 + 12x + 18$ is *not* $(2x + 6)(x + 3)$. Why?

4.4   Factoring $ax^2 + bx + c$

In this section we learn to factor trinomials of the form $ax^2 + bx + c$ with $a \neq 1$.

EXAMPLE 1   Factor $2x^2 + 7x + 3$.

Solution   Consider all combinations of binomial factors whose first terms multiply to $2x^2$ and whose last terms multiply to 3. We prefer that the first term in each binomial be positive, so we consider only positive factors of 2.

Possible factors	*Middle term*
$(2x + 3)(x + 1)$	$5x$
$(2x + 1)(x + 3)$	$7x$
$(2x - 3)(x - 1)$	$-5x$
$(2x - 1)(x - 3)$	$-7x$

The second factorization produces the correct middle term, $7x$. Therefore

$$2x^2 + 7x + 3 = (2x + 1)(x + 3).$$

Try Problem 1 >   To check, find the product of $2x + 1$ and $x + 3$.   ■

In Example 1 we could have eliminated immediately the last two factorizations using the following rule.

TRINOMIAL FACTORING SHORTCUT

If all terms of a trinomial are positive, all terms of its binomial factors will be positive.

EXAMPLE 2   Factor $6y^2 - y - 2$.

Solution   Consider binomials whose first terms multiply to $6y^2$ and whose last terms multiply to -2. Since the last term of the trinomial is negative, the last terms of the binomials must have different signs.

Possible factors	Middle term
$(6y + 1)(y - 2)$	$-11y$
$(6y - 1)(y + 2)$	$11y$
$(3y + 2)(2y - 1)$	y
$(3y - 2)(2y + 1)$	$-y$

Try Problem 11 >   Therefore $6y^2 - y - 2 = (3y - 2)(2y + 1)$. Check by multiplication.   ■

Note that we did not consider factorizations such as $(6y + 2)(y - 1)$ in Example 2. Since $6y + 2$ has the common factor 2, this factorization can be written as $2(3y + 1)(y - 1)$. But this would mean the original trinomial, $6y^2 - y - 2$, has the common factor 2, which it does not. This suggests the following rule.

TRINOMIAL FACTORING SHORTCUT

If a trinomial has no common factor, neither of its binomial factors will have a common factor.

EXAMPLE 3   Factor $4m^2 + 5m - 6$.

Solution   The trinomial has no common factor. Therefore neither of its binomial factors will have a common factor. This leaves only the following factorizations to consider.

(Thừa số)

Possible factors	Middle term
$(4m + 1)(m - 6)$	$-23m$
$(4m - 1)(m + 6)$	$23m$
$(4m + 3)(m - 2)$	$-5m$
$(4m - 3)(m + 2)$	$5m$

Try Problem 23 >   Therefore $4m^2 + 5m - 6 = (4m - 3)(m + 2)$. Check by multiplication.   ■

EXAMPLE 4   Factor $3z^2 + 2z + 5$.

Solution   Since all terms of the trinomial are positive, all terms of its binomial factors will be positive.

$$\begin{array}{ll} \underline{\textit{Possible factors}} & \underline{\textit{Middle term}} \\ (3z + 5)(z + 1) & 8z \\ (3z + 1)(z + 5) & 16z \end{array}$$

Try Problem 27 >

Neither factorization yields the correct middle term, so the trinomial $3z^2 + 2z + 5$ is a prime polynomial.   ■

We can use the same technique to factor a trinomial in two variables.

EXAMPLE 5   Factor $21a^2 - 19ab + 4b^2$.

Solution   The last term is positive, so the last terms of the factors must have the same sign. That common sign is negative, since the middle term of the trinomial is negative.

$$\begin{array}{ll} \underline{\textit{Possible factors}} & \underline{\textit{Middle term}} \\ (21a - 4b)(a - b) & -25ab \\ (21a - b)(a - 4b) & -85ab \\ (21a - 2b)(a - 2b) & -44ab \\ (7a - 4b)(3a - b) & -19ab \\ (7a - b)(3a - 4b) & -31ab \\ (7a - 2b)(3a - 2b) & -20ab \end{array}$$

Try Problem 35 >

Therefore $21a^2 - 19ab + 4b^2 = (7a - 4b)(3a - b)$. Check by multiplication.   ■

Remember to factor out the greatest common factor before attempting any other type of factoring.

EXAMPLE 6   Write $-12r^2 + 26r + 16$ in prime factored form.

Solution
$$\begin{aligned} -12r^2 + 26r + 16 &= -2(6r^2 - 13r - 8) && \textit{Factor out the GCF, } -2 \\ &= -2(3r - 8)(2r + 1) && \textit{Factor the trinomial in} \\ &&& \textit{parentheses} \end{aligned}$$

Try Problem 55 >   Check by multiplication.   ■

An Alternate Method for Factoring $ax^2 + bx + c$

Another method for factoring $ax^2 + bx + c$ uses factoring by grouping. This method often takes longer than trial and error, but it is more systematic.

TO FACTOR $ax^2 + bx + c$ $(a \neq 1)$ BY GROUPING

1. List all pairs of integers whose product is ac.
2. Find the pair of integers listed in Step 1, say m and n, whose sum is b.
3. Rewrite the trinomial, splitting the middle term as follows.

   $bx = mx + nx$

4. Factor the resulting polynomial of four terms by grouping.
5. Check by multiplication.

We illustrate this method using the trinomials originally given in Examples 1, 2, and 3.

EXAMPLE 7   Factor $2x^2 + 7x + 3$.

Solution   First note that $a = 2$, $b = 7$, and $c = 3$. Therefore $ac = 2 \cdot 3 = 6$.

Step 1 List all pairs of integers whose product is 6.

↓

Product

$1 \cdot 6$
$2 \cdot 3$

Step 2 Find the pair whose sum is 7.

↓

Sum

$1 + 6 = 7$ *Stop*

Since 6 is positive, the factors of 6 must have the same sign. Since their sum must be 7, we considered only those factors whose sum is positive. Therefore 1 and 6 are the integers whose product is 6 and whose sum is 7.

Step 3 Rewrite the trinomial, splitting the middle term as follows: $7x = 1x + 6x$.

   $2x^2 + 7x + 3 = 2x^2 + x + 6x + 3$

Step 4 Factor by grouping.

$$
\begin{aligned}
&= (2x^2 + x) + (6x + 3) &&\text{\textit{Group}} \\
&= x(2x + 1) + 3(2x + 1) &&\text{\textit{Factor each group}} \\
&= (2x + 1)(x + 3) &&\text{\textit{Factor out } 2x + 1}
\end{aligned}
$$

Try Problem 1 >   **Step 5** Check by multiplication.   ∎

If we had written the middle term in Example 7 as $6x + x$ rather than $x + 6x$, the result would have been the same.

$$2x^2 + 7x + 3 = 2x^2 + 6x + x + 3 \quad \textit{Split the middle term}$$
$$= 2x(x + 3) + 1(x + 3) \quad \textit{Factor out } 2x, \textit{ factor out } 1$$
$$= (x + 3)(2x + 1) \quad \textit{Factor out } x + 3$$

Only the order of the factors has been changed. Since multiplication is commutative, the two answers are equal.

EXAMPLE 8   Factor $6y^2 - y - 2$.

Solution   List all pairs of integers whose product is $ac = 6(-2) = -12$. Then find the pair whose sum is $b = -1$.

Product	Sum
$1(-12)$	$1 + (-12) = -11$
$2(-6)$	$2 + (-6) = -4$
$3(-4)$	$3 + (-4) = -1$ *Stop*

Since -12 is negative, the factors of -12 must have different signs. Since their sum must be -1, we considered only those factors whose sum is negative.

$$6y^2 - y - 2 = 6y^2 + 3y - 4y - 2 \quad \textit{Rewrite, splitting the middle}$$
$$\textit{term as follows:}$$
$$-y = 3y - 4y$$
$$= 3y(2y + 1) - 2(2y + 1) \quad \textit{Factor by grouping}$$
$$= (2y + 1)(3y - 2)$$

Try Problem 11 >   Check by multiplication.   ■

EXAMPLE 9   Factor $4m^2 + 5m - 6$.

Solution   Note that $ac = 4(-6) = -24$ and $b = 5$. Consider only those factors of -24 whose sum is positive.

Product	Sum
$-1 \cdot 24$	23
$-2 \cdot 12$	10
$-3 \cdot 8$	5 *Stop*
$-4 \cdot 6$	

$$4m^2 + 5m - 6 = 4m^2 - 3m + 8m - 6 \quad \textit{Rewrite, splitting the}$$
$$\textit{middle term}$$
$$= m(4m - 3) + 2(4m - 3) \quad \textit{Factor by grouping}$$
$$= (4m - 3)(m + 2)$$

Try Problem 23 >   Check by multiplication.   ■

4.4 Problem Set

LEARNING THROUGH WRITING

☐ Describe the steps in factoring $ax^2 + bx + c$.

Factor each trinomial.

1. $2x^2 + 11x + 5$
2. $3x^2 + 7x + 2$
3. $2z^2 - 7z + 5$
4. $3z^2 - 10z + 7$
5. $7p^2 - 16p + 4$
6. $5p^2 - 12p + 4$
7. $5m^2 + 2m - 3$
8. $7m^2 + 4m - 3$
9. $6r^2 + 11r - 2$
10. $6r^2 + r - 7$
11. $6y^2 - 7y - 5$
12. $6y^2 - 7y - 3$
13. $6t^2 + 19t + 10$
14. $6t^2 + 25t + 14$
15. $6 + 11x + 4x^2$
16. $6 + 29x + 9x^2$
17. $4y^2 - 12y + 9$
18. $9y^2 - 12y + 4$
19. $8k^2 - 10k - 3$
20. $8k^2 - 18k - 5$
21. $48z + 20z^2 - 5$
22. $28z + 20z^2 - 3$
23. $4m^2 + m - 14$
24. $4m^2 + 3m - 10$
25. $20p^2 - 9p - 20$
26. $12p^2 - 7p - 12$
27. $3z^2 + 11z + 7$
28. $2z^2 + 8z + 5$
29. $36r^2 - 5r - 24$
30. $36r^2 - 13r - 40$

Factor each trinomial.

31. $2x^2 + 5xy + 3y^2$
32. $2x^2 + 7xy + 5y^2$
33. $4p^2 - 8pq + 3q^2$
34. $4p^2 - 12pq + 5q^2$
35. $10a^2 - 23ab + 9b^2$
36. $15x^2 - 17xy + 4y^2$
37. $3r^2 + 14rs - 5s^2$
38. $3r^2 + 20rs - 7s^2$
39. $8m^2 - 2mn - 21n^2$
40. $12m^2 - 7mn - 10n^2$
41. $12c^2 + 7cd - 12d^2$
42. $20c^2 + 9cd - 20d^2$
43. $6x^2 + 3xy - 8y^2$
44. $6a^2 + 5ab - 8b^2$
45. $25p^2 - 30pq + 9q^2$
46. $49p^2 - 28pq + 4q^2$
47. $12m^2 + 10n^2 - 23mn$
48. $10m^2 - 12n^2 - 7mn$

Write in prime factored form.

49. $10x^2 + 16x + 6$
50. $14x^2 + 18x + 4$
51. $24y^2 - 28y + 8$
52. $24y^2 - 52y + 20$
53. $-4x^2 - 13x - 3$
54. $-4x^2 - 7x - 3$
55. $-12r^2 + 26r + 10$
56. $-30r^2 + 4r + 2$
57. $9z^5 + 6z^4 + z^3$
58. $4z^6 + 4z^5 + z^4$
59. $10p^2 - 210p + 100p^3$
60. $10p^2 - 60p + 150p^3$
61. $24m^4n - 7m^3n^2 - 6m^2n^3$
62. $40m^4n - m^3n^2 - 6m^2n^3$
63. $12p^6q - 15p^5q + 30p^4q$
64. $20p^6q - 15p^5q + 75p^4q$
65. $-18a^3b - 3a^2b^2 + 105ab^3$
66. $-30a^3b - 5a^2b^2 + 200ab^3$

Factor each polynomial.

67. $2x^4 - x^2y^2 - 3y^4$
68. $3x^4 + x^2y^2 - 2y^4$
69. $5x^6 + 8x^3y + 3y^2$
70. $7x^6 + 9x^3y + 2y^2$

71. What polynomial has $(3x - 4)(3x + 4)$ as its factored form?
72. What polynomial has $(x + 2)(x^2 - 2x + 4)$ as its factored form?

4.5 Special Factorizations

In this section we discuss three special types of polynomials, each of which can be factored using a specific rule. By memorizing these rules, we can avoid trial and error in factoring such polynomials.

Difference of Two Squares

Recall that the product of the sum and the difference of two terms is

$$(a + b)(a - b) = a^2 - b^2.$$

If we turn this equation around, we have the rule for factoring the expression on the right side of the equation. This expression is called the *difference of two squares*.

DIFFERENCE OF TWO SQUARES

$$a^2 - b^2 = (a + b)(a - b)$$

EXAMPLE 1   Factor $x^2 - 36$.

Solution   Since x^2 is the square of x, and 36 is the square of 6, we say that $x^2 - 36$ is the difference of two squares. Apply the difference-of-two-squares rule, and factor as follows.

$$x^2 - 36 = x^2 - 6^2$$
$$= (x + 6)(x - 6)$$

Try Problem 1 >   Check by multiplication.   ■

EXAMPLE 2   Factor $4r^2 - 25$.

Solution   Since $4r^2 = (2r)^2$ and $25 = 5^2$, we have a difference of two squares.

$$4r^2 - 25 = (2r)^2 - 5^2$$
$$= (2r + 5)(2r - 5)$$

Try Problem 5 >   Check by multiplication.   ■

Caution! ■   The *sum* of two squares, $a^2 + b^2$, is a prime polynomial and cannot be factored
■   using integers.
■
■
■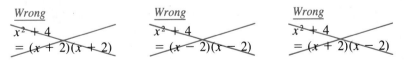
■
■

EXAMPLE 3   Factor each polynomial.

a. $y^2 - \dfrac{9}{16} = y^2 - \left(\dfrac{3}{4}\right)^2 = \left(y + \dfrac{3}{4}\right)\left(y - \dfrac{3}{4}\right)$

b. $100x^2 - 81y^2 = (10x)^2 - (9y)^2 = (10x + 9y)(10x - 9y)$

c. $m^4 - 49 = (m^2)^2 - 7^2 = (m^2 + 7)(m^2 - 7)$

Try Problem 17 >   Neither $m^2 + 7$ nor $m^2 - 7$ can be factored further using integers.   ■

As before, factor out the greatest common factor before attempting any other type of factoring.

EXAMPLE 4   Factor $-8t^6 + 8t^2$.

Solution

$$-8t^6 + 8t^2 = -8t^2(t^4 - 1) \qquad \text{\textit{Factor out the GCF,} } -8t^2$$
$$= -8t^2(t^2 + 1)(t^2 - 1) \qquad \text{\textit{Factor the difference of two}}$$
$$\text{\textit{squares, }} t^4 - 1$$
$$= -8t^2(t^2 + 1)(t + 1)(t - 1) \qquad \text{\textit{Factor }} t^2 - 1 \text{ \textit{(remember,}}$$
$$t^2 + 1 \text{ \textit{is prime})}$$

Try Problem 25 >

Perfect-Square Trinomials

The expressions 121, $9x^2$, and $25p^4$ are called *perfect squares*, since each can be written as the square of another quantity.

$$121 = 11^2 \qquad 9x^2 = (3x)^2 \qquad 25p^4 = (5p^2)^2$$

Recall the rules for squaring a binomial.

$$(a + b)^2 = a^2 + 2ab + b^2$$
$$(a - b)^2 = a^2 - 2ab + b^2$$

If we turn these equations around, we have rules for factoring the two expressions on the right. The expressions $a^2 + 2ab + b^2$ and $a^2 - 2ab + b^2$ are called **perfect-square trinomials,** since each is the square of a binomial.

PERFECT-SQUARE TRINOMIALS

$$a^2 + 2ab + b^2 = (a + b)^2$$
$$a^2 - 2ab + b^2 = (a - b)^2$$

We can recognize a perfect-square trinomial by its terms: Its first and last terms are perfect squares, and its middle term is twice the product of the two terms of the squared binomial.

$$a^2 \quad + \quad 2ab \quad + \quad b^2 \quad = \quad (a + b)^2$$

a^2	$2ab$	b^2	$(a + b)^2$
↑	↑	↑	↑
perfect square	*twice the product of the terms of the squared binomial*	*perfect square*	*squared binomial*
↓	↓	↓	↓

$$a^2 \quad - \quad 2ab \quad + \quad b^2 \quad = \quad (a - b)^2$$

EXAMPLE 5   Factor $x^2 + 6x + 9$.

Solution   Note that x^2 and 9 are perfect squares. Since the middle term is positive, this suggests that

$$x^2 + 6x + 9 = (x + 3)^2.$$

To check, take twice the product of the two terms of the squared binomial.

$$2(x)(3) = 6x$$

Try Problem 29 >

Since $6x$ is the middle term of the trinomial, the trinomial is a perfect-square trinomial, and its factored form is $(x + 3)^2$. Check by multiplication.   ■

EXAMPLE 6   Factor $y^2 - 24y + 144$.

Solution   Note that y^2 and 144 are perfect squares. Since the middle term is negative, this suggests that

$$y^2 - 24y + 144 = (y - 12)^2.$$

To check, take twice the product of the two terms of the squared binomial.

$$2(y)(-12) = -24y$$

Since $-24y$ is the middle term of the trinomial, the trinomial is a perfect-square trinomial, and its factored form is $(y - 12)^2$. Check by multiplication.

Try Problem 31 >

■

Caution! ■ The first and last terms of $x^2 + 13x + 36$ are perfect squares, but the middle
■ term is not twice the product of x and 6. Therefore $x^2 + 13x + 36$ is not a
■ perfect-square trinomial.
■
■
■   *Correct*   *Wrong*
■ $x^2 + 13x + 36 = (x + 4)(x + 9)$ $\cancel{x^2 + 13x + 36 = (x + 6)^2}$

EXAMPLE 7   Factor $4m^2 - 20m + 25$.

Solution   Since $4m^2 = (2m)^2$ and $25 = 5^2$, the first and last terms are perfect squares. Also, the middle term is twice the product of $2m$ and -5. Therefore $4m^2 - 20m + 25$ is a perfect-square trinomial, and

Try Problem 35 >

$$4m^2 - 20m + 25 = (2m - 5)^2.$$ ■

EXAMPLE 8   Factor $45p^2 - 120pq + 80q^2$.

Solution

$$\begin{aligned} 45p^2 - 120pq + 80q^2 &= 5(9p^2 - 24pq + 16q^2) && \textit{Factor out the GCF, 5} \\ &= 5(3p - 4q)^2 && \textit{Factor the perfect-} \end{aligned}$$

Try Problem 43 >

square trinomial   ■

Sum and Difference of Two Cubes

We can factor both the sum and the difference of two cubes using the following rules. (It may help you remember them if you keep in mind that each factorization has exactly one negative sign.)

SUM AND DIFFERENCE OF TWO CUBES

$$a^3 + b^3 = (a + b)(a^2 - ab + b^2)$$
$$a^3 - b^3 = (a - b)(a^2 + ab + b^2)$$

We verify the first rule simply by computing the product on the right side of the equation.

$$
\begin{array}{r}
a^2 - ab\ + b^2 \\
a\ + b \\
\hline
a^2 b\ - ab^2 + b^3 \\
a^3 - a^2 b\ + ab^2 \\
\hline
a^3 \qquad\qquad + b^3
\end{array}
$$

To verify the second rule, compute the product $(a - b)(a^2 + ab + b^2)$.

EXAMPLE 9 Factor $x^3 + 8$.

Solution Since x^3 is the cube of x and 8 is the cube of 2, we say that $x^3 + 8$ is the sum of two cubes. Apply the sum-of-two-cubes rule and factor.

$$
\begin{aligned}
x^3 + 8 &= x^3 + 2^3 \\
&= (x + 2)(x^2 - x \cdot 2 + 2^2) \\
&= (x + 2)(x^2 - 2x + 4)
\end{aligned}
$$

Try Problem 47 >   Check by multiplication.   ∎

Caution! ∎ Do not confuse $a^2 - ab + b^2$, the second factor in the sum-of-two-cubes rule, with the perfect-square trinomial $a^2 - 2ab + b^2$. We cannot factor $a^2 - ab + b^2$.

EXAMPLE 10 Factor $m^3 - 125$.

Solution Since m^3 is the cube of m and 125 is the cube of 5, apply the difference-of-two-cubes rule.

$$
\begin{aligned}
m^3 - 125 &= m^3 - 5^3 \\
&= (m - 5)(m^2 + m \cdot 5 + 5^2) \\
&= (m - 5)(m^2 + 5m + 25)
\end{aligned}
$$

Try Problem 49 >   Check by multiplication.   ∎

EXAMPLE 11   Factor $64r^3 + 1$.

Solution   Since $64r^3 = (4r)^3$ and $1 = 1^3$, apply the sum-of-two-cubes rule.

$$64r^3 + 1 = (4r)^3 + 1^3$$
$$= (4r + 1)[(4r)^2 - (4r)(1) + 1^2]$$
$$= (4r + 1)(16r^2 - 4r + 1)$$

Try Problem 51 >

EXAMPLE 12   Factor $x^6 + 216y^3$.

Solution

$$x^6 + 216y^3 = (x^2)^3 + (6y)^3$$
$$= (x^2 + 6y)[(x^2)^2 - (x^2)(6y) + (6y)^2]$$
$$= (x^2 + 6y)(x^4 - 6x^2y + 36y^2)$$

Try Problem 59 >

4.5   Problem Set

LEARNING THROUGH WRITING

☐ Describe how to recognize and factor a difference of two squares.

☐ Describe how to recognize and factor a perfect-square trinomial.

☐ Describe how to recognize and factor both a sum and a difference of two cubes.

Factor as much as possible.

1. $x^2 - 4$ **2.** $y^2 - 49$ **3.** $m^2 - n^2$ **4.** $p^2 - q^2$

5. $9r^2 - 25$ **6.** $4r^2 - 81$ **7.** $x^2 + 9$ **8.** $x^2 + 25$

9. $y^2 - \dfrac{16}{81}$ **10.** $y^2 - \dfrac{49}{100}$ **11.** $36 - z^2$ **12.** $64 - z^2$

13. $4p^2 - q^2$ **14.** $9m^2 - n^2$ **15.** $m^2 + n^2$ **16.** $p^2 + q^2$

17. $121x^2 - 81y^2$ **18.** $144x^2 - 25y^2$ **19.** $r^2s^2 - 169$ **20.** $r^2s^2 - 225$

21. $m^4 - 9$ **22.** $m^4 - 25$ **23.** $7x^4 - 7$ **24.** $5x^4 - 5$

25. $-3t^6 + 48t^2$ **26.** $-2t^7 + 162t^3$ **27.** $324x^5 - 64xy^4$ **28.** $48x^4y - 243y^5$

Factor as much as possible.

29. $x^2 + 10x + 25$ **30.** $x^2 - 8x + 16$ **31.** $y^2 - 22y + 121$

32. $y^2 - 26y + 169$ **33.** $1 + 6r + 9r^2$ **34.** $1 + 10r + 25r^2$

35. $4m^2 - 12m + 9$ **36.** $9m^2 - 24m + 16$ **37.** $x^2 + 10x + 16$

38. $x^2 + 20x + 64$ **39.** $y^2 - 7y + 49$ **40.** $y^2 - 5y + 25$

41. $25a^2 + 20ab + 4b^2$ **42.** $25a^2 + 30ab + 9b^2$ **43.** $2p^2 - 40pq + 200q^2$

44. $10p^2 - 120pq + 360q^2$ **45.** $5x^3 + 30x^2y + 45xy^2$ **46.** $3x^3 - 12x^2y + 12xy^2$

Factor as much as possible.

47. $x^3 + 27$ **48.** $x^3 - 64$ **49.** $m^3 - 8$ **50.** $m^3 - 1000$

51. $125r^3 + 1$ **52.** $27r^3 + 1$ **53.** $1000r^3 + s^3$ **54.** $8r^3 + s^3$

55. $8y^3 - 125$

56. $64y^3 - 27$

57. $27a^3 + 64b^3$

58. $125a^3 + 8b^3$

59. $x^6 + 343y^3$

60. $x^6 + 512y^3$

61. $-3k^4 - 648k$

62. $-2k^4 - 686k$

63. $320p^6 - 625q^3$

64. $2916p^6 - 256q^3$

65. $8x^9 - 125y^3$

66. $27x^9 - 64y^3$

Factor as much as possible.

67. $x^2 - (y + 3)^2$

68. $x^2 - (y + 7)^2$

69. $100x^4 - 140x^2y + 49y^2$

70. $121x^4 - 176x^2y + 64y^2$

71. $(x^2 + 4x + 4) - y^2$

72. $(x^2 + 6x + 9) - y^2$

73. $(x + 1)^3 - y^3$

74. $(x - 5)^3 + y^3$

4.6   **Factoring Strategy**

To be successful at factoring, you must be able to recognize which factoring technique to use on a given polynomial. Then you must be able to apply that factoring technique correctly. We can summarize our factoring strategy as follows.

FACTORING STRATEGY

1. Write the polynomial in descending order.
2. Always factor out the GCF first. Factor out -1 if needed.
3. To factor a binomial, try one of the following factorizations.

   $a^2 - b^2 = (a + b)(a - b)$ *Difference of two squares*
   $a^3 + b^3 = (a + b)(a^2 - ab + b^2)$ *Sum of two cubes*
   $a^3 - b^3 = (a - b)(a^2 + ab + b^2)$ *Difference of two cubes*

   Remember that $a^2 + b^2$ is a prime polynomial.
4. To factor a trinomial, try one of the following factorizations.

   $a^2 + 2ab + b^2 = (a + b)^2$ *Perfect-square trinomial*
   $a^2 - 2ab + b^2 = (a - b)^2$ *Perfect-square trinomial*
   $x^2 + bx + c$ *See Section 4.3*
   $ax^2 + bx + c$ *See Section 4.4*

5. To factor a polynomial with four terms, try grouping.
6. Continue to factor until you reach prime factored form.
7. Check by multiplication.

We illustrate this strategy with several examples.

EXAMPLE 1   Factor $xy - 5y + 2x - 10$.

Solution   There is no common factor (except 1). Since there are four terms, try grouping.

$$xy - 5y + 2x - 10 = y(x - 5) + 2(x - 5) \quad \textit{Factor out y, factor out 2}$$
$$= (x - 5)(y + 2) \quad \textit{Factor out } x - 5$$

Try Problem 9 >   Check by multiplication.   ∎

EXAMPLE 2   Factor $81 - 18t + t^2$.

Solution   Write the trinomial in descending order.

$$81 - 18t + t^2 = t^2 - 18t + 81$$

Since the first and last terms are perfect squares, this may be a perfect-square trinomial. Try $(t - 9)^2$. Since $2(t)(-9) = -18t$, the middle term of the trinomial, the polynomial is a perfect-square trinomial. Therefore

$$81 - 18t + t^2 = t^2 - 18t + 81 = (t - 9)^2.$$

Try Problem 13 >   Check by multiplication.   ∎

EXAMPLE 3   Factor $-9r^3 + 6r^2 - 3r$.

Solution   The factor $3r$ is common to all three terms, and the leading coefficient is negative. Therefore factor out the GCF, $-3r$.

$$-9r^3 + 6r^2 - 3r = -3r(3r^2 - 2r + 1)$$

Since $3r^2 - 2r + 1$ is prime, we cannot factor any further. Check by
Try Problem 19 >   multiplication.   ∎

EXAMPLE 4   Factor $10m^2 + 35mn - 75n^2$.

Solution
$$10m^2 + 35mn - 75n^2 = 5(2m^2 + 7mn - 15n^2) \quad \textit{Factor out the GCF, 5}$$
$$= 5(2m - 3n)(m + 5n) \quad \textit{Factor the trinomial using the methods of Section 4.4}$$

Try Problem 39 >   Check by multiplication.   ∎

EXAMPLE 5   Factor $8p^4 - 27pq^3$.

Solution
$$8p^4 - 27pq^3 = p(8p^3 - 27q^3) \qquad\qquad \textit{Factor out the GCF, p}$$

$$= p[(2p)^3 - (3q)^3] \qquad\qquad \textit{Factor the difference of two cubes}$$

$$= p\{(2p - 3q)[(2p)^2 + (2p)(3q) + (3q)^2]\}$$
$$= p(2p - 3q)(4p^2 + 6pq + 9q^2)$$

Try Problem 51 >   Check by multiplication.   ∎

EXAMPLE 6   Factor $x^3 + 5x^2 - 16x - 80$.

Solution   Since there are four terms, try grouping.

$$x^3 + 5x^2 - 16x - 80 = x^2(x + 5) - 16(x + 5)$$ *Factor out x^2, factor out -16*

$$= (x + 5)(x^2 - 16)$$ *Factor out $x + 5$*

$$= (x + 5)(x + 4)(x - 4)$$ *Factor the difference of two squares*

Try Problem 57 >   Check by multiplication.

4.6 Problem Set

LEARNING THROUGH WRITING

☐ Describe the various elements in factoring strategy.

Write in prime factored form.

1. $x^2 - 5x - 14$

2. $x^2 - 10x - 11$

3. $y^2 - 64$

4. $y^2 - 100$

5. $6z^2 + 18z - 3$

6. $4z^2 + 14z - 2$

7. $4p^2 + 4$

8. $9p^2 + 9$

9. $xy - 7y + 2x - 14$

10. $xy - 3y + 2x - 6$

11. $k^3 + 9k^2 + k + 9$

12. $k^3 + 4k^2 + k + 4$

13. $36 - 12t + t^2$

14. $64 - 16t + t^2$

15. $18m - 45$

16. $16m - 24$

17. $c^3 + 8d^3$

18. $c^3 - 27d^3$

19. $-15r^3 + 10r^2 - 5r$

20. $-20r^3 + 12r^2 - 4r$

21. $a^3 - a^2$

22. $a^4 - a^3$

23. $16p^2 - 40pq + 25q^2$

24. $4p^2 - 28pq + 49q^2$

25. $4x^2 + 9$

26. $16x^2 + 25$

27. $z^3 - 1$

28. $z^3 + 1$

29. $2y^2 + 3y - 20$

30. $3y^2 + y - 10$

31. $12c^2 + cd - 6d^2$

32. $15c^2 + 14cd - 8d^2$

33. $1 - 49k^2$

34. $1 - 36k^2$

35. $2xy - 5y - 2x + 5$

36. $3xy - 4y - 3x + 4$

37. $x^{11}y^3z^5 + x^4y^3z^7 - x^8y^3z^9$

38. $x^{10}y^2z^4 - x^6y^3z^4 + x^7y^8z^4$

39. $4m^2 + 6mn - 70n^2$

40. $25m^2 + 35mn - 30n^2$

41. $-12 - 11b + b^2$

42. $-18 - 17b + b^2$

43. $r^3s^3 - 27$

44. $r^3s^3 + 8$

45. $96a^2 - 150b^2$

46. $54a^2 - 24b^2$

47. $-4t^3 - 19t^2 + 30t$

48. $-6t^3 - 19t^2 + 20t$

49. $4\pi R^2 - 4\pi r^2$

50. $\pi R^2h - \pi r^2h$

51. $8p^4 + 125pq^3$

52. $27p^4 - 64pq^3$

53. $6x^7 - 486x^3$

54. $8x^8 - 128x^4$

55. $-12 - 29m - 14m^2$

56. $-12 - 32m - 21m^2$

57. $x^3 + 3x^2 - 4x - 12$

58. $x^3 + 2x^2 - 9x - 18$

59. $12a^2b + 24ab - 20a - 40$

60. $48a^2b - 24ab - 36a + 18$

Write in prime factored form.

61. $121x^4 - 154x^2y^2 + 49y^4$

62. $144x^4 - 120x^2y^2 + 25y^4$

63. $6x^6 + 7x^3y - 20y^2$

64. $4x^6 - 7x^3y - 15y^2$

65. $m^3 - (n + 3)^3$

66. $m^3 + (n - 4)^3$

67. $4p^6 - 4$

68. $2p^6 - 128$

69. $x^2 - y^2 - 2y - 1$

70. $x^2 - y^2 - 4y - 4$

71. $a^2 - b^2 + 5a + 5b$

72. $a^2 - b^2 + 3a - 3b$

| 4.7 | **Solving Quadratic Equations by Factoring** |

An equation that contains a variable to the second power (and no higher power) is called a *quadratic equation*.

DEFINITION OF A QUADRATIC EQUATION

A **quadratic equation,** or **second-degree equation,** in the variable x is an equation that can be expressed in the form

$$ax^2 + bx + c = 0,$$

where a, b, and c are constants and $a \neq 0$. This form is called the *standard form* of a quadratic equation.

Here are three examples of quadratic equations. Only the first equation is in standard form.

$$x^2 - 5x + 6 = 0 \qquad 2y^2 + 7y = 4 \qquad 9m^2 = 16$$

We can solve each of these equations by writing the equation in standard form, factoring the left side, and applying the **zero factor property.**

ZERO FACTOR PROPERTY

If $p \cdot q = 0$, then $p = 0$ or $q = 0$.

In other words, if the product of two numbers is 0, then one or both of the numbers must be 0.

EXAMPLE 1   Solve $x^2 - 5x + 6 = 0$.

Solution   The equation is already in standard form. Therefore factor the left side.

$$x^2 - 5x + 6 = 0 \quad \textit{Standard form}$$
$$(x - 2)(x - 3) = 0 \quad \textit{Factor the left side}$$

According to the zero factor property, if the product of $x - 2$ and $x - 3$ is 0, then

$$x - 2 = 0 \qquad \text{or} \qquad x - 3 = 0.$$

Now solve each of these linear equations.

$$x = 2 \qquad \text{or} \qquad x = 3$$

Try Problem 7 >

Therefore the solutions to the equation $x^2 - 5x + 6 = 0$ are 2 and 3. Check each solution by substituting it into the original equation.   ∎

TO SOLVE A QUADRATIC EQUATION BY FACTORING

1. Write the equation in standard form.
2. Factor the left side.
3. Set each factor equal to 0, and solve the resulting linear equations.
4. Check each solution in the original equation.

EXAMPLE 2   Solve $2y^2 + 7y = 4$.

Solution

Step 1   *Write the equation in standard form.*

$$2y^2 + 7y = 4 \quad \textit{Original equation}$$
$$2y^2 + 7y - 4 = 0 \quad \textit{Subtract 4 from both sides}$$

Step 2   *Factor the left side.*

$$(2y - 1)(y + 4) = 0$$

Step 3   *Set each factor equal to 0, and solve the resulting linear equations.*

$$2y - 1 = 0 \qquad \text{or} \qquad y + 4 = 0$$
$$2y = 1$$
$$y = \frac{1}{2} \qquad \text{or} \qquad y = -4$$

The solutions are $1/2$ and -4.

Step 4   *Check each solution in the original equation.*

$$\underline{\textit{Check } y = 1/2}$$
$$2y^2 + 7y = 4$$
$$2\left(\frac{1}{2}\right)^2 + 7\left(\frac{1}{2}\right) = 4$$
$$2\left(\frac{1}{4}\right) + \frac{7}{2} = 4$$
$$\frac{1}{2} + \frac{7}{2} = 4$$
$$\frac{8}{2} = 4 \quad \textit{True}$$

$$\underline{\textit{Check } y = -4}$$
$$2y^2 + 7y = 4$$
$$2(-4)^2 + 7(-4) = 4$$
$$2(16) - 28 = 4$$
$$32 - 28 = 4$$
$$4 = 4 \quad \textit{True}$$

Try Problem 13 >

∎

Caution! ∎
∎
∎
∎

We must write a quadratic equation in standard form before we can apply the zero factor property. The fact that a product equals 4, for example, does not mean that either factor equals 4.

EXAMPLE 3   Solve $-t^2 + 14t - 49 = 0$

Solution   The equation is already in standard form, but it will be easier to factor the left side if we multiply both sides by -1.

$$-1(-t^2 + 14t - 49) = -1 \cdot 0 \quad \textit{Multiply both sides by } -1$$
$$t^2 - 14t + 49 = 0 \qquad \textit{Distribute } -1 \textit{ over every term}$$
$$(t - 7)(t - 7) = 0 \qquad \textit{Factor the left side}$$

Set each factor equal to 0, and solve each linear equation for t.

$$t - 7 = 0 \qquad \text{or} \qquad t - 7 = 0$$
$$t = 7 \qquad \text{or} \qquad t = 7$$

Try Problem 17 >   The only solution is 7. Check in the original equation.   ■

Note that the equations of Examples 1 and 2 had two real solutions, but the equation of Example 3 had only one real solution. On the other hand, the equation $x^2 = -4$ has no real solutions, since no real number squared is -4. **A quadratic equation will have 0, 1, or 2 real solutions.**

EXAMPLE 4   Solve $9m^2 = 16$.

Solution

$$9m^2 - 16 = 0 \qquad \textit{Write in standard form}$$
$$(3m + 4)(3m - 4) = 0 \qquad \textit{Factor the left side}$$

$$3m + 4 = 0 \qquad \text{or} \qquad 3m - 4 = 0 \quad \textit{Set each factor equal to 0}$$
$$3m = -4 \qquad \text{or} \qquad 3m = 4$$
$$m = -\frac{4}{3} \qquad \text{or} \qquad m = \frac{4}{3} \quad \textit{Solve each linear equation}$$

Try Problem 23 >   The solutions are $-4/3$ and $4/3$. Check in the original equation.   ■

EXAMPLE 5   Solve $10x^2 + 64x + 24 = 0$.

Solution   The equation is in standard form, so factor the left side.

$$2(5x^2 + 32x + 12) = 0 \quad \textit{Factor out the GCF, 2}$$
$$2(5x + 2)(x + 6) = 0 \quad \textit{Factor the trinomial}$$

The factor 2 cannot equal 0. Therefore set the other two factors equal to 0 and solve for x.

$$5x + 2 = 0 \qquad \text{or} \qquad x + 6 = 0$$
$$5x = -2$$
$$x = -\frac{2}{5} \qquad \text{or} \qquad x = -6$$

Try Problem 29 >   The solutions are $-2/5$ and -6. Check in the original equation.   ■

EXAMPLE 6   Solve $3r^2 = 15r$.

Solution

$$3r^2 - 15r = 0 \quad \text{\textit{Write in standard form}}$$
$$3r(r - 5) = 0 \quad \text{\textit{Factor the left side}}$$

$$3r = 0 \quad \text{or} \quad r - 5 = 0 \quad \text{\textit{Set each factor equal to 0}}$$
$$r = 0 \quad \text{or} \quad r = 5 \quad \text{\textit{Solve each linear equation}}$$

Try Problem 35 >   The solutions are 0 and 5. Check in the original equation.   ∎

Caution! ∎
∎
∎
∎

Do not divide both sides of the equation in Example 6 by $3r$. In doing so you would lose the solution $r = 0$. The danger in dividing both sides by a variable expression, such as $3r$, is that you may be dividing by 0.

EXAMPLE 7   Solve $(p - 3)(p - 5) = 24$.

Solution

$$p^2 - 8p + 15 = 24 \quad \text{\textit{Multiply out the left side}}$$
$$p^2 - 8p - 9 = 0 \quad \text{\textit{Subtract 24, to express the equation in standard form}}$$
$$(p - 9)(p + 1) = 0 \quad \text{\textit{Factor the left side}}$$

$$p - 9 = 0 \quad \text{or} \quad p + 1 = 0 \quad \text{\textit{Set each factor equal to 0}}$$
$$p = 9 \quad \text{or} \quad p = -1 \quad \text{\textit{Solve for p}}$$

Try Problem 39 >   The solutions are 9 and -1. Check in the original equation.   ∎

Higher-Degree Equations

A method for solving any quadratic equation was known by the Babylonians, perhaps as early as 2000 B.C. However, it wasn't until the sixteenth century that algebraic methods for solving general third-degree and fourth-degree equations were discovered. Later, it was proven that no such algebraic methods could ever be found for solving general fifth-degree or higher-degree equations.

We can use the method of factoring to solve certain types of higher-degree equations.

EXAMPLE 8   Solve $x^3 + 9x^2 = 10x$.

Solution   Since the equation contains a variable to the third power (and no higher power), it is a third-degree equation. Collect all terms on the left side.

$$x^3 + 9x^2 - 10x = 0 \quad \text{\textit{Subtract 10x from both sides}}$$
$$x(x^2 + 9x - 10) = 0 \quad \text{\textit{Factor out x on the left side}}$$
$$x(x - 1)(x + 10) = 0 \quad \text{\textit{Factor the trinomial}}$$

The product of the three factors x, $x - 1$, and $x + 10$ will be 0 if any of the factors is 0. Therefore set each factor equal to 0 and solve for x.

$$x = 0 \quad \text{or} \quad x - 1 = 0 \quad \text{or} \quad x + 10 = 0$$
$$x = 1 \quad \text{or} \quad x = -10$$

Try Problem 55 >   The solutions are 0, 1, and -10. Check in the original equation.   ∎

Sometimes we cannot solve a quadratic equation (or a higher-degree equation) by factoring, because we cannot factor the left side. In Chapter 9 you will learn methods for solving any quadratic equation, including those that can't be solved by factoring.

4.7   Problem Set

LEARNING THROUGH WRITING

☐ Define a *quadratic equation*.

☐ How do you write a quadratic equation in standard form?

☐ State the *zero factor property*.

☐ Describe the steps in solving a quadratic equation by factoring.

Use the zero factor property to solve each equation.

1. $(y - 1)(y + 3) = 0$

2. $(y - 5)(y + 1) = 0$

3. $(m - 9)(m - 9) = 0$

4. $(m + 3)(m + 3) = 0$

5. $3t(7t - 4) = 0$

6. $5t(9t - 2) = 0$

Solve each equation.

7. $x^2 - 3x + 2 = 0$

8. $x^2 - 4x + 3 = 0$

9. $z^2 - 2z - 35 = 0$

10. $p^2 + 6p - 16 = 0$

11. $3m^2 + 2m - 1 = 0$

12. $2m^2 + m - 1 = 0$

13. $2y^2 + 11y = 6$

14. $3y^2 + 11y = 4$

15. $5r^2 - 18r = 8$

16. $3r^2 - 16r = 12$

17. $-t^2 + 6t - 9 = 0$

18. $-t^2 + 4t - 4 = 0$

19. $r^2 - 81 = 0$

20. $r^2 - 49 = 0$

21. $p^2 + 8p = 0$

22. $p^2 + 9p = 0$

23. $4m^2 = 25$

24. $16m^2 = 25$

25. $9t^2 + 4 = 12t$

26. $9t^2 + 16 = 24t$

27. $6x^2 = 0$

28. $8x^2 = 0$

29. $10x^2 + 46x + 24 = 0$

30. $21x^2 + 51x + 18 = 0$

31. $8y^2 - 4y = 0$

32. $6y^2 - 3y = 0$

33. $1 + 12m = -36m^2$

34. $1 + 16m = -64m^2$

35. $5r^2 = 20r$

36. $4r^2 = 24r$

37. $m(m + 1) = 2$

38. $m(m + 1) = 6$

39. $(p - 3)(p + 1) = 12$

40. $(p - 2)(p - 3) = 12$

41. $(2y + 1)^2 = (y + 2)^2 + 9$

42. $(3y + 1)^2 = (y + 3)^2 + 64$

43. $2k(k - 6) = (3k + 4)(k - 5)$

44. $3k(k - 1) = (4k + 5)(k - 4)$

45. $(2r - 1)^2 - (r + 3)^2 = 0$

46. $(2r + 1)^2 - (r + 5)^2 = 0$

Solve each equation.

47. $(x - 2)(x + 7)(4x - 3) = 0$

48. $(x - 3)(x + 8)(5x - 4) = 0$

49. $(y - 4)(y^2 + 7y - 8) = 0$

50. $(y - 6)(y^2 + 8y - 9) = 0$

51. $p^3 - 49p = 0$

52. $p^3 - 64p = 0$

53. $m^3 - 13m^2 = 0$

54. $m^3 - 11m^2 = 0$

55. $x^3 + 5x^2 = 6x$

56. $x^3 + 2x^2 = 15x$

57. $r^4 = r^3 + 20r^2$

58. $r^4 = r^3 + 30r^2$

Solve each word problem.

59. If four times a number is added to the square of the number, the result is 21. Find the number.

60. If two times a number is added to the square of the number, the result is 15. Find the number.

61. The square of a number is four more than three times the number. Find the number.

62. The square of a number is eight more than seven times the number. Find the number.

4.8   Problem Solving with Quadratic Equations

We will now see how quadratic equations can be used to solve certain types of word problems. We can solve each word problem in this section using the same four steps we used to solve the word problems in Chapter 2. The only difference in this section is that the equation we write in Step 2 will be a quadratic equation.

EXAMPLE 1   The product of two consecutive odd integers is 35. Find the integers.

Solution

Step 1   *Write down the unknown quantities. Call one x and write the other in terms of x.* Since the unknown quantities are consecutive odd integers, the larger integer is 2 more than the smaller.

$$x = \text{smaller integer}$$
$$x + 2 = \text{larger integer}$$

Step 2   *Write an equation involving x.*

$$
\begin{array}{ccc}
\textit{Product} & & \\
\textit{of the} & & \\
\textit{integers} & \textit{is} & 35 \\
\downarrow & \downarrow & \downarrow \\
x(x + 2) & = & 35
\end{array}
$$

Step 3   *Solve the equation.*

$$x^2 + 2x = 35 \qquad \textit{Multiply the left side}$$
$$x^2 + 2x - 35 = 0 \qquad \textit{Write in standard form}$$
$$(x - 5)(x + 7) = 0 \qquad \textit{Factor the left side}$$

$$x - 5 = 0 \quad \text{or} \quad x + 7 = 0 \qquad \textit{Set each factor equal to 0}$$
$$x = 5 \quad \text{or} \qquad x = -7 \qquad \textit{Solve each linear equation}$$

If $x = 5$, then $x + 2 = 7$. If $x = -7$, then $x + 2 = -5$. Therefore one solution is the pair of integers 5 and 7. Another solution is the pair -7 and -5.

Step 4 *Check in the words of the original problem.* Five and 7 are consecutive odd integers whose product is 35. Also, −7 and −5 are consecutive odd integers whose product is 35. ∎

Try Problem 1 >

EXAMPLE 2   A rancher has 12 miles of fencing to enclose a rectangular pasture. One side of the pasture lies along the base of a straight cliff and needs no additional fencing (see Fig. 4.3). What should the width and length of the pasture be if the area is to be 16 square miles?

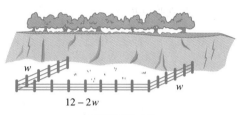

FIGURE 4.3

Solution   Suppose we call the width of the pasture w. To write the length, we must subtract two widths from the total amount of fencing, which is 12 miles (see Fig. 4.3).

$$w = \text{width of pasture}$$
$$12 - 2w = \text{length of pasture}$$

Area of the
pasture　　*is*　16
　 ↓　　　 ↓ 　↓
$w(12 - 2w)$　=　16

Solve the equation.

$$
\begin{array}{ll}
12w - 2w^2 = 16 & \textit{Multiply the left side} \\
-2w^2 + 12w - 16 = 0 & \textit{Write in standard form} \\
-2(w^2 - 6w + 8) = 0 & \textit{Factor out } -2 \\
-2(w - 2)(w - 4) = 0 & \textit{Factor the trinomial}
\end{array}
$$

$$
\begin{array}{lll}
w - 2 = 0 & \text{or} & w - 4 = 0 \quad \textit{Set each factor equal to 0} \\
w = 2 & \text{or} & w = 4 \quad\quad \textit{Solve each linear equation}
\end{array}
$$

If $w = 2$, then $12 - 2w = 8$. If $w = 4$, then $12 - 2w = 4$. Therefore one solution is to make the pasture 2 miles by 8 miles. Another solution is to make the pasture 4 miles by 4 miles. Check in the words of the original problem. ∎

Try Problem 11 >

One of the most important formulas in plane geometry is the **Pythagorean theorem.**

The Pythagorean theorem is named after the Greek mathematician Pythagoras (ca. 572–495 B.C.). The theorem was known to the Babylonians more than a thousand years earlier, but Pythagoras was probably the first to give a proof of the theorem.

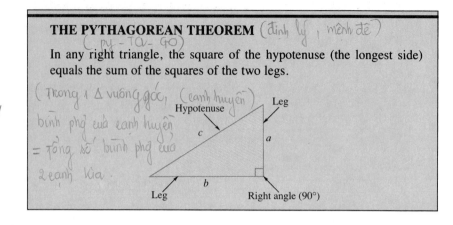

THE PYTHAGOREAN THEOREM (định lý, mệnh đề)
(py - Ta- GO)

In any right triangle, the square of the hypotenuse (the longest side) equals the sum of the squares of the two legs.

(Trong 1 △ vuông góc, (cạnh huyền)
bình phg của cạnh huyền
= tổng số bình phg của
2 cạnh kia.

Hypotenuse   Leg
c
a
Leg
b
Right angle (90°)

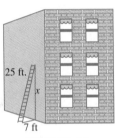

FIGURE 4.4

EXAMPLE 3   A 25-foot ladder is placed so that the base of the ladder is 7 feet from the side of a building (see Fig. 4.4). How high up on the building will the ladder reach?

Solution   Let x = the height of the top of the ladder. Use the Pythagorean theorem to write the equation (see Fig. 4.4).

$$a^2 + b^2 = c^2$$
$$\downarrow \quad \downarrow \quad \downarrow$$
$$x^2 + 7^2 = 25^2$$

Solve the equation.

$$x^2 + 49 = 625 \quad \textit{Square 7, square 25}$$
$$x^2 - 576 = 0 \quad \textit{Write in standard form}$$
$$(x - 24)(x + 24) = 0 \quad \textit{Factor the left side}$$

$$x - 24 = 0 \quad \text{or} \quad x + 24 = 0 \quad \textit{Set each factor equal to 0}$$
$$x = 24 \quad \text{or} \quad x = -24 \quad \textit{Solve each linear equation}$$

The ladder reaches 24 feet high on the side of the building. Ignore the solution -24, since the height of the ladder cannot be a negative number. Check in the words of the original problem.   ∎

Try Problem 15 >

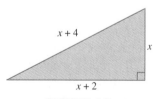

FIGURE 4.5

EXAMPLE 4   One leg of a right triangle is 2 inches longer than the other leg. The hypotenuse is 4 inches longer than the shorter leg (see Fig. 4.5). Find the length of each side.

Solution   Use the Pythagorean theorem to write the equation (see Fig. 4.5).

$$c^2 \quad = a^2 + \quad b^2$$
$$\downarrow \qquad \downarrow \qquad \downarrow$$
$$(x + 4)^2 = x^2 + (x + 2)^2$$
$$x^2 + 8x + \ 16 = x^2 + x^2 + 4x + 4 \qquad \textit{Square } x + 4 \textit{ and } x + 2$$
$$0 = x^2 - 4x - 12 \qquad \textit{Collect terms on the right side}$$
$$0 = (x - 6)(x + 2) \qquad \textit{Factor the right side}$$

$$x - 6 = 0 \quad \text{or} \quad x + 2 = 0 \qquad \textit{Set each factor equal to } 0$$
$$x = 6 \quad \text{or} \qquad x = -2 \quad \textit{Solve each linear equation}$$

Ignore the solution -2, since the shorter leg cannot be negative. Therefore the shorter leg is $x = 6$ inches, the longer leg is $x + 2 = 8$ inches, and the hypotenuse is $x + 4 = 10$ inches. Check in the words of the original problem.

Try Problem 19 >

■

4.8 | Problem Set

LEARNING THROUGH WRITING

☐ State the *Pythagorean theorem* in words.

☐ Describe the steps in solving a word problem.

Solve the following number problems.

1. The product of two consecutive odd integers is 63. Find the integers.

2. The product of two consecutive even integers is 48. Find the integers.

3. The sum of the squares of two consecutive positive integers is 41. Find the integers.

4. The sum of the squares of two consecutive positive integers is 61. Find the integers.

5. One positive number is twice another. If the larger number is subtracted from the square of the smaller, the result is five times the sum of the two numbers. Find the numbers.

6. One positive number is three times another. If the larger number is subtracted from the square of the smaller, the result is five times the sum of the two numbers. Find the numbers.

7. The square of the sum of two consecutive negative integers is 221 more than twice the product of the integers. Find the integers.

8. The square of the sum of two consecutive negative integers is 421 more than three times the product of the integers. Find the integers.

Solve the following area problems.

9. The length of a rectangular rug is 1 meter more than three times the width. The area of the rug is 30 square meters. Find the width and length.

10. The length of a rectangular dance floor is 3 meters more than twice the width. The area of the floor is 44 square meters. Find the width and length.

11. A rancher has 6 miles of fencing to enclose a rectangular pasture. One side of the pasture lies along a straight river and needs no additional fencing. What should the width and length of the pasture be if the area is to be 4 square miles?

12. A farmer wants to fence in a rectangular pig pen along one side of a barn. The farmer has 18 yards of fencing and wants the area of the pen to be 36 square yards. What should the width and length of the pen be?

13. The length of a rectangle is 3 centimeters more than the width. If the width and length are each increased by 4 centimeters, the area is increased by 44 square centimeters. Find the original width and length.

Solve the following Pythagorean theorem problems.

15. A 50-foot extension ladder from a fire engine leans against the side of a building. How high up on the building does the ladder reach if the truck is parked 30 feet from the side of the building?

14. The length of a rectangle is twice the width. If the width and length are each increased by 5 centimeters, the area is increased by 70 square centimeters. Find the original width and length.

16. The roof on an A-frame ski lodge is 34 feet long (see Fig. 4.6). How high is the peak of the roof if the width of the base of the lodge is 32 feet?

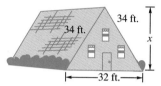

FIGURE 4.6

17. How long must a cable be to reach from the top of a 24-foot TV antenna to a point on the ground 7 feet from the base of the pole?

19. One leg of a right triangle is 1 inch longer than the other leg. The hypotenuse is 2 inches longer than the shorter leg. Find the length of each side.

21. The length of a rectangle is 1 yard less than twice the width. The diagonal is 1 yard more than twice the width. Find the width and length.

Solve each word problem.

23. A square piece of sheet metal is to be made into a cake pan by cutting a 2-inch square from each corner and then turning up the sides (see Fig. 4.7). What size piece of sheet metal is needed if the volume of the pan is to be 128 cubic inches?

18. Two ships leave the same port simultaneously. One ship travels north at 30 mph, and the other travels east at 40 mph. How far apart are the ships after 30 minutes?

20. One leg of a right triangle is 7 inches longer than the other leg. The hypotenuse is 8 inches longer than the shorter leg. Find the length of each side.

22. The length of a rectangle is 4 yards more than twice the width. The diagonal is 4 yards less than three times the width. Find the width and length.

24. An art gallery wants to put a frame of uniform width around a 4-foot by 6-foot painting (see Fig. 4.8). The gallery wants the area of the frame to equal the area of the painting. How wide should the frame be made?

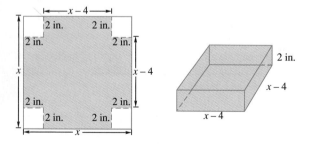

FIGURE 4.7

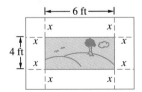

FIGURE 4.8

25. Ignoring air resistance, the distance, d, in feet, that an object falls in t seconds is given by the formula $d = 16t^2$. A piece of concrete falls from a bridge 144 feet high. How long does it take to hit the water below?

26. A slingshot fires a pellet vertically upward with an initial velocity of 96 feet per second. The height, h, of the pellet (in feet) after t seconds is given by the formula $h = -16t^2 + 96t$.

    a. When will the height, h, be 128 feet?
    b. When will the height, h, be 144 feet?
    c. When will the height, h, be 0 feet?

C H A P T E R 4   S U M M A R Y

Key Terms

Constant term, p. 183
Factor, p. 176
Greatest common factor (GCF), p. 175
Leading coefficient, p. 185

Middle coefficient, p. 183
Perfect-square trinomial, p. 196
Prime factored form, p. 174
Prime number, p. 174

Prime polynomial, p. 177
Quadratic equation, p. 203
Second-degree equation, p. 203

Key Rules

Divisibility Tests
A number is divisible by 2 if it ends in 0, 2, 4, 6, or 8.
A number is divisible by 3 if the sum of its digits is divisible by 3.
A number is divisible by 5 if it ends in 0 or 5.

Perfect-Square Trinomials

$a^2 + 2ab + b^2 = (a + b)^2$
$a^2 - 2ab + b^2 = (a - b)^2$

Difference of Two Squares

$a^2 - b^2 = (a + b)(a - b)$

Sum and Difference of Two Cubes

$a^3 + b^3 = (a + b)(a^2 - ab + b^2)$
$a^3 - b^3 = (a - b)(a^2 + ab + b^2)$

Zero Factor Property
If $p \cdot q = 0$, then $p = 0$ or $q = 0$.

Pythagorean Theorem

$a^2 + b^2 = c^2$

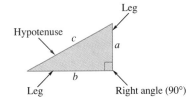

C H A P T E R 4   R E V I E W   P R O B L E M S

[4.1] *Write each number in prime factored form.*

  1. 40   **2.** 2475

Find the GCF of each collection of numbers.

  3. 180, 54, 450   **4.** 56, 33, 25

Find the GCF of each collection of terms.

5. x^3y^5, x^2y^7

6. $48m^{11}, 60m^{22}$

Factor out the GCF, including -1 if the highest-degree term has a negative coefficient.

7. $7a - 35b$

8. $8r^{30}s^{15} - 12r^{20}s^{10} - 4r^{10}s^5$

9. $q(p^2 + 9) - 4(p^2 + 9)$

10. $-20k^4 - 30k^3 + 50k^2 + 10k$

[4.2] *Factor by grouping.*

11. $xy + 5y + 3x + 15$

12. $5m^2 + 35m - 2m - 14$

13. $t^3 - 8t^2 + t - 8$

Write in prime factored form.

14. $12r^2 - 6rs + 18rs - 9s^2$

15. $6a^3b + 10a^2b^2 - 12a^2b^2 - 20ab^3$

[4.3] *Factor each trinomial. Factor out -1 if the highest-degree term has a negative coefficient.*

16. $x^2 + 10x + 21$

17. $m^2 + 2m - 35$

18. $p^2 - 5p - 36$

19. $r^2 + 2rs - 24s^2$

20. $a^2 + 8b^2 - 9ab$

21. $-z^2 - 13z - 42$

Write in prime factored form.

22. $2x^3 - 2x^2 - 60x$

23. $5y^4a + 40y^3a^2 + 80y^2a^3$

[4.4] *Factor each trinomial.*

24. $3x^2 + 10x - 8$

25. $2y^2 + 7y + 1$

26. $4p^2 - 16p - 9$

27. $6m^2 + 19m - 20$

28. $5r^2 - 26rs + 5s^2$

29. $15 + 2k - 8k^2$

Write in prime factored form.

30. $18x^2 + 42x + 12$

31. $24m^3n - 7m^2n^2 - 6mn^3$

[4.5] *Factor as much as possible.*

32. $25r^2 - 16s^2$

33. $1 - x^2y^2$

34. $m^4 - 81$

35. $x^2 - 20x + 100$

36. $4p^2 + 12pq + 9q^2$

37. $9a^3 - 24a^2b + 16ab^2$

38. $a^3 + 8$

39. $b^3 - 1000$

40. $8m^4n + 27mn^4$

[4.6] *Write in prime factored form.*

41. $4z^2 + 12z - 8$

42. $c^3 + 64d^3$

43. $a^4 - 4a^2$

44. $b^4 - b$

45. $xy - 9y + 2x - 18$

46. $8r^3 - 16r^2 - 42r$

47. $24m^2 + 56mn - 160n^2$

48. $az^2 - 25a + z^2 - 25$

49. $16k - k^2 - 64$

[4.7] *Solve each equation.*

50. $(5x - 2)(x + 3) = 0$

51. $3m^2 - 11m - 4 = 0$

52. $t^2 + 9t = 0$

53. $r^2 + 16 = 8r$

54. $9p^2 = 25$

55. $2t^2 = 14t$

56. $(4a - 1)^2 = (2a + 3)^2 + 40$

57. $-16z^2 + 48z + 160 = 0$

58. $x^3 - 36x = 0$

[4.8] *Solve each word problem.*

59. The product of two consecutive even integers is 6 more than three times their sum. Find the integers.

60. The length of a rectangle is 1 meter less than twice the width. The area of the rectangle is 28 square meters. Find the width and length.

61. A farmer has 24 yards of fencing to enclose a rectangular corral. One side of the corral will lie along an existing fence and needs no additional fencing. What should the width and length of the corral be if the area is to be 72 square yards?

62. Find the length, x, of the roof in Fig. 4.9.

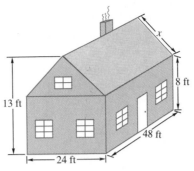

13 ft

8 ft

48 ft

24 ft

FIGURE 4.9

1. Write 20 in prime factored form. $\times$

2. Find the GCF of $280x^4y^3$ and $360x^{12}y$.

Write in prime factored form.

3. $x^2 - 49$

4. $y^2 + 2y + 1$

5. $m^2 - 4m - 12$

6. $pq + 5p + 2q + 10$

7. $k^3 + 8$

8. $6a^2 + 11a - 35$

9. $12x^2y + 16xy - 4xy^2$

10. $9x^2 - 64y^2$

11. $27t^3 - s^3$

12. $100r^8s^6 - 10r^4s^3$

13. $4x^2 - 20ax + 25a^2$

14. $m^3 - 6m^2 - 4m + 24$

15. $24c^3 + 10c^2d - 56cd^2$

16. $5p^4 - 80$

17. $-10k - 24 - k^2$

Solve each equation.

18. $x^2 - 2x - 8 = 0$

19. $y(3y + 13) = 10$

20. $25p^2 - 16 = 0$

21. $4m^2 + 24m = 0$

22. $t^2 + 81 = 18t$

23. $k^3 = k$

Solve each word problem.

24. One integer is twice another. The product of the integers is 8 more than five times their sum. Find the integers.

(Tên ,mũi tên) (đung thẳ) Cgióc)

26. An arrow is shot vertically upward with an initial velocity of 112 feet per second. The height, h, of the arrow (in feet) after t seconds is given by the formula $h = -16t^2 + 112t$. When will the arrow be at a height of 192 feet?

25. One leg of a right triangle is 7 inches longer than the other leg. The hypotenuse is 1 inch longer than twice the shorter leg. Find the length of each side.

Rational Expressions

Did you ever wonder how a game warden determines the number of fish in a lake? In Section 5.9 we show how this can be done: First, a certain number of fish are tagged and placed in the lake. Later, a sample of fish is caught from the lake and the number of tagged fish in the sample noted. By setting up a proportion, which is a type of equation with rational expressions, the approximate number of fish in the lake can be calculated.

5.1   Simplifying Rational Expressions

Recall that the quotient of two integers is called a *rational number,* so long as the divisor is not 0. In a similar way, the quotient of two polynomials is called a *rational expression.*

DEFINITION OF A RATIONAL EXPRESSION

A **rational expression,** also called an **algebraic fraction,** is an expression of the form

$$\frac{P}{Q},$$

where P and Q are polynomials and $Q \neq 0$.

All of the expressions

$$\frac{2x}{x-4}, \qquad \frac{3y+4}{y^2-7y+10}, \qquad \text{and} \qquad \frac{m^3+1}{6}$$

are rational expressions, since each is the quotient of two polynomials.

EXAMPLE 1   Find the value(s) of x that make $\dfrac{2x}{x-4}$ undefined.

Solution   Since division by zero is undefined, a rational expression is undefined when its denominator is 0. Therefore set the denominator equal to 0, and solve.

$$x - 4 = 0$$
$$x = 4$$

Try Problem 3 >   The rational expression $\dfrac{2x}{x-4}$ is undefined when $x = 4$.   ∎

EXAMPLE 2   Find the value(s) of y that make $\dfrac{3y+4}{y^2-7y+10}$ undefined.

Solution   Set the denominator equal to 0 and solve.

$$y^2 - 7y + 10 = 0$$
$$(y-2)(y-5) = 0$$

$$y - 2 = 0 \quad \text{or} \quad y - 5 = 0$$
$$y = 2 \quad \text{or} \quad y = 5$$

Try Problem 7 >   The rational expression is undefined when $y = 2$ or when $y = 5$.   ∎

EXAMPLE 3   Find the value(s) of m that make $\dfrac{m^3 + 1}{6}$ undefined.

Solution   Since the denominator is never 0, there are no values of m that
Try Problem 9 >   make the rational expression undefined.   ∎

From now on when we write a rational expression we will assume that
those values that make the denominator 0 are excluded.

We perform operations on rational expressions in much the same way that
we perform operations on ordinary fractions. Recall that we simplify a fraction
by dividing out common factors from the numerator and the denominator.

$$\frac{14}{21} = \frac{2 \cdot 7}{3 \cdot 7} = \frac{2 \cdot \overset{1}{\cancel{7}}}{3 \cdot \underset{1}{\cancel{7}}} = \frac{2}{3}$$

We can simplify a rational expression in the same way.

FUNDAMENTAL PROPERTY OF RATIONAL EXPRESSIONS

If P, Q, and K are polynomials and neither Q nor K is zero, then

$$\frac{P \cdot K}{Q \cdot K} = \frac{P}{Q}.$$

EXAMPLE 4   Simplify $\dfrac{-10m}{15m^2}$.

Solution

$$\frac{-10m}{15m^2} = \frac{-2 \cdot 5 \cdot m}{3 \cdot 5 \cdot m \cdot m} \qquad \text{\textit{Write the numerator and the denominator in prime}}$$
$$\text{\textit{factored form}}$$

$$= \frac{-2 \cdot \overset{1}{\cancel{5}} \cdot \overset{1}{\cancel{m}}}{3 \cdot \underset{1}{\cancel{5}} \cdot \underset{1}{\cancel{m}} \cdot m} \qquad \text{\textit{Divide out factors common to the numerator and the}}$$
$$\text{\textit{denominator}}$$

$$= \frac{-2}{3m}$$

Both $\dfrac{-2}{3m}$ and $-\dfrac{2}{3m}$ are correct answers. The form $\dfrac{2}{-3m}$ is also correct, but we
Try Problem 15 >   prefer to write a fraction with a positive denominator.   ∎

TO SIMPLIFY A RATIONAL EXPRESSION

1. Write the numerator and the denominator in prime factored form.
2. Divide both the numerator and the denominator by any factors they have in common.

EXAMPLE 5   Simplify $\dfrac{3p - 15}{4p - 20}$.

Solution

Step 1   *Write the numerator and the denominator in prime factored form.*

$$\frac{3p - 15}{4p - 20} = \frac{3(p - 5)}{4(p - 5)}$$

Step 2   *Divide out the common factor, p − 5.*

$$= \frac{3(p - 5)}{4(p - 5)}$$

Try Problem 23 >

$$= \frac{3}{4}$$

■

EXAMPLE 6   Simplify $\dfrac{x^2 - 4}{x^2 + x - 6}$.

Solution

$$\frac{x^2 - 4}{x^2 + x - 6} = \frac{(x + 2)(x - 2)}{(x + 3)(x - 2)} \qquad \text{\textit{Factor the numerator and the denominator}}$$

$$= \frac{x + 2}{x + 3} \qquad \text{\textit{Divide out the common factor, x − 2}}$$

Try Problem 33 >   This answer cannot be simplified further.   ■

Caution! ■   Remember that factors are related by multiplication; we can divide out common
■   factors. Terms are related by addition; we cannot divide out common terms.
■
■
■
■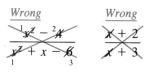
■
■
■

EXAMPLE 7   Simplify $\dfrac{5r - 7}{7 - 5r}$.

Solution   Factor out 1 from the numerator and −1 from the denominator.
Then simplify.

Try Problem 49 > $$\frac{5r - 7}{7 - 5r} = \frac{1(5r - 7)}{-1(-7 + 5r)} = \frac{1(5r - 7)}{-1(5r - 7)} = \frac{1}{-1} = -1$$ ■

Did you notice in Example 7 that $5r - 7$ and $7 - 5r$ are opposites? Whenever the numerator and the denominator of a fraction are opposites, the fraction always simplifies to -1.

Caution! ■
■
■
■

Note the difference in the following three fractions.

$$\frac{a + b}{b + a} = 1 \qquad \frac{a - b}{b - a} = -1 \qquad \frac{a + b}{a - b} \text{ cannot be simplified}$$

EXAMPLE 8   Simplify $\dfrac{(m + 4)3 - 12}{(m + 4)m}$.

Solution   Do not divide out $(m + 4)$; the binomial $m + 4$ is not a factor of the entire numerator. Instead, proceed as follows.

$$\frac{(m + 4)3 - 12}{(m + 4)m} = \frac{3m + 12 - 12}{(m + 4)m} \qquad \textit{Distribute 3}$$

$$= \frac{3m}{(m + 4)m} \qquad \textit{Simplify the numerator}$$

Try Problem 59 > $$= \frac{3}{m + 4} \qquad \textit{Divide out the common factor m}$$ ■

P R O B L E M   S O L V I N G

This formula was known to the early Greeks.

EXAMPLE 9   Rational expressions are used in many formulas. For example, a polygon is a plane figure consisting of three or more sides. Triangles, rectangles, and pentagons are examples of polygons. If the sides are equal and the interior angles are equal, the polygon is said to be regular. The number of degrees, a, in each interior angle of a regular polygon having n sides is given by the formula

$$a = \frac{180n - 360}{n}.$$

Find the number of degrees in each interior angle of a regular pentagon.

Solution   Since a pentagon has 5 sides, replace n with 5.

$$a = \frac{180n - 360}{n} = \frac{180(5) - 360}{5} = \frac{900 - 360}{5} = \frac{540}{5} = 108$$

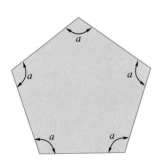

Try Problem 65>   Each angle measures $108°$.

5.1   Problem Set

Find the value(s) of the variable that make each rational expression undefined.

1. $\dfrac{1}{2x}$

2. $\dfrac{1}{3x}$

3. $\dfrac{5x}{x - 6}$

4. $\dfrac{7x}{x + 4}$

5. $\dfrac{r + 8}{r^2 - 25}$

6. $\dfrac{r - 9}{r^2 - 100}$

7. $\dfrac{4y + 5}{y^2 - 4y - 21}$

8. $\dfrac{5y + 3}{y^2 - 8y + 15}$

9. $\dfrac{m^3 - 27}{3}$

10. $\dfrac{m^3 - 8}{2}$

11. $\dfrac{t^2}{t^2 + 4}$

12. $\dfrac{t^2}{t^2 + 9}$

Simplify each rational expression.

13. $\dfrac{36x^3}{9x}$

14. $\dfrac{24x^2}{4x}$

15. $\dfrac{-6m}{21m^2}$

16. $\dfrac{-10m}{14m^2}$

17. $\dfrac{-22p^3}{-99p^3}$

18. $\dfrac{-26p^4}{-39p^4}$

19. $\dfrac{30a^2b^4}{-24a^3b}$

20. $\dfrac{45a^3b^2}{-30ab^4}$

21. $\dfrac{12x + 18}{6}$

22. $\dfrac{24x - 16}{8}$

23. $\dfrac{2p - 6}{5p - 15}$

24. $\dfrac{5p - 10}{7p - 14}$

25. $\dfrac{3m + 3}{9m + 9}$

26. $\dfrac{2m + 2}{4m + 4}$

27. $\dfrac{10y^2}{25y^2 - 5y}$

28. $\dfrac{6y^2}{9y^2 - 3y}$

29. $\dfrac{x^2 + 8x}{8x + 64}$

30. $\dfrac{x^2 + 6x}{6x + 36}$

31. $\dfrac{t - 4}{t^2 - 16}$

32. $\dfrac{t - 9}{t^2 - 81}$

33. $\dfrac{x^2 - 25}{x^2 + 2x - 35}$

34. $\dfrac{x^2 - 36}{x^2 + x - 42}$

35. $\dfrac{(r + s)^2}{(r + s)^6}$

36. $\dfrac{(r - s)^3}{(r - s)^6}$

37. $\dfrac{(c + d)^2}{c^2 - d^2}$

38. $\dfrac{c^2 - d^2}{(c - d)^2}$

39. $\dfrac{z^2 - 4z + 3}{z^2 - 2z + 1}$

40. $\dfrac{z^2 - z - 2}{z^2 - 4z + 4}$

41. $\dfrac{2m^2 - 9mn - 5n^2}{m^2 - 25n^2}$

42. $\dfrac{3m^2 + 11mn - 4n^2}{m^2 - 16n^2}$

43. $\dfrac{8x^2 + 2x - 6}{4x^2 + 5x - 6}$

44. $\dfrac{6x^2 - 9x - 15}{2x^2 + x - 15}$

Simplify each rational expression.

45. $\dfrac{x + 3}{3 + x}$

46. $\dfrac{x + y}{y + x}$

47. $\dfrac{x - 3}{3 - x}$

48. $\dfrac{x - y}{y - x}$

49. $\dfrac{2r - 5}{5 - 2r}$

50. $\dfrac{3r - 4}{4 - 3r}$

51. $\dfrac{a^2 - ab - 2b^2}{6b^2 - ab - a^2}$

52. $\dfrac{a^2 - 2ab - 3b^2}{6b^2 + ab - a^2}$

Simplify each rational expression.

53. $\dfrac{4 + 2(t + 3)}{5t - 7(t + 2)}$

54. $\dfrac{6 + 3(t + 4)}{4t - 7(t + 3)}$

55. $\dfrac{2(x + 3) - (x + 9)}{x^2 - 9}$

56. $\dfrac{2(x + 2) - (x + 6)}{x^2 - 4}$

57. $\dfrac{(p-5)p+6}{(p-2)p-3}$

58. $\dfrac{(p-7)p+12}{(p-2)p-3}$

59. $\dfrac{(m+2)3-6}{(m+2)m}$

60. $\dfrac{(m+1)5-5}{(m+1)m}$

61. $\dfrac{x^3+27}{x+3}$

62. $\dfrac{k^2+k+1}{k^3-1}$

63. $\dfrac{m^3+m^2+4m+4}{m^2-2m-3}$

64. $\dfrac{xy-3y-9x+27}{3-x}$

Solve each word problem.

65. The number of degrees, a, in each interior angle of a regular polygon having n sides is

$$a = \frac{180n-360}{n}.$$

Find the number of degrees in each interior angle of a regular hexagon (six sides).

66. The number of degrees, a, in each interior angle of a regular polygon having n sides is

$$a = \frac{180n-360}{n}.$$

Find the number of degrees in each interior angle of a regular octagon (eight sides).

67. According to experiments conducted by A. J. Clark, the response, r, of a frog's heart to the injection of x units of acetylcholine is

$$r = \frac{100x}{15+x}.$$

Find r when $x = 22.5$ units.

68. According to the cube law of politics, the percent, y, of seats won by a political party is

$$y = \frac{x^3}{3x^2-300x+10,000},$$

where x is the percent of total votes for that party. Find y if $x = 60$.

5.2 # Multiplying and Dividing Rational Expressions

Multiplying Rational Expressions

Recall that we multiply two fractions by multiplying their numerators and multiplying their denominators.

$$\frac{3}{4} \cdot \frac{5}{7} = \frac{3 \cdot 5}{4 \cdot 7} = \frac{15}{28}$$

We multiply two rational expressions in the same way.

MULTIPLYING RATIONAL EXPRESSIONS

If P/Q and R/S are rational expressions, then

$$\frac{P}{Q} \cdot \frac{R}{S} = \frac{P \cdot R}{Q \cdot S}.$$

EXAMPLE 1   Multiply $\dfrac{m^2}{15} \cdot \dfrac{6}{m}$.

Solution

$$\frac{m^2}{15} \cdot \frac{6}{m} = \frac{6m^2}{15m} \qquad \textit{Multiply the numerators, multiply the denominators}$$

$$= \frac{2 \cdot \overset{1}{\cancel{3}} \cdot m \cdot \overset{1}{\cancel{m}}}{\underset{1}{\cancel{3}} \cdot 5 \cdot \underset{1}{\cancel{m}}} \qquad \textit{Factor and divide out common factors}$$

$$= \frac{2m}{5}$$

Try Problem 1 >   Therefore the product of the rational expressions $m^2/15$ and $6/m$ is the rational expression $2m/5$.   ∎

Multiplying fractions is easier if we divide out common factors *before* we multiply.

$$\frac{3}{4} \cdot \frac{14}{15} = \frac{\overset{1}{\cancel{3}}}{2 \cdot 2} \cdot \frac{\overset{1}{\cancel{2}} \cdot 7}{\underset{1}{\cancel{3}} \cdot 5} = \frac{7}{10}$$

The same can be said about multiplying rational expressions.

TO MULTIPLY RATIONAL EXPRESSIONS

1. Write the numerators and the denominators in prime factored form.
2. Divide out common factors.
3. Multiply the numerators and multiply the denominators.

EXAMPLE 2   Multiply $\dfrac{x^2 - 4}{2x} \cdot \dfrac{6}{3x - 6}$.

Solution

Step 1 *Write the numerators and the denominators in prime factored form.*

$$\frac{x^2 - 4}{2x} \cdot \frac{6}{3x - 6} = \frac{(x + 2)(x - 2)}{2x} \cdot \frac{2 \cdot 3}{3(x - 2)}$$

Step 2 *Divide out common factors.*

$$= \frac{(x + 2)\overset{1}{\cancel{(x - 2)}}}{2x} \cdot \frac{\overset{1}{\cancel{2}} \cdot \overset{1}{\cancel{3}}}{\cancel{3}(x \cancel{- 2})}$$

Step 3 *Multiply the numerators and multiply the denominators.*

$$= \frac{x + 2}{x}$$

Try Problem 19 >   This answer cannot be simplified further.   ∎

EXAMPLE 3   Multiply $\dfrac{p^2 - 4p}{p^2 + 3p + 2} \cdot \dfrac{p^2 + 5p + 6}{p^2 - p - 12}$.

Solution

$$\frac{p^2 - 4p}{p^2 + 3p + 2} \cdot \frac{p^2 + 5p + 6}{p^2 - p - 12}$$

$$= \frac{p(p - 4)}{(p + 1)(p + 2)} \cdot \frac{(p + 2)(p + 3)}{(p - 4)(p + 3)}$$

Try Problem 27 > $= \dfrac{p}{p + 1}$ ∎

Dividing Rational Expressions

We divide two fractions by multiplying the first fraction by the *reciprocal* of the second fraction. Recall that the **reciprocal** of a/b is b/a.

$$\frac{5}{6} \div \frac{3}{10} = \frac{5}{6} \cdot \frac{10}{3} = \frac{5}{\cancel{2} \cdot 3} \cdot \frac{\cancel{2} \cdot 5}{3} = \frac{25}{9}$$

We divide two rational expressions in the same way.

DIVIDING RATIONAL EXPRESSIONS

If P/Q and R/S are rational expressions and $R/S \neq 0$, then

$$\frac{P}{Q} \div \frac{R}{S} = \frac{P}{Q} \cdot \frac{S}{R} = \frac{P \cdot S}{Q \cdot R}.$$

EXAMPLE 4   Divide $\dfrac{x}{y+3} \div \dfrac{y+6}{x}$.

Solution

$$\dfrac{x}{y+3} \div \dfrac{y+6}{x} = \dfrac{x}{y+3} \cdot \dfrac{x}{y+6} \qquad \textit{Multiply by the reciprocal of } (y+6)/x$$

$$= \dfrac{x^2}{(y+3)(y+6)}$$

Try Problem 33 >

You can multiply out the denominator of the answer, but it is common to leave it in factored form. ∎

Caution! ∎
∎
∎
∎
∎
∎
∎
∎

Do not divide out the x's in Example 4. You can divide out common factors only when the operation is multiplication.

Correct

$$\dfrac{\cancel{x}}{a-5} \cdot \dfrac{a+7}{\cancel{x}}$$

Wrong

$$\dfrac{\cancel{x}}{a-5} \cdot \dfrac{a+7}{\cancel{x}}$$

EXAMPLE 5   Divide $\dfrac{5a+10b}{a^2-ab} \div \dfrac{a^2+ab-2b^2}{a^2-b^2}$.

Solution

$$\dfrac{5a+10b}{a^2-ab} \div \dfrac{a^2+ab-2b^2}{a^2-b^2}$$

$$= \dfrac{5a+10b}{a^2-ab} \cdot \dfrac{a^2-b^2}{a^2+ab-2b^2} \qquad \textit{Multiply by the reciprocal}$$

$$= \dfrac{5(a+2b)}{a(a-b)} \cdot \dfrac{(a+b)(a-b)}{(a-b)(a+2b)} \qquad \textit{Factor}$$

$$= \dfrac{5\cancel{(a+2b)}}{a\cancel{(a-b)}} \cdot \dfrac{(a+b)\cancel{(a-b)}}{(a-b)\cancel{(a+2b)}} \qquad \textit{Divide out common factors}$$

Try Problem 41 >

$$= \dfrac{5(a+b)}{a(a-b)} \qquad \textit{Multiply} \qquad ∎$$

EXAMPLE 6   Divide $\dfrac{4-r^2}{4r+8} \div (r^2-2r)$.

Solution   The reciprocal of the rational expression $\dfrac{r^2-2r}{1}$ is $\dfrac{1}{r^2-2r}$.

$$\dfrac{4-r^2}{4r+8} \div (r^2-2r) = \dfrac{4-r^2}{4r+8} \cdot \dfrac{1}{r^2-2r} \qquad \textit{Multiply by the reciprocal}$$

$$= \dfrac{(2+r)(2-r)}{4(r+2)} \cdot \dfrac{1}{r(r-2)} \qquad \textit{Factor}$$

Now, $\dfrac{2 + r}{r + 2} = 1$ and $\dfrac{2 - r}{r - 2} = -1$. Therefore continue as follows.

$$= \frac{\overset{1}{\cancel{(2 + r)}}\overset{-1}{\cancel{(2 - r)}}}{\underset{1}{\cancel{4(r + 2)}}} \cdot \frac{1}{\underset{1}{\cancel{r(r - 2)}}} \qquad \textit{Divide out common factors}$$

$$= \frac{-1}{4r} \qquad\qquad\qquad \textit{Multiply}$$

Try Problem 45 >   You can also write the answer as $-\dfrac{1}{4r}$. ∎

5.2 Problem Set

LEARNING THROUGH WRITING

☐ Describe the steps in multiplying rational expressions.

☐ Why do we factor and divide out common factors *before* we multiply rational expressions?

☐ What are *reciprocals*?

☐ Explain in words how to divide two rational expressions.

Multiply or divide as indicated. Write your answer in simplest form.

1. $\dfrac{m^2}{14} \cdot \dfrac{10}{m}$

2. $\dfrac{m^2}{21} \cdot \dfrac{15}{m}$

3. $\dfrac{a^3}{9b} \cdot \dfrac{27}{ab}$

4. $\dfrac{a^4}{4b} \cdot \dfrac{8}{a^2b}$

5. $\dfrac{y}{3} \div \dfrac{3}{y}$

6. $\dfrac{y}{5} \div \dfrac{5}{y}$

7. $\dfrac{-25k^{10}}{9k^7} \div \dfrac{20k^8}{6k^4}$

8. $\dfrac{-27k^9}{45k^4} \div \dfrac{18k^{12}}{12k^6}$

9. $\dfrac{36d}{3c} \div (4cd)$

10. $\dfrac{50d}{2c} \div (5cd)$

11. $\dfrac{(2r)^2}{15r^4} \cdot \dfrac{5r^3}{2(3r)^2} \cdot \dfrac{(3r)^3}{20r}$

12. $\dfrac{7r^5}{3(2r)^2} \cdot \dfrac{(3r)^2}{12r^4} \cdot \dfrac{(2r)^3}{14r^3}$

13. $\dfrac{(3x)^2y^5}{3(z^2y)^4} \div \dfrac{6(xy)^3}{(-3z^2y)^3}$

14. $\dfrac{8(x^4y)^4}{(2z^3y)^2} \div \dfrac{(-2x^5)^3y}{3(zy^2)^3}$

15. $\dfrac{x^2}{6} \div \dfrac{x^3}{4} \div \dfrac{x}{y}$

16. $\dfrac{x^4}{9} \div \dfrac{x^3}{12} \div \dfrac{x^2}{y^2}$

Multiply or divide as indicated. Write your answer in simplest form.

17. $\dfrac{7a + 14}{5} \cdot \dfrac{15a}{6a + 12}$

18. $\dfrac{21a}{6a + 18} \cdot \dfrac{5a + 15}{7}$

19. $\dfrac{x^2 - 9}{5x} \cdot \dfrac{10}{2x - 6}$

20. $\dfrac{x^2 - 16}{6x} \cdot \dfrac{18}{3x - 12}$

21. $\dfrac{m - 5}{m} \cdot \dfrac{m^3}{5 - m}$

22. $\dfrac{m^4}{m - 3} \cdot \dfrac{3 - m}{m^2}$

23. $\dfrac{4t + 6}{t^2 + t} \div \dfrac{6t + 9}{t}$

24. $\dfrac{6t + 8}{t^2 - t} \div \dfrac{9t + 12}{t}$

25. $\dfrac{x^4 + x^3}{y + xy} \div \dfrac{x^3}{y^2}$

26. $\dfrac{x^3 + x^2}{y + xy} \div \dfrac{x^2}{y^2}$

27. $\dfrac{p^2 - 6p}{p^2 + 6p + 5} \cdot \dfrac{p^2 + 7p + 10}{p^2 - 4p - 12}$

28. $\dfrac{p^2 - 9p}{p^2 + 8p + 7} \cdot \dfrac{p^2 + 9p + 14}{p^2 - 7p - 18}$

29. $\dfrac{m^2 + 3m - 10}{m^2 - 25} \cdot \dfrac{m^2 - 2m - 15}{8m^2 - 16m}$

30. $\dfrac{m^2 + 6m - 7}{m^2 - 49} \cdot \dfrac{m^2 - 5m - 14}{9m^2 - 9m}$

31. $\dfrac{(c + d)^2}{8c} \cdot \dfrac{24c}{c^2 - d^2}$

32. $\dfrac{30d}{(c - d)^2} \cdot \dfrac{c^2 - d^2}{6d}$

33. $\dfrac{x}{y - 2} \div \dfrac{y - 6}{x}$

34. $\dfrac{x}{y + 2} \div \dfrac{y + 4}{x}$

35. $\dfrac{t + 2}{t - 1} \div \dfrac{1}{t^2 - 1}$

36. $\dfrac{t - 3}{t + 1} \div \dfrac{1}{t^2 - 1}$

37. $\dfrac{9z^2 - 1}{6z + 2} \div \dfrac{3z - 1}{2}$

38. $\dfrac{3}{4z - 1} \div \dfrac{12z + 3}{16z^2 - 1}$

39. $\dfrac{6y^2 + 7y - 20}{2y^2 + 9y + 10} \div \dfrac{3y^2 - y - 4}{y^2 - y - 2}$

40. $\dfrac{8y^2 - 2y - 15}{2y^2 + 3y - 9} \div \dfrac{4y^2 + 9y + 5}{y^2 - 2y - 3}$

41. $\dfrac{7a + 35b}{a^2 + ab} \div \dfrac{a^2 + 6ab + 5b^2}{a^2 - b^2}$

42. $\dfrac{11a + 33b}{a^2 - ab} \div \dfrac{a^2 + 2ab - 3b^2}{a^2 - b^2}$

43. $\dfrac{c^2 + c - 6}{c^2 - 6c + 8} \div \dfrac{c^2 + 2c - 8}{c^2 - c - 12}$

44. $\dfrac{c^2 + 4c + 3}{c^2 + c - 2} \div \dfrac{c^2 + 2c + 1}{c^2 + 5c + 6}$

45. $\dfrac{36 - r^2}{2r + 12} \div (r^2 - 6r)$

46. $\dfrac{64 - r^2}{3r + 24} \div (r^2 - 8r)$

47. $\dfrac{12}{x} \div \dfrac{x + 3}{x - 3} \cdot \dfrac{3x^2 + 9x}{x^2 - 9}$

48. $\dfrac{6}{x} \div \dfrac{x + 2}{x - 2} \cdot \dfrac{2x^2 + 4x}{x^2 - 4}$

49. $\dfrac{x^2 + 10x + 25}{2x^2 + 10x} \cdot \dfrac{20x}{2x^2 + 3x - 2} \div \dfrac{2x + 10}{x + 2}$

50. $\dfrac{x^2 + 6x + 9}{2x^2 + 6x} \cdot \dfrac{30x}{2x^2 + 7x - 4} \div \dfrac{3x + 9}{x + 4}$

51. $\dfrac{x^2 + 8x + 16}{5x^2 + 19x - 4} \div \dfrac{9x + 36}{3x^2 - 6x} \cdot \dfrac{15x^2 + 2x - 1}{x^2 - 4}$

52. $\dfrac{x^2 + 6x + 9}{4x^2 + 11x - 3} \div \dfrac{8x + 24}{4x^2 + 12x} \cdot \dfrac{8x^2 + 2x - 1}{x^2 - 9}$

53. $\dfrac{pq + 4p + 2q + 8}{pq + 4p + 3q + 12} \cdot \dfrac{p^2 - 9}{12p^2 + 24p}$

54. $\dfrac{a^3 - b^3}{a^2 - b^2} \div \dfrac{a^2b + ab^2 + b^3}{a + b}$

5.3 Adding and Subtracting Rational Expressions Having Like Denominators

We add (or subtract) two fractions having the same denominator by adding (or subtracting) their numerators and placing the sum (or difference) over the common denominator.

$$\frac{7}{13} + \frac{2}{13} = \frac{9}{13} \qquad \frac{7}{13} - \frac{2}{13} = \frac{5}{13}$$

We add and subtract rational expressions in the same way.

ADDING AND SUBTRACTING RATIONAL EXPRESSIONS

If P/Q and R/Q are rational expressions, then

$$\frac{P}{Q} + \frac{R}{Q} = \frac{P + R}{Q} \quad \text{and} \quad \frac{P}{Q} - \frac{R}{Q} = \frac{P - R}{Q}.$$

EXAMPLE 1   Add $3x/8 + x/8$.

Solution   The denominators are the same, so add the numerators.

$$\frac{3x}{8} + \frac{x}{8} = \frac{3x + x}{8} = \frac{4x}{8}$$

Simplify by factoring and dividing out common factors.

$$\frac{4x}{8} = \frac{\cancel{2} \cdot \cancel{2} \cdot x}{\cancel{2} \cdot \cancel{2} \cdot 2} = \frac{x}{2}$$

The sum of the rational expressions $3x/8$ and $x/8$ is the rational expression $x/2$.

Try Problem 3 >

■

EXAMPLE 2   Add $\dfrac{3p}{p + 2} + \dfrac{6}{p + 2}$.

Solution

$$\frac{3p}{p + 2} + \frac{6}{p + 2} = \frac{3p + 6}{p + 2} \qquad \textit{Add the numerators, keep the same}$$
$$\textit{denominator}$$
$$= \frac{3(p + 2)}{p + 2} \qquad \textit{Factor the numerator}$$
$$= 3 \qquad \textit{Divide out } p + 2$$

Try Problem 11 >

■

EXAMPLE 3   Subtract $\dfrac{r + 7}{r^2} - \dfrac{1}{r^2}$.

Solution   The denominators are the same, so subtract the numerators.

$$\frac{r + 7}{r^2} - \frac{1}{r^2} = \frac{r + 7 - 1}{r^2} = \frac{r + 6}{r^2}$$

Try Problem 17 >   This answer cannot be simplified further.

■

> **TO ADD OR SUBTRACT RATIONAL EXPRESSIONS HAVING THE SAME DENOMINATOR**
>
> 1. Add or subtract the numerators and place the sum or difference over the common denominator.
> 2. If possible, simplify the answer by writing the numerator and the denominator in prime factored form and dividing out common factors.

EXAMPLE 4   Subtract $\dfrac{2p}{p^2 + 3p - 28} - \dfrac{8}{p^2 + 3p - 28}$.

Solution

Step 1   *Subtract the numerators and place the difference over the common denominator.*

$$\frac{2p}{p^2 + 3p - 28} - \frac{8}{p^2 + 3p - 28} = \frac{2p - 8}{p^2 + 3p - 28} \qquad \text{\textit{Subtract the numerators}}$$

Step 2   *Simplify the answer by writing the numerator and the denominator in prime factored form and dividing out common factors.*

$$= \frac{2(p - 4)}{(p + 7)(p - 4)} \qquad \text{\textit{Factor}}$$

Try Problem 25 >

$$= \frac{2}{p + 7} \qquad \text{\textit{Divide out }} p - 4$$

■

EXAMPLE 5   Subtract $\dfrac{4x + 7}{x - 5} - \dfrac{3x + 2}{x - 5}$.

Solution

$$\frac{4x + 7}{x - 5} - \frac{3x + 2}{x - 5} = \frac{4x + 7 - (3x + 2)}{x - 5} \qquad \begin{array}{l}\text{\textit{Subtract the numerators,}}\\ \text{\textit{write parentheses around the}}\\ \text{\textit{second numerator}}\end{array}$$

$$= \frac{4x + 7 - 3x - 2}{x - 5} \qquad \text{\textit{Distribute}} -1$$

Try Problem 31 >

$$= \frac{x + 5}{x - 5} \qquad \text{\textit{Combine like terms}}$$

■

Caution! ■

When you subtract two rational expressions, make sure you write parentheses around the second numerator if it contains two or more terms.

Correct

$$\frac{9}{x} - \frac{x - 1}{x} = \frac{9 - (x - 1)}{x}$$

Wrong

$$\frac{9}{x} - \frac{x - 1}{x} \quad \frac{9 - x - 1}{x}$$

EXAMPLE 6   Add $\dfrac{9}{m-3} + \dfrac{2}{3-m}$.

Solution   The denominators are not the same, but they are opposites. To make them the same, multiply the numerator and the denominator of the second rational expression by -1.

$$\frac{9}{m-3} + \frac{2}{3-m} = \frac{9}{m-3} + \frac{2}{3-m} \cdot \frac{-1}{-1}$$

$$= \frac{9}{m-3} + \frac{-2}{m-3}$$

$$= \frac{9+(-2)}{m-3} \qquad \textit{Add the numerators}$$

$$= \frac{7}{m-3}$$

Try Problem 41 >   You could also solve this problem by multiplying the numerator and the denominator of the first rational expression by -1.   ∎

5.3 Problem Set

LEARNING THROUGH WRITING

☐ Describe the steps in adding or subtracting rational expressions having the same denominator.

☐ How can you add or subtract two rational expressions if their denominators are opposites?

Add or subtract as indicated. Write your answer in simplest form.

1. $\dfrac{a}{3} + \dfrac{a}{3}$

2. $\dfrac{a}{5} + \dfrac{a}{5}$

3. $\dfrac{5x}{8} + \dfrac{x}{8}$

4. $\dfrac{2x}{9} + \dfrac{x}{9}$

5. $\dfrac{1}{p} + \dfrac{1}{p}$

6. $\dfrac{3}{p} + \dfrac{3}{p}$

7. $\dfrac{1}{6y} + \dfrac{5}{6y}$

8. $\dfrac{1}{4y} + \dfrac{3}{4y}$

9. $\dfrac{9}{10r} - \dfrac{7}{10r}$

10. $\dfrac{11}{12r} - \dfrac{7}{12r}$

11. $\dfrac{2p}{p+5} + \dfrac{10}{p+5}$

12. $\dfrac{4p}{p+3} + \dfrac{12}{p+3}$

13. $\dfrac{b+3}{b} - \dfrac{3}{b}$

14. $\dfrac{b+7}{b} - \dfrac{7}{b}$

15. $\dfrac{m+3}{7x} + \dfrac{m-2}{7x}$

16. $\dfrac{m-5}{9x} + \dfrac{m+8}{9x}$

17. $\dfrac{r + 8}{r^2} - \dfrac{1}{r^2}$

18. $\dfrac{r + 5}{r^2} - \dfrac{1}{r^2}$

19. $\dfrac{x}{x^2} + \dfrac{2}{x^2}$

20. $\dfrac{x}{x^2} + \dfrac{3}{x^2}$

21. $\dfrac{t^2}{t - 3} - \dfrac{9}{t - 3}$

22. $\dfrac{t^2}{t - 2} - \dfrac{4}{t - 2}$

23. $\dfrac{m + 5}{m - 1} - \dfrac{m + 2}{m - 1}$

24. $\dfrac{m + 9}{m - 2} - \dfrac{m + 3}{m - 2}$

25. $\dfrac{3p}{p^2 + 5p - 14} - \dfrac{6}{p^2 + 5p - 14}$

26. $\dfrac{5p}{p^2 + 4p - 21} - \dfrac{15}{p^2 + 4p - 21}$

27. $\dfrac{a^2 + b^2}{a + b} + \dfrac{2ab}{a + b}$

28. $\dfrac{a^2 + b^2}{a - b} - \dfrac{2ab}{a - b}$

29. $\dfrac{3y + 5}{y^2 + 2y} + \dfrac{y + 3}{y^2 + 2y}$

30. $\dfrac{k}{k^2 - 81} - \dfrac{9}{k^2 - 81}$

31. $\dfrac{6x + 7}{x - 4} - \dfrac{5x + 3}{x - 4}$

32. $\dfrac{4x + 3}{x + 5} - \dfrac{3x + 8}{x + 5}$

33. $\dfrac{x(x + 5)}{(x - 5)(x + 5)} - \dfrac{5(x - 5)}{(x + 5)(x - 5)}$

34. $\dfrac{x(x + 6)}{(x - 6)(x + 6)} - \dfrac{6(x - 6)}{(x + 6)(x - 6)}$

35. $\dfrac{2(x + 8)}{x^2 - 2x - 15} - \dfrac{5(x + 1)}{x^2 - 2x - 15}$

36. $\dfrac{3(x + 5)}{x^2 - 4x - 21} - \dfrac{5(x + 2)}{x^2 - 4x - 21}$

37. $\dfrac{(m + 2)(m + 3)}{(m + 4)(m + 3)} + \dfrac{(m + 2)(m - 1)}{(m + 3)(m + 4)}$

38. $\dfrac{(m + 3)(m + 5)}{(m + 2)(m + 5)} + \dfrac{(m + 3)(m - 3)}{(m + 2)(m + 5)}$

39. $\dfrac{y^2 + y + 7}{(y + 5)(y + 2)} - \dfrac{(y - 4)(y + 2)}{(y + 5)(y + 2)}$

40. $\dfrac{y^2 + 3y + 2}{(y + 7)(y + 4)} - \dfrac{(y - 3)(y + 4)}{(y + 7)(y + 4)}$

Add or subtract as indicated. Write your answer in simplest form.

41. $\dfrac{8}{m - 2} + \dfrac{3}{2 - m}$

42. $\dfrac{12}{m - 4} + \dfrac{5}{4 - m}$

43. $\dfrac{4}{x - y} - \dfrac{5}{y - x}$

44. $\dfrac{2}{x - y} - \dfrac{6}{y - x}$

45. $\dfrac{2r + 1}{3 - r} - \dfrac{5r - 8}{r - 3}$

46. $\dfrac{7r + 1}{5 - r} - \dfrac{9r - 3}{r - 5}$

47. $\dfrac{x^2 + x - 1}{(x - 1)^2} - \dfrac{x(x + 1)}{(x - 1)^2} + \dfrac{x}{(x - 1)^2}$

48. $\dfrac{-9x^2}{3x + y} - \dfrac{y^2}{3x + y} - \dfrac{6xy}{3x + y}$

5.4 **Finding the Least Common Denominator**

To add or subtract rational expressions that do not have the same denominator, we begin by finding the least common denominator. The **least common denominator (LCD)** of a collection of rational expressions is the simplest polynomial that can be divided (without remainder) by all of the denominators in the collection. When the denominators are simple, we can determine the LCD by inspection. When the LCD is not obvious from a simple inspection, we can find the LCD as follows.

TO FIND THE LEAST COMMON DENOMINATOR (LCD)

1. Write each denominator in prime factored form using exponents.
2. Multiply together the highest power of each factor.

EXAMPLE 1   Find the LCD of $\dfrac{1}{16xy^3}$ and $\dfrac{1}{36x^2y^5}$.

Solution

Step 1   *Write each denominator in prime factored form using exponents.*

$$16xy^3 = 2^4 \cdot x \cdot y^3$$
$$36x^2y^5 = 2^2 \cdot 3^2 \cdot x^2 \cdot y^5$$

Step 2   *Multiply together the highest power of each factor.* The highest power of 2 is 2^4, the highest power of 3 is 3^2, the highest power of x is x^2, and the highest power of y is y^5. Multiply these powers together to get the LCD.

$$LCD = 2^4 \cdot 3^2 \cdot x^2 \cdot y^5 = 144x^2y^5$$

Try Problem 13 >   Note that the numerators play no role in determining the LCD.   ■

EXAMPLE 2   Find the LCD of $\dfrac{8}{m+4}$ and $\dfrac{6}{5m+20}$.

Solution   Write each denominator in prime factored form.

$m + 4$ is already in prime factored form
$5m + 20 = 5(m + 4)$

Multiply together the highest power of each factor. The highest power of 5 is 5^1. The highest power of $m + 4$ is $(m + 4)^1$.

$$LCD = 5^1 \cdot (m + 4)^1 = 5(m + 4)$$

Try Problem 15 >   Note that we generally leave the LCD in factored form.   ■

EXAMPLE 3   Find the LCD of $3/x$ and $9x/(x + 1)$.

Solution   Write each denominator in prime factored form.

x is already in prime factored form
$x + 1$ is already in prime factored form

Multiply together the highest power of each factor.

$$LCD = x(x + 1)$$

Note that the LCD in this case was simply the product of the two denominators. This is because the denominators had no common factor (except 1).

Try Problem 21 >

EXAMPLE 4 Find the LCD of $\dfrac{y - 1}{y + 2}$ and $\dfrac{y}{y + 3}$.

Solution Both denominators are already in prime factored form. Since the denominators have no common factor (except 1),

Try Problem 27 >

$$LCD = (y + 2)(y + 3).$$

EXAMPLE 5 Find the LCD of $\dfrac{6}{a + 5}$ and a.

Solution Note that $a = a/1$. The denominators have no common factor (except 1), so

Try Problem 33 >

$$LCD = 1 \cdot (a + 5) = a + 5.$$

EXAMPLE 6 Find the LCD of $\dfrac{5}{p^2 + 6p}$ and $\dfrac{7}{6p}$.

Solution

$$p^2 + 6p = p(p + 6)$$
$$6p = 2 \cdot 3 \cdot p$$ $\Big\}$ *Prime factored form*

$$LCD = 2 \cdot 3 \cdot p(p + 6) \quad \text{\textit{Highest power of each factor}}$$
$$= 6p(p + 6)$$

Try Problem 41 >

EXAMPLE 7 Find the LCD of $\dfrac{r}{r^2 - 1}$ and $\dfrac{r + 3}{r^2 - 2r + 1}$.

Solution

$$r^2 - 1 = (r + 1)(r - 1)$$
$$r^2 - 2r + 1 = (r - 1)^2$$ $\Big\}$ *Prime factored form*

Try Problem 45 >

$$LCD = (r + 1)(r - 1)^2 \quad \text{\textit{Highest power of each factor}}$$

P R O B L E M   S O L V I N G

EXAMPLE 8 Suppose hot dogs come in a package of 10 and buns come in a package of 12. What is the fewest number of packages of each that must be purchased to obtain the same number of hot dogs and buns?

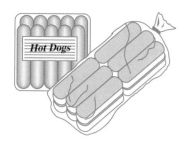

Solution   We need to find the smallest number that can be divided (without remainder) by both 12 and 10. But that is the LCD of 12 and 10.

$$12 = 2^2 \cdot 3$$
$$10 = 2 \cdot 5$$
$\left.\rule{0pt}{22pt}\right\}$*Prime factored form*

$$\text{LCD} = 2^2 \cdot 3 \cdot 5 = 60 \quad \textit{Highest power of each factor}$$

Therefore 60 hot dogs (6 packages) and 60 buns (5 packages) must be purchased.

Try Problem 51 >

5.4 Problem Set

LEARNING THROUGH WRITING

☐ Describe the steps in finding the least common denominator.

☐ Define the term *least common denominator.*

Find the LCD for each collection of rational expressions.

1. $\dfrac{5}{y^2}, \dfrac{15}{y^6}$

2. $\dfrac{27}{y^8}, \dfrac{9}{y^4}$

3. $\dfrac{z}{9}, \dfrac{12}{z}$

4. $\dfrac{z}{4}, \dfrac{6}{z}$

5. $k, \dfrac{2}{3k}$

6. $k, \dfrac{3}{2k}$

7. $\dfrac{3}{5p}, \dfrac{8}{9p}$

8. $\dfrac{2}{5p}, \dfrac{7}{8p}$

9. $\dfrac{m-2}{6m^2}, \dfrac{1}{18m}$

10. $\dfrac{1}{16m^3}, \dfrac{m+2}{4m^2}$

11. $\dfrac{5}{a^3b}, \dfrac{8}{a^2b^2}$

12. $\dfrac{6}{a^2b^4}, \dfrac{7}{a^3b^3}$

13. $\dfrac{1}{12xy^4}, \dfrac{1}{45x^3y^2}$

14. $\dfrac{1}{24x^5y}, \dfrac{1}{80x^3y^6}$

15. $\dfrac{8}{m+4}, \dfrac{10}{3m+12}$

16. $\dfrac{6}{m-3}, \dfrac{9}{4m-12}$

17. $\dfrac{r^2}{2r-6}, \dfrac{17}{3r-9}$

18. $\dfrac{r^2}{3r+6}, \dfrac{19}{5r+10}$

19. $\dfrac{k+4}{k^2+k}, \dfrac{k-3}{k+1}$

20. $\dfrac{k-6}{k^2-k}, \dfrac{k+2}{k-1}$

21. $\dfrac{2}{x}, \dfrac{7x}{x-1}$

22. $\dfrac{5}{x}, \dfrac{8x}{x+1}$

23. $\dfrac{t+5}{t^2-4t}, \dfrac{t-4}{t^2+5t}$

24. $\dfrac{t-3}{t^2+2t}, \dfrac{t+2}{t^2-3t}$

25. $\dfrac{11z}{18z+12}, \dfrac{-z}{27z+18}$

26. $\dfrac{-z}{8z+12}, \dfrac{13z}{20z+30}$

27. $\dfrac{y-1}{y+3}, \dfrac{y}{y+5}$

28. $\dfrac{y}{y+2}, \dfrac{y-5}{y+4}$

29. $\dfrac{6m+1}{5m-3}, \dfrac{7m-4}{10m+9}$

30. $\dfrac{9m-2}{4m+3}, \dfrac{3m+5}{8m-9}$

31. $\dfrac{-3r^2}{4r+8}, \dfrac{4r^2}{3r-6}$

32. $\dfrac{5r^2}{2r-4}, \dfrac{-2r^2}{5r+10}$

33. $\dfrac{9}{a+7}, a$

34. $\dfrac{5}{a-6}, a$

35. $\dfrac{6}{x^2-4}, \dfrac{x}{x+2}$

36. $\dfrac{3}{x^2-9}, \dfrac{x}{x+3}$

37. $\dfrac{x}{3x+18}, \dfrac{x+1}{x^2-36}$

38. $\dfrac{x}{2x+14}, \dfrac{x-1}{x^2-49}$

39. $\dfrac{xy}{x^2-y^2}, \dfrac{2xy}{x^2+2xy+y^2}$

40. $\dfrac{2xy}{x^2-2xy+y^2}, \dfrac{xy}{x^2-y^2}$

41. $\dfrac{7}{p^2+10p}, \dfrac{3}{10p}$

42. $\dfrac{2}{p^2+14p}, \dfrac{5}{14p}$

43. $\dfrac{1}{2x+8}, \dfrac{1}{x^2+3x-4}$

44. $\dfrac{1}{6x+12}, \dfrac{1}{x^2-x-6}$

45. $\dfrac{r}{r^2-25}, \dfrac{r+2}{r^2-10r+25}$

46. $\dfrac{r}{r^2-16}, \dfrac{r+5}{r^2-8r+16}$

47. $\dfrac{3m-2}{m^2-8m-9}, \dfrac{2m}{m^2-5m-6}$

48. $\dfrac{2m-3}{m^2-2m-8}, \dfrac{3m}{m^2-4m-12}$

49. $\dfrac{a^2-1}{6a^2-11a-10}, \dfrac{a+1}{3a^2-4a-4}$

50. $\dfrac{a^2-4}{4a^2+4a-3}, \dfrac{a+2}{2a^2-3a-9}$

Solve each word problem.

51. Suppose that x number of oranges can be packed either in crates that hold 24 oranges or in crates that hold 36 oranges, with none left over in either case. What is the smallest number that x can be?

52. It takes Jupiter 12 years to revolve around the sun, Saturn 30 years, and Neptune 165 years. Suppose that on a particular night all three planets are lined up. How many years will pass before the planets line up again?

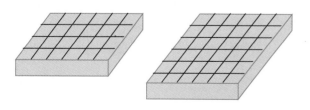

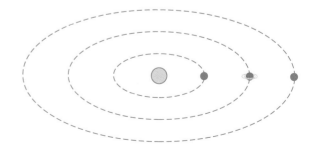

5.5   Adding and Subtracting Rational Expressions Having Unlike Denominators

In this section we add and subtract rational expressions that do not have the same denominator.

TO ADD OR SUBTRACT RATIONAL EXPRESSIONS HAVING UNLIKE DENOMINATORS

1. Factor the denominators to find the LCD.
2. Write each rational expression with the LCD. This is done by using the property

$$\frac{P}{Q} = \frac{P}{Q} \cdot \frac{K}{K} = \frac{PK}{QK} \, .$$

3. Add or subtract the numerators, and place the sum or difference over the LCD.
4. If possible, simplify your answer by factoring and dividing out common factors.

EXAMPLE 1   Add $\dfrac{1}{3x} + \dfrac{1}{4x}$.

Solution

Step 1   *Factor the denominators to find the LCD.*

$$\left. \begin{aligned} 3x &= 3 \cdot x \\ 4x &= 2^2 \cdot x \end{aligned} \right\} \text{\textit{Prime factored form}}$$

$$\text{LCD} = 2^2 \cdot 3 \cdot x = 12x \quad \textit{Highest power of each factor}$$

Step 2   *Write each rational expression with the LCD.* Since $12x \div 3x = 4$, multiply the first rational expression by 4/4.

$$\frac{1}{3x} = \frac{1}{3x} \cdot \frac{4}{4} = \frac{4}{12x}$$

Since $12x \div 4x = 3$, multiply the second rational expression by 3/3.

$$\frac{1}{4x} = \frac{1}{4x} \cdot \frac{3}{3} = \frac{3}{12x}$$

Step 3 *Add the numerators, and place the sum over the LCD.*

$$\frac{1}{3x} + \frac{1}{4x} = \frac{4}{12x} + \frac{3}{12x} = \frac{4+3}{12x} = \frac{7}{12x}$$

Try Problem 5 >   **Step 4** This answer cannot be simplified further.   ■

EXAMPLE 2   Subtract $\dfrac{6}{y} - \dfrac{2}{y^2}$.

Solution   The LCD is y^2. Write each rational expression with the LCD.

$$\frac{6}{y} - \frac{2}{y^2} = \frac{6}{y} \cdot \frac{y}{y} - \frac{2}{y^2} \qquad \textit{Multiply the first rational expression by y/y}$$

$$= \frac{6y}{y^2} - \frac{2}{y^2}$$

$$= \frac{6y - 2}{y^2} \qquad \textit{Subtract the numerators, and place the difference over the LCD}$$

Try Problem 11 >   This answer cannot be simplified further.   ■

EXAMPLE 3   Subtract $a - \dfrac{a^2}{a+5}$.

Solution   Since $a = a/1$, the LCD is $a + 5$. Write each rational expression with the LCD.

$$a - \frac{a^2}{a+5} = \frac{a}{1} - \frac{a^2}{a+5}$$

$$= \frac{a}{1} \cdot \frac{a+5}{a+5} - \frac{a^2}{a+5} \qquad \textit{Multiply the first rational expression by (a + 5)/(a + 5)}$$

$$= \frac{a^2 + 5a}{a+5} - \frac{a^2}{a+5}$$

$$= \frac{a^2 + 5a - a^2}{a+5} \qquad \textit{Subtract the numerators, keep the same denominator}$$

$$= \frac{5a}{a+5} \qquad \textit{Combine like terms}$$

Try Problem 23 >   This answer cannot be simplified further.   ■

EXAMPLE 4   Add $\dfrac{m}{m+4} + \dfrac{1}{m}$.

Solution

$$\frac{m}{m+4} + \frac{1}{m} = \frac{m}{m+4} \cdot \frac{m}{m} + \frac{1}{m} \cdot \frac{m+4}{m+4}$$

Write each rational expression with the LCD, $m(m+4)$

$$= \frac{m^2}{m(m+4)} + \frac{m+4}{m(m+4)}$$

$$= \frac{m^2 + m + 4}{m(m+4)}$$

Add the numerators, keep the same denominator

This answer cannot be simplified further. Note that we usually leave the denominator in factored form.

Try Problem 27 >

■

Caution! ■ You can divide out common factors only when multiplying rational expressions.
■
■
■
■ *Correct*   *Wrong*
■
■ $\dfrac{a}{1} + \dfrac{1}{a} = \dfrac{a}{1} \cdot \dfrac{a}{a} + \dfrac{1}{a} = \dfrac{a^2 + 1}{a}$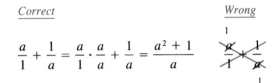
■
■

EXAMPLE 5   Subtract $\dfrac{t-2}{t+6} - \dfrac{t+3}{t-9}$.

Solution   Write each rational expression with the LCD, $(t+6)(t-9)$.

$$\frac{t-2}{t+6} - \frac{t+3}{t-9} = \frac{t-2}{t+6} \cdot \frac{t-9}{t-9} - \frac{t+3}{t-9} \cdot \frac{t+6}{t+6}$$

$$= \frac{t^2 - 11t + 18}{(t+6)(t-9)} - \frac{t^2 + 9t + 18}{(t+6)(t-9)}$$

Subtract the numerators (be sure to write parentheses around the second numerator).

$$= \frac{t^2 - 11t + 18 - (t^2 + 9t + 18)}{(t+6)(t-9)}$$

$$= \frac{t^2 - 11t + 18 - t^2 - 9t - 18}{(t+6)(t-9)}$$ *Distribute -1*

$$= \frac{-20t}{(t+6)(t-9)}$$ *Combine like terms*

Try Problem 33 >   This answer cannot be simplified further.   ■

EXAMPLE 6   Add $\dfrac{15}{p^2 - 1} + \dfrac{15}{2p + 2}$.

Solution   Factor the denominators to find the LCD.

$$\frac{15}{p^2 - 1} + \frac{15}{2p + 2} = \frac{15}{(p + 1)(p - 1)} + \frac{15}{2(p + 1)}$$

Write each rational expression with the LCD, $2(p + 1)(p - 1)$.

$$= \frac{15}{(p + 1)(p - 1)} \cdot \frac{2}{2} + \frac{15}{2(p + 1)} \cdot \frac{p - 1}{p - 1}$$

$$= \frac{30}{2(p + 1)(p - 1)} + \frac{15p - 15}{2(p + 1)(p - 1)}$$

$$= \frac{30 + 15p - 15}{2(p + 1)(p - 1)} \qquad \text{Add the numerators}$$

$$= \frac{15p + 15}{2(p + 1)(p - 1)}$$

$$= \frac{15(p + 1)}{2(p + 1)(p - 1)} \qquad \text{Factor the numerator}$$

Try Problem 39 >

$$= \frac{15}{2(p - 1)} \qquad \text{Simplify.}$$ ■

EXAMPLE 7   Subtract $\dfrac{r}{r^2 + 6r + 9} - \dfrac{r + 1}{r^2 + 5r + 6}$.

Solution   Factor the denominators to find the LCD.

$$\frac{r}{r^2 + 6r + 9} - \frac{r + 1}{r^2 + 5r + 6}$$

$$= \frac{r}{(r + 3)^2} - \frac{r + 1}{(r + 3)(r + 2)}$$

Write each rational expression with the LCD, $(r + 3)^2(r + 2)$.

$$= \frac{r}{(r + 3)^2} \cdot \frac{r + 2}{r + 2} - \frac{r + 1}{(r + 3)(r + 2)} \cdot \frac{r + 3}{r + 3}$$

$$= \frac{r^2 + 2r}{(r + 3)^2(r + 2)} - \frac{r^2 + 4r + 3}{(r + 3)^2(r + 2)}$$

Subtract the numerators (be sure to write parentheses around the second numerator).

$$= \frac{r^2 + 2r - (r^2 + 4r + 3)}{(r + 3)^2(r + 2)}$$

$$= \frac{r^2 + 2r - r^2 - 4r - 3}{(r + 3)^2(r + 2)}$$

Try Problem 45 >

$$= \frac{-2r - 3}{(r + 3)^2(r + 2)}$$ ■

EXAMPLE 8   Subtract $\dfrac{7x + 21}{x^2 + x - 12} - \dfrac{5x + 9}{x^2 - 2x - 3}$.

Solution   Factor the denominators to find the LCD.

$$\dfrac{7x + 21}{x^2 + x - 12} - \dfrac{5x + 9}{x^2 - 2x - 3}$$

$$= \dfrac{7x + 21}{(x - 3)(x + 4)} - \dfrac{5x + 9}{(x + 1)(x - 3)}$$

Write each rational expression with the LCD, $(x - 3)(x + 4)(x + 1)$.

$$= \dfrac{7x + 21}{(x - 3)(x + 4)} \cdot \dfrac{x + 1}{x + 1} - \dfrac{5x + 9}{(x + 1)(x - 3)} \cdot \dfrac{x + 4}{x + 4}$$

$$= \dfrac{7x^2 + 28x + 21}{(x - 3)(x + 4)(x + 1)} - \dfrac{5x^2 + 29x + 36}{(x - 3)(x + 4)(x + 1)}$$

Subtract the numerators (be sure to write parentheses around the second numerator).

$$= \dfrac{7x^2 + 28x + 21 - (5x^2 + 29x + 36)}{(x - 3)(x + 4)(x + 1)}$$

$$= \dfrac{7x^2 + 28x + 21 - 5x^2 - 29x - 36}{(x - 3)(x + 4)(x + 1)}$$

$$= \dfrac{2x^2 - x - 15}{(x - 3)(x + 4)(x + 1)}$$

Factor the numerator, then simplify.

$$= \dfrac{(2x + 5)(x - 3)}{(x - 3)(x + 4)(x + 1)}$$

Try Problem 49 >

$$= \dfrac{2x + 5}{(x + 4)(x + 1)}$$ ∎

5.5 Problem Set

LEARNING THROUGH WRITING

☐ Describe the steps in adding or subtracting rational expressions having unlike denominators.

☐ Discuss situations where you can and situations where you cannot divide out common factors when performing operations on rational expressions.

Add or subtract as indicated. Write your answer in simplest form.

1. $\dfrac{x}{10} + \dfrac{x}{5}$

2. $\dfrac{x}{15} + \dfrac{x}{5}$

3. $\dfrac{a}{2} - \dfrac{2}{a}$

4. $\dfrac{a}{3} - \dfrac{3}{a}$

5. $\dfrac{1}{2x} + \dfrac{1}{9x}$

6. $\dfrac{1}{5x} + \dfrac{1}{4x}$

7. $\dfrac{5}{12m} - \dfrac{1}{8m}$

8. $\dfrac{8}{15m} - \dfrac{1}{10m}$

9. $\dfrac{1}{r^2} + \dfrac{3}{r}$

10. $\dfrac{1}{r^2} + \dfrac{2}{r}$

11. $\dfrac{4}{y} - \dfrac{2}{y^2}$

12. $\dfrac{6}{y} - \dfrac{3}{y^2}$

13. $\dfrac{8}{a^2} + \dfrac{6}{ab}$

14. $\dfrac{9}{ab} + \dfrac{4}{b^2}$

15. $\dfrac{3}{12x^2y^4} - \dfrac{5}{18x^2y^5}$

16. $\dfrac{9}{80x^4y^2} - \dfrac{7}{90x^3y^3}$

17. $\dfrac{2}{xy^2} - \dfrac{3}{x^2y} + \dfrac{1}{xy}$

18. $\dfrac{5}{x^2y} - \dfrac{4}{xy^2} + \dfrac{1}{xy}$

19. $7 + \dfrac{1}{x}$

20. $5 + \dfrac{1}{x}$

21. $\dfrac{1}{4t} + t$

22. $\dfrac{1}{9t} + t$

23. $a - \dfrac{a^2}{a+4}$

24. $a - \dfrac{a^2}{a+6}$

Add or subtract as indicated. Write your answer in simplest form.

25. $\dfrac{1}{x} - \dfrac{1}{x-4}$

26. $\dfrac{1}{x} - \dfrac{1}{x-6}$

27. $\dfrac{m}{m+6} + \dfrac{1}{m}$

28. $\dfrac{m}{m+8} + \dfrac{1}{m}$

29. $\dfrac{3}{a+2} + \dfrac{8}{a-4}$

30. $\dfrac{4}{a+3} + \dfrac{2}{a-1}$

31. $\dfrac{x}{x-3} - \dfrac{1}{x+3}$

32. $\dfrac{x}{x-4} - \dfrac{1}{x+4}$

33. $\dfrac{t-4}{t+8} - \dfrac{t+1}{t-2}$

34. $\dfrac{t-2}{t+3} - \dfrac{t+4}{t-6}$

35. $\dfrac{10}{3m+12} + \dfrac{1}{m+4}$

36. $\dfrac{8}{5m-10} + \dfrac{1}{m-2}$

37. $\dfrac{6}{r^2-1} + \dfrac{3}{r+1}$

38. $\dfrac{30}{r^2-9} + \dfrac{5}{r+3}$

39. $\dfrac{22}{p^2-4} + \dfrac{11}{2p+4}$

40. $\dfrac{27}{p^2-81} + \dfrac{3}{2p+18}$

41. $\dfrac{2}{t^2-3t} + \dfrac{3}{5t}$

42. $\dfrac{5}{t^2-4t} + \dfrac{2}{3t}$

43. $\dfrac{6k}{(k-1)^2} - \dfrac{2}{k^2-1}$

44. $\dfrac{2k}{(k+2)^2} - \dfrac{3}{k^2-4}$

45. $\dfrac{r}{r^2+4r+4} - \dfrac{r+3}{r^2+3r+2}$

46. $\dfrac{r}{r^2+8r+16} - \dfrac{r+1}{r^2+7r+12}$

47. $\dfrac{m-3}{m^2+4m-5} + \dfrac{m-2}{m^2+11m+30}$

48. $\dfrac{m-3}{m^2+m-6} - \dfrac{m+2}{m^2+3m-10}$

49. $\dfrac{9x-20}{x^2+x-12} - \dfrac{6x-13}{x^2-x-6}$

50. $\dfrac{3x-2}{x^2-3x-4} - \dfrac{x+2}{x^2-5x+4}$

51. $\dfrac{1}{x-3} + \dfrac{2}{x+3} - \dfrac{6}{x^2-9}$

52. $\dfrac{1}{x+1} + \dfrac{1}{x-1} - \dfrac{2}{x^2-1}$

53. $\dfrac{2y}{y - 6} + \dfrac{1}{y + 4} + \dfrac{10}{y^2 - 2y - 24}$

54. $\dfrac{2y}{y + 7} + \dfrac{1}{y - 5} - \dfrac{12}{y^2 + 2y - 35}$

55. $\dfrac{4z}{z^2 - 16} - \dfrac{2}{z} - \dfrac{2}{z - 4}$

56. $\dfrac{6z}{z^2 - 36} - \dfrac{3}{z} - \dfrac{3}{z - 6}$

57. $\left[\dfrac{-x}{2 - x} - \dfrac{3}{(x - 2)^2} \right] \dfrac{x^3 - 8}{x^3 - 3x^2 + 4x - 12}$

58. $\left[\dfrac{-x}{3 - x} - \dfrac{4}{(x - 3)^2} \right] \dfrac{x^3 - 27}{x^3 - 4x^2 + x - 4}$

Show that each formula is true.

59. $\dfrac{a}{b} + \dfrac{c}{d} = \dfrac{ad + bc}{bd}$

60. $\dfrac{a}{b} - \dfrac{c}{d} = \dfrac{ad - bc}{bd}$

5.6   Complex Fractions

Sometimes a rational expression contains fractions in its numerator or in its denominator.

DEFINITION OF A COMPLEX FRACTION

A **complex fraction** is a fraction that contains other fractions in its numerator or denominator or both. A fraction that is not a complex fraction is called a **simple fraction.**

Here are some examples of complex fractions.

$$\dfrac{1 + \dfrac{1}{2}}{5} \qquad \dfrac{x + y}{\dfrac{1}{x} + \dfrac{1}{y}} \qquad \dfrac{1 - \dfrac{1}{p^2}}{\dfrac{1}{5} + \dfrac{1}{5p}}$$

We identify the parts of a complex fraction as follows:

$$\textit{Main fraction bar} \rightarrow \dfrac{\left. \dfrac{1}{a} + \dfrac{1}{b} \right\} \leftarrow\textit{Numerator of complex fraction}}{\left. \dfrac{a + b}{b} \right\} \leftarrow\textit{Denominator of complex fraction}}$$

We call the fractions $1/a$, $1/b$, and $(a + b)/b$ **secondary fractions** of the complex fraction above.

Because of their various fractional parts, complex fractions are difficult to interpret. Therefore we need to know how to simplify a complex fraction. The two methods for simplifying a complex fraction are illustrated in Example 1.

EXAMPLE 1   Simplify $\dfrac{\dfrac{2}{3} + \dfrac{1}{6}}{\dfrac{1}{3} + \dfrac{3}{4}}$.

Solution
Method 1   *Write the numerator of the complex fraction as a single fraction and the denominator as a single fraction.*

$$\frac{\dfrac{2}{3} + \dfrac{1}{6}}{\dfrac{1}{3} + \dfrac{3}{4}} = \frac{\dfrac{4}{6} + \dfrac{1}{6}}{\dfrac{4}{12} + \dfrac{9}{12}} = \frac{\dfrac{5}{6}}{\dfrac{13}{12}}$$

Now divide the two fractions.

$$\frac{\dfrac{5}{6}}{\dfrac{13}{12}} = \frac{5}{6} \div \frac{13}{12} = \frac{5}{6} \cdot \frac{12}{13} = \frac{60}{78} = \frac{10}{13}$$

Method 2   *Multiply both the numerator and the denominator of the complex fraction by the least common denominator of all the secondary fractions.* Since the LCD of 2/3, 1/6, 1/3, and 3/4 is 12, we write

$$\frac{\dfrac{2}{3} + \dfrac{1}{6}}{\dfrac{1}{3} + \dfrac{3}{4}} = \frac{\left(\dfrac{2}{3} + \dfrac{1}{6}\right)12}{\left(\dfrac{1}{3} + \dfrac{3}{4}\right)12} = \frac{\left(\dfrac{2}{3}\right)12 + \left(\dfrac{1}{6}\right)12}{\left(\dfrac{1}{3}\right)12 + \left(\dfrac{3}{4}\right)12} = \frac{8 + 2}{4 + 9} = \frac{10}{13}.$$

Try Problem 3 >

Note that the original complex fraction simplifies to 10/13 no matter which method is used. ■

TO SIMPLIFY A COMPLEX FRACTION

Method 1   Write the numerator of the complex fraction as a single fraction and the denominator as a single fraction.

Method 2   Multiply both the numerator and the denominator of the complex fraction by the least common denominator of all the secondary fractions.

EXAMPLE 2   Simplify $\dfrac{\dfrac{2r^3}{s}}{\dfrac{4r^3}{s^2}}$.

Solution

Method 1   Both the numerator and the denominator of the complex fraction are already a single fraction. Therefore divide the two fractions.

$$\frac{\dfrac{2r^3}{s}}{\dfrac{4r^3}{s^2}} = \frac{2r^3}{s} \div \frac{4r^3}{s^2}$$

$$= \frac{2r^3}{s} \cdot \frac{s^2}{4r^3}$$

$$= \frac{2r^3 s^2}{4r^3 s}$$

$$= \frac{s}{2}$$

Try Problem 7 >

Method 2   The LCD of the secondary fractions is s^2. Therefore multiply both the numerator and the denominator of the complex fraction by s^2.

$$\frac{\dfrac{2r^3}{s}}{\dfrac{4r^3}{s^2}} = \frac{\left(\dfrac{2r^3}{s}\right)s^2}{\left(\dfrac{4r^3}{s^2}\right)s^2}$$

$$= \frac{2r^3 s}{4r^3}$$

$$= \frac{s}{2}$$

■

Caution! ■ When using Method 2, make sure you multiply both the numerator and the denominator of the complex fraction by the same quantity.

Correct

$$\frac{\dfrac{1}{a}}{\dfrac{1}{a^2}} = \frac{\left(\dfrac{1}{a}\right)a^2}{\left(\dfrac{1}{a^2}\right)a^2}$$

Wrong

$$\frac{\dfrac{1}{a}}{\dfrac{1}{a^2}} = \frac{\left(\dfrac{1}{a}\right)a}{\left(\dfrac{1}{a^2}\right)a^2}$$

EXAMPLE 3   Simplify $\dfrac{\dfrac{1}{a} + \dfrac{1}{b}}{\dfrac{a+b}{a}}$.

Solution

Method 1   The denominator is already a single fraction. Write the numerator as a single fraction.

$$\frac{\dfrac{1}{a}+\dfrac{1}{b}}{\dfrac{a+b}{a}}=\frac{\dfrac{1}{a}\cdot\dfrac{b}{b}+\dfrac{1}{b}\cdot\dfrac{a}{a}}{\dfrac{a+b}{a}}$$

$$=\frac{\dfrac{b+a}{ab}}{\dfrac{a+b}{a}}$$

$$=\frac{b+a}{ab}\cdot\frac{a}{a+b}$$

$$=\frac{1}{b}$$

Method 2   The LCD of the secondary fractions is ab. Multiply both the numerator and denominator by ab.

$$\frac{\dfrac{1}{a}+\dfrac{1}{b}}{\dfrac{a+b}{a}}=\frac{\left(\dfrac{1}{a}+\dfrac{1}{b}\right)ab}{\left(\dfrac{a+b}{a}\right)ab}$$

$$=\frac{\dfrac{1}{a}\cdot ab+\dfrac{1}{b}\cdot ab}{\dfrac{a+b}{a}\cdot ab}$$

$$=\frac{b+a}{(a+b)b}$$

$$=\frac{1}{b}\qquad\blacksquare$$

Try Problem 13 >

Note that in Method 1 we are working with the numerator and the denominator of the complex fraction separately. In Method 2 we are working with the entire complex fraction at once.

EXAMPLE 4   Simplify $\dfrac{1+\dfrac{3}{x}}{\dfrac{1}{9}-\dfrac{1}{x^2}}$.

Solution

Method 1

$$\frac{1+\dfrac{3}{x}}{\dfrac{1}{9}-\dfrac{1}{x^2}}=\frac{\dfrac{1}{1}\cdot\dfrac{x}{x}+\dfrac{3}{x}}{\dfrac{1}{9}\cdot\dfrac{x^2}{x^2}-\dfrac{1}{x^2}\cdot\dfrac{9}{9}}$$

$$=\frac{\dfrac{x+3}{x}}{\dfrac{x^2-9}{9x^2}}$$

$$=\frac{x+3}{x}\cdot\frac{9x^2}{x^2-9}$$

$$=\frac{x+3}{x}\cdot\frac{9x^2}{(x+3)(x-3)}$$

$$=\frac{9x}{x-3}$$

Method 2

$$\frac{1+\dfrac{3}{x}}{\dfrac{1}{9}-\dfrac{1}{x^2}}=\frac{\left(1+\dfrac{3}{x}\right)9x^2}{\left(\dfrac{1}{9}-\dfrac{1}{x^2}\right)9x^2}$$

$$=\frac{1\cdot 9x^2+\dfrac{3}{x}\cdot 9x^2}{\dfrac{1}{9}\cdot 9x^2-\dfrac{1}{x^2}\cdot 9x^2}$$

$$=\frac{9x^2+27x}{x^2-9}$$

$$=\frac{9x(x+3)}{(x+3)(x-3)}$$

$$=\frac{9x}{x-3}\qquad\blacksquare$$

Try Problem 21 >

PROBLEM SOLVING

EXAMPLE 5   A path up a hill is 1 mile long. A hiker walks up the path at 3 mph and down the path at 5 mph. Find the hiker's average speed for the round trip.

Solution   The average speed is *not* 4 mph (the average of 3 mph and 5 mph). That is because the hiker walks at the rate of 3 mph for a longer period of time than the hiker walks at 5 mph. Therefore the average speed for the round trip is closer to 3 mph than it is to 5 mph. Let r denote the hiker's average speed for the round trip. Since $r = d/t$, we write

$$r = \frac{\text{distance of round trip}}{\text{time of round trip}}$$

$$r = \frac{\text{distance up hill } + \text{ distance down hill}}{\text{time up hill } + \text{ time down hill}}$$

Since $t = d/r$, we have

$$r = \frac{1 + 1}{\dfrac{\text{distance up hill}}{\text{rate up hill}} + \dfrac{\text{distance down hill}}{\text{rate down hill}}}$$

$$r = \frac{2}{\dfrac{1}{3} + \dfrac{1}{5}}.$$

Now simplify the complex fraction.

$$r = \frac{(2)15}{\left(\dfrac{1}{3} + \dfrac{1}{5}\right)15} = \frac{30}{5 + 3} = \frac{30}{8} = \frac{15}{4} = 3\frac{3}{4}$$

Try Problem 49 >   The hiker's average speed was 3 3/4 mph.

5.6 Problem Set

LEARNING THROUGH WRITING

☐ Define the term *complex fraction*.

☐ Define the term *simple fraction*.

☐ Define the term *secondary fraction*.

☐ Describe the two methods for simplifying a complex fraction.

Simplify each complex fraction.

1. $\dfrac{1 + \dfrac{1}{5}}{2}$

2. $\dfrac{3}{1 + \dfrac{1}{11}}$

3. $\dfrac{\dfrac{1}{3} + \dfrac{1}{6}}{\dfrac{3}{4} + \dfrac{1}{3}}$

4. $\dfrac{\dfrac{2}{5} + \dfrac{1}{15}}{\dfrac{1}{5} + \dfrac{1}{3}}$

5. $\dfrac{\dfrac{x + 1}{x}}{\dfrac{x - 1}{x}}$

6. $\dfrac{\dfrac{x - 2}{x}}{\dfrac{x + 2}{x}}$

7. $\dfrac{\dfrac{2r^3}{s^2}}{\dfrac{6r^3}{s^3}}$

8. $\dfrac{\dfrac{4r^5}{s^2}}{\dfrac{8r^4}{s^2}}$

9. $\dfrac{\dfrac{1}{m^2 - 16}}{\dfrac{1}{m + 4}}$

10. $\dfrac{\dfrac{1}{m^2 - 36}}{\dfrac{1}{m + 6}}$

11. $\dfrac{\dfrac{1}{b} + a}{\dfrac{1}{a} + b}$

12. $\dfrac{\dfrac{1}{b} - a}{\dfrac{1}{a} - b}$

13. $\dfrac{\dfrac{1}{a} + \dfrac{1}{b}}{\dfrac{a + b}{b}}$

14. $\dfrac{\dfrac{1}{a} - \dfrac{1}{b}}{\dfrac{b - a}{a}}$

15. $\dfrac{1 - \dfrac{x}{y}}{1 - \dfrac{x^2}{y^2}}$

16. $\dfrac{3 - \dfrac{x}{y}}{9 - \dfrac{x^2}{y^2}}$

17. $\dfrac{\dfrac{1}{xy} + 1}{\dfrac{1}{x} - \dfrac{y}{x^2}}$

18. $\dfrac{\dfrac{x}{y^2} + 1}{\dfrac{1}{x} + \dfrac{1}{xy}}$

19. $\dfrac{\dfrac{1}{ab} - \dfrac{1}{b}}{\dfrac{1}{b} - \dfrac{1}{ab}}$

20. $\dfrac{\dfrac{1}{a} - \dfrac{1}{ab}}{\dfrac{1}{ab} - \dfrac{1}{a}}$

21. $\dfrac{1 + \dfrac{2}{x}}{\dfrac{1}{4} - \dfrac{1}{x^2}}$

22. $\dfrac{1 + \dfrac{5}{x}}{\dfrac{1}{25} - \dfrac{1}{x^2}}$

23. $\dfrac{t^2 - 1}{1 - \dfrac{1}{t}}$

24. $\dfrac{t^2 - 1}{1 + \dfrac{1}{t}}$

25. $\dfrac{\dfrac{3}{4z} - \dfrac{2}{3z^2}}{\dfrac{1}{2z} + \dfrac{5}{6z^2}}$

26. $\dfrac{\dfrac{2}{3z} + \dfrac{7}{10z^2}}{\dfrac{4}{5z} - \dfrac{1}{2z^2}}$

27. $\dfrac{1 - \dfrac{9}{p^2}}{1 - \dfrac{1}{p} - \dfrac{6}{p^2}}$

28. $\dfrac{1 - \dfrac{4}{p^2}}{1 - \dfrac{1}{p} - \dfrac{6}{p^2}}$

29. $\dfrac{2 + \dfrac{5}{x} - \dfrac{12}{x^2}}{3 + \dfrac{11}{x} - \dfrac{4}{x^2}}$

30. $\dfrac{3 - \dfrac{5}{x} - \dfrac{2}{x^2}}{4 - \dfrac{11}{x} + \dfrac{6}{x^2}}$

31. $\dfrac{1}{1 + \dfrac{1}{x + 1}}$

32. $\dfrac{1}{1 + \dfrac{1}{x - 1}}$

33. $\dfrac{\dfrac{5}{m + 2} + 1}{1 - \dfrac{5}{m + 2}}$

34. $\dfrac{\dfrac{3}{m + 1} + 1}{1 - \dfrac{3}{m + 1}}$

35. $\dfrac{k - 7 + \dfrac{5}{k - 1}}{k - 3 + \dfrac{1}{k - 1}}$

36. $\dfrac{k + 4 + \dfrac{5}{k - 2}}{k + 6 + \dfrac{15}{k - 2}}$

37. $\dfrac{\dfrac{1}{y} - \dfrac{1}{y + 2}}{\dfrac{1}{y} + \dfrac{1}{y + 2}}$

38. $\dfrac{\dfrac{1}{y} + \dfrac{1}{y + 4}}{\dfrac{1}{y} - \dfrac{1}{y + 4}}$

39. $1 + \dfrac{1}{1 - \dfrac{1}{1 + 1}}$

40. $1 + \dfrac{1}{1 + \dfrac{1}{1 + 1}}$

Write each expression with positive exponents. Then simplify the resulting complex fraction.

41. $\dfrac{a^{-1}}{b^{-2}}$

42. $\dfrac{a^{-3}}{b^{-1}}$

43. $\dfrac{x^{-2} - 1}{x^{-1} - 1}$

44. $\dfrac{x^{-1} + 1}{x^{-2} - 1}$

45. $\dfrac{m - 2}{8m^{-2} - m}$

46. $\dfrac{m - 3}{27m^{-2} - m}$

The efficiency, E, of a jack is given by the formula

$$E = \dfrac{\dfrac{x}{2}}{x + \dfrac{1}{2}}.$$

47. Determine E if $x = 3/4$.

48. Determine E if $x = 2/5$.

The average speed, r, for a round trip is given by the formula

$$r = \dfrac{2}{\dfrac{1}{a} + \dfrac{1}{b}},$$

where a is the speed to the destination and b is the speed on the return trip.

49. A path up a hill is 1 mile long. A hiker walks up the path at 2 mph and down the path at 6 mph. Find the hiker's average speed for the round trip.

50. You drive the 10 miles to work at 60 mph. You drive home at 40 mph. Find your average speed for the round trip.

51. A lumberjack travels 4 mph going up a 50-foot tree and 20 mph coming down. Find the lumberjack's average speed for the round trip.

52. A skier rides the ski lift up a 750-foot slope at 4 mph and skis down at 40 mph. Find the skier's average speed for the round trip.

5.7   Equations Involving Rational Expressions

In earlier chapters we learned how to solve linear equations and quadratic equations. In this section we learn how to solve equations that involve rational expressions.

When solving an equation containing fractions, it is usually best to clear the equation of fractions as soon as possible. This is done by multiplying both sides of the equation by the least common denominator.

EXAMPLE 1   Solve $\dfrac{x}{2} + \dfrac{x}{4} = 6$.

Solution

$$4 \cdot \left(\dfrac{x}{2} + \dfrac{x}{4} \right) = 4 \cdot 6 \qquad \textit{Multiply both sides by the LCD, 4}$$

$$\overset{2}{\cancel{4}}\left(\dfrac{x}{\cancel{2}} \right) + \cancel{4}\left(\dfrac{x}{\cancel{4}} \right) = 4 \cdot 6 \qquad \textit{Distribute 4 on the left side}$$

$$2x + x = 24$$

This equation has no fractions and is easily solved.

$$3x = 24 \qquad \textit{Simplify the left side}$$
$$x = 8 \qquad \textit{Divide both sides by 3}$$

Try Problem 1 >   The solution is 8. Check in the original equation.   ■

Caution! ■   Students often confuse the following two problems.

PROBLEM 1 Solve $\dfrac{x}{2} + \dfrac{x}{4} = 6$.	**PROBLEM 2** Add $\dfrac{x}{2} + \dfrac{x}{4}$.
Solution We solve the equation to get a value for x.	**Solution** We add the two rational expressions to get a third rational expression.

$$\frac{x}{2} + \frac{x}{4} = 6$$
$$4\left(\frac{x}{2} + \frac{x}{4}\right) = 4 \cdot 6$$
$$2x + x = 24$$
$$3x = 24$$
$$x = 8$$

$$\frac{x}{2} + \frac{x}{4} = \frac{x}{2} \cdot \frac{2}{2} + \frac{x}{4}$$
$$= \frac{2x}{4} + \frac{x}{4}$$
$$= \frac{2x + x}{4}$$
$$= \frac{3x}{4}$$

EXAMPLE 2   Solve $\dfrac{1}{4x} - \dfrac{1}{3x} = \dfrac{1}{12}$.

Solution

$$12x \cdot \left(\frac{1}{4x} - \frac{1}{3x}\right) = 12x\left(\frac{1}{12}\right) \qquad \textit{Multiply both sides by the LCD, } 12x$$

$$\overset{3}{\cancel{12x}}\left(\frac{1}{\cancel{4x}}\right) - \overset{4}{\cancel{12x}}\left(\frac{1}{\cancel{3x}}\right) = x \qquad \textit{Distribute } 12x \textit{ on the left side}$$

$$3 - 4 = x \qquad \textit{Simplify the left side}$$
$$-1 = x$$

Try Problem 9 >   The solution is -1. Check in the original equation.   ■

Caution! ■   Students often make the mistake of inverting each term of an equation. They think they are performing the same operation on each side, when actually they are performing the same operation on each term. Notice how this mistake produces an incorrect solution to Example 2.

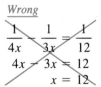

Wrong

EXAMPLE 3   Solve $\dfrac{m - 4}{4} - \dfrac{m - 3}{6} = \dfrac{1}{12}$.

Solution

$$12 \cdot \left(\frac{m - 4}{4} - \frac{m - 3}{6} \right) = 12\left(\frac{1}{12} \right) \quad \textit{Multiply both sides by the LCD, } 12$$

$$\overset{3}{\cancel{12}}\left(\frac{m - 4}{\cancel{4}} \right) - \overset{2}{\cancel{12}}\left(\frac{m - 3}{\cancel{6}} \right) = 1 \quad \textit{Distribute } 12$$

$$3(m - 4) - 2(m - 3) = 1 \qquad \textit{Simplify the left side, and}$$
$$3m - 12 - 2m + 6 = 1 \qquad \textit{solve (make sure you write}$$
$$m - 6 = 1 \qquad\qquad \textit{parentheses around } m - 4$$
$$m = 7 \qquad\qquad\quad \textit{and } m - 3)$$

Try Problem 29 >   he solution is 7. Check in the original equation.   ■

EXAMPLE 4   Solve $\dfrac{y + 1}{y - 3} = \dfrac{4}{y - 3} + 6$.

Solution

$$\cancel{(y - 3)}\left(\frac{y + 1}{\cancel{y - 3}} \right) = \cancel{(y - 3)}\left(\frac{4}{\cancel{y - 3}} \right) + (y - 3)6 \quad \textit{Multiply both sides by the LCD, } y - 3$$

$$y + 1 = 4 + 6y - 18$$
$$y + 1 = 6y - 14$$
$$-5y = -15$$
$$y = 3$$

The proposed solution is 3. However, 3 does not check in the original equation because it makes both denominators 0.

Check:

$$\frac{y + 1}{y - 3} = \frac{4}{y - 3} + 6 \qquad \textit{Original equation}$$

$$\frac{3 + 1}{3 - 3} = \frac{4}{3 - 3} + 6 \qquad \textit{Replace } y \textit{ with } 3$$

$$\frac{4}{0} = \frac{4}{0} + 6 \qquad\qquad \textit{4/0 is undefined}$$

Try Problem 35 >   Therefore the equation has no solution.   ■

Caution! ■
■
■
■
■

When you solve an equation that contains a variable in a denominator, you must check your answer to make sure it does not yield a denominator of 0. A solution obtained during the solving process that does not check in the original equation is called an **extraneous solution,** and must be discarded.

EXAMPLE 5   Solve $\dfrac{4}{3p - 3} + \dfrac{1}{3} = \dfrac{1}{p^2 - 1}$.

Solution   Factor the denominators to find the LCD.

$$\frac{4}{3(p - 1)} + \frac{1}{3} = \frac{1}{(p + 1)(p - 1)}$$

Multiply both sides by the LCD, $3(p - 1)(p + 1)$.

$$\cancel{3}\cancel{(p - 1)}(p + 1) \frac{4}{\cancel{3}\cancel{(p - 1)}} + \cancel{3}(p - 1)(p + 1) \frac{1}{\cancel{3}}$$

$$= 3\cancel{(p - 1)}\cancel{(p + 1)} \frac{1}{\cancel{(p + 1)}\cancel{(p - 1)}}$$

$$(p + 1)4 + (p - 1)(p + 1) = 3$$
$$4p + 4 + p^2 - 1 = 3$$
$$p^2 + 4p = 0$$

Factor the left side of this quadratic equation, set each factor equal to 0, and solve.

$$p(p + 4) = 0$$

$$p = 0 \quad \text{or} \quad p + 4 = 0$$
$$p = -4$$

Try Problem 43 >   Both numbers check, so the solutions are 0 and -4.   ∎

TO SOLVE AN EQUATION INVOLVING RATIONAL EXPRESSIONS

1. Factor the denominators to find the LCD.
2. Multiply both sides of the equation by the LCD. This will result in every term's being multiplied by the LCD. The equation should be clear of fractions after this step.
3. Solve the equation resulting from Step 2.
4. Check all solutions in the original equation. If any solution yields a denominator of 0, it is an extraneous solution and must be discarded.

EXAMPLE 6   Solve $\dfrac{3}{r} + \dfrac{8}{r^2 - 4} = \dfrac{2}{r - 2}$.

Solution
Step 1   *Factor the denominators to find the LCD.*

$$\frac{3}{r} + \frac{8}{(r + 2)(r - 2)} = \frac{2}{r - 2}$$

The LCD is $r(r + 2)(r - 2)$.

Step 2 *Multiply both sides of the equation by the LCD. This will result in every term's being multiplied by the LCD.*

$$\cancel{r}(r + 2)(r - 2)\frac{3}{\cancel{r}} + r\cancel{(r + 2)}\cancel{(r - 2)}\frac{8}{\cancel{(r + 2)}\cancel{(r - 2)}}$$

$$= r(r + 2)\cancel{(r - 2)}\frac{2}{\cancel{r - 2}}$$

$$(r + 2)(r - 2)3 + 8r = 2r(r + 2)$$

Step 3 *Solve the equation resulting from Step 2.*

$$\left.\begin{array}{l}(r^2 - 4)3 + 8r = 2r^2 + 4r \\ 3r^2 - 12 + 8r = 2r^2 + 4r\end{array}\right\}\text{Simplify both sides}$$

$$r^2 + 4r - 12 = 0 \qquad \text{Write in standard form}$$

$$(r + 6)(r - 2) = 0 \qquad \text{Factor the left side}$$

$$\begin{array}{llll} r + 6 = 0 & \text{or} & r - 2 = 0 & \text{Set each factor equal to 0} \\ r = -6 & \text{or} & r = 2 & \text{Solve each linear equation}\end{array}$$

Step 4 *Check both solutions in the original equation.*

$$\underline{Check\ r = -6}$$

$$\frac{3}{r} + \frac{8}{r^2 - 4} = \frac{2}{r - 2}$$

$$\frac{3}{-6} + \frac{8}{(-6)^2 - 4} = \frac{2}{-6 - 2}$$

$$-\frac{1}{2} + \frac{8}{32} = -\frac{1}{4}$$

$$-\frac{1}{4} = -\frac{1}{4} \qquad True$$

$$\underline{Check\ r = 2}$$

$$\frac{3}{r} + \frac{8}{r^2 - 4} = \frac{2}{r - 2}$$

$$\frac{3}{2} + \frac{8}{2^2 - 4} = \frac{2}{2 - 2}$$

$$\frac{3}{2} + \frac{8}{0} = \frac{2}{0} \qquad Undefined$$

The number -6 checks, but the number 2 makes two of the denominators 0. Therefore 2 is an extraneous solution and must be discarded. The only solution is -6.   ■

Try Problem 49 >

Solving a Formula for a Variable

We can use the same technique to solve a formula containing rational expressions for one of its variables.

EXAMPLE 7   Solve $I = \dfrac{E}{R + r}$ for R.

Solution

$$I = \frac{E}{R + r} \qquad \text{Original formula}$$

$$(R + r)I = (R + r)\frac{E}{R + r} \qquad \text{Multiply both sides by } R + r$$

$$RI + rI = E \qquad \text{Distribute } I$$

$$RI + rI - rI = E - rI \qquad \text{Subtract } rI \text{ from both sides}$$

$$RI = E - rI \qquad \text{Simplify the left side}$$

$$\frac{RI}{I} = \frac{E - rI}{I} \qquad \text{Divide both sides by } I$$

Try Problem 61 >

$$R = \frac{E - rI}{I} \qquad \text{Simplify the left side}$$

5.7 Problem Set

LEARNING THROUGH WRITING

☐ Define the term *extraneous solution*.

☐ Describe the steps in solving an equation involving rational expressions.

Solve each equation.

1. $\dfrac{x}{3} + \dfrac{x}{6} = 2$

2. $\dfrac{x}{2} + \dfrac{x}{4} = 9$

3. $\dfrac{3r}{2} - \dfrac{3r}{4} = 6$

4. $\dfrac{5r}{3} - \dfrac{5r}{6} = 5$

5. $\dfrac{y}{3} - 2 = \dfrac{y}{4}$

6. $\dfrac{y}{2} - 3 = \dfrac{y}{3}$

7. $t + \dfrac{3}{2} = \dfrac{3t}{4} - \dfrac{t}{8}$

8. $t + \dfrac{5}{4} = \dfrac{5t}{6} - \dfrac{t}{12}$

9. $\dfrac{1}{4x} - \dfrac{1}{2x} = \dfrac{1}{8}$

10. $\dfrac{1}{6x} - \dfrac{1}{2x} = \dfrac{1}{12}$

11. $\dfrac{1}{2m} + \dfrac{1}{3m} = \dfrac{1}{6}$

12. $\dfrac{1}{3m} + \dfrac{1}{5m} = \dfrac{1}{15}$

13. $\dfrac{4}{y} + \dfrac{3}{5} = 1$

14. $\dfrac{3}{y} + \dfrac{2}{5} = 1$

15. $7 - \dfrac{5}{2p} = \dfrac{3}{p} + \dfrac{3}{2}$

16. $3 - \dfrac{4}{3p} = \dfrac{2}{p} + \dfrac{7}{3}$

17. $1 + \dfrac{1}{x} - \dfrac{6}{x^2} = 0$

18. $1 + \dfrac{1}{x} - \dfrac{2}{x^2} = 0$

Solve each equation and check your answer.

19. $\dfrac{x + 4}{x - 5} = \dfrac{2}{3}$

20. $\dfrac{x - 3}{x + 7} = \dfrac{4}{5}$

21. $\dfrac{z + 4}{z - 1} = \dfrac{5}{z - 1}$

22. $\dfrac{z + 7}{z + 6} = \dfrac{1}{z + 6}$

23. $\dfrac{r^2}{r + 3} = \dfrac{9}{r + 3}$

24. $\dfrac{r^2}{r - 5} = \dfrac{25}{r - 5}$

25. $\dfrac{x + 3}{2} + \dfrac{x + 1}{4} = 4$

26. $\dfrac{x + 2}{3} + \dfrac{x + 5}{6} = 4$

27. $\dfrac{2p - 1}{3} - 4 = \dfrac{p - 6}{2}$

28. $\dfrac{3p - 1}{5} - 3 = \dfrac{p - 5}{2}$

29. $\dfrac{m - 3}{8} - \dfrac{m - 10}{12} = \dfrac{5}{12}$

30. $\dfrac{m - 1}{6} - \dfrac{m - 2}{9} = \dfrac{5}{18}$

31. $\dfrac{h + 7}{2} - \dfrac{1}{3} = \dfrac{1}{2} - \dfrac{h + 9}{9}$

32. $\dfrac{h + 5}{4} - \dfrac{1}{3} = \dfrac{1}{4} - \dfrac{h + 6}{6}$

33. $\dfrac{x}{x + 4} + 1 = \dfrac{16}{x + 4}$

34. $\dfrac{x}{x + 6} + 1 = \dfrac{8}{x + 6}$

35. $\dfrac{y + 1}{y - 2} = \dfrac{3}{y - 2} + 5$

36. $\dfrac{y + 3}{y - 4} = \dfrac{7}{y - 4} + 6$

Solve each equation and check your answer.

37. $\dfrac{5}{x} - \dfrac{2}{x + 2} = \dfrac{4}{x}$

38. $\dfrac{7}{x} - \dfrac{2}{x + 1} = \dfrac{6}{x}$

39. $\dfrac{k}{2k + 2} = \dfrac{2k}{4k + 4} - \dfrac{k + 3}{k + 1}$

40. $\dfrac{k}{3k - 3} = \dfrac{2k}{6k - 6} - \dfrac{k + 4}{k - 1}$

41. $\dfrac{2}{t} + \dfrac{3}{t - 5} = \dfrac{2(3t + 2)}{t^2 - 5t}$

42. $\dfrac{4}{t} + \dfrac{5}{t - 6} = \dfrac{5(2t - 3)}{t^2 - 6t}$

43. $\dfrac{3}{2p - 2} + \dfrac{1}{2} = \dfrac{1}{p^2 - 1}$

44. $\dfrac{6}{5p - 5} + \dfrac{1}{5} = \dfrac{1}{p^2 - 1}$

45. $\dfrac{1}{m - 3} - \dfrac{3}{m + 3} = \dfrac{11}{m^2 - 9}$

46. $\dfrac{1}{m - 2} - \dfrac{5}{m + 2} = \dfrac{11}{m^2 - 4}$

47. $\dfrac{2x}{2x - 4} + \dfrac{8}{x^2 - 4} = \dfrac{3x}{3x + 6}$

48. $\dfrac{3x}{3x + 9} - \dfrac{18}{x^2 - 9} = \dfrac{4x}{4x - 12}$

49. $\dfrac{2}{r} + \dfrac{8}{r^2 - 16} = \dfrac{1}{r - 4}$

50. $\dfrac{2}{r} + \dfrac{10}{r^2 - 25} = \dfrac{1}{r - 5}$

51. $\dfrac{4y}{y^2 - y - 2} = \dfrac{7y}{y^2 + y - 6} - \dfrac{3y - 1}{y^2 + 4y + 3}$

52. $\dfrac{3y}{y^2 + 5y + 6} = \dfrac{5y}{y^2 + 2y - 3} - \dfrac{2y + 1}{y^2 + y - 2}$

53. $\dfrac{3}{x^2 + x - 2} - \dfrac{1}{x^2 - 1} = \dfrac{7}{2(x^2 + 3x + 2)}$

54. $\dfrac{4}{x^2 - x - 2} - \dfrac{1}{x^2 - 1} = \dfrac{5}{2(x^2 - 3x + 2)}$

Solve each formula for the specified variable.

55. $T = \dfrac{n}{4} + 40$ for n

56. $F = \dfrac{m}{3} - 30$ for m

57. $\dfrac{PV}{T} = \dfrac{pv}{t}$ for P

58. $\dfrac{PV}{T} = \dfrac{pv}{t}$ for p

59. $\dfrac{PV}{T} = \dfrac{pv}{t}$ for T

60. $\dfrac{PV}{T} = \dfrac{pv}{t}$ for t

61. $I = \dfrac{E}{R + r}$ for r

62. $S = \dfrac{a}{1 - r}$ for r

63. $y = \dfrac{x + 1}{x - 1}$ for x

64. $y = \dfrac{x - 2}{x + 2}$ for x

65. $\dfrac{1}{z} = \dfrac{1}{x} + \dfrac{1}{y}$ for x

66. $\dfrac{1}{z} = \dfrac{1}{x} - \dfrac{1}{y}$ for y

5.8   Problem Solving with Rational Equations

In this section we use the techniques learned in the previous section to solve certain types of word problems. We solve each word problem using the same four steps used in Chapter 2. The only difference here is that the equation we write in Step 2 is an equation involving rational expressions.

Number Problems

EXAMPLE 1   One number is twice another. The sum of their reciprocals is 1/2. Find the numbers.

Solution

Step 1   *Write down the unknown quantities. Call one x, and write the other in terms of x.*

$$x = \text{first number}$$
$$2x = \text{second number}$$

Step 2   *Write an equation involving x.*

$$
\begin{array}{ccc}
\text{Sum of} & & \dfrac{1}{2} \\
\text{reciprocals} & \text{is} & \\
\downarrow & \downarrow & \downarrow \\
\dfrac{1}{x} + \dfrac{1}{2x} & = & \dfrac{1}{2}
\end{array}
$$

Step 3   *Solve the equation to find x and 2x.*

$$2x\left(\frac{1}{x} + \frac{1}{2x}\right) = 2x\left(\frac{1}{2}\right) \qquad \text{\textit{Multiply by the LCD, }} 2x$$

$$2x\left(\frac{1}{x}\right) + 2x\left(\frac{1}{2x}\right) = 2x\left(\frac{1}{2}\right) \qquad \text{\textit{Distribute }} 2x \text{\textit{ on the left side}}$$

$$2 + 1 = x \qquad \text{\textit{Find each product}}$$

$$3 = x \qquad \text{\textit{Simplify the left side}}$$

The numbers are $x = 3$ and $2x = 6$.

Try Problem 5 >

Step 4   *Check in the words of the original problem.* Six is twice 3, and the sum of 1/3 and 1/6 is 1/2.   ■

Motion Problems

To solve motion problems we use the formula

$$d = rt,$$

where d is distance, r is rate, and t is time.

EXAMPLE 2   A paddleboat can travel 8 mph in still water. If the boat takes the same amount of time to travel 3 miles upstream as it does to travel 5 miles downstream, find the speed of the current.

Solution

$$x = \text{speed of the current}$$

To find the rate of the boat upstream (against the current), subtract the speed of the current from the speed of the boat. To find the rate downstream (with the current), add the speed of the current to the speed of the boat.

	Distance	Rate	Time
Upstream	3	$8 - x$	$\dfrac{3}{8 - x}$
Downstream	5	$8 + x$	$\dfrac{5}{8 + x}$

Since $t = \dfrac{d}{r}$

$$\begin{array}{ccc} Time & & time \\ upstream & = & downstream \\ \downarrow \;\; \downarrow & & \downarrow \end{array}$$

$$\frac{3}{8 - x} = \frac{5}{8 + x}$$

Multiply both sides by the LCD, $(8 - x)(8 + x)$.

$$(8 - x)(8 + x)\frac{3}{8 - x} = (8 - x)(8 + x)\frac{5}{8 + x}$$

$(8 + x)3 = (8 - x)5$	*Simplify*
$24 + 3x = 40 - 5x$	*Distributive property*
$8x = 16$	*Add 5x, subtract 24*
$x = 2$	*Divide by 8*

Try Problem 11 >   The speed of the current is 2 mph.   ■

Work Problems

To solve work problems, we make the following assumption: If it takes 3 hours to do a job, then the portion of the job completed in 1 hour is 1/3. More generally, we have the following rule.

RULE FOR SOLVING WORK PROBLEMS

If it takes x hours to do a job, then the portion of the job completed in 1 hour is $1/x$.

EXAMPLE 3   A large pump can empty a tank in 4 hours. A smaller pump takes 6 hours. How long would it take the two pumps working together to empty the tank?

Solution

x = time it takes both pumps working together to empty the tank

	Time to Do Job	Portion of Job Done in 1 Hour	
Large pump	4	$\dfrac{1}{4}$	←
Small pump	6	$\dfrac{1}{6}$	←
Both pumps	x	$\dfrac{1}{x}$	←

Sum equals this

Portion emptied by large pump in 1 hour	+	portion emptied by small pump in 1 hour	=	portion emptied by both pumps in 1 hour
↓	↓	↓	↓	↓
$\dfrac{1}{4}$	+	$\dfrac{1}{6}$	=	$\dfrac{1}{x}$

$$12x\left(\frac{1}{4}\right) + 12x\left(\frac{1}{6}\right) = 12x\left(\frac{1}{x}\right) \quad \textit{Multiply both sides by the LCD, } 12x$$

$$3x + 2x = 12 \qquad \textit{Find each product}$$

$$5x = 12 \qquad \textit{Combine like terms}$$

$$x = \frac{12}{5} \qquad \textit{Divide by 5}$$

Try Problem 19 > It would take both pumps working together 2 2/5 hours to empty the tank. ∎

EXAMPLE 4 An old copier takes 8 hours longer to copy the flyers for an advertising campaign than does a new copier. If the two copiers work together, the job takes 3 hours. How long does it take each copier to do the job on its own?

Solution

$$x = \text{time it takes fast copier to do the job}$$
$$x + 8 = \text{time it takes slow copier to do the job}$$

	Time to Do Job	Portion of Job Done in 1 Hour	
Fast copier	x	$\dfrac{1}{x}$	←
Slow copier	$x + 8$	$\dfrac{1}{x+8}$	←
Both copiers	3	$\dfrac{1}{3}$	←

Sum equals this

Portion of job done by fast copier in 1 hour		portion of job done by slow copier in 1 hour		portion of job done by both copiers in 1 hour
↓	+	↓	=	↓
$\dfrac{1}{x}$	+	$\dfrac{1}{x+8}$	=	$\dfrac{1}{3}$

Multiply both sides by the LCD, $3x(x + 8)$.

$$3x(x + 8)\,\frac{1}{x} + 3x(x + 8)\,\frac{1}{x + 8} = 3x(x + 8)\,\frac{1}{3}$$
$$3(x + 8) + 3x = x(x + 8)$$
$$3x + 24 + 3x = x^2 + 8x$$

Collect terms on the right side of this quadratic equation, and solve by factoring.

$$0 = x^2 + 2x - 24$$
$$0 = (x + 6)(x - 4)$$

$$x + 6 = 0 \qquad \text{or} \qquad x - 4 = 0$$
$$x = -6 \qquad \text{or} \qquad x = 4$$

Try Problem 23 >

The fast copier's time could not be -6 hours. Therefore the fast copier's time is $x = 4$ hours, and the slow copier's time is $x + 8 = 12$ hours. ∎

5.8 Problem Set

LEARNING THROUGH WRITING

☐ State the rule for solving a work problem.

☐ Describe the steps in solving a word problem.

Solve the following number problems.

1. One-half of a number is 3 more than one-fifth of the number. Find the number.

2. One-third of a number is 2 more than one-fifth of the number. Find the number.

3. Four plus three times the reciprocal of a number is 8. Find the number.

4. Six plus twice the reciprocal of a number is 9. Find the number.

5. One number is three times another. The sum of their reciprocals is 2/3. Find the numbers.

6. One number is five times another. The sum of their reciprocals is 3/10. Find the numbers.

7. What number must be added to the numerator and the denominator of 5/8 to make the result equal 2/3?

8. What number must be added to the numerator and the denominator of 7/10 to make the result equal 3/4?

9. A worker's 2-week salary is decreased by 3/8. If the new salary is $1345, what was the original salary?

10. A company states that its light beer has 1/3 fewer calories than its regular beer. If a 12-ounce bottle of its light beer has 96 calories, how many calories does a 12-ounce bottle of its regular beer have?

Solve the following motion problems.

11. A motorboat can travel 12 mph in still water. If the boat takes the same amount of time to travel 4 miles upstream as it does to travel 5 miles downstream, what is the speed of the current?

12. A canoeist can paddle 4 mph in still water. If it takes the canoeist as long to row 1 mile upstream as it does to row 2 miles downstream, what is the speed of the current?

13. A plane takes the same amount of time to fly 30 miles against the wind as it does to fly 50 miles with the wind. If the speed of the wind is 25 mph, what is the speed of the plane in still air?

14. A helicopter takes the same amount of time to fly 20 miles against the wind as it does to fly 30 miles with the wind. If the speed of the wind is 16 mph, what is the speed of the helicopter in still air?

15. One racer can cycle 60 miles in the same time that another racer cycles 45 miles. If the first racer cycles 10 mph faster than the second, what is the speed of each?

16. A plane travels 100 miles in the same time that a train travels 40 miles. If the plane travels 90 mph faster than the train, what is the speed of each?

17. A motorist drove 110 miles before running out of gas and walking 2 miles to a gas station. The rate at which the motorist drove was ten times the rate at which the motorist walked. If the total time spent driving and walking was 3 hours, what was the rate at which the motorist walked?

18. A racer cycled 75 miles of a 78-mile course before breaking a wheel and walking the rest of the way. The rate at which the racer cycled was five times the rate at which the racer walked. If the total time spent cycling and walking was 4 hours, what was the rate at which the racer walked?

	Distance	Rate	Time
Drove	110	10x	
Walked	2	x	

	Distance	Rate	Time
Cycled	75	5x	
Walked	3	x	

Solve the following work problems.

19. Two landscape employees work at different rates. The first employee can mow a particular customer's lawn in 3 hours. The second employee can mow the same lawn in 2 hours. How long would it take the two employees to mow the lawn working together?

20. Two painters work at different rates. The first painter can paint a garage in 9 hours. The second painter can paint the same garage in 6 hours. How long would it take the two painters working together to paint the garage?

21. One typist can type twice as fast as another. Together they can type the 800-page annual report in 4 days. How long would it take each typist to type the annual report working alone?

22. One clerk can stuff envelopes twice as fast as another. Together they can stuff 75,000 envelopes in 8 days. How long would it take each clerk to stuff the envelopes working alone?

23. An old printing press takes 5 hours longer to put out a daily paper than does a new press. If the two presses work together, the job takes 6 hours. How long does it take each press to put out the paper on its own?

24. An old computer takes 6 hours longer to process the company payroll than does a new computer. If the two computers work together, the job takes 4 hours. How long does it take each computer to process the payroll on its own?

25. A pipe can fill an empty tank in 3 hours. A pump can empty a full tank in 5 hours. If by mistake the pipe is open and the pump is on, how long will it take to fill an empty tank?

26. A swimming pool can be filled by an inlet pipe in 4 days. A pump can empty a full pool in 10 days. If by mistake the inlet pipe is open and the pump is on, how long will it take to fill an empty pool?

Two resistors, one of size R_1 and the other of size R_2, are connected in parallel as shown in Fig. 5.1. The total resistance, R, in the electrical circuit is given by the formula

$$\frac{1}{R} = \frac{1}{R_1} + \frac{1}{R_2}.$$

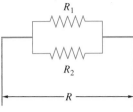

R_1

R_2

R

FIGURE 5.1

The numbers 1 and 2 in the expressions R_1 and R_2 are called subscripts. The subscripts allow us to use the same letter R to represent two different resistors. They do not indicate an operation. The expressions R_1 and R_2 are read "R sub-1" and "R sub-2," respectively.

27. Find the total resistance in a parallel-wired circuit if the resistance in one branch is 6 ohms and the resistance in the other branch is 12 ohms.

28. Find the total resistance in a parallel-wired circuit if the resistance in one branch is 5 ohms and the resistance in the other branch is 20 ohms.

29. Find the resistance in one branch of a parallel-wired circuit if the resistance in the other branch is 16 ohms and the total resistance is 11 ohms.

30. Find the resistance in one branch of a parallel-wired circuit if the resistance in the other branch is 13 ohms and the total resistance is 8 ohms.

5.9   Ratio and Proportion

One of the most useful types of applied problems that results in an equation involving rational expressions is a problem that deals with ratio and proportion. We begin our discussion of this type of problem with a definition of the term *ratio*.

Ratio

Suppose your boss earns $600 per week and you earn $200. One way to compare the two salaries is by subtraction. Since $600 − $200 = $400, your boss earns $400 more per week than you do. You can also compare the two salaries by division. Since $600/$200 = 3, your boss earns 3 times as much as you do. A comparison by division is called a *ratio*.

> **DEFINITION OF A RATIO**
>
> The **ratio** of the number a to the number b ($b \neq 0$) is the quotient
>
> $$\frac{a}{b}.$$

EXAMPLE 1   Express each ratio as a fraction in lowest terms.

a. 6 miles to 10 miles   b. 10 miles to 6 miles

Solution

a. The ratio of 6 miles to 10 miles is

$$\frac{6 \text{ miles}}{10 \text{ miles}} = \frac{2 \cdot 3 \text{ miles}}{2 \cdot 5 \text{ miles}} = \frac{3}{5} \; .$$

b. The ratio of 10 miles to 6 miles is

Try Problem 5 >

$$\frac{10 \text{ miles}}{6 \text{ miles}} = \frac{2 \cdot 5 \text{ miles}}{2 \cdot 3 \text{ miles}} = \frac{5}{3} \; .$$

Note that the units "miles" in Example 1 divide out of the ratio just as the constant 2 does. This leaves a number that has no units.

EXAMPLE 2   Express each ratio as a fraction in lowest terms.

a. 28 hours to 1 day   b. 243 miles to 9 gallons

Solution

a. To make the units the same, we convert 1 day to 24 hours. (We would get the same answer if we converted 28 hours to 1 1/6 days.)

$$\frac{28 \text{ hours}}{1 \text{ day}} = \frac{28 \text{ hours}}{24 \text{ hours}} = \frac{7}{6}$$

b. We cannot convert miles to gallons or gallons to miles. Therefore we write

$$\frac{243 \text{ miles}}{9 \text{ gallons}} = \frac{27 \text{ miles}}{1 \text{ gallon}} \, ,$$

Try Problem 17 >

or 27 mi/gal.

Proportion

Now that we understand what a ratio is, we can define a *proportion*.

DEFINITION OF A PROPORTION

A statement that two ratios are equal is called a **proportion.**

Since a/b and c/d are ratios, the equation

$$\frac{a}{b} = \frac{c}{d}$$

is a proportion. This proportion is read "*a* is to *b* as *c* is to *d*." The letters *a*, *b*, *c*, and *d* are called the **terms** of the proportion. Further, *a* and *d* are called the **extremes** of the proportion, and *b* and *c* are called the **means.** If we multiply both sides of this proportion by the least common denominator, *bd*, we have

$$bd \cdot \frac{a}{b} = bd \cdot \frac{c}{d}$$
$$ad = bc.$$

Note that the products *ad* and *bc* can be found by "cross-multiplying."

$$\frac{a}{b} \diagdown\mkern-12mu\diagup \frac{c}{d}$$

This gives the following rule for solving proportions.

CROSS-PRODUCT RULE

In any proportion, the product of the extremes is equal to the product of the means. In symbols,

$$\text{if } \frac{a}{b} = \frac{c}{d}, \text{ then } ad = bc.$$

If we know any three of the four terms of a proportion, we can use the cross-product rule to find the fourth.

EXAMPLE 3   Solve the proportion $\dfrac{x}{54} = \dfrac{5}{6}$.

Solution

$$\frac{x}{54} = \frac{5}{6} \qquad \textit{Original proportion}$$
$$x \cdot 6 = 54 \cdot 5 \quad \textit{Cross-product rule}$$
$$6x = 270 \qquad \textit{Simplify}$$
$$x = 45 \qquad \textit{Divide by 6}$$

Try Problem 23 >   Check in the original proportion.   ■

Caution! ■   Do not divide out common factors across the equality sign of a proportion.
   ■
   ■
   ■   *Wrong*
   ■
   ■
   ■
   ■
   ■

EXAMPLE 4   Solve the proportion $\dfrac{8}{x} = \dfrac{3\frac{3}{4}}{30}$.

Solution

$$3\frac{3}{4} \cdot x = 8 \cdot 30 \qquad \textit{Cross-product rule}$$

$$\frac{15}{4}x = 240 \qquad \textit{Simplify each side}$$

$$\frac{4}{15} \cdot \frac{15}{4}x = \frac{4}{15} \cdot 240 \qquad \textit{Multiply by the reciprocal of 15/4}$$

$$x = 64 \qquad \textit{Simplify each side}$$

Try Problem 33 >   Check in the original proportion.

■

EXAMPLE 5   Solve the proportion $\dfrac{4}{9} = \dfrac{p}{p+2}$.

Solution

$$4(p + 2) = 9p \qquad \textit{Cross-product rule}$$
$$4p + 8 = 9p \qquad \textit{Distribute 4}$$
$$8 = 5p \qquad \textit{Subtract 4p}$$
$$\frac{8}{5} = p \qquad \textit{Divide by 5}$$

Try Problem 39 >   Check in the original proportion.

■

P R O B L E M   S O L V I N G

EXAMPLE 6   A fish warden tags 60 fish and then returns them to their lake. Later, she catches a sample of 48 fish from the lake and finds that 5 of the 48 are tagged. How many fish are in the lake?

Solution   Let x represent the total number of fish in the lake. To set up a proportion, we assume the ratio of tagged fish to total fish is the same in both the lake and the sample.

$$\begin{array}{c}\textit{Tagged fish in lake} \rightarrow \\ \textit{Total fish in lake} \; \rightarrow\end{array} \dfrac{60}{x} = \dfrac{5}{48} \begin{array}{c}\leftarrow \textit{Tagged fish in sample} \\ \leftarrow \textit{Total fish in sample}\end{array}$$

$$5x = 60 \cdot 48 \qquad \textit{Cross-product rule}$$
$$5x = 2880 \qquad \textit{Simplify the right side}$$
$$x = 576 \qquad \textit{Divide by 5}$$

Try Problem 55 >   There are 576 fish in the lake. Check in the words of the original problem.   ■

5.9 Problem Set

LEARNING THROUGH WRITING

☐ Define the term *ratio*.

☐ Define the term *proportion*.

☐ What are the *terms* of a proportion?

☐ What are the *means* and the *extremes* of a proportion?

☐ State the *cross-product rule* in words.

Express each ratio as a fraction in lowest terms.

1. 1 inch to 5 inches

2. 1 foot to 7 feet

3. 5 inches to 1 inch

4. 7 feet to 1 foot

5. 4 miles to 6 miles

6. 8 gallons to 10 gallons

7. 5 days to 20 hours

8. 6 minutes to 24 seconds

9. 80 cents to 3 dollars

10. 60 cents to 5 dollars

11. 7 1/2 feet to 6 yards

12. 13.5 pints to 2.25 quarts

13. 54 males to 30 females

14. 28 females to 20 males

15. 162 cents to 3 ounces

16. 178 cents to 2 pounds

17. 371 miles to 7 hours

18. 248 miles to 8 gallons

19. 2 ounces of shampoo to 2 ounces of water

20. 9 quarts of antifreeze to 9 quarts of water

21. One runner on an oval track completes 3/4 of a lap while another runner completes 1/2 of a lap. What is the ratio of the first runner's speed to the second runner's speed?

22. One runner finishes a marathon in 3 hours while a second runner finishes in 3 hours and 20 minutes. What is the ratio of the first runner's time to the second runner's time?

Solve each proportion.

23. $\dfrac{x}{16} = \dfrac{3}{4}$

24. $\dfrac{x}{18} = \dfrac{2}{3}$

25. $\dfrac{5}{7} = \dfrac{20}{y}$

26. $\dfrac{6}{11} = \dfrac{24}{y}$

27. $\dfrac{3}{5} = \dfrac{m}{4}$

28. $\dfrac{5}{2} = \dfrac{m}{3}$

29. $\dfrac{12}{r} = \dfrac{8}{2}$

30. $\dfrac{15}{r} = \dfrac{9}{3}$

31. $\dfrac{x}{3} = \dfrac{3}{5}$

32. $\dfrac{x}{2} = \dfrac{2}{7}$

33. $\dfrac{8}{x} = \dfrac{6\,2/3}{35}$

34. $\dfrac{10}{x} = \dfrac{4\,4/5}{36}$

35. $\dfrac{1/2}{1/3} = \dfrac{3/4}{z}$

36. $\dfrac{2/3}{1/2} = \dfrac{1/6}{z}$

37. $\dfrac{3.6}{2.4} = \dfrac{t}{6.5}$

38. $\dfrac{4.8}{3.2} = \dfrac{t}{9.5}$

39. $\dfrac{5}{8} = \dfrac{p}{p+1}$

40. $\dfrac{2}{5} = \dfrac{p}{p+4}$

41. $\dfrac{k-2}{k+4} = \dfrac{4}{k}$

42. $\dfrac{k-1}{k+5} = \dfrac{2}{k}$

Solve each word problem by setting up a proportion.

43. A flagpole casts a shadow of 28 feet at the same time that a 5-foot tree casts a shadow of 4 feet. Find the height of the flagpole.

44. A tree casts a shadow of 45 feet at the same time that a 4-foot bush casts a shadow of 3 feet. Find the height of the tree.

45. The ratio of males to females in a school is 9 to 7. If there are 910 females, how many males are there?

46. The ratio of females to males in a school is 7 to 5. If there are 630 males, how many females are there?

47. An enlargement of a photograph is 10 inches wide. If the original photograph is 4 inches wide and 5 inches long, how long is the enlargement?

48. A scale drawing of a rectangular room is 5 inches wide. If the room is 16 feet wide and 24 feet long, how long is the drawing?

49. A light bulb manufacturer advertises that only 8 out of 1000 of its bulbs are defective. If that is true, how many defective bulbs can be expected in a shipment of 2250 bulbs?

50. If you drive 4300 miles during the first five months of the year, how many miles can you expect to drive for the entire year?

51. If 3 1/2 bags of fertilizer cover 2800 square feet of lawn, how many square feet of lawn will 5 1/2 bags cover?

52. If 2 1/2 inches on a map represent 5 miles on the ground, then how many miles on the ground do 3 1/2 inches represent?

53. A secretary can type 12 pages in 1 hour and 20 minutes. How long will it take him to type 99 pages?

54. A secretary can address 200 envelopes in 1 hour and 20 minutes. How many envelopes can she address in 5 hours?

55. A game warden tags 62 deer and then returns them to their park. Later he catches a sample of 45 deer and finds that 6 of the 45 are tagged. How many deer are in the park?

56. A fish warden tags 80 fish and then returns them to their pond. Later, she catches a sample of 65 fish and finds that 10 of the 65 are tagged. How many fish are in the pond?

57. Two persons decide to share profits in the ratio of 5 to 7. If the profits total $6120, how much will each person receive?

58. Two persons decide to share profits in the ratio of 5 to 9. If the profits total $6300, how much will each person receive?

Consider a pool table that is 42 inches by 84 inches. For a player to make the shot pictured in Fig. 5.2, the angle ABD must equal the angle CBE. This means that triangle ABD is similar to triangle CBE. Similar triangles have the same shape but not necessarily the same size. If two triangles are similar, the ratios of their corresponding sides are equal. Therefore we can find x by setting up a proportion. For example, from Fig. 5.2 we can write the proportion

$$\frac{BD}{AD} = \frac{BE}{CE}.$$

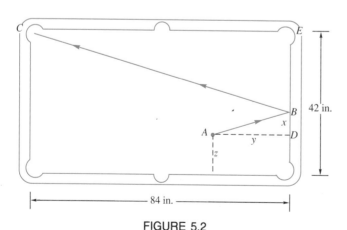

FIGURE 5.2

59. Find x if $y = 14$ inches and $z = 7$ inches.

60. Find x if $y = 28$ inches and $z = 10$ inches.

C H A P T E R 5	S U M M A R Y

Key Terms

Algebraic fraction, p. 218
Complex fraction, p. 243
Extraneous solution, p. 251
Extremes, p. 263
Least common denominator (LCD), p. 232
Means, p. 263
Proportion, p. 262

Ratio, p. 261
Rational expression, p. 218
Reciprocal, p. 225
Secondary fraction, p. 243
Simple fraction, p. 243
Terms, p. 263

Key Rules

Fundamental Property of Rational Expressions

$$\frac{P \cdot K}{Q \cdot K} = \frac{P}{Q} \qquad (Q \neq 0,\ K \neq 0)$$

Operations on Rational Expressions

Addition: $\dfrac{P}{Q} + \dfrac{R}{Q} = \dfrac{P + R}{Q} \qquad (Q \neq 0)$

Subtraction: $\dfrac{P}{Q} - \dfrac{R}{Q} = \dfrac{P - R}{Q} \qquad (Q \neq 0)$

Multiplication: $\dfrac{P}{Q} \cdot \dfrac{R}{S} = \dfrac{P \cdot R}{Q \cdot S} \qquad (Q \neq 0,\ S \neq 0)$

Division: $\dfrac{P}{Q} \div \dfrac{R}{S} = \dfrac{P}{Q} \cdot \dfrac{S}{R} \qquad (Q \neq 0,\ R \neq 0,\ S \neq 0)$

Cross-Product Rule

If $\dfrac{a}{b} = \dfrac{c}{d}$, then $ad = bc$.

C H A P T E R 5	R E V I E W P R O B L E M S

[5.1] *Find the value(s) of the variable that make each rational expression undefined.*

1. $\dfrac{x}{x - 3}$

2. $\dfrac{5}{m^2 - 3m - 4}$

3. $\dfrac{r}{r^2 + 1}$

Simplify each rational expression.

4. $\dfrac{-42a^4b}{6a^2b^3}$

5. $\dfrac{5p + 20}{3p + 12}$

6. $\dfrac{4k^2 - 8k}{4k^2 + 8k}$

7. $\dfrac{m^2 - 16}{m^2 + 2m - 24}$

8. $\dfrac{r^2 - 2rs + s^2}{s - r}$

9. $\dfrac{(x + 2)4 - 8}{(x + 2)x}$

10. Suppose the percent, p, of certain information that is remembered t days after it is studied is

$$p = \frac{100}{1 + t}.$$

Find the percent of information that is remembered
4 days after it is studied.

[5.2] *Multiply or divide as indicated. Write your answer in simplest form.*

11. $\dfrac{(3m)^2}{4m^4} \cdot \dfrac{10m^5}{(6m)^2}$

12. $\dfrac{(a-b)^2}{a^2b} \div \dfrac{a^2-b^2}{ab^2}$

13. $\dfrac{p^2-4p+4}{p^2+5p+6} \cdot \dfrac{6p^2+12p}{p-2p}$

14. $\dfrac{x-5}{x} \div (5-x)$

15. $\dfrac{y}{x} \div \dfrac{1}{xy+x}$

16. $\dfrac{2r^2-11r+15}{4r^2-25} \cdot \dfrac{3r+9}{r^2-9}$

[5.3] *Add or subtract as indicated. Write your answer in simplest form.*

17. $\dfrac{a}{4} + \dfrac{a}{4}$

18. $\dfrac{k+9}{10k^2} + \dfrac{k-9}{10k^2}$

19. $\dfrac{x-7}{x+8} - \dfrac{x+1}{x+8}$

20. $\dfrac{2y}{y^2+3y-4} - \dfrac{2}{y^2+3y-4}$

21. $\dfrac{10}{p-5} + \dfrac{5}{5-p}$

22. $\dfrac{r^2+1}{(r+1)} + \dfrac{2r}{(r+1)^2}$

[5.4] *Find the LCD for each collection of rational expressions.*

23. $\dfrac{1}{28x^2y}, \dfrac{1}{42x^3}$

24. $\dfrac{6}{r}, r+1$

25. $\dfrac{2}{y+2}, \dfrac{3y}{y+3}$

26. $\dfrac{m}{m+6}, \dfrac{7}{m^2+6m}$

27. $\dfrac{p-4}{p^2+5p+4}, \dfrac{3p}{p^2-1}$

28. $\dfrac{9}{4k}, \dfrac{k^2}{k-4}, \dfrac{k-1}{k^2-4k}$

[5.5] *Add or subtract as indicated. Write your answer in simplest form.*

29. $\dfrac{y}{4} + \dfrac{y}{20}$

30. $\dfrac{5}{2r} - \dfrac{8}{r^2}$

31. $a + \dfrac{1}{a^2}$

32. $\dfrac{x+2}{3} - \dfrac{x+2}{7}$

33. $\dfrac{3}{p} - \dfrac{2}{p+1}$

34. $\dfrac{4}{m-2} + \dfrac{6}{m+3}$

35. $\dfrac{9}{2x+8} + \dfrac{1}{x+4}$

36. $\dfrac{r}{r^2+2r+1} + \dfrac{2}{r^2+3r+2}$

37. $\dfrac{1}{x+2} + \dfrac{2}{x-2} - \dfrac{8}{x^2-4}$

[5.6] *Simplify each complex fraction.*

38. $\dfrac{1+\dfrac{1}{6}}{\dfrac{2}{3}+\dfrac{3}{4}}$

39. $\dfrac{\dfrac{x}{x-5}}{\dfrac{x}{x+5}}$

40. $\dfrac{\dfrac{1}{ab}+1}{\dfrac{ab+1}{b}}$

41. $\dfrac{\dfrac{1}{x^2}-\dfrac{1}{9}}{\dfrac{1}{3}+\dfrac{1}{x}}$

42. $\dfrac{1-\dfrac{4}{r^2}}{1+\dfrac{1}{r}-\dfrac{6}{r^2}}$

43. $\dfrac{\dfrac{6}{p+4}+1}{1-\dfrac{6}{p+4}}$

44. Write $\dfrac{1+x^{-1}}{1-x^{-1}}$ with positive exponents and simplify.

[5.7] *Solve each equation.*

45. $\dfrac{x}{4} + \dfrac{x}{12} = 1$

46. $\dfrac{y}{2} - 2 = \dfrac{y}{3}$

47. $p + \dfrac{5}{6} = \dfrac{7p}{9} - \dfrac{p}{18}$

48. $\dfrac{1}{2r} + \dfrac{1}{5r} = \dfrac{1}{10}$

49. $1 - \dfrac{3}{m} - \dfrac{4}{m^2} = 0$

50. $\dfrac{t-4}{3} + \dfrac{1}{6} = \dfrac{13}{2} - \dfrac{t+5}{4}$

51. $\dfrac{x+4}{x+3} = \dfrac{1}{x+3} + 5$

52. $\dfrac{6}{y-1} + \dfrac{2}{y} = \dfrac{4}{y}$

53. $\dfrac{1}{3p+9} + \dfrac{1}{3} = \dfrac{-p}{p^2-9}$

Solve each formula for the specified variable.

54. $a = \dfrac{km}{d}$ for d

55. $y = \dfrac{x}{x+3}$ for x

[5.8] *Solve each word problem.*

56. One-half of a number is 5 more than one-fourth of the number. Find the number.

57. One number is three times another. The sum of their reciprocals is 2/9. Find the numbers.

58. Jack can run 5 miles in the same time that Diane can run 4 miles. If Jack runs 2 mph faster than Diane, what is the rate of each?

59. A kyaker can paddle 6 mph in still water. If it takes her as long to paddle 2 miles upstream as it does to paddle 3 miles downstream, what is the speed of the current?

60. Erin can chalk all the school's softball fields in 3 hours, whereas Pat takes 5 hours. How long would it take Erin and Pat working together to chalk the fields?

61. An old copier takes twice as long to copy the weekly flyers for a shopping center as a new copier. If the two copiers work together, the job takes 6 hours. How long does it take each copier to do the job on its own?

[5.9] *Express each ratio as a fraction in lowest terms.*

62. 6 feet to 18 feet

63. 90 cents to 3.75 dollars

64. 120 females to 48 males

Solve each proportion.

65. $\dfrac{x}{12} = \dfrac{3}{8}$

66. $\dfrac{6}{m} = \dfrac{15}{5}$

67. $\dfrac{4}{5} = \dfrac{p - 4}{p}$

68. $\dfrac{k + 1}{k + 3} = \dfrac{2}{k}$

Solve each word problem by setting up a proportion.

69. A silo casts a shadow of 80 feet at the same time that a 6-foot-high stack of hay bales casts a shadow of 15 feet. How high is the silo?

70. Two cities that are 68 miles apart are 6 centimeters apart on a map. How far apart are two cities that are 18 centimeters apart on the map?

71. If 12 quarts of antifreeze should be mixed with 15 quarts of water, how much antifreeze should be mixed with 20 quarts of water?

72. A fish warden tags 48 fish and then returns them to their lake. Later, he catches a sample of 32 fish and finds that 12 of the 32 are tagged. How many fish are in the lake?

C H A P T E R   5   **T E S T**

1. Express the following ratio as a fraction in lowest terms: 3 feet to 24 inches.

2. Find the value(s) that make $\dfrac{x}{x^2 - 16}$ undefined.

Solve each proportion.

3. $\dfrac{42}{x} = \dfrac{7}{5}$

4. $\dfrac{5}{2} = \dfrac{2p}{p + 1}$

Simplify each rational expression.

5. $\dfrac{6m^2}{9m^2 + 12m}$

6. $\dfrac{a^2 - b^2}{a^2 + 2ab + b^2}$

Find the LCD for each collection of rational expressions.

7. $\dfrac{1}{8r}, \dfrac{1}{12r^2}, \dfrac{1}{18r^3}$

8. $\dfrac{y + 1}{y^2 + y - 12}, \dfrac{y}{5y - 15}$

Simplify each complex fraction.

9. $\dfrac{\dfrac{4}{r + 3} + 1}{1 - \dfrac{4}{r + 3}}$

10. $\dfrac{1 + \dfrac{1}{x}}{1 - \dfrac{1}{x^2}}$

Solve each equation.

11. $\dfrac{5m}{6} - 4 = \dfrac{m}{3}$

12. $1 - \dfrac{3}{x} - \dfrac{10}{x^2} = 0$

13. $\dfrac{h+1}{4} + \dfrac{1}{3} = \dfrac{1}{2} - \dfrac{h-3}{6}$

14. $\dfrac{y}{y+3} + \dfrac{2}{y-8} = \dfrac{22}{y^2 - 5y - 24}$

Perform the indicated operation. Write your answer in simplest form.

15. $\dfrac{7}{10x} - \dfrac{3}{10x}$

16. $\dfrac{4}{m-6} - \dfrac{1}{6-m}$

17. $\dfrac{(4a)^2}{4ab^3} \cdot \dfrac{6a^2 b}{(2a)^3}$

18. $\dfrac{y^2 - 25}{y+4} \cdot \dfrac{y+4}{y^2 - y - 20}$

19. $\dfrac{p^2 + p}{6p+6} \div \dfrac{p^2 - p}{3p-3}$

20. $1 - \dfrac{1}{a+1}$

21. $\dfrac{m}{4m+20} + \dfrac{3}{4m}$

22. $\dfrac{2}{x+6} + \dfrac{24}{x^2 - 36}$

23. $\dfrac{3x^2 + x - 10}{2x^2 + 3x - 2} \div (5 - 3x)$

Solve each word problem.

24. Eight plus six times the reciprocal of a number is 16. Find the number.

25. One inlet pipe can fill a swimming pool in 4 days, whereas another pipe takes 5 days. How long would it take both pipes together to fill the pool?

26. Six out of every 150 parts produced by a stamping machine are defective. How many defective parts can be expected in a production run of 1350 parts?

27. A car travels 285 miles in the same time that a bus travels 210 miles. If the car travels 15 mph faster than the bus, find the speed of each.

Linear Equations and Inequalities in Two Variables

The demand for a certain video game and the price of that video game are two separate variable quantities, although they are related: As the price increases, the demand usually decreases. In Section 6.2 we show how to use two known pairs of values for price and demand to graph a straight line that enables us to predict other pairs of values for price and demand.

6.1 The Rectangular Coordinate System

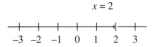

$x = 2$

$x < 1$

FIGURE 6.2

In Chapters 1 and 2 we learned how to graph equations and inequalities in one variable. For example, the graph of the equation $x = 2$ is shown in Fig. 6.1, and the graph of the inequality $x < 1$ is shown in Fig. 6.2.

To graph an equation in two variables, such as $x + y = 4$, we need two number lines, one for x and one for y. These two number lines are drawn perpendicular to each other, as shown in Fig. 6.3. The horizontal number line is called the **x-axis,** and the vertical number line is called the **y-axis.** The point of intersection of the two axes is called the **origin.** The axes divide the plane on which they are drawn into four separate regions, called **quadrants.** The quadrants are always numbered counterclockwise, as in Fig. 6.3. **The axes themselves are not part of any quadrant.**

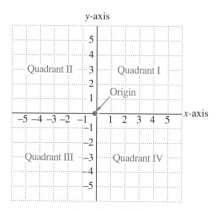

FIGURE 6.3

To identify a point in the plane, we must give a value for x and a value for y. For simplicity we write the pair of values $x = 4$ and $y = 2$ as (4, 2). The expression (4, 2) is called an **ordered pair** of numbers, because it consists of two numbers in a specified order. The first number in an ordered pair is known as the **x-coordinate,** and the second number as the **y-coordinate.**

(4, 2)

x-coordinate *y-coordinate* = (ordinate)
(hoành độ)   (Tung độ)

Caution! ▪

Do not confuse the ordered pair (4, 2) with the ordered pair (2, 4).

(4, 2)   means $x = 4$ and $y = 2$
(2, 4)   means $x = 2$ and $y = 4$

Here is how we locate the point that corresponds to the ordered pair (4, 2) on a rectangular coordinate system: Since the x-coordinate is 4, start at the ori-

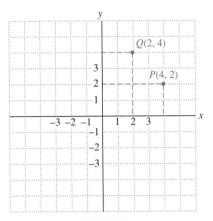

FIGURE 6.4

gin and go 4 units to the right. Since the y-coordinate is 2, turn and go up 2 units. At that location draw a point and label it P, as shown in Fig. 6.4. We call point P the **graph** of the ordered pair (4, 2). We call (4, 2) the **coordinates** of point P. The act of drawing P is referred to as *plotting* the point whose coordinates are (4, 2) or, more simply, as plotting the point (4, 2). Note that the point $Q(2, 4)$ is different from the point $P(4, 2)$, as shown in Fig. 6.4. This system of assigning ordered pairs of numbers to points in the plane is known as the **rectangular coordinate system.**

This system of assigning ordered pairs of numbers to points in a plane is also called a **Cartesian coordinate system,** in honor of its inventor, René Descartes (1596–1650). Some say the idea for this coordinate system came to Descartes while he was lying in bed watching a fly crawl on the ceiling of his room.

EXAMPLE 1   Plot each point and state the quadrant in which it lies.

a. $A(4, -2)$ b. $B(-3, -1)$ c. $C(5, 0)$ d. $D\left(-\dfrac{3}{2}, \dfrac{5}{2}\right)$

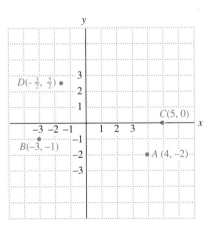

FIGURE 6.5

Solution

a. To plot (4, −2), go 4 units to the right and 2 units down. The point is in quadrant IV, as shown in Fig. 6.5.

b. To plot $(-3, -1)$, go 3 units to the left and 1 unit down. The point is in quadrant III, as shown in Fig. 6.5.

c. To plot $(5, 0)$, go 5 units to the right. This gives the point on the positive part of the x-axis between quadrants I and IV, as shown in Fig. 6.5.

d. To plot $(-3/2, 5/2)$, go 1 1/2 units to the left and 2 1/2 units up. The point is in quadrant II, as shown in Fig. 6.5.   ■

Try Problem 3 >

EXAMPLE 2   State five ordered pairs whose y-coordinate is twice their x-coordinate. Then plot the five points on the same rectangular coordinate system.

Solution   Five ordered pairs whose y-coordinate is twice their x-coordinate are $(1, 2)$, $(2, 4)$, $(3, 6)$, $(0, 0)$, and $(-1, -2)$ (there are many others). These five points are plotted in Fig. 6.6.   ■

Try Problem 47 >

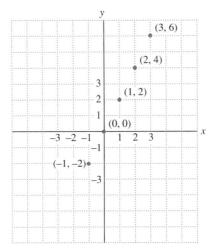

FIGURE 6.6

Often the units in an applied problem are large, so we must make appropriate adjustments when we label the hash marks. In the next example we let the distance between successive hash marks represent 5 units.

PROBLEM   SOLVING

EXAMPLE 3   A hardware store has $60 in its weekly budget for ordering hammers. A tack hammer costs the store $2 and a claw hammer costs $3. Suppose x represents the number of tack hammers and y represents the number of claw hammers. Three possible ways of ordering hammers are represented by the three ordered pairs graphed in Fig. 6.7. Interpret each ordered pair.

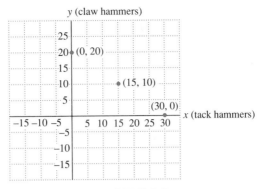

FIGURE 6.7

Solution

Ordered Pair	Interpretation
(0, 20)	0 tack hammers and 20 claw hammers
(15, 10)	15 tack hammers and 10 claw hammers
(30, 0)	30 tack hammers and 0 claw hammers

Try Problem 57 >

Note that each order utilizes the weekly budget of $60. For example, 15 tack hammers at $2 each and 10 claw hammers at $3 each would cost a total of $60.

6.1 Problem Set

Plot each point on a rectangular coordinate system. Then state the quadrant in which each point lies.

1. (3, 2)

2. (4, 1)

3. (3, −2)

4. (4, −1)

5. (−5, 1)

6. (−3, 5)

7. (−4, −2)

8. (−6, −2)

9. (0, −3)

10. (0, 4)

11. (6, 0)

12. (−5, 0)

13. (0, 0)

14. (1, 1)

15. $\left(3, -\dfrac{3}{2}\right)$

16. $\left(-\dfrac{9}{2}, -\dfrac{1}{2}\right)$

Solve each word problem.

17. The points (2, 2), (−6, −2), and (2, −2) form a triangle. Find the area of the triangle.

18. The points (−1, 3), (−1, −1), (4, −1), and (4, 3) form a rectangle. Find the perimeter of the rectangle.

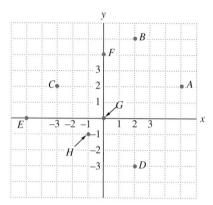

FIGURE 6.8

19. State the coordinates of points *A, C, E,* and *G* in Fig. 6.8.

20. State the coordinates of points *B, D, F,* and *H* in Fig. 6.8.

Plot all of the given points on the same rectangular coordinate system. Let the distance between successive hash marks on the axes represent 5 units.

21. (35, 10)   **22.** (−20, 15)   **23.** (35, −20)   **24.** (30, −5)

Plot all of the given points on the same rectangular coordinate system. Let the distance between successive hash marks on the x-axis represent 1 unit, and that on the y-axis 10 units.

25. (3, 50)   **26.** (5, −70)   **27.** (−6, 50)   **28.** (2, 75)

State the quadrant(s) in which the point whose coordinates satisfy the given conditions lie.

29. The *x*-coordinate is positive and the *y*-coordinate is negative.

30. The *x*-coordinate is negative and the *y*-coordinate is positive.

31. Both coordinates are positive.

32. Both coordinates are negative.

33. The *y*-coordinate is positive.

34. The *x*-coordinate is negative.

Describe the coordinates of a point P satisfying the given conditions.

35. *P* lies in quadrant III.

36. *P* lies in quadrant I.

37. *P* lies in quadrant II.

38. *P* lies in quadrant IV.

39. *P* lies on the *x*-axis between quadrants I and IV.

40. *P* lies on the *y*-axis between quadrants III and IV.

If a > 0 and b < 0, state the quadrant in which each point lies.

41. (*a, b*)   **42.** (*b, a*)   **43.** (*a, −b*)   **44.** (−*a, b*)

45. (*a, b − a*)   **46.** (*ab, a − b*)

Plot five points on the same rectangular coordinate system whose coordinates satisfy the given conditions.

47. The *y*-coordinate is three times the *x*-coordinate.

48. The *y*-coordinate is one-half the *x*-coordinate.

49. The *y*-coordinate equals the *x*-coordinate.

50. The *y*-coordinate is the opposite of the *x*-coordinate.

51. The sum of the *x*-coordinate and the *y*-coordinate is 5.

52. The *y*-coordinate is one more than the *x*-coordinate.

53. The *x*-coordinate is 2.

54. The *y*-coordinate is 3.

55. The *y*-coordinate is the square of the *x*-coordinate.

56. The *y*-coordinate is the square root of the *x*-coordinate.

Solve each word problem.

57. Suppose *x* represents the number of hours a car is parked in a parking garage and *y* represents the number of dollars it costs to park. Interpret each ordered pair graphed in Fig. 6.9.

58. Suppose *x* represents the number of minutes a dancer works out and *y* represents the dancer's heart rate, in beats per minute. Interpret each ordered pair graphed in Fig. 6.10.

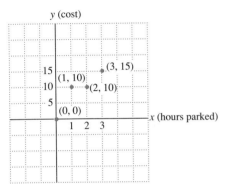

FIGURE 6.9

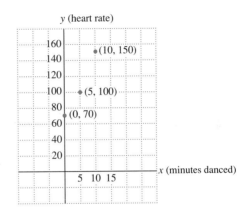

FIGURE 6.10

59. Suppose *x* represents the number of minutes after chemicals are mixed in a laboratory experiment and *y* represents the temperature of the chemicals. Interpret each ordered pair graphed in Fig. 6.11.

60. Suppose *x* represents the number of lawnmowers manufactured each week by a company and *y* represents the weekly profit, in dollars. Interpret each ordered pair graphed in Fig. 6.12.

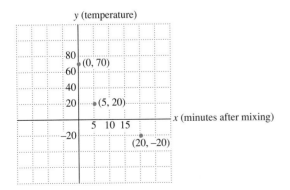

FIGURE 6.11

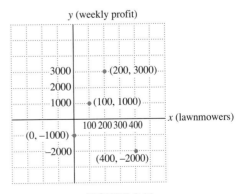

FIGURE 6.12

The rectangular coordinate system can be used to display the collection of all possible outcomes when two dice (one red and one green) are rolled. Suppose x represents the number rolled on the red die and y represents the number rolled on the green die (see Fig. 6.13).

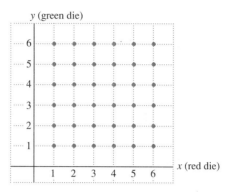

FIGURE 6.13

61. List all ordered pairs that represent a total of 5 on the two dice.

62. List all ordered pairs that represent a total of 10 on the two dice.

63. List all ordered pairs that represent a total between 6 and 9 on the two dice.

64. List all ordered pairs that represent a total less than 4 on the two dice.

6.2 Graphing Linear Equations

From Chapter 2 we know that the equation $2x + 1 = 7$ is a linear equation in one variable. We can verify that 3 is a solution of this equation as follows.

$$2x + 1 = 7 \quad \textit{Original equation}$$
$$2(3) + 1 = 7 \quad \textit{Replace x with 3}$$
$$7 = 7 \quad \textit{True}$$

Now consider the equation $2x + y = 7$. The first thing we notice is that there are two variables rather than one. Therefore a **solution** of this equation consists of a pair of values, one for x and one for y, that makes the equation a true statement. One pair of values that forms a solution is $x = 1$ and $y = 5$. We can verify this as follows.

$$2x + y = 7 \quad \textit{Original equation}$$
$$2(1) + 5 = 7 \quad \textit{Replace x with 1 and y with 5}$$
$$7 = 7 \quad \textit{True}$$

For simplicity we write the solution $x = 1$ and $y = 5$ as the ordered pair $(1, 5)$. Since the ordered pair $(1, 5)$ is a solution of $2x + y = 7$, we say that $(1, 5)$ *satisfies* the equation $2x + y = 7$.

EXAMPLE 1   Determine which of the ordered pairs listed are solutions of $2x + y = 7$.

a. $(5, -3)$ b. $(-4, 10)$

Solution   Substitute each ordered pair into the equation.

a.
$$2x + y = 7$$
$$2(5) + (-3) = 7 \quad \textit{Let } (x, y) = (5, -3)$$
$$10 - 3 = 7$$
$$7 = 7 \quad \textit{True}$$

Therefore $(5, -3)$ is a solution. (bài giải : nghiệm số´, Trị số´)

b.
$$2x + y = 7$$
$$2(-4) + 10 = 7 \quad \textit{Let } (x, y) = (-4, 10)$$
$$-8 + 10 = 7$$
$$2 = 7 \quad \textit{False}$$

Try Problem 1 >   Therefore $(-4, 10)$ is not a solution.   ∎

Equations like $2x + y = 7$ are called *linear equations* in two variables.

DEFINITION OF A LINEAR EQUATION IN TWO VARIABLES

A **linear equation** in two variables (say x and y) is an equation that can be expressed in the form

$$ax + by = c,$$

where a, b, and c are constants and a and b are not both 0. This form is called the *standard form* of a linear equation.

The following three linear equations are all in two variables. Only the first equation is in standard form.

$$4x + 3y = 12 \qquad y = \frac{1}{2}x \qquad x - y + 5 = 0$$

A linear equation in two variables has an infinite number of solutions. The **graph** of a linear equation in two variables is the graph of all the ordered pairs that are solutions of the equation. Since there is an infinite number of solutions, we can graph several solutions and then look for a pattern.

EXAMPLE 2   Graph $y = x + 2$.

Solution   To find solutions, substitute any convenient value for either variable, then solve for the other variable. For instance,

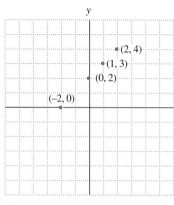

FIGURE 6.14

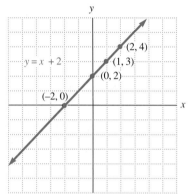

FIGURE 6.15

Try Problem 9 >

if $x = 0$, then

$$y = x + 2 = 0 + 2 = 2;$$

if $x = 1$, then

$$y = x + 2 = 1 + 2 = 3;$$

if $x = 2$, then

$$y = x + 2 = 2 + 2 = 4;$$

if $y = 0$, then

$$y = x + 2$$
$$0 = x + 2$$
$$-2 = x.$$

Therefore four solutions of the equation $y = x + 2$ are (0, 2), (1, 3), (2, 4), and (−2, 0). An easy way to collect these solutions is in a *table of values,* such as the following.

x	y
0	2
1	3
2	4
−2	0

Plot the points from the table to obtain the graph shown in Fig. 6.14. Note that all four points lie on the same straight line. In fact, *every* solution to $y = x + 2$ produces a point on this line. Likewise, every point on this line represents a solution of $y = x + 2$. Therefore complete the graph by drawing a straight line through the four points, as shown in Fig. 6.15. This graph is a "picture" of all the solutions of $y = x + 2$. ∎

Now you know why an equation like $y = x + 2$ is called a *linear* equation. Its graph is a straight line. Since a line is determined when any two points on the line are known, we need to find only two solutions of the equation to graph the entire line. It is a good idea, however, to find a third solution as a check. If the three points do not line up, we have made a mistake.

EXAMPLE 3   Graph $x + 2y = 4$.

Solution   We need two points to determine the line. To make the computations easy, let $x = 0$ and solve for y. Then let $y = 0$ and solve for x.

$$x + 2y = 4 \qquad\qquad x + 2y = 4$$
$$0 + 2y = 4 \quad \text{Let } x = 0 \qquad x + 2 \cdot 0 = 4 \quad \text{Let } y = 0$$
$$2y = 4 \qquad\qquad x + 0 = 4$$
$$y = 2 \qquad\qquad x = 4$$

As a check, find a third point. For example, let $x = 2$.

$$x + 2y = 4$$
$$2 + 2y = 4 \quad \text{Let } x = 2$$
$$2y = 2$$
$$y = 1$$

Collect the three ordered pairs in the following table of values. Then plot the points and draw a straight line through them to produce the graph shown in Fig. 6.16.   ∎

Try Problem 11 >

x	y
0	2
4	0
2	1

Since the line in Fig. 6.16 crosses the y-axis at (0, 2), we call 2 the **y-intercept** of the line. Since the line crosses the x-axis at (4, 0), we call 4 the **x-intercept** of the line. You should draw enough of the line to display both intercepts.

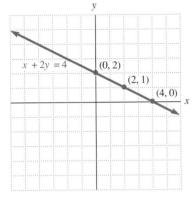

FIGURE 6.16

FINDING THE INTERCEPTS OF A LINE

To find the y-intercept, let $x = 0$.
To find the x-intercept, let $y = 0$.

EXAMPLE 4   Graph $2x + 3y = -6$.

Solution   To find the y-intercept, let $x = 0$. To find the x-intercept, let $y = 0$.

$$2x + 3y = -6 \qquad\qquad\qquad 2x + 3y = -6$$
$$2 \cdot 0 + 3y = -6 \quad \text{Let } x = 0 \qquad 2x + 3 \cdot 0 = -6 \quad \text{Let } y = 0$$
$$3y = -6 \qquad\qquad\qquad\qquad 2x = -6$$
$$y = -2 \qquad\qquad\qquad\qquad x = -3$$

Then find a check point.

$$2x + 3y = -6$$
$$2 \cdot 3 + 3y = -6 \quad \text{Let } x = 3$$
$$6 + 3y = -6$$
$$3y = -12$$
$$y = -4$$

Collect the three ordered pairs in the following table of values. Plot the points and draw a straight line through them to produce the graph shown in Fig. 6.17.   ∎

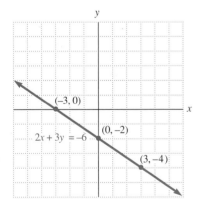

FIGURE 6.17

Try Problem 21 >

x	y
0	-2
-3	0
3	-4

EXAMPLE 5   Graph $y = 2x$.

Solution   When $x = 0$, we get $y = 0$, which gives the ordered pair $(0, 0)$. When $y = 0$, we get $x = 0$, which gives the same ordered pair $(0, 0)$. This means that both intercepts occur at the same point $(0, 0)$. Therefore we need to find two other points on the line. When $x = 2$, we get $y = 4$. When $x = -2$, we get $y = -4$. This gives the following table of values. Plot the points and draw a straight line through them to produce the graph shown in Fig. 6.18.   ∎

Try Problem 27 >

x	y
0	0
2	4
−2	−4

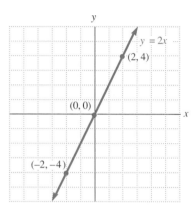

FIGURE 6.18

TO GRAPH A LINEAR EQUATION IN TWO VARIABLES

1. Let $x = 0$ to find the y-intercept.
2. Let $y = 0$ to find the x-intercept.
3. Substitute any convenient value for one of the variables, and then solve for the other variable. This gives a check point.
4. Plot the three points found in Steps 1, 2, and 3 and draw a straight line through them.
5. The graph of $y = ax$ is a line through $(0, 0)$. Since both intercepts occur at the point $(0, 0)$, you should find *two* other points in Step 3.

Horizontal and Vertical Lines

When a linear equation in one variable is graphed on a rectangular coordinate system, the result is either a horizontal line or a vertical line.

EXAMPLE 6   Graph $y = 3$ on a rectangular coordinate system.

Solution   We can write the equation $y = 3$ as

$$0 \cdot x + y = 3.$$

Note that no matter what x-value we choose, the corresponding y-value is 3. For example, suppose we choose $x = 5$.

$$0 \cdot x + y = 3$$
$$0 \cdot 5 + y = 3 \quad \textit{Let } x = 5$$
$$0 + y = 3$$
$$y = 3$$

Therefore we can construct the following table of values. Plotting the points from the table and drawing a straight line through them produces the horizontal line shown in Fig. 6.19. ■

Try Problem 43 >

x	y
0	3
5	3
−5	3

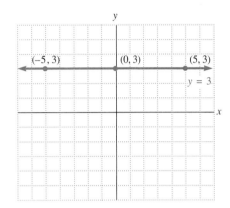

FIGURE 6.19

EXAMPLE 7   Graph $x = -4$ on a rectangular coordinate system.

Solution   We can write this equation as $x + 0 \cdot y = -4$. This means that for any y-value we choose, the x-value is -4. Therefore we can construct the following table of values. Plotting the points from the table and drawing a straight line through them produces the vertical line shown in Fig. 6.20. ■

Try Problem 45 >

x	y
−4	0
−4	3
−4	−4

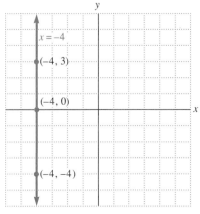

FIGURE 6.20

From Example 6 we see that the graph of $y = 3$ is a horizontal line with y-intercept 3. From Example 7 we see that the graph of $x = -4$ is a vertical line with x-intercept -4. These two observations suggest the following rules.

HORIZONTAL AND VERTICAL LINES

The graph of $y = c$ is a horizontal line with y-intercept c.
The graph of $x = c$ is a vertical line with x-intercept c.

Using these rules we can graph a horizontal line or a vertical line without constructing a table of values.

EXAMPLE 8   Graph $y = -2$ on a rectangular coordinate system.

Solution   The graph is a horizontal line with y-intercept -2 (see Fig. 6.21).

Try Problem 49 >

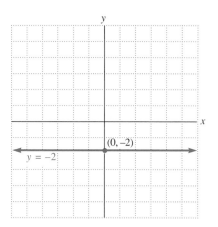

FIGURE 6.21

EXAMPLE 9   Graph $2x - 9 = 0$ on a rectangular coordinate system.

Solution   First solve the equation for x.

$$2x - 9 = 0$$
$$2x = 9$$
$$x = \frac{9}{2}$$

Try Problem 55 >   The graph is a vertical line with x-intercept 9/2 (see Fig. 6.22).

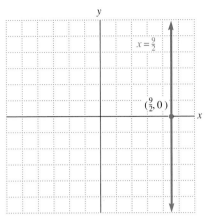

FIGURE 6.22

PROBLEM SOLVING

EXAMPLE 10   Suppose the demand for a certain video game is 5000 when the price is $25, but only 1500 when the price is $35. Let y represent the number of video games demanded and x represent the price.

a. Graph the two ordered pairs described.
b. Draw a line through the two ordered pairs. Then use this line to estimate what the demand would be if the price drops to $20.

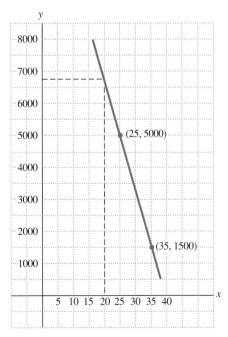

FIGURE 6.23

Solution

a. Since the demand, y, is 5000 when the price, x, is \$25, one of the ordered pairs is $(x, y) = (25, 5000)$. Since the demand, y, is 1500 when the price, x, is \$35, the other ordered pair is $(x, y) = (35, 1500)$. These two ordered pairs are graphed in Fig. 6.23.

b. Draw a line through the two ordered pairs. Using this line we estimate the demand would be 6700 video games if the price drops to \$20. (If the relationship between price and demand is strictly linear, the actual demand would be 6750 video games.)

Try Problem 67 >

6.2 Problem Set

LEARNING THROUGH WRITING

☐ Define the term *linear equation in two variables*.

☐ Define the term *solution of a linear equation in two variables*.

☐ How many solutions does a linear equation in two variables have?

☐ What is meant by *the graph of a linear equation in two variables?*

☐ Define the terms *x-intercept of a line* and *y-intercept of a line*.

☐ Describe how to find the intercepts of a line.

☐ Describe the steps in graphing a linear equation in two variables.

☐ Describe the graph of the equation $y = c$, in words.

☐ Describe the graph of the equation $x = c$, in words.

Determine which of the ordered pairs listed are solutions of the given equation.

1. $3x + 2y = 8$
 a. $(0, 4)$ b. $(2, -1)$ c. $(-2, 7)$

2. $2x + 3y = 12$
 a. $(6, 0)$ b. $(-3, 2)$ c. $(9, -2)$

3. $y = -4x + 7$
 a. $(3, 5)$ b. $\left(\dfrac{1}{2}, 5\right)$ c. $(-4, 23)$

4. $y = -6x + 5$
 a. $(1, 11)$ b. $\left(\dfrac{1}{3}, 3\right)$ c. $(-6, 41)$

5. $y = 4$
 a. $(0, 0)$ b. $(5, 4)$ c. $(4, 5)$

6. $y = -8$
 a. $(0, 0)$ b. $(-8, 9)$ c. $(9, -8)$

7. $x = -6$
 a. $(1, -6)$ b. $(-6, 0)$ c. $(-6, 10)$

8. $x = 7$
 a. $(1, 7)$ b. $(7, 0)$ c. $(7, -11)$

Complete each table of values using the given equation. Then plot the points and draw a straight line through them.

9. $y = x + 1$

x	y
0	
1	
2	
	0

10. $y = x + 3$

x	y
0	
1	
2	
	0

11. $x + 2y = 6$

x	y
0	
	0
2	

12. $x + 3y = 6$

x	y
0	
	0
3	

13. $y = \dfrac{3}{4}x$

x	y
0	
4	
−4	

14. $y = \dfrac{2}{3}x$

x	y
0	
3	
−3	

Graph each equation. Label the x-intercept and the y-intercept.

15. $y = 2x - 4$ **16.** $y = 3x - 6$ **17.** $x + y = 4$ **18.** $x - y = 3$

19. $4x + y = 4$ **20.** $5x + y = 5$ **21.** $3x + 5y = -15$ **22.** $3x + 4y = -12$

23. $2x - 3y = 6$ **24.** $2x - 5y = 10$ **25.** $y = x$ **26.** $y = -x$

27. $y = 3x$ **28.** $y = 4x$ **29.** $y = -2x$ **30.** $y = -5x$

31. $y = -x + 7$ **32.** $y = -2x + 8$ **33.** $6x - 5y = -30$ **34.** $7x - 5y = -35$

35. $-2x + 7y = 21$ **36.** $-2x + 9y = 27$ **37.** $-9x - 18y = 24$ **38.** $-6x - 12y = 20$

39. $y = \dfrac{1}{2}x$ **40.** $y = \dfrac{1}{3}x$ **41.** $y = \dfrac{2}{3}x + 6$ **42.** $y = \dfrac{3}{4}x + 9$

Complete each table of values using the given equation. Then plot the points and draw a straight line through them.

43. $y = 2$

x	y
0	
4	
−4	

44. $y = 4$

x	y
0	
3	
−3	

45. $x = -3$

x	y
	0
	5
	−3

46. $x = -5$

x	y
	0
	2
	−5

Graph each equation on a rectangular coordinate system. Label the appropriate intercept.

47. $x = 4$ **48.** $y = 1$ **49.** $y = -1$ **50.** $y = -4$

51. $x + 7 = 0$ **52.** $x + 9 = 0$ **53.** $y - 3 = 0$ **54.** $y - 6 = 0$

55. $2x - 5 = 0$ **56.** $3y + 8 = 0$ **57.** $y = 0$ **58.** $x = 0$

Write an equation that describes each statement. Then graph the equation.

59. The y-value is 5 more than twice the x-value.

60. The y-value is 2 less than three times the x-value.

61. The sum of the x-value and six times the y-value is 9.

62. The difference of the x-value and four times the y-value is 10.

63. The y-value is 5.

64. The x-value is 2.

Solve each word problem.

65. The daily cost, y, of a firm that manufactures x calculators per day is $5 per calculator plus a daily overhead of $100. The relationship between x and y is graphed in Fig. 6.24 (next page). Use this graph to estimate each of the following.

   a. The daily cost of manufacturing 0 calculators per day

   b. The daily cost of manufacturing 10 calculators per day

   c. The number of calculators that must be manufactured each day to yield a daily cost of $250

66. The daily profit, y, of a company that manufactures x radios per day is $10 per radio minus a daily overhead of $150. The relationship between x and y is graphed in Fig. 6.25 (next page). Use this graph to estimate each of the following.

   a. The daily profit when 10 radios per day are manufactured

   b. The daily profit when 20 radios per day are manufactured

   c. The number of radios that must be manufactured each day to yield a daily profit of $250

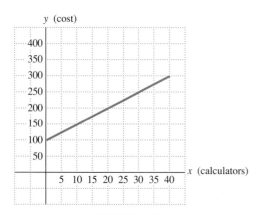

FIGURE 6.24

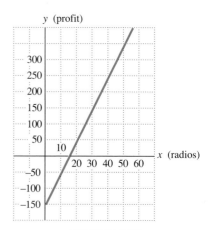

FIGURE 6.25

67. Suppose the demand for a certain watch is 3000 when the price is $20, but only 500 when the price is $40. Let *y* represent the number of watches demanded and *x* represent the price.
a. Graph the two ordered pairs described.
b. Draw a line through the two ordered pairs. Then use this line to estimate what the demand would be if the price drops to $15.

68. Suppose the demand for a certain necklace is 4500 when the price is $30, but only 2000 when the price is $40. Let *y* represent the number of necklaces demanded and *x* represent the price.
a. Graph the two ordered pairs described.
b. Draw a line through the two ordered pairs. Then use this line to estimate what the demand would be if the price increases to $45.

6.3 The Slope of a Line

Consider the two skiers in Fig. 6.26. The skier on the right has a steeper hill to negotiate than does the skier on the left. Note that the horizontal change (called the *run*) is 100 yards for both skiers. However, the vertical change (called the *rise*) is 30 yards for the skier on the left and 70 yards for the skier on the right.

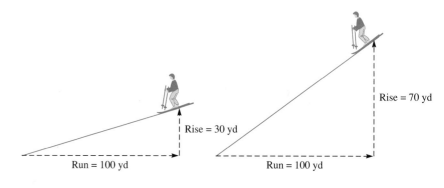

$$\text{Slope} = \frac{\text{rise}}{\text{run}} = \frac{30}{100} = \frac{3}{10} \qquad\qquad \text{Slope} = \frac{\text{rise}}{\text{run}} = \frac{70}{100} = \frac{7}{10}$$

FIGURE 6.26

We can measure the steepness of each hill by finding the ratio of rise to run. This ratio is called the *slope* of the hill.

$$\text{slope} = \frac{\text{rise}}{\text{run}}$$

Note that the slope of the hill on the left is 3/10 and the slope of the hill on the right is 7/10.

We can measure the steepness of a line in the same way. In Example 1 we show how to use the two known points on the line in Fig. 6.27 to find the slope of that line.

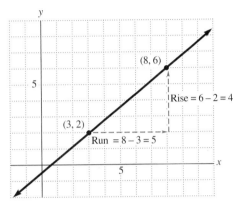

FIGURE 6.27

EXAMPLE 1   Find the slope of the line through (3, 2) and (8, 6).

Solution   Calculate the rise between the two known points by subtracting the y-values.

$$\text{rise} = 6 - 2 = 4$$

Calculate the run by subtracting the two x-values.

$$\text{run} = 8 - 3 = 5$$

The slope of the line is the ratio of rise to run.

Try Problem 1 > $$\text{slope} = \frac{\text{rise}}{\text{run}} = \frac{4}{5}$$ ■

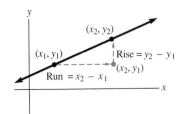

FIGURE 6.28

Now consider the line that passes through the two points (x_1, y_1) and (x_2, y_2). This line is shown in Fig. 6.28. (The numbers 1 and 2 are called *subscripts*, and x_1 and x_2 are read "x sub-1" and "x sub-2," respectively. Subscripts are not exponents. Subscripts simply allow us to use the same letter to represent different numbers.)

From Fig. 6.28 we see that the **rise** (the *change in y*) is $y_2 - y_1$. The **run** (the *change in x*) is $x_2 - x_1$. Therefore we define the slope of the line as follows.

The letter m is taken from the French word *monter*, meaning "to climb."

DEFINITION OF SLOPE

The **slope** of the line through (x_1, y_1) and (x_2, y_2) is denoted m and is given by

$$m = \frac{\text{rise}}{\text{run}} = \frac{y_2 - y_1}{x_2 - x_1}.$$

It can be shown that **the slope of a line is the same no matter which two points on the line are used to calculate the slope.**

EXAMPLE 2   Find the slope of the line through $(0, 1)$ and $(4, 3)$.

Solution   Let $(x_1, y_1) = (0, 1)$ and $(x_2, y_2) = (4, 3)$.

Try Problem 3 >
$$m = \frac{y_2 - y_1}{x_2 - x_1} = \frac{3 - 1}{4 - 0} = \frac{2}{4} = \frac{1}{2}$$ ∎

A slope of 1/2 means that a rise of 1 unit produces a run of 2 units. Since $1/2 = 2/4 = 3/6 = \ldots$, a slope of 1/2 also means that a rise of 2 units produces a run of 4 units, a rise of 3 units produces a run of 6 units, and so on (see Fig. 6.29).

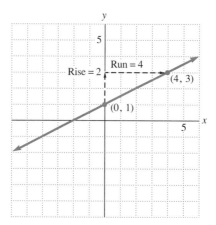

FIGURE 6.29

We can also calculate the slope in Example 2 by letting $(x_1, y_1) = (4, 3)$ and $(x_2, y_2) = (0, 1)$.

$$m = \frac{y_2 - y_1}{x_2 - x_1} = \frac{1 - 3}{0 - 4} = \frac{-2}{-4} = \frac{1}{2}$$

Caution!

When calculating the slope of the line through two points, say (2, 1) and (14, 6), do not start with the *y*-value of one point and the *x*-value of the other. This would give the *opposite* of the correct slope.

Correct   *Correct*   *Wrong*

$$m = \frac{6-1}{14-2} = \frac{5}{12} \qquad m = \frac{1-6}{2-14} = \frac{-5}{-12} = \frac{5}{12} \qquad m = \frac{1-6}{14-2} = \frac{-5}{12}$$

EXAMPLE 3   Find the slope of the line through $(-2, 3)$ and $(1, -6)$.

Solution

Try Problem 7 >

$$m = \frac{-6-3}{1-(-2)} = \frac{-9}{3} = -3$$

Since $-3 = -3/1 = -6/2 = \ldots$, the slope of -3 found in Example 3 means that a rise of -3 produces a run of 1 unit, a rise of -6 produces a run of 2 units, and so on (see Fig. 6.30). The slope of the line in Fig. 6.30 is a negative number, because the line is falling from left to right. **A negative slope means the line is falling from left to right. A positive slope means the line is rising from left to right.**

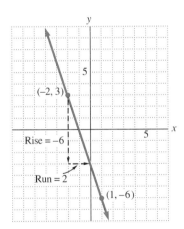

FIGURE 6.30

EXAMPLE 4   Find the slope of the line through $(4, 2)$ and $(-5, 2)$.

Solution

Try Problem 11 >

$$m = \frac{2-2}{-5-4} = \frac{0}{-9} = 0$$

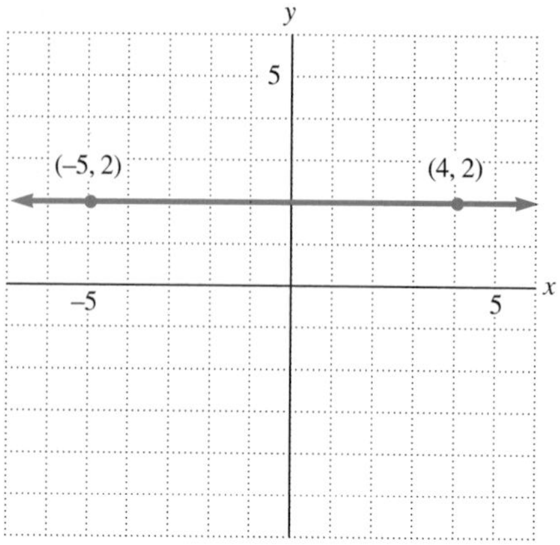

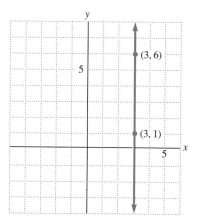

FIGURE 6.31

The slope in Example 4 is 0 because the line is horizontal, and there-fore the y-values are the same (see Fig. 6.31). **The slope of any horizontal line is 0.**

EXAMPLE 5   Find the slope of the line through (3, 1) and (3, 6).

Solution

$$m = \frac{6-1}{3-3} = \frac{5}{0}$$

Try Problem 13 >   The slope is undefined.   ■

The slope in Example 5 is undefined because the line is vertical, and there-fore the x-values are the same (see Fig. 6.32). **The slope of any vertical line is undefined.**

FIGURE 6.32

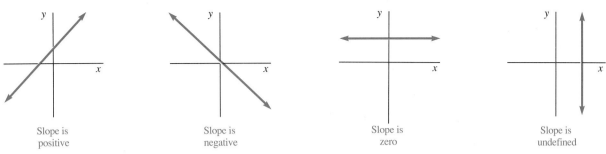

FIGURE 6.33

We summarize some of our findings about slope in Fig. 6.33.

Graphing a Line Using One Point and the Slope

In Section 6.2 we graphed a line by finding two points on the line. We can also graph a line if we know one point on the line and the slope of the line.

EXAMPLE 6   Graph the line that passes through (0, 2) and has slope 3/7.

Solution   First plot the point (0, 2), as in Fig. 6.34. Then note that

$$m = \frac{3}{7} = \frac{\text{rise}}{\text{run}}.$$

Now, from (0, 2) go up 3 units (since the rise is 3) and go right 7 units (since the run is 7). This brings us to the point (7, 5). Draw a line through (0, 2) and (7, 5), as shown in Fig. 6.34.   ∎

Try Problem 29 >

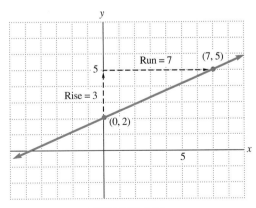

FIGURE 6.34

EXAMPLE 7 Graph the line that passes through $(-1, 2)$ and has slope $-(5/4)$.

Solution First plot the point $(-1, 2)$, as shown in Fig. 6.35. Then write the slope as

$$m = -\frac{5}{4} = \frac{-5}{4} = \frac{\text{rise}}{\text{run}}.$$

Now, from $(-1, 2)$ go down 5 units (since the rise is -5) and go right 4 units (since the run is 4). This brings us to the point $(3, -3)$. Draw a line through $(-1, 2)$ and $(3, -3)$, as shown in Fig. 6.35. ∎

Try Problem 35 >

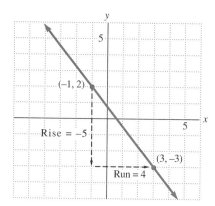

FIGURE 6.35

TO GRAPH A LINE USING ONE POINT AND THE SLOPE

1. Plot the known point.
2. Starting at the known point, travel up (if the slope is positive) or down (if the slope is negative) a distance equal to the rise. Then travel to the right a distance equal to the run. Plot a second point at this new location.
3. Draw a line through the two points plotted in Steps 1 and 2.

6.3 | Problem Set

LEARNING THROUGH WRITING

☐ Define the terms *rise* and *run*.

☐ Give the definition for the *slope* of a line.

☐ What can be said about a line whose slope is each of the following?
   a. positive   b. negative   c. 0   d. undefined

☐ Describe the steps in graphing a line using one point and the slope.

Find the slope of the line through each pair of points.

1. (2, 1), (8, 6)   **2.** (3, 2), (11, 5)   **3.** (0, 1), (6, 3)   **4.** (0, 1), (8, 3)

5. (−2, −3), (5, −6)   **6.** (−1, −1), (6, −5)   **7.** (−1, 1), (1, −3)   **8.** (−1, 2), (1, −4)

9. (4, −11), (0, −2)   **10.** (3, −12), (0, −4)   **11.** (2, 3), (−4, 3)   **12.** (−5, 4), (2, 4)

13. (6, 1), (6, 4)   **14.** (4, 2), (4, 7)   **15.** $\left(\frac{1}{3}, \frac{1}{2}\right), \left(\frac{11}{12}, \frac{1}{4}\right)$ **16.** $\left(\frac{5}{12}, \frac{3}{4}\right), \left(\frac{5}{6}, \frac{1}{2}\right)$

17. (8.4, 1.9), (2.7, 5.8)   **18.** (4.8, 6.7), (9.4, 3.3)

Graph the line that passes through the given point and has the given slope.

19. (0, 0), $m = 2$ **20.** (0, 0), $m = 3$ **21.** (0, 0), $m = \frac{1}{2}$ **22.** (0, 0), $m = \frac{1}{3}$

23. (0, 0), $m = 1$ **24.** (0, 0), $m = -1$ **25.** (0, 0), $m = -10$ **26.** (0, 0), $m = -8$

27. (0, 0), $m = -\frac{3}{4}$ **28.** (0, 0), $m = -\frac{2}{5}$ **29.** (0, 1), $m = \frac{2}{3}$ **30.** (0, 2), $m = \frac{3}{4}$

31. (−4, 0), $m = -\frac{1}{2}$ **32.** (−6, 0), $m = -\frac{1}{3}$ **33.** (0, −3), $m = \frac{4}{5}$ **34.** (0, −5), $m = \frac{7}{2}$

35. (−2, 3), $m = -\frac{5}{4}$ **36.** (−1, 2), $m = -\frac{3}{5}$ **37.** (−5, −4), $m = \frac{7}{9}$ **38.** (−7, −3), $m = \frac{8}{11}$

39. (0, 4), $m = 0$ **40.** (0, −2), $m = 0$ **41.** (−6, −1), m undefined   **42.** (5, −1), m undefined

Determine the slope of each line graphed in Problems 43–48.

43.

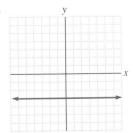

44.

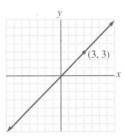

45.

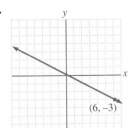

(6, −3)

46.

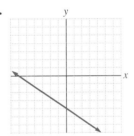

(3, 3)

47.

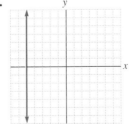

48.

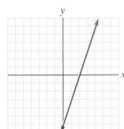

Solve each word problem.

49. Show that the three points A(6, 1), B(2, −1), and C(−2, −3) lie on the same straight line.

50. Show that the three points A(9, 5), B(2, 1), and C(−5, −4) do not lie on the same straight line.

51. Architects refer to the slope of a roof as the *pitch* of the roof. Determine the pitch of the roof shown in Fig. 6.36.

52. Engineers refer to the slope of a road as the *grade* of the road. Determine the grade of the bridge roadway shown in Fig. 6.37. (Hint: Use the Pythagorean theorem.)

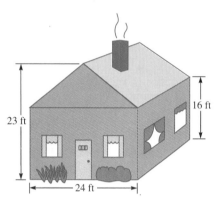

FIGURE 6.36

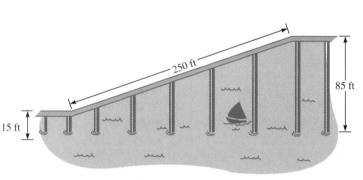

FIGURE 6.37

53. The length of a particular ski trail from the top of a mountain to the bottom is 3718 feet (see Fig. 6.38). If the slope of the trail is 5/12, find the height, *x,* of the mountain. (Hint: Apply the Pythagorean theorem to the triangle on the left. Then use the two triangles to set up a proportion.)

54. The slope of a conical pile of sand is 3/4 (see Fig. 6.39). If the height of the pile is 10 feet, find the diameter, *x,* of the base. (Hint: Use the two triangles to set up a proportion.)

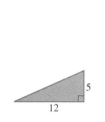

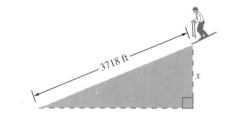

FIGURE 6.38

FIGURE 6.39

6.4   Forms of a Linear Equation

In this section we learn how to use information about a line to write an equation of the line.

Point-Slope Form of a Linear Equation

Consider the line that passes through the point (x_1, y_1) and has slope m, as shown in Fig. 6.40. If (x, y) is any other point on the line, we can use the definition of slope to write the following equation.

$$\frac{y - y_1}{x - x_1} = m$$

Multiply both sides by $x - x_1$ and simplify.

$$(x - x_1) \cdot \frac{y - y_1}{x - x_1} = m \cdot (x - x_1)$$
$$y - y_1 = m(x - x_1)$$

This last equation is called the *point-slope form* of a linear equation.

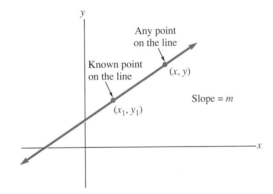

FIGURE 6.40

POINT-SLOPE FORM

An equation of the line through (x_1, y_1) with slope m is

$$y - y_1 = m(x - x_1).$$

To find an equation of a line using the point-slope form, we must know one point on the line and the slope of the line.

EXAMPLE 1   Find an equation of the line through $(3, 7)$ with slope 2. Then write the equation in standard form.

Solution   Since one point and the slope are given, use the point-slope form.

$$y - y_1 = m(x - x_1) \quad \text{\textit{Point-slope form}}$$
$$y - 7 = 2(x - 3) \quad \text{\textit{Let }} (x_1, y_1) = (3, 7) \text{ \textit{and }} m = 2$$

Now write the equation in standard form.

$$y - 7 = 2x - 6 \qquad \textit{Distribute 2}$$
$$-2x + y = 1 \qquad \textit{Subtract 2x, add 7}$$
$$-1(-2x + y) = -1(1) \qquad \textit{Multiply by } -1, \textit{ to make the first coefficient a}$$
$$\textit{positive number}$$
$$2x - y = -1 \qquad \textit{Simplify}$$

Try Problem 1 >   Both of the answers, $-2x + y = 1$ and $2x - y = -1$, are correct.   ∎

EXAMPLE 2   Find an equation of the line through $(-1, 4)$ and $(5, -6)$.
Then write the equation in standard form.

Solution   First use the two given points to find the slope of the line.

$$m = \frac{-6 - 4}{5 - (-1)} = \frac{-10}{6} = -\frac{5}{3}$$

Now substitute either of the given points and the slope into the point-slope
form.

$$y - y_1 = m(x - x_1) \qquad \textit{Point-slope form}$$
$$y - 4 = -\frac{5}{3}[x - (-1)] \qquad \textit{Let } (x_1, y_1) = (-1, 4) \textit{ and } m = -5/3$$
$$y - 4 = -\frac{5}{3}(x + 1) \qquad \textit{Simplify}$$

Finally, write the equation in standard form.

$$3(y - 4) = -5(x + 1) \qquad \textit{Multiply by 3}$$
$$3y - 12 = -5x - 5 \qquad \textit{Distributive property}$$
$$5x + 3y = 7 \qquad \textit{Add 5x, add 12}$$

Try Problem 19 >   We can check this answer by showing that both $(-1, 4)$ and $(5, -6)$ are solutions of $5x + 3y = 7$.   ∎

Slope-Intercept Form

We can also find an equation of a line if we know the slope and the y-intercept
of the line. Consider the line with slope m and y-intercept b. Since the y-inter-
cept is b, the line passes through the point $(0, b)$, as shown in Fig. 6.41. Substitute the point $(x_1, y_1) = (0, b)$ and the slope m into the point-slope form.

$$y - y_1 = m(x - x_1) \qquad \textit{Point-slope form}$$
$$y - b = m(x - 0) \qquad \textit{Let } (x_1, y_1) = (0, b) \textit{ and } m = m$$
$$y - b = mx \qquad \textit{Simplify the right side}$$
$$y = mx + b \qquad \textit{Add b}$$

This last equation is called the *slope-intercept form* of a linear equation.

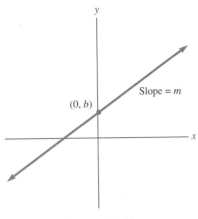

FIGURE 6.41

SLOPE-INTERCEPT FORM

An equation of the line with slope m and y-intercept b is

$$y = mx + b.$$

The slope-intercept form illustrates that **when an equation of a line is solved for y, the coefficient of x is the slope and the constant term is the y-intercept.**

Equation	Slope	y-intercept
$y = 6x + 7$	6	7
$y = x - 4$	1	-4
$y = \dfrac{8}{3}x - \dfrac{2}{5}$	$\dfrac{8}{3}$	$-\dfrac{2}{5}$
$y = -\dfrac{x}{2}$	$-\dfrac{1}{2}$	0

EXAMPLE 3   Find an equation of the line with slope $-1/4$ and y-intercept 1.

Solution   Since the slope and the y-intercept are given, use the slope-intercept form.

$$y = mx + b \qquad \textit{Slope-intercept form}$$

Try Problem 29 > $$y = -\frac{1}{4}x + 1 \qquad \textit{Let } m = -1/4 \textit{ and } b = 1$$ ∎

EXAMPLE 4   Find the slope and the y-intercept of the line whose equation is $3x + 2y = 10$.

Solution   Solve for y to put the equation in slope-intercept form.

$$3x + 2y = 10 \qquad \textit{Original equation}$$
$$2y = -3x + 10 \qquad \textit{Subtract 3x}$$
$$y = \frac{-3x + 10}{2} \qquad \textit{Divide both sides by 2}$$
$$y = \frac{-3x}{2} + \frac{10}{2} \qquad \textit{Divide each term by 2}$$
$$y = -\frac{3}{2}x + 5 \qquad \textit{Simplify}$$

Try Problem 39 >   The slope is $-3/2$ and the y-intercept is 5.   ■

EXAMPLE 5   Find the slope and the y-intercept of the line whose equation is $y = 6$.

Solution   You can write the equation in slope-intercept form as $y = 0 \cdot x + 6$. Therefore the slope is 0 (which means the line is horizontal) and the y-intercept is 6.   ■

Try Problem 43 >

We can use the slope and the y-intercept of a line to graph the line without constructing a table of values.

EXAMPLE 6   Find the slope and the y-intercept of the line whose equation is $2x - y = 4$. Then use this information to graph the line.

Solution   Write the equation in slope-intercept form.

$$2x - y = 4 \qquad \textit{Original equation}$$
$$-y = -2x + 4 \qquad \textit{Subtract 2x}$$
$$y = 2x - 4 \qquad \textit{Multiply by -1}$$

The y-intercept is -4. Therefore plot the point $(0, -4)$ as shown in Fig. 6.42.

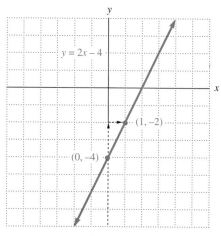

FIGURE 6.42

Since the slope is 2/1, start at $(0, -4)$ and go 2 units up (the rise) and 1 unit right (the run). This brings you to the point $(1, -2)$. Draw a line through $(0, -4)$ and $(1, -2)$ as shown in Fig. 6.42. ■

Try Problem 49 >

Here is a summary of the various forms of a linear equation.

FORMS OF A LINEAR EQUATION

$ax + by = c$	**Standard Form** Let $x = 0$ to find the y-intercept Let $y = 0$ to find the x-intercept
$y = c$	**Horizontal Line** The y-intercept is c
$x = c$	**Vertical Line** The x-intercept is c
$y - y_1 = m(x - x_1)$	**Point-Slope Form** Passes through (x_1, y_1) The slope is m
$y = mx + b$	**Slope-Intercept Form** The slope is m The y-intercept is b

---

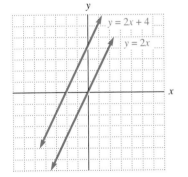

FIGURE 6.43

Parallel and Perpendicular Lines

We can determine whether two lines are parallel, or perpendicular, or neither parallel nor perpendicular by comparing the slopes of the two lines. Consider the two lines graphed in Fig. 6.43. The lines are parallel, since they do not intersect no matter how far they are extended. Note that their slopes are equal (both slopes are 2). This suggests the following rule.

PARALLEL LINES

Two (nonvertical) lines are parallel if their slopes are equal.

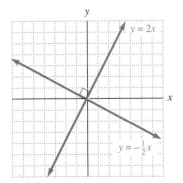

FIGURE 6.44

Now consider the two lines graphed in Fig. 6.44. The lines are perpendicular, since they intersect at right angles (90° angles). Note that the product of their slopes is -1, since $2[-(1/2)] = -1$. This suggests the following rule.

> **PERPENDICULAR LINES**
>
> Two (nonvertical) lines are perpendicular if the product of their slopes is -1.

EXAMPLE 7   Determine whether the lines represented by the given pair of equations are parallel, perpendicular, or neither.

a. $y = 2x - 6$ b. $3x - y = 7$ c. $8x + 10y = 20$
    $y = -2x + 1$ $-6x + 2y = 8$ $5x - 4y = 6$

Solution

a. The slope of the first line is 2, and the slope of the second line is -2. Since $2 \neq -2$, the slopes are not equal. Since $2(-2) = -4$, the product of the slopes is not -1. Therefore the lines are neither parallel nor perpendicular.

b. Write each equation in slope-intercept form to determine the slope.

$$3x - y = 7 \qquad\qquad -6x + 2y = 8$$
$$-y = -3x + 7 \qquad\qquad 2y = 6x + 8$$
$$y = 3x - 7 \qquad\qquad y = 3x + 4$$
$$m = 3 \qquad\qquad m = 3$$

The slopes are equal, so the lines are parallel.

Try Problem 59 >

c. If we write each equation in slope-intercept form, we find that the slope of the first line is $-(4/5)$ and the slope of the second line is $5/4$. Since $[-(4/5)][5/4] = -1$, the lines are perpendicular.   ∎

P R O B L E M   S O L V I N G

EXAMPLE 8   Suppose the demand for a certain telephone is 3000 when the price is \$20, but only 1000 when the price is \$25. Let y represent the number of telephones demanded and x represent the price.

a. Assuming the relationship between price and demand is linear, write an equation relating x (price) and y (demand).

b. Use this equation to determine what the demand would be if the price drops to \$10.

Solution

a. One point on the line is $(x_1, y_1) = (20, 3000)$. Another point is $(x_2, y_2) = (25, 1000)$. Use the two points to find the slope.

$$m = \frac{1000 - 3000}{25 - 20} = \frac{-2000}{5} = -400$$

Then use the point-slope form to write an equation of the line.

$$y - y_1 = m(x - x_1) \qquad \textit{Point-slope form}$$
$$y - 3000 = -400(x - 20) \qquad \textit{Let } (x_1, y_1) = (20, 3000) \textit{ and } m = -400$$
$$y - 3000 = -400x + 8000 \qquad \textit{Distribute } -400$$
$$y = -400x + 11,000 \qquad \textit{Add } 3000$$

b. If the price, x, is \$10, then

$$y = -400(10) + 11,000 = -4000 + 11,000 = 7000$$

Try Problem 73 >   If the price were \$10, the demand would be 7000 telephones.

6.4 Problem Set

LEARNING THROUGH WRITING

☐ Discuss the line whose equation is $y - y_1 = m(x - x_1)$.

☐ Discuss the line whose equation is $y = mx + b$.

☐ Describe the slopes of parallel lines.

☐ Describe the slopes of perpendicular lines.

Find an equation of the line through the given point and with the given slope. Then write the equation in standard form.

1. $(2, 5)$, $m = 3$

2. $(4, 6)$, $m = 2$

3. $(-1, 7)$, $m = 4$

4. $(-3, 1)$, $m = 5$

5. $(6, -4)$, $m = \dfrac{1}{2}$

6. $(5, -2)$, $m = \dfrac{1}{3}$

7. $(-3, -2)$, $m = \dfrac{7}{3}$

8. $(-1, -4)$, $m = \dfrac{7}{2}$

9. $(0, 9)$, $m = -1$

10. $(0, -7)$, $m = -1$

11. $(-8, 0)$, $m = -\dfrac{2}{5}$

12. $(0, 0)$, $m = -\dfrac{4}{5}$

Find an equation of the line through the given pair of points. Then write the equation in standard form.

13. $(4, 3)$, $(5, 5)$

14. $(2, 5)$, $(3, 8)$

15. $(-3, 4)$, $(1, 6)$

16. $(-1, 2)$, $(5, 4)$

17. $(2, -3)$, $(-5, 4)$

18. $(4, -8)$, $(-6, 2)$

19. $(-5, 6)$, $(1, -9)$

20. $(-2, 3)$, $(6, -7)$

21. $(0, 0)$, $(-10, -8)$

22. $(3, 0)$, $(-11, -10)$

23. $(6, 7)$, $(3, 7)$

24. $(9, 8)$, $(4, 8)$

Find an equation of the line with the given slope and the given y-intercept.

25. $m = 5$, $b = 3$

26. $m = 6$, $b = 4$

27. $m = 1$, $b = -12$

28. $m = 1$, $b = -15$

29. $m = -\dfrac{1}{2}$, $b = 1$

30. $m = -\dfrac{1}{5}$, $b = 2$

31. $m = \dfrac{4}{7}$, $b = 0$

32. $m = \dfrac{5}{8}$, $b = 0$

33. $m = -8$, $b = -\dfrac{2}{3}$

34. $m = -9$, $b = -\dfrac{3}{4}$

35. $m = 0$, $b = -5$

36. $m = 0$, $b = -7$

Find the slope and the y-intercept of the line with the given equation.

37. $y = 4x + 8$

38. $y = -x + 2$

39. $5x + 3y = 12$

40. $5x + 4y = 16$

41. $4x - 6y = 0$

42. $8x - 10y = 0$

43. $y = 9$

44. $y = 7$

Find the slope and the y-intercept of the line with the given equation. Then use this information to graph the line. Do not construct a table of values.

45. $y = x + 3$

46. $y = -x + 4$

47. $y = -3x$

48. $y = 4x$

49. $3x - y = 6$

50. $2x - y = 2$

51. $2x - 5y = 10$

52. $5x + 4y = 12$

Determine whether the lines represented by the given pair of equations are parallel, perpendicular, or neither.

53. $y = 6x - 1$
$y = 6x + 1$

54. $y = -4x + 1$
$y = -4x - 1$

55. $y = -5x$
$y = \dfrac{x}{5}$

56. $y = -3x$
$y = \dfrac{x}{3}$

57. $y = -\dfrac{x}{3} + \dfrac{2}{3}$
$x + 3y = 0$

58. $y = -\dfrac{x}{2} + \dfrac{3}{2}$
$x + 2y = 0$

59. $4x - y = 9$
$-8x + 2y = 10$

60. $5x - y = 11$
$-15x + 3y = 9$

61. $-2x + y = 0$
$x - 2y = 5$

62. $-6x + y = 0$
$x - 6y = 7$

63. $9x + 6y = 18$
$2x - 3y = 6$

64. $12x + 10y = 30$
$5x - 6y = 12$

Solve each word problem.

65. What is the slope and the y-intercept of the line $x = 3$?

66. What is the slope and the y-intercept of the line $x = -2$?

67. Find an equation of the line through $(-1, 5)$ and $(-1, 3)$.

68. Find an equation of the line through $(7, 2)$ and $(7, 4)$.

69. Write an equation of the line that passes through $(1, 3)$ and is parallel to the line whose equation is $y = 4x - 5$.

70. Write an equation of the line that passes through $(6, 7)$ and is parallel to the line whose equation is $y = 5x + 1$.

71. Write an equation of the line that passes through $(2, -4)$ and is perpendicular to the line whose equation is $3x - y = 7$.

72. Write an equation of the line that passes through $(-3, 5)$ and is perpendicular to the line whose equation is $2x - y = 9$.

73. Suppose the demand for a certain pair of sunglasses is 5000 when the price is \$30, but only 4000 when the price is \$35. Let y represent the number of sunglasses demanded and x represent the price.
  a. Assuming the relationship between price and demand is linear, write an equation relating x (price) and y (demand).
  b. Use this equation to determine what the demand would be if the price drops to \$20.

74. Suppose that when the monthly dues at a certain health club are \$20 the demand for memberships is 450. However, when the dues are \$25 the demand drops to 375. Let y represent the number of memberships demanded and x represent the monthly dues.
  a. Assuming the relationship between dues and demand is linear, write an equation relating x (monthly dues) and y (demand).
  b. Use this equation to determine what the demand would be if the monthly dues were raised to \$35.

6.5   Graphing Linear Inequalities

If we replace the equality symbol in a linear equation with an inequality symbol, we get a **linear inequality.** Therefore

$$x > 2, \qquad y \le 4, \qquad \text{and} \qquad x + y < 3$$

are linear inequalities. The **graph** of a linear inequality is the graph of all the solutions of the inequality.

EXAMPLE 1   Graph $x > 2$ on a rectangular coordinate system.

Solution   Any ordered pair (x, y) with an x-value greater than 2 is a solution of $x > 2$. We graph the solutions by shading the region to the right of the vertical line $x = 2$, as shown in Fig. 6.45. The boundary line $x = 2$ is drawn as a dashed line to indicate that points on the line $x = 2$ are not part of the solution.

Try Problem 13 >

■

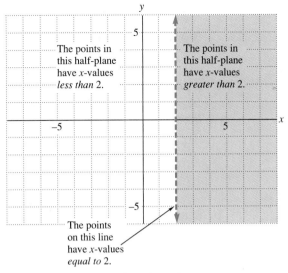

FIGURE 6.45

Each line in the plane divides the plane into two regions, called **half-planes.** A half-plane that includes its boundary line is called a *closed half-plane*. A half-plane that does not include its boundary line is called an *open half-plane*. The graph in Fig. 6.45 is an open half-plane.

EXAMPLE 2   Graph $y \leq 4$ on a rectangular coordinate system.

Solution   The graph is the closed half-plane that lies on and below the horizontal line $y = 4$ (see Fig. 6.46). The boundary line $y = 4$ is solid, since the inequality symbol is $\leq$ and not $<$.   ■

Try Problem 15 >

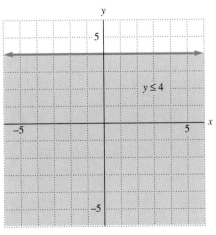

FIGURE 6.46

EXAMPLE 3   Graph $x + y < 3$.

Solution   First graph the boundary line $x + y = 3$, as shown in Fig. 6.47. The boundary line divides the plane into two half-planes, one above the boundary line and one below. To determine which half-plane represents the solution to $x + y < 3$, choose a test point that does *not* lie on the boundary line itself. It's a good idea to choose $(0, 0)$ as your test point to make the arithmetic easy, but any point not on the boundary line can be used. Substitute $(x, y) = (0, 0)$ into the original inequality.

$$x + y < 3 \quad \textit{Original inequality}$$
$$0 + 0 < 3 \quad \textit{Let } x = 0 \textit{ and } y = 0$$
$$0 < 3 \quad \textit{True}$$

Try Problem 21 >

Since $(0, 0)$ is a solution of $x + y < 3$, shade the open half-plane that contains $(0, 0)$, as shown in Fig. 6.48.   ∎

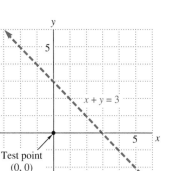

FIGURE 6.47

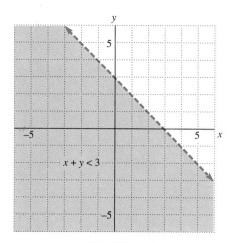

FIGURE 6.48

TO GRAPH A LINEAR INEQUALITY

1. Replace the inequality symbol with an equality symbol and graph the resulting boundary line. Draw a solid line if the symbol is $\leq$ or $\geq$. Draw a dashed line if the symbol is $<$ or $>$.
2. Choose a test point not on the boundary line and substitute it into the original inequality. If the result is a true statement, shade the half-plane that contains the test point; if the result is a false statement, shade the half-plane that does not contain the test point.

EXAMPLE 4   Graph $y \geq 2x$.

Solution

Step 1 *Replace the inequality symbol* $\geq$ *with the equality symbol* $=$ *and graph the resulting boundary line,* $y = 2x$. *Draw a solid line, since the original inequality symbol is* $\geq$. The boundary line, $y = 2x$, is shown in Fig. 6.49.

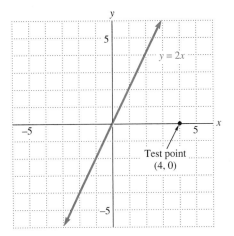

FIGURE 6.49

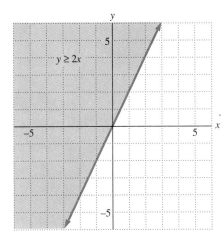

FIGURE 6.50

Step 2 *Choose a test point not on the boundary line—say* (4, 0)—*and substitute it into the original inequality.* We cannot use (0, 0), since it is on the boundary line.

$$y \geq 2x \qquad \text{\textit{Original inequality}}$$
$$0 \geq 2(4) \qquad \text{\textit{Let} } x = 4 \text{ \textit{and} } y = 0$$
$$0 \geq 8 \qquad \text{\textit{False}}$$

Try Problem 29 >

Since the result is a false statement, shade the closed half-plane that does not contain (4, 0). The graph is shown in Fig. 6.50. ∎

PROBLEM SOLVING

EXAMPLE 5   A patient is to consume no more than 10 grams of fat at any one meal. For breakfast, the patient decides to eat bagels and cream cheese. Each bagel contains 2 grams of fat, and each ounce of cream cheese contains 5 grams of fat. Therefore the patient can eat x bagels and y ounces of cream cheese, so long as

$$2x + 5y \leq 10.$$

Grams of fat in   *Grams of fat in y oz*   *Total grams of fat allowed*
x bagels   *of cream cheese*

Graph all of the breakfast possibilities.

Solution   First graph the boundary line $2x + 5y = 10$, as shown in Fig. 6.51. Then substitute the test point $(0, 0)$ into the original inequality.

$$2x + 5y \leq 10 \quad \textit{Original inequality}$$
$$2(0) + 5(0) \leq 10 \quad \textit{Let } x = 0 \textit{ and } y = 0$$
$$0 \leq 10 \quad \textit{True}$$

Since the result is a true statement, shade the closed half-plane that contains the test point, as shown in Fig. 6.52. But neither x (the number of bagels) nor y (the number of ounces of cream cheese) can be a negative number. Therefore only that portion of the half-plane shown in Fig. 6.53 applies to this problem. Any ordered pair taken from the shaded region in Fig. 6.53 represents a breakfast possibility. For example, the ordered pair $(x, y) = (2, 1)$ represents 2 bagels and 1 ounce of cream cheese. This gives a total of

Try Problem 37 > $\qquad 2x + 5y = 2(2) + 5(1) = 4 + 5 = 9$ grams of fat.

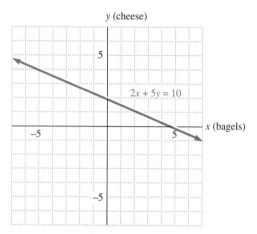

FIGURE 6.51

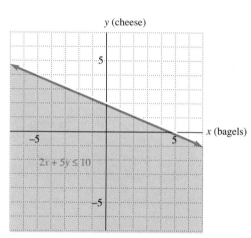

FIGURE 6.52

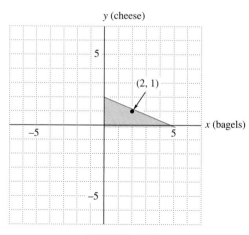

FIGURE 6.53

6.5 Problem Set

For Problems 1–12 the boundary line for the given inequality has been drawn. Complete the graph of the inequality by shading the appropriate half-plane.

1. $x < 5$

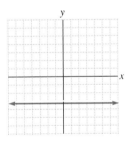

2. $y > 2$

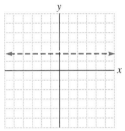

3. $y \geq -3$

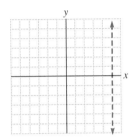

4. $x \leq -1$

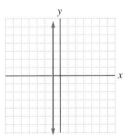

5. $x + y < 4$

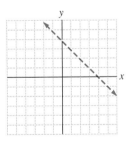

6. $x + y < 3$

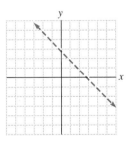

7. $x + y > 4$

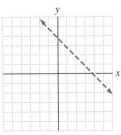

8. $x + y > 3$

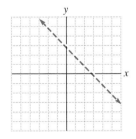

9. $4x - 5y \leq 20$

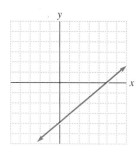

10. $3x - 4y \geq 12$

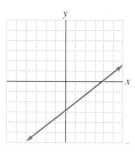

11. $y \geq 2x$

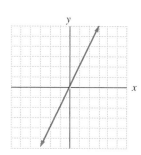

12. $y \leq \dfrac{1}{2}x$

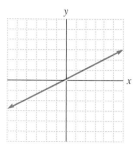

Graph each linear inequality on a rectangular coordinate system.

13. $x > 1$	**14.** $x > 3$	**15.** $y \leq 3$	**16.** $y \leq 2$
17. $y < x + 2$	**18.** $y < x + 4$	**19.** $y \leq 2x - 4$	**20.** $y \leq 2x - 6$
21. $x + y < 1$	**22.** $x + y < 2$	**23.** $x + 2y > 4$	**24.** $x + 2y > 6$
25. $x \leq -2$	**26.** $x \leq -4$	**27.** $3x - 2y \geq 6$	**28.** $5x - 2y \geq 10$
29. $y \geq 3x$	**30.** $y \geq 4x$	**31.** $y > -5$	**32.** $y > -1$
33. $x \geq 0$	**34.** $y \leq 0$	**35.** $x - 2y > 0$	**36.** $x + 3y > 0$

For Problems 37–40:

a. Graph the inequality. Since neither x nor y can be a negative number, graph only that portion of the half-plane that lies in quadrant I.

b. List three ordered pairs that lie in the region graphed in part (a).

37. A patient consumes x hamburger buns and y slices of bologna. Each hamburger bun contains 2 grams of fat, and each slice of bologna contains 8 grams of fat. If the total fat consumed is to be no more than 16 grams, then

$$2x + 8y \leq 16.$$

38. A clothing manufacturer makes x shirts and y suits each day. It takes 2 hours of labor to produce a shirt and 6 hours of labor to produce a suit. If the firm is willing to spend no more than 18 hours of labor each day producing shirts and suits, then

$$2x + 6y \leq 18.$$

39. A drugstore orders x units of Drug A and y units of Drug B from a particular supplier. Drug A costs $3 per unit and Drug B costs $5 per unit. If the drugstore must order a minimum of $600 worth of drugs from this supplier to keep the account open, then

$$3x + 5y \geq 600.$$

40. Protein and carbohydrates both contain about 4 calories in each gram. Fat contains 9 calories in each gram. A bodybuilder eats x grams of protein and carbohydrates combined and y grams of fat. If the total calories consumed each day must be at least 2700, then

$$4x + 9y \geq 2700.$$

6.6 Functions and Function Notation

Suppose you earn $5 an hour. Then your earnings are related to the number of hours you work. One way to express this relationship is to write a set of ordered pairs. For example, the ordered pair (2, 10) means if you work 2 hours you earn $10. The ordered pair (8, 40) means if you work 8 hours you earn $40. In this way a set of ordered pairs defines a *relation* between two variable quantities.

> **DEFINITION OF A RELATION**
>
> A **relation** is a set of ordered pairs. (cặp)
> (hệ thức
>   Tập hợp các phần tử thứ tự)

Domain   Range

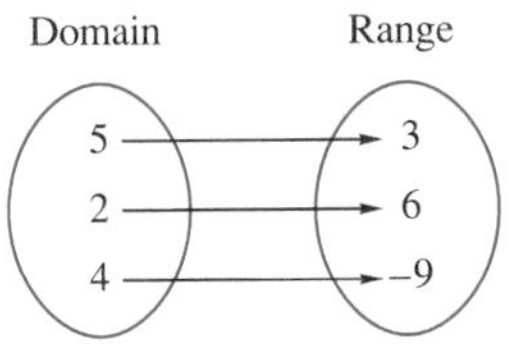

FIGURE 6.54

The set of all first coordinates of the ordered pairs of a relation is called the **domain** of the relation; the set of all second coordinates is called the **range.** The set of ordered pairs {(5, 3), (2, 6), (4, −9)} is an example of a relation. The domain of this relation is the set {5, 2, 4}. The range is {3, 6, −9}. One way to picture this relation is shown in Fig. 6.54. Notice that the relation corresponds each value in the domain to a value in the range.

A special kind of relation, called a *function*, is the most useful kind of relation for solving applied problems.

> **DEFINITION OF A FUNCTION**
>
> A **function** is a set of ordered pairs in which each first coordinate corresponds to exactly one second coordinate.

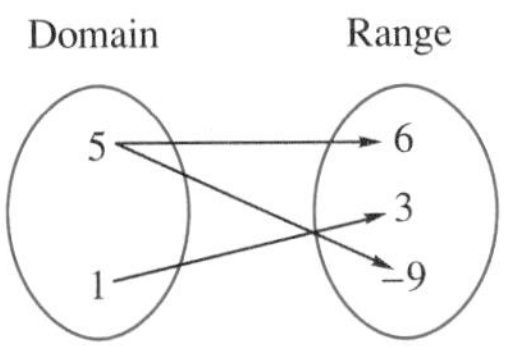

Domain   Range

FIGURE 6.55

(miền)

EXAMPLE 1 State the domain and the range of each relation. Determine whether the relation is a function. (khoảng biến thiên , miền trị số) (xác định)
(hàm số)

a. {(1, 4), (−3, 2), (0, 7), (8, 4)}   b. {(5, 6), (1, 3), (5, −9)}

Solution

a. The domain is {1, −3, 0, 8}. The range is {4, 2, 7}. Since each first coordinate corresponds to exactly one second coordinate, this relation is a function.

b. The domain is {5, 1}. The range is {6, 3, −9}. Since the first coordinate 5 corresponds to two different second coordinates, namely 6 and −9, this relation is not a function (see Fig. 6.55).   ∎

Try Problem 3 >

We can also define a function by writing a rule that tells us how to get the second coordinate of the ordered pair when we are given the first coordinate.

For example, suppose you earn $5 an hour. Then your daily earnings, y, are a function of the number of hours, x, that you work each day. The rule that defines this function is

$$y = 5x.$$

The domain of this function is the set of all possible values of x. Since you cannot work a negative number of hours, nor can you work more than 24 hours in a day, the domain of this function is $0 \le x \le 24$. The range of this function is the set of all possible values of y. If you work 0 hours, your daily earnings are $0. If you work 24 hours, your daily earnings are $120. Therefore the range of this function is $0 \le y \le 120$.

EXAMPLE 2   Determine whether the given rule defines y as a function of x.

a. $y = 4x + 1$ b. $y < x + 3$

Solution

a. If you substitute any value for x, multiply by 4 and add 1, you get exactly one value for y. Therefore $y = 4x + 1$ defines y as a function of x.
b. For each value of x, there is an infinite number of values for y. For example, if $x = 1$, then y can be any number less than 4. Therefore $y < x + 3$ does not define y as a function of x. ∎

Try Problem 13 >

Caution! ■

Any rule that relates x and y defines a relation. However, not all relations are functions. Both of the following rules define relations, but only the first rule defines a function.

A Function	*Not a Function*
$y = x^2$	$y^2 = x$
Each value of x produces exactly one value of y.	When $x = 4$, the value of y can be 2 or -2.

EXAMPLE 3   Find the domain of the function defined by the given equation.

a. $y = x + 3$ b. $y = \dfrac{5}{x^2 - 4}$

Solution

a. If we substitute any real value for x and add 3, the result is a real value for y. Therefore the domain is all real numbers.
b. We can substitute any real value for x except those values that make the denominator 0. Therefore the domain consists of all real numbers except 2 and -2, written $x \ne 2, -2$. ∎

Try Problem 29 >

EXAMPLE 4   Find the range of the function defined by the given equation.

a. $y = 2x$ b. $y = x^2$

Solution

a. Since any real number can be used for y, the range is all real numbers.

b. Note that y is the square of a real number. Since the square of a real number cannot be negative, the range is all non-negative real numbers, written $y \geq 0$.

Try Problem 33 >

We can determine whether a graph is the graph of a function by applying the *vertical line test*.

VERTICAL LINE TEST

A graph in the plane represents a function provided that no vertical line intersects the graph at more than one point.

EXAMPLE 5   Determine whether the graphs in Figs. 6.56 and 6.57 represent functions.

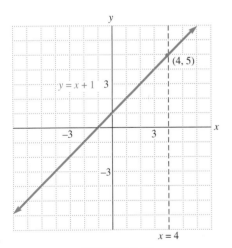

FIGURE 6.56

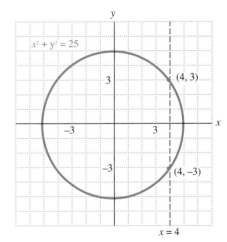

FIGURE 6.57

Solution

a. Since no vertical line intersects the graph in Fig. 6.56 at more than one point, this graph represents a function.

b. In Fig. 6.57, the vertical line $x = 4$ intersects the graph at two points, namely (4, 3) and (4, -3). This means that the x-value 4 leads to two y-values, namely 3 and -3. Therefore this graph does not represent a function.

Try Problem 43 >

Function Notation

To denote that y is a function of x we write

$$y = f(x).$$

The notation $f(x)$ is read "f of x." It does *not* mean "f times x."

Since y and $f(x)$ are equal, they can be used interchangeably. This means that we can use either of the following notations to define the function whose second coordinate is the square of the first coordinate.

$$y = x^2 \qquad \text{or} \qquad f(x) = x^2$$

The function notation $f(x) = x^2$ has certain advantages over the notation $y = x^2$. For example, using $y = x^2$ we must write

$$\text{if } x = 3, \text{ then } y = 3^2 = 9.$$

Using $f(x) = x^2$ we write

$$f(3) = 3^2 = 9.$$

The equation $f(3) = 9$ is read "f of 3 equals 9." Note that $f(3)$ is the range value that corresponds to the domain value 3 (see Fig. 6.58). As such, $f(3)$ is called the *value of the function f* at 3.

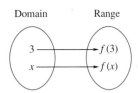

Domain   Range

FIGURE 6.58

Swiss mathematician Leonhard Euler (1707–1783) was the first to formulate a definition of the term *function* that is somewhat similar to the contemporary definition. He was also the first to use the function notation $f(x)$. Euler wrote more on the subject of mathematics than any other writer in history. He continued writing even after he became totally blind in 1768. Euler's definition of a function was later modified by the German mathematician Lejeune Dirichlet (1805–1859), and essentially it is Dirichlet's definition that is in use today.

FUNCTION NOTATION

The equation $y = f(x)$ is read "y equals f of x."

1. f is the name of the function.
2. x is the domain value.
3. $f(x)$ is the range value (or the value of the function) for the domain value x.

EXAMPLE 6   If $f(x) = 6x + 5$, find (a) $f(2)$, (b) $f(0)$, (c) $f(-1)$.

Solution

a. Replace x with 2.

$$f(x) = 6x + 5 \qquad \textit{Original function}$$
$$f(2) = 6(2) + 5 \qquad \textit{Replace x with 2}$$
$$f(2) = 12 + 5$$
$$f(2) = 17 \qquad \left.\vphantom{\begin{array}{c}a\\b\end{array}}\right\}\textit{Simplify the right side}$$

b. Replace x with 0.

$$f(0) = 6(0) + 5 = 0 + 5 = 5$$

c. Replace x with -1.

Try Problem 53 >

$$f(-1) = 6(-1) + 5 = -6 + 5 = -1$$

∎

Although we usually use the letter f to name a function, any letter can be used. Therefore the functions

$$g(x) = x^2 \quad \text{and} \quad h(x) = x^2$$

are equivalent to the function $f(x) = x^2$, since each has the range value a^2 when the domain value is a.

EXAMPLE 7 If $g(x) = 3x^2 - 5x + 8$, find (a) $g(1)$, (b) $g(0)$, (c) $g(-3)$.

Solution
a. Replace x with 1.

$$
\begin{aligned}
g(x) &= 3x^2 - 5x + 8 \qquad &\textit{Original function} \\
g(1) &= 3(1)^2 - 5(1) + 8 \qquad &\textit{Replace x with 1} \\
g(1) &= 3 - 5 + 8 \\
g(1) &= 6
\end{aligned}
\right\} \textit{Simplify the right side}
$$

b. Replace x with 0.

$$g(0) = 3(0)^2 - 5(0) + 8 = 8$$

c. Replace x with -3.

Try Problem 59 >

$$g(-3) = 3(-3)^2 - 5(-3) + 8 = 3(9) + 15 + 8 = 50$$

■

PROBLEM SOLVING

EXAMPLE 8 A sales representative earns a salary of $250 per week plus a commission of 15% of the dollar value of all sales she makes. If $E(x)$ denotes her total weekly earnings based on sales totaling x dollars, write an equation that defines weekly earnings as a function of sales. Then find and interpret $E(900)$.

Solution An equation that defines weekly earnings as a function of sales is

Weekly earnings	*equal*	*commissions*	*plus*	*weekly salary*
↓	↓	↓	↓	↓
$E(x)$	$=$	15% of x	$+$	250.

Simplify the right side.

$$E(x) = 0.15x + 250$$

Therefore

$$E(900) = 0.15(900) + 250 = 135 + 250 = 385.$$

This means that if $900 worth of goods are sold that week, the representative's

Try Problem 81 > earnings are $385.

6.6 Problem Set

State the domain and the range of each relation. Determine whether the relation is a function.

1. $\{(2, 5), (-6, 4), (0, 3), (9, 5)\}$

2. $\{(8, 1), (-5, 7), (10, 1), (0, 2)\}$

3. $\{(3, 9), (1, 7), (3, -8)\}$

4. $\{(6, 9), (4, 8), (4, -3)\}$

5. $\{(1, 1), (2, 2), (3, 3)\}$

6. $\{(0, 0), (-1, -1), (-2, -2)\}$

7. $\{(-5, 0), (-6, 0), (-7, 0)\}$

8. $\{(1, 3), (2, 3), (3, 3)\}$

9. Domain   Range

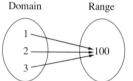

10. Domain   Range

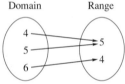

11. Domain   Range

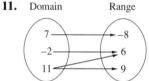

12. Domain   Range

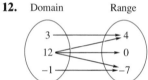

Determine whether the given rule defines y as a function of x.

13. $y = 2x + 6$

14. $y = 4x - 8$

15. $y = x^2 - 3$

16. $y = x^2 + 7$

17. $y < x + 4$

18. $y > x + 4$

19. $y = \dfrac{1}{x}$

20. $y = \dfrac{1}{x - 1}$

21. $y^2 = x$

22. $|y| = x$

23. $x^2 + y^2 = 4$

24. $x^2 + y^2 = 9$

Find the domain of the function defined by the given equation.

25. $y = x - 2$

26. $y = 2x^2 - 9$

27. $y = \dfrac{7}{x - 3}$

28. $y = \dfrac{11}{x + 4}$

29. $y = \dfrac{x}{x^2 - 1}$

30. $y = \dfrac{x}{x^2 - 25}$

31. $y = \dfrac{x - 1}{x^2 + 8x}$

32. $y = \dfrac{21}{x^2 + 4x - 21}$

Find the range of the function defined by the given equation.

33. $y = 4x$

34. $y = 6x$

35. $y = 2x + 5$

36. $y = 9x - 7$

37. $y = (x - 1)^2$

38. $y = (x + 3)^2$

39. $y = x^2 + 1$

40. $y = x^2 - 3$

Determine whether each graph represents a function.

41.

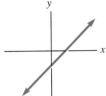

42.

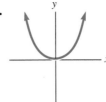

43.

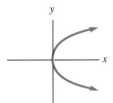

44.

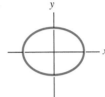

45.

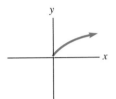

46.

47.

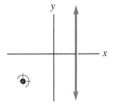

48.

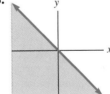

For each function, find (a) f(2), (b) f(0), and (c) f(−1).

49. $f(x) = x + 1$ **50.** $f(x) = x - 1$ **51.** $f(x) = -6x$ **52.** $f(x) = 4x$

53. $f(x) = 4x + 3$ **54.** $f(x) = -2x + 7$ **55.** $f(x) = |x - 2|$ **56.** $f(x) = |x - 1|$

For each function, find (a) g(1), (b) g(0), and (c) g(−3).

57. $g(x) = x^2 + x$ **58.** $g(x) = x^2 - x$ **59.** $g(x) = 2x^2 - 5x + 9$

60. $g(x) = 3x^2 - 4x + 6$ **61.** $g(x) = -x^2 + 6x + 4$ **62.** $g(x) = -x^2 + 5x + 7$

63. $g(x) = x^3 - 5x^2 + 7x - 4$ **64.** $g(x) = x^3 + 6x^2 - 8x - 9$

The starting roster of a coed volleyball team is as follows.

Player	Age (in years)	Weight (in pounds)	Height (in inches)
Sean	18	160	70
Cindy	19	110	64
Dan	20	165	68
Kim	18	100	62
Mike	21	195	73
Beth	19	145	68

If $f(x)$ = age of x, $g(x)$ = weight of x, and $h(x)$ = height of x, determine each of the following.

65. $f(\text{Kim})$ **66.** $h(\text{Dan})$ **67.** $g(\text{Kim})$ **68.** $f(\text{Dan})$

69. $h(\text{Cindy})$ **70.** $g(\text{Mike})$ **71.** $f(\text{Sean})$ **72.** $h(\text{Beth})$

Determine whether each relation is a function. In each case the domain is the set of all United States citizens who have a social security number

73. $f(x)$ = social security number of x **74.** $g(x)$ = phone number of x **75.** $h(x)$ = child of x

76. $p(x)$ = birthdate of x

Solve each word problem.

77. Write an equation that gives the area, A, of a square as a function of its side, x. Then state the domain and range.

78. Write an equation that gives the perimeter, P, of a square as a function of its side, x. Then state the domain and range.

79. The maximum pulse rate, R, that a healthy person aged 18 to 55 should attain while exercising is determined by subtracting the person's age, a, from 220. Write R as a function of a. Then state the domain and range.

80. The target heart rate, T, that a healthy person aged 20 to 55 should maintain while exercising is determined by subtracting 80% of the person's age, a, from 176. Write T as a function of a. Then state the domain and range.

81. A sales representative earns a salary of $100 per week plus a commission of 25% of the dollar value of all sales he makes. If $E(x)$ denotes his total weekly earnings based on sales totaling x dollars, write an equation that defines weekly earnings as a function of sales. Then find and interpret (a) $E(0)$, (b) $E(700)$.

82. A company can manufacture tennis shoes at a cost of $8 per pair plus a daily overhead of $350. If $C(x)$ denotes the total daily cost of producing x pairs of tennis shoes, write an equation that defines daily cost as a function of number of pairs of tennis shoes produced. Then find and interpret (a) $C(0)$, (b) $C(125)$.

CHAPTER 6 SUMMARY

Key Terms

Cartesian coordinate system, p. 273
Coordinates, p. 273
Domain, p. 311
Function, p. 311
Function notation, p. 314
Graph, pp. 273, 279, 304
Half-plane, p. 305
Linear equation, p. 279
Linear inequality, p. 304

Ordered pair, p. 272
Origin, p. 272
Quadrant, p. 272
Range, p. 311
Rectangular coordinate system, p. 273
Relation, p. 311
Rise, p. 289
Run, p. 289

Slope, p. 290
Solution, p. 278
x-axis, p. 272
x-coordinate, p. 272
x-intercept, p. 281
y-axis, p. 272
y-coordinate, p. 272
y-intercept, p. 281

Key Rules

Definition of Slope

$$m = \frac{\text{rise}}{\text{run}} = \frac{y_2 - y_1}{x_2 - x_1}$$

Forms of a Linear Equation

$ax + by = c$	Standard Form
$y = c$	Horizontal Line
$x = c$	Vertical Line
$y - y_1 = m(x - x_1)$	Point-Slope Form
$y = mx + b$	Slope-Intercept Form

Parallel and Perpendicular Lines

Two (nonvertical) lines are parallel if their slopes are equal.

Two (nonvertical) lines are perpendicular if the product of their slopes is -1.

Vertical Line Test

A graph in the plane represents a function provided that no vertical line intersects the graph at more than one point.

CHAPTER 6 REVIEW PROBLEMS

[6.1] *Plot each point and state the quadrant in which it lies.*

1. (5, 2)

2. (−3, 1)

3. $\left(0, -\dfrac{9}{2}\right)$

4. (−2, −80)

5. On a rectangular coordinate system, plot five points whose x-coordinate is -4.

6. Suppose your algebra grade is determined by your performance on four tests. If x represents the test number and y represents your grade on that test, interpret each ordered pair graphed in Fig. 6.59.

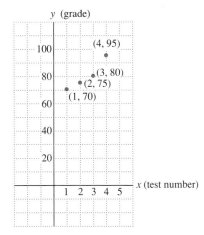

FIGURE 6.59

[6.2] *Determine which of the ordered pairs listed are solutions of the given equation.*

7. $x + 2y = 6$
   a. (−4, 5)   b. (3, 1)

8. $3x - 6y = 15$
   a. (−3, −1)   b. (1, −2)

Complete each table of values using the given equation. Then plot the points and draw a straight line through them.

9. $y = \dfrac{1}{4}x$

x	y
0	
4	
-4	

10. $3x + y = 6$

x	y
0	
	0
1	

11. $y = 6$

x	y
0	
-2	
3	

12. $x = -2$

x	y
	0
	-2
	5

(hoành độ góc)   (tung độ góc)

Graph each equation. Label the x-intercept and the y-intercept, if they exist.

13. $y = x + 2$ **14.** $4x - 3y = 24$ **15.** $y = 5x$ **16.** $y + 3 = 0$

17. $2x + 5y = -12$ **18.** $2x - 9 = 0$

19. Write an equation that describes the following statement: The *y*-value is 3 less than the opposite of the *x*-value. Then graph the equation.

[6.3] *Find the slope of the line through each pair of points.*

20. $(-2, -9), (1, 6)$ **21.** $(-3, 4), (5, -2)$ **22.** $(3, 7), (-4, 7)$ **23.** $(-1, 0), (-1, 8)$

Graph the line that passes through the given point and has the given slope.

24. $(0, 0), m = 4$ **25.** $(2, 1), m = -\dfrac{4}{5}$ **26.** $(0, -4), m = 1$ **27.** $(-3, 2), m$ undefined

Determine the slope of each line graphed in Problems 28 and 29.

28.

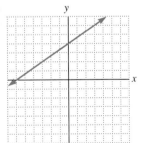

29.

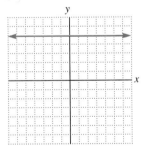

[6.4] *Find an equation of the line through the given point and with the given slope. Then write the equation in standard form.*

30. $(4, 8), m = -2$ **31.** $(-5, 1), m = \dfrac{3}{7}$

Find an equation of the line through the given pair of points. Then write the equation in standard form.

32. $(6, -4), (3, 2)$ **33.** $(-7, 6), (1, -4)$ **34.** $(-1, 10), (1, 10)$

Find an equation of the line with the given slope and the given y-intercept.

35. $m = 7, b = -2$ **36.** $m = -\dfrac{1}{3}, b = 0$

Find the slope and the y-intercept of the line with the given equation. Then use that information to graph the line.

37. $y - 2x = 0$ **38.** $2x - 3y = 6$ **39.** $y + 7 = 0$

Determine whether the lines represented by the given pair of equations are parallel, perpendicular, or neither.

40. $-x + 2y = 8$ **41.** $2x - 3y = 3$ **42.** $y = x + 6$
       $x - 2y = -5$ $3x - 2y = 2$ $x + y = -9$

43. Write an equation of the line that passes through $(-2, 5)$ and is perpendicular to the line whose equation is $y = 3x - 4$.

[6.5] *Complete the graph of each inequality by shading the appropriate half-plane.*

44. $x \geq 4$ **45.** $2x + 3y < 6$

 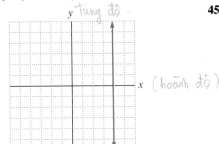 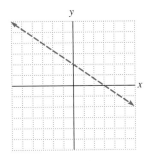

Graph each linear inequality on a rectangular coordinate system.

46. $y > -2$ **47.** $y \geq 3x - 6$ **48.** $2x + 5y > 10$ **49.** $y \leq -2x$

[6.6] *State the domain and the range of each relation. Determine whether the relation is a function.*

50. $\{(7, 1), (-3, 8), (7, -4)\}$ **51.** $\{(1, 2), (3, 4), (5, 6)\}$

52. Domain   Range   **53.** Domain   Range

Determine whether the given rule defines y as a function of x.

54. $6x - y = 0$ **55.** $y^2 = x + 9$ **56.** $y = \dfrac{1}{x + 4}$

Find the domain of the function defined by the given equation.

57. $y = 3x - 8$ **58.** $y = \dfrac{x}{x^2 - 9}$ **59.** $y = \dfrac{5}{x^2 + 1}$

Find the range of the function defined by the given equation.

60. $y = 6x + 1$ **61.** $y = |x|$ **62.** $y = x^2 - 2$

Determine whether each graph represents a function.

63.

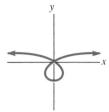

64.

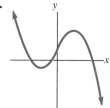

For each function, find (a) f(0), (b) f(3), and (c) f(−2).

65. $f(x) = 3x + 5$

66. $f(x) = -x^2 + 1$

For each function, find (a) g(0), (b) g(1), and (c) g(−4).

67. $g(x) = 2x^2 - 4x + 3$

68. $g(x) = |x - 2| - 3$

69. It costs $25 to join a video club and an additional $3 for each video that you rent. If C is the cost of renting x videos, write an equation that defines C as a function of x.

C H A P T E R 6 TEST

1. Determine whether each ordered pair is a solution of $2x - 5y = 26$.
  a. $(3, -4)$ b. $(-8, 2)$

2. Determine whether each relation is a function.
  a. $\{(4, 9), (-2, 1), (0, 9)\}$ b. $y < 3x - 1$

3. Determine whether each graph represents a function.
  a.

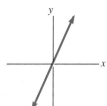

  b.

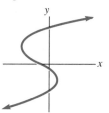

4. For the function $f(x) = 3x^2 - 7x + 1$, find each of the following.
  a. $f(1)$ b. $f(-2)$

5. Find the domain of each function.
  a. $\{(-2, 0), (5, 7), (1, 3)\}$ b. $y = \dfrac{8}{x + 6}$

6. Find the range of each function.
  a. $\{(8, -6), (10, 4), (3, -1)\}$ b. $y = 2x$

Find an equation of the line with the given slope and the given y-intercept.

7. $m = \dfrac{1}{3}, b = 9$

8. $m = -1, b = -\dfrac{4}{5}$

Find the slope and the y-intercept of the line with the given equation.

9. $5x + y = 0$

10. $3x - 2y = 6$

Find the slope of the line through each pair of points.

11. $(4, 5), (1, 8)$

12. $(4, -2), (-10, 2)$

Find an equation of the line satisfying the given conditions. Then write the equation in standard form.

13. Through $(5, -1)$ with slope 6

14. Through $(-2, 9)$ and $(4, 6)$

15. Through $(3, 8)$ and perpendicular to $y = 2x + 1$

16. Through $(2, 7)$ and $(2, 3)$

Graph the line that passes through the given point and has the given slope.

17. $(0, 1)$, $m = \dfrac{3}{4}$

18. $(4, 3)$, $m = 0$

Graph each linear equation. Label the x-intercept and the y-intercept, if they exist.

19. $y = 3x - 6$

20. $4x + 5y = 20$

21. $y = 4$

22. $x + 6 = 0$

Graph each linear inequality.

23. $x + 2y \geq -4$

24. $x < -3$

25. Suppose you earn \$4.75 an hour. Write your daily earnings, y, as a function of the number of hours, x, that you work each day. Then state the domain and range.

Linear Systems

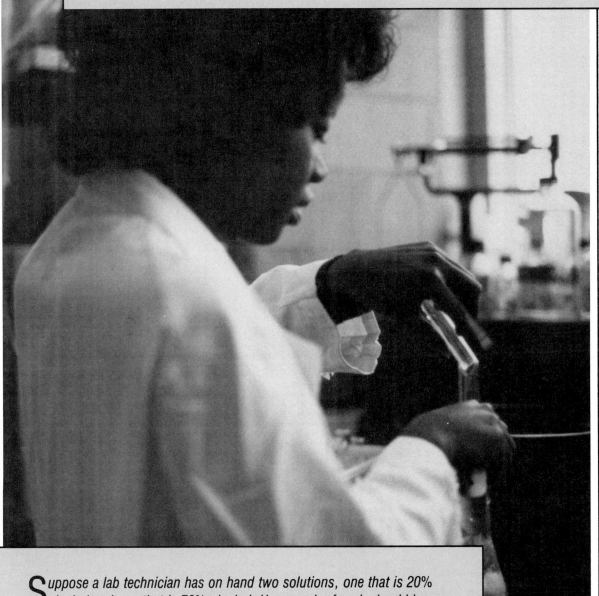

Suppose a lab technician has on hand two solutions, one that is 20% alcohol and one that is 70% alcohol. How much of each should be mixed to produce 100 kilograms of a solution that is 50% alcohol? In Section 7.4 we show how to solve this problem by setting up a system of equations.

7.1   The Graphing Method

In Chapter 2 we solved word problems that involved two unknown quantities by representing one unknown quantity by x and writing the other unknown quantity in terms of x and then writing an equation involving x. Sometimes it is easier to solve such a word problem by representing one unknown quantity by x and the other unknown quantity by y and then writing two equations involving x and y. For example, suppose a record and a tape together cost \$11 and the record costs \$3 more than the tape. If x is the cost of the record and y the cost of the tape, then we can write the following two equations.

$$x + y = 11$$
$$x - y = 3$$

Systems of equations were studied by the Greek mathematician Diophantus (ca. 250), among others. A particular type of system of equations is still known as a Diophantine system.

Two linear equations in the same variables are called a **system of linear equations.** A **solution of a system** of two linear equations in x and y is an ordered pair of numbers (x, y) that makes both equations true.

EXAMPLE 1   Determine whether the ordered pair $(7, 4)$ is a solution of the system

$$x + y = 11$$
$$x - y = 3.$$

Solution   Replace x with 7 and y with 4 in both equations.

$$
\begin{array}{ll}
x + y = 11 & \qquad x - y = 3 \\
7 + 4 = 11 & \qquad 7 - 4 = 3 \\
\quad\ 11 = 11 \quad \textit{True} & \qquad \quad 3 = 3 \quad \textit{True}
\end{array}
$$

Try Problem 1 >   Since $(7, 4)$ satisfies both equations, it is a solution of the system.   ■

EXAMPLE 2   Determine whether the ordered pair $(-2, -1)$ is a solution of the system

$$y = 4x + 7$$
$$5x - 3y = 7.$$

Solution   Substitute $(x, y) = (-2, -1)$ into both equations.

$$
\begin{array}{ll}
y = 4x + 7 & \qquad 5x - 3y = 7 \\
-1 = 4(-2) + 7 & \qquad 5(-2) - 3(-1) = 7 \\
-1 = -8 + 7 & \qquad -10 + 3 = 7 \\
-1 = -1 \quad \textit{True} & \qquad \qquad -7 = 7 \quad \textit{False}
\end{array}
$$

Try Problem 5 >   Since $(-2, -1)$ does not satisfy both equations, it is not a solution of the system.   ■

Solving a Linear System by Graphing

One way to find the solution of a linear system is to graph both equations on the same rectangular coordinate system. The intersection point of the two lines represents the solution. This method of solution is called the *graphing method*.

EXAMPLE 3   Solve the following system by the graphing method.

$$x - y = 4$$
$$2x + y = 5$$

Solution   Graph both equations using the methods of Chapter 6 (see Fig. 7.1).

$$x - y = 4 \qquad\qquad 2x + y = 5$$

x	y
0	-4
4	0
2	-2

x	y
0	5
$\dfrac{5}{2}$	0
2	1

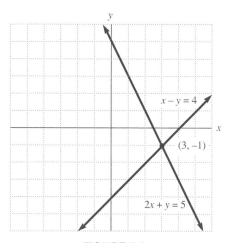

FIGURE 7.1

Each equation has an infinite number of ordered-pair solutions. The solutions of $x - y = 4$ are represented by the points on the rising line in Fig. 7.1. The solutions of $2x + y = 5$ are represented by the points on the falling line in Fig. 7.1. The only point that represents a solution of both equations is the intersection point, $(3, -1)$, since this is the only point that lies on both lines. Therefore $(3, -1)$ is the solution of the system. Check in both equations.   ■

Try Problem 15 >

If the two linear equations that form a system represent two different lines, the system is said to be an **independent system.** If they represent the same line, the system is a **dependent system.** If the system has at least one solution, the system is said to be a **consistent system.** If the system has no solution, it is an **inconsistent system.** Thus the system of Example 3 is both independent (since the lines are different) and consistent (since there is at least one solution).

EXAMPLE 4   Solve the following system by the graphing method.

$$x + 2y = 0$$
$$x = 4$$

Try Problem 19 >

Solution   The graphs of the the two equations are shown in Fig. 7.2. Since the lines intersect at the point (4, −2), the ordered pair (4, −2) is the solution of the system. Check in both equations.   ∎

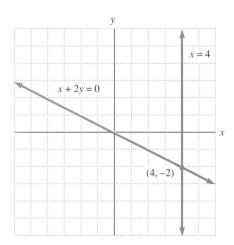

FIGURE 7.2

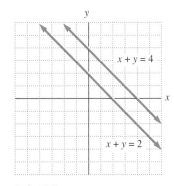

FIGURE 7.3

Try Problem 23 >

EXAMPLE 5   Solve the following system by the graphing method.

$$x + y = 2$$
$$x + y = 4$$

Solution   The graphs of the two equations (see Fig. 7.3) are parallel lines. Since parallel lines do not intersect, the system has no solution. Thus the system is both independent (since the lines are different) and inconsistent (since there is no solution).   ∎

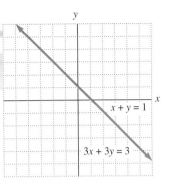

FIGURE 7.4

Try Problem 27 >

EXAMPLE 6   Solve the following system by the graphing method.

$$x + y = 1$$
$$3x + 3y = 3$$

Solution   Figure 7.4 shows that the graphs of the two equations are the same line (actually, the second equation is simply the first equation multiplied by 3). This means that any ordered pair that satisfies one of the equations will also satisfy the other equation. Since every point on the line represents a solution, there is an infinite number of solutions. Thus the system is both dependent (since the lines are the same) and consistent (since there is at least one solution).

■

Classifying Linear Systems

Here is a summary of the three possibilities for the solution of a linear system.

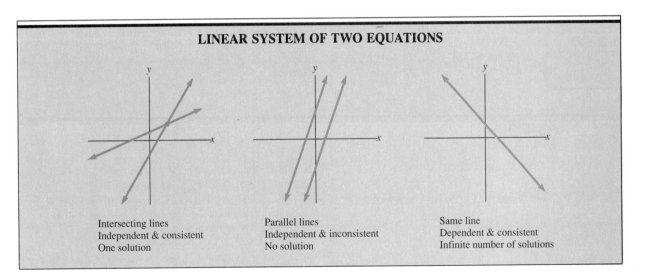

We can determine which of the three categories a linear system falls into without actually graphing the lines. We simply write both equations in slope-intercept form and observe the slope and the y-intercept of each line.

EXAMPLE 7   Without graphing, classify each system as dependent or independent and as consistent or inconsistent, and then determine the number of solutions.

a. $y = 3x + 6$
   $y = 3x - 1$

b. $6x + 2y = -10$
   $-3x - y = 5$

c. $2x - y = 4$
   $-x + 3y = 6$

Solution

a. Both equations are already in slope-intercept form. The slope of both lines is 3, so the lines are either parallel or they are the same line. The y-intercept of the first line is 6 and the y-intercept of the second line is -1, so they are not the same line. Therefore the lines are parallel, and the system is both independent and inconsistent. There is no solution.

b. Write both equations in slope-intercept form.

$$6x + 2y = -10 \qquad\qquad -3x - y = 5$$
$$2y = -6x - 10 \qquad\qquad -y = 3x + 5$$
$$y = -3x - 5 \qquad\qquad y = -3x - 5$$

Both lines have the same slope, -3, and the same y-intercept, -5. Therefore they are the same line, and the system is both dependent and consistent. There is an infinite number of solutions.

c. Write both equations in slope-intercept form.

$$2x - y = 4 \qquad\qquad -x + 3y = 6$$
$$-y = -2x + 4 \qquad\qquad 3y = x + 6$$
$$y = 2x - 4 \qquad\qquad y = \frac{1}{3}x + 2$$

Try Problem 43 >

Since the slopes are different, the lines are not parallel, and they are not the same line. Therefore the lines are intersecting lines, and the system is both independent and consistent. There is one solution. ∎

7.1 Problem Set

LEARNING THROUGH WRITING

☐ Define the term *linear system of two equations*.

☐ Define the term *solution of a linear system of two equations*.

☐ Describe how to solve a linear system of two equations by the graphing method.

☐ Explain the difference between a *dependent* and an *independent* linear system of two equations.

☐ Explain the difference between a *consistent* and an *inconsistent* linear system of two equations.

☐ Discuss the number of solutions that a linear system of two equations may have.

Determine whether the given ordered pair is a solution of the given system.

1. (11, 4)
$$x + y = 15$$
$$x - y = 7$$

2. (14, 5)
$$x + y = 19$$
$$x - y = 9$$

3. (−1, 1)
$$y = 3x - 2$$
$$y = -4x + 5$$

4. (−2, 2)
$$y = -x + 4$$
$$y = 2x - 6$$

5. (−3, −2)
$$y = 2x + 4$$
$$6x - 5y = 8$$

6. (−4, −1)
$$y = 3x + 11$$
$$2x - 5y = 3$$

7. (6, 0)
$$x - 9y = 6$$
$$y = \frac{1}{3}x - 2$$

8. (0, 8)
$$10x - y = -8$$
$$x = \frac{1}{2}y - 4$$

9. $(5, -4)$
$x - y = 9$
$y + 4 = 0$

10. $(-3, 7)$
$x + y = 4$
$x + 3 = 0$

11. $\left(-\dfrac{1}{4}, \dfrac{1}{2}\right)$
$8x - 6y = -5$
$x = \dfrac{3}{2}y - 1$

12. $\left(\dfrac{1}{3}, -\dfrac{1}{2}\right)$
$9x - 4y = 5$
$y = \dfrac{3}{2}x - 1$

Solve each system by the graphing method. Classify each system as dependent or independent and as consistent or inconsistent.

13. $x + y = 4$
$x - y = 2$

14. $x + y = 5$
$x - y = 3$

15. $x - y = 6$
$2x + y = 6$

16. $x - y = 4$
$2x + y = 2$

17. $y = 5x$
$y = -x$

18. $y = 4x$
$y = -x$

19. $x + 3y = 0$
$x = 6$

20. $x + 2y = 0$
$y = 1$

21. $2x + 3y = 12$
$x - 2y = -1$

22. $2x - 3y = -6$
$x + 3y = 6$

23. $x + y = 3$
$x + y = 5$

24. $x + y = 1$
$x + y = 4$

25. $y = \dfrac{1}{2}x$
$y = 2$

26. $y = \dfrac{1}{3}x$
$x = 3$

27. $x + y = 2$
$2x + 2y = 4$

28. $x - y = 1$
$3x - 3y = 3$

29. $y = x$
$y = -x - 3$

30. $y = -x$
$y = x + 3$

31. $x + 2 = 0$
$y - 3 = 0$

32. $x - 4 = 0$
$y + 1 = 0$

33. $\dfrac{x}{2} + y = -5$
$\dfrac{x}{4} - \dfrac{y}{5} = 1$

34. $x - \dfrac{y}{2} = -3$
$\dfrac{x}{3} + \dfrac{y}{4} = -1$

35. $\dfrac{1}{4}x - \dfrac{1}{3}y = \dfrac{1}{2}$
$6x = 8y$

36. $\dfrac{1}{5}x - \dfrac{1}{2}y = \dfrac{1}{2}$
$4x = 10y$

Without graphing, classify each system as dependent or independent and as consistent or inconsistent, and then determine the number of solutions.

37. $y = 2x - 4$
$y = 2x + 3$

38. $y = -4x + 8$
$y = -4x - 6$

39. $5y = 7x$
$5x = 7y$

40. $3y = 8x$
$3x = 8y$

41. $8x - 2y = 6$
$-4x + y = -3$

42. $-10x + 2y = 4$
$5x - y = -2$

43. $3x - y = 9$
$-x + 4y = 8$

44. $2x - y = 7$
$-x + 3y = 9$

45. $4x + 6y = -2$
$\dfrac{2}{3}x + y = \dfrac{1}{3}$

46. $6x + 10y = -4$
$\dfrac{3}{5}x + y = \dfrac{2}{5}$

47. $\dfrac{x}{2} - 2y = 1$
$y = \dfrac{1}{4}x - \dfrac{1}{2}$

48. $\dfrac{x}{2} - 3y = 1$
$y = \dfrac{1}{6}x - \dfrac{1}{3}$

7.2   The Addition Method

We have used the graphing method for solving a linear system of two equations primarily to illustrate the three different possibilities that can occur when such a system is solved. In practice, the graphing method is seldom used to solve a system, because it is often difficult to determine the exact coordinates of the intersection point, for example, the intersection point (31/23, 20/23). In this section we discuss a different method for solving a linear system of equations, called the *addition method*.

The addition method is similar to the Gauss-Jordan method, named after the German mathematician Carl Friedrich Gauss (1777–1855) and Camille Jordan (1838–1922). Gauss is considered by many to be one of the three greatest mathematicians in history [along with Archimedes (287–212 B.C.) and Isaac Newton (1642–1727)]. Stories abound attesting to his status as an infant prodigy, such as the one in which Gauss detected an error in his father's bookkeeping when only 2 years old.

EXAMPLE 1   Solve the following system by the addition method.

$$x + y = 6$$
$$x - y = 4$$

Solution   Add the corresponding sides of the two equations to eliminate y.

$$
\begin{array}{ll}
x + y = 6 & \textit{First equation} \\
\underline{x - y = 4} & \textit{Second equation} \\
2x + 0 = 10 & \textit{Add corresponding sides}
\end{array}
$$

Now solve the equation $2x + 0 = 10$ for x.

$$
\begin{array}{ll}
2x = 10 & \textit{Simplify the left side} \\
x = 5 & \textit{Divide by 2}
\end{array}
$$

To find y, substitute $x = 5$ into either of the original equations. If we use the first equation, we get the following.

$$
\begin{array}{ll}
x + y = 6 & \textit{First equation} \\
5 + y = 6 & \textit{Replace x with 5} \\
y = 1 & \textit{Subtract 5}
\end{array}
$$

The solution is $(5, 1)$. Check in both of the original equations, as follows.

$$
\begin{array}{ll}
x + y = 6 \qquad\qquad & x - y = 4 \\
5 + 1 = 6 & 5 - 1 = 4 \\
6 = 6 \quad \textit{True} & 4 = 4 \quad \textit{True}
\end{array}
$$

■

Try Problem 1 >

EXAMPLE 2   Solve the following system by the addition method.

$$4x + 9y = 9$$
$$2x + 3y = 2$$

Solution   In this case adding the two equations will not eliminate either variable. Therefore multiply the second equation by -2. This will make the coefficient of x in the second equation the opposite of the coefficient of x in the first equation.

$$
\begin{array}{ll}
2x + 3y = 2 & \textit{Second equation} \\
-2(2x + 3y) = -2(2) & \textit{Multiply by} -2 \\
-4x - 6y = -4 & \textit{Simplify}
\end{array}
$$

Now add the new second equation to the first equation to eliminate x.

$$
\begin{array}{ll}
4x + 9y = 9 & \textit{First equation} \\
\underline{-4x - 6y = -4} & \textit{New second equation} \\
0 + 3y = 5 & \textit{Add}
\end{array}
$$

Solve $0 + 3y = 5$ for y.

$$
\begin{array}{ll}
3y = 5 & \textit{Simplify the left side} \\
y = \dfrac{5}{3} & \textit{Divide by 3}
\end{array}
$$

To find x, substitute $y = 5/3$ into either of the original equations. If we use the second equation we get the following.

$$2x + 3y = 2 \quad \textit{Second equation}$$
$$2x + 3\left(\frac{5}{3}\right) = 2 \quad \textit{Replace y with 5/3}$$
$$2x + 5 = 2 \quad \textit{Simplify the left side}$$
$$2x = -3 \quad \textit{Subtract 5}$$
$$x = -\frac{3}{2} \quad \textit{Divide by 2}$$

Try Problem 23 > The solution is $-\dfrac{3}{2}, \dfrac{5}{3}$. Check in the original system. ■

Sometimes we must multiply *both* equations by a number that will act to eliminate one variable when the equations are added.

EXAMPLE 3 Solve the following system by the addition method.

$$4x + 5y - 3 = 0$$
$$3x = 2y + 8$$

Solution   First write each equation in the standard form $ax + by = c$.

$$4x + 5y = 3 \quad \textit{First equation in standard form}$$
$$3x - 2y = 8 \quad \textit{Second equation in standard form}$$

Now multiply the first equation by 2 and the second equation by 5. This will make the coefficients of y opposites of each other.

$$8x + 10y = 6 \quad \textit{First equation multiplied by 2}$$
$$\underline{15x - 10y = 40} \quad \textit{Second equation multiplied by 5}$$
$$23x = 46 \quad \textit{Add}$$
$$x = 2 \quad \textit{Divide by 23}$$

To find y, substitute $x = 2$ into either of the original equations. If we use the first equation we get the following.

$$4x + 5y = 3 \quad \textit{First equation}$$
$$4(2) + 5y = 3 \quad \textit{Replace x with 2}$$
$$8 + 5y = 3 \quad \textit{Simplify}$$
$$5y = -5 \quad \textit{Subtract 8}$$
$$y = -1 \quad \textit{Divide by 5}$$

Try Problem 25 > The solution is $(2, -1)$. Check in the original system. ■

EXAMPLE 4 Solve the following system by the addition method.

$$-6x + 3y = 1$$
$$2x - y = 0$$

Solution   Multiply the second equation by 3, and add the result to the first equation.

$$\begin{array}{rl} -6x + 3y = 1 & \textit{First equation} \\ \underline{6x - 3y = 0} & \textit{Second equation multiplied by 3} \\ 0 = 1 & \textit{Add} \end{array}$$

Try Problem 29 >

The false statement $0 = 1$ means that the two lines are parallel. Therefore there is no solution.   ■

EXAMPLE 5   Solve the following system by the addition method.

$$x + 2y = 3$$
$$4x + 8y = 12$$

Solution   Multiply the first equation by -4, and add the result to the second equation.

$$\begin{array}{rl} -4x - 8y = -12 & \textit{First equation multiplied by } -4 \\ \underline{4x + 8y = 12} & \textit{Second equation} \\ 0 = 0 & \textit{Add} \end{array}$$

Try Problem 33 >

The true statement $0 = 0$ means that the two equations represent the same line. Therefore there is an infinite number of solutions.   ■

TO SOLVE A LINEAR SYSTEM OF TWO EQUATIONS BY ADDITION

1. Write both equations in the standard form $ax + by = c$. If either equation contains fractions or decimals, multiply that equation by a number designed to clear the equation of fractions and decimals.
2. If necessary, multiply one or both equations by a number that will make the coefficients of x or y opposites.
3. Add the two equations, and solve the resulting equation in one variable. (Note: If a false statement results, the lines are parallel and there is no solution; if a true statement results, the lines are the same line and there is an infinite number of solutions.)
4. To find the value of the other variable, substitute the value found in Step 3 into either of the original equations.
5. Check the solution in both of the original equations.

EXAMPLE 6   Solve the following system by addition.

$$\frac{1}{3}x + \frac{1}{4}y = \frac{2}{3}$$
$$0.6x - 0.7y = 0.2$$

Solution

Step 1   *Both equations are already in standard form. Multiply the first equation by* 12 *(to clear fractions) and the second equation by* 10 *(to clear decimals).*

$$\frac{1}{3}x + \frac{1}{4}y = \frac{2}{3}$$

$$12\left(\frac{1}{3}x + \frac{1}{4}y\right) = 12\left(\frac{2}{3}\right)$$

$$4x + 3y = 8$$

$$0.6x - 0.7y = 0.2$$
$$10(0.6x - 0.7y) = 10(0.2)$$
$$6x - 7y = 2$$

Step 2   *Multiply* $4x + 3y = 8$ *by* 7 *and* $6x - 7y = 2$ *by* 3 *so that the coefficients of y are opposites.*

$$28x + 21y = 56$$
$$18x - 21y = 6$$

Step 3   *Add the two equations and solve the resulting equation in one variable.*

$$28x + 21y = 56$$
$$\underline{18x - 21y = 6} \quad$$
$$46x = 62 \quad \text{\textit{Add}}$$
$$x = \frac{62}{46} \quad \text{\textit{Divide by} 46}$$
$$x = \frac{31}{23} \quad \text{\textit{Write in lowest terms}}$$

Step 4   *To find y, we could substitute* $x = 31/23$ *into either of the original equations (or either equation from Step 1).* However, this calculation would be messy. It may be easier to start over and eliminate the variable x. Multiply the first equation from Step 1 by 3 and the second equation by -2.

$$12x + 9y = 24$$
$$\underline{-12x + 14y = -4}$$
$$23y = 20 \quad \text{\textit{Add}}$$
$$y = \frac{20}{23} \quad \text{\textit{Divide by} 23}$$

Try Problem 39 >   **Step 5**   *Check the solution* (31/23, 20/23) *in both of the original equations.* ∎

EXAMPLE 7   Two numbers, x and y, are such that the sum of twice x and y is 15, and the difference of x and three times y is 11. Find the numbers.

Solution   Use the statements in the problem to write a system of two equations in x and y.

Statement	*Equation*
The sum of twice x and y is 15.	$2x + y = 15$
The difference of x and three times y is 11.	$x - 3y = 11$

Now solve the system by multiplying the first equation by 3 and adding the resulting equation to the second equation.

$$
\begin{array}{ll}
6x + 3y = 45 & \textit{First equation multiplied by 3} \\
\underline{x - 3y = 11} & \textit{Second equation} \\
7x \qquad = 56 & \textit{Add} \\
x = 8 & \textit{Divide by 7}
\end{array}
$$

To find y, substitute $x = 8$ into the first equation. This gives $y = -1$. Therefore the numbers are $x = 8$ and $y = -1$. Check in the words of the original problem.

Try Problem 45 >

7.2 Problem Set

LEARNING THROUGH WRITING

☐ Describe the steps in solving a linear system of two equations by addition.

☐ When solving a linear system by the addition method, how do you know if the system has one solution, no solution, or an infinite number of solutions?

Solve each system by the addition method.

1. $x + y = 4$
   $x - y = 2$

2. $x + y = 5$
   $x - y = 3$

3. $2x - y = 1$
   $x + y = 5$

4. $3x - y = 2$
   $x + y = 6$

5. $x + y = 0$
   $-x + 3y = -4$

6. $x + y = 0$
   $-x + 2y = -9$

7. $2x + y = 7$
   $3x - y = 13$

8. $3x + y = 1$
   $4x - y = 6$

9. $4x - 2y = -12$
   $5x + 2y = -33$

10. $5x + 3y = -45$
    $2x - 3y = 3$

11. $-3x - 5y = -8$
    $3x - 5y = 8$

12. $-5x - 4y = -9$
    $5x - 4y = 9$

Solve each system by the addition method.

13. $3x - 2y = -3$
    $x + y = 4$

14. $2x - 3y = 1$
    $x + y = 3$

15. $2x - y = 0$
    $4x + 3y = -20$

16. $3x - y = 0$
    $5x + 2y = -33$

17. $2x + 7y = 3$
    $2x + 3y = 7$

18. $3x + 5y = 2$
    $3x + 2y = 8$

19. $7x + 2y = 60$
    $-4x + 2y = -6$

20. $9x + 3y = 66$
    $-4x + 3y = 1$

21. $x - 2y = -5$
    $4x - 3y = -20$

22. $x - 2y = -6$
    $5x - 3y = -30$

23. $4x + 9y = 6$
    $2x + 3y = 1$

24. $8x + 9y = 1$
    $2x + 6y = 9$

Solve each system by the addition method.

25. $5x + 3y - 4 = 0$
    $3x = 2y + 10$

26. $7x + 5y - 9 = 0$
    $2x = 3y + 7$

27. $2x + 7y - 7 = 0$
    $5x + 2y - 2 = 0$

28. $5x + 4y - 8 = 0$
    $2x + 3y - 6 = 0$

29. $-6x + 2y = 5$
    $3x - y = 0$

30. $8x - 4y = 3$
    $-2x + y = 0$

31. $3x - 7y = 0$
    $4x + 5y = 0$

32. $4x + 3y = 0$
    $5x - 2y = 0$

33. $x + 3y = -2$
$2x + 6y = -4$

34. $x - 4y = -2$
$3x - 12y = -6$

35. $8x + 12y = -35$
$5y = -14 - 3x$

36. $9x + 3y = -22$
$8y = -33 - 10x$

Solve each system by the addition method.

37. $\dfrac{x}{2} + \dfrac{y}{3} = \dfrac{2}{3}$
$\dfrac{x}{3} + \dfrac{y}{5} = \dfrac{1}{3}$

38. $\dfrac{x}{2} + \dfrac{y}{5} = -\dfrac{1}{2}$
$\dfrac{x}{3} + \dfrac{y}{4} = \dfrac{1}{4}$

39. $\dfrac{1}{5}x + \dfrac{1}{3}y = \dfrac{2}{5}$
$0.2x - 0.7y = 0.1$

40. $\dfrac{1}{9}x - \dfrac{1}{3}y = \dfrac{1}{2}$
$0.5x + 0.4y = 0.2$

41. $4.8x - 3.6y = 2.4$
$-7.2x + 5.4y = -9$

42. $2.8x - 4.2y = -7$
$-3.2x + 4.8y = 10.8$

Write a system of equations that describes each word problem. Then solve the system by the addition method.

43. Two angles, x and y, have a sum of 90° and a difference of 38°. Find the angles.

44. Two angles, x and y, have a sum of 180° and a difference of 52°. Find the angles.

45. Two numbers, x and y, are such that the sum of four times x and y is 26, and the difference of x and twice y is 38. Find the numbers.

46. Two numbers, x and y, are such that the sum of three times x and y is 19, and the difference of x and twice y is 18. Find the numbers.

47. One-fourth of a number x is 2 less than 1/3 of another number y. Three-fourths of y is 5 more than 1/2 of x. Find x and y.

48. One-third of a number x is 4 less than 1/4 of another number y. Two-thirds of y is 6 more than 1/2 of x. Find x and y.

7.3 The Substitution Method

A third method for solving a system of linear equations is called the *substitution method*. The substitution method is effective when one of the equations is solved for one of the variables.

EXAMPLE 1   Solve the following system by the substitution method.

$$5x + 2y = 44$$
$$y = 3x$$

Solution   The second equation is solved for y. Therefore replace y in the first equation with $3x$.

$5x + 2y = 44$ *First equation*
$5x + 2(3x) = 44$ *Replace y with 3x*

This is an equation in one variable and is easily solved.

$5x + 6x = 44$ ⎫
$11x = 44$ ⎬ *Simplify the left side*
$x = 4$ *Divide by 11*

To find y, substitute $x = 4$ into either of the original equations. The second equation is easier to use.

$y = 3x$ *Second equation*
$y = 3(4) = 12$ *Replace x with 4*

Try Problem 1 > The solution is (4, 12). Check in the original system. ■

EXAMPLE 2   Solve the following system by substitution.

$x = 9 - 2y$
$4x + 3y = 11$

Solution   The first equation is solved for x. Therefore replace x in the second equation with $9 - 2y$.

$4x + 3y = 11$ *Second equation*
$4(9 - 2y) + 3y = 11$ *Replace x with 9 − 2y*

Solve for y.

$36 - 8y + 3y = 11$ *Distributive property*
$36 - 5y = 11$ *Combine like terms*
$-5y = -25$ *Subtract 36*
$y = 5$ *Divide by −5*

To find x, substitute $y = 5$ into $x = 9 - 2y$.

$x = 9 - 2y$ *First equation*
$x = 9 - 2(5) = 9 - 10 = -1$ *Replace y with 5*

Try Problem 5 > The solution is (−1, 5). Check in the original system. ■

EXAMPLE 3   Solve the following system by substitution.

$x - 2y = 8$
$3x + y = 3$

Solution   Neither equation is solved for a variable. To avoid fractions, solve the first equation for x, or the second equation for y. We decide to solve the first equation for x.

$x - 2y = 8$ *First equation*
$x = 8 + 2y$ *Add 2y to both sides*

Replace x in the second equation with $8 + 2y$.

$3x + y = 3$ *Second equation*
$3(8 + 2y) + y = 3$ *Replace x with 8 + 2y*

Solve for y.

$$24 + 6y + y = 3 \qquad \textit{Distributive property}$$
$$24 + 7y = 3 \qquad \textit{Combine like terms}$$
$$7y = -21 \qquad \textit{Subtract 24}$$
$$y = -3 \qquad \textit{Divide by 7}$$

To find x, substitute $y = -3$ into $x = 8 + 2y$. (The substitution can also be made into either of the original equations.)

$$x = 8 + 2y$$
$$x = 8 + 2(-3) = 8 + (-6) = 2$$

Try Problem 13 >   The solution is $(2, -3)$. Check in the original system.   ∎

Caution! ∎

When you solve one equation for one of the variables, make sure you substitute the result into the *other* equation. Note what happens in Example 3 if you substitute $x = 8 + 2y$ into the first equation instead of the second equation.

Wrong

$$x - 2y = 8 \qquad \textit{First equation}$$
$$(8 + 2y) - 2y = 8 \qquad \textit{Replace x with 8 + 2y}$$
$$8 = 8 \qquad \textit{Simplify}$$

The result is a true statement, not because the two lines are the same line, but because you substituted the value of x obtained from the first equation back into the first equation. This approach will *not* lead to a solution.

EXAMPLE 4   Solve the following system by the substitution method.

$$6x + 3y = 5$$
$$2x + y = 1$$

Solution   To avoid fractions, solve the second equation for y.

$$2x + y = 1 \qquad \textit{Second equation}$$
$$y = 1 - 2x \qquad \textit{Subtract 2x}$$

Replace y in the first equation with $1 - 2x$.

$$6x + 3y = 5 \qquad \textit{First equation}$$
$$6x + 3(1 - 2x) = 5 \qquad \textit{Replace y with 1 - 2x}$$

Solve for x.

$$6x + 3 - 6x = 5 \qquad \textit{Distributive property}$$
$$3 = 5 \qquad \textit{Combine like terms}$$

The false statement $3 = 5$ means that the two lines are parallel. Therefore there *Try Problem 17 >*   is no solution.   ∎

> ## TO SOLVE A LINEAR SYSTEM OF TWO EQUATIONS BY SUBSTITUTION
>
> 1. If either equation contains fractions or decimals, multiply that equation by a number chosen to clear the equation of fractions and decimals.
> 2. If necessary, solve one of the equations for one of the variables. Try to avoid fractions.
> 3. Substitute the result of Step 2 into the other equation, and solve the resulting equation in one variable. (Note: If a false statement results, the lines are parallel and there is no solution; if a true statement results, the lines are the same line and there is an infinite number of solutions.)
> 4. To find the value of the other variable, substitute the value found in Step 3 into the equation resulting from Step 2.
> 5. Check the solution in both of the original equations.

EXAMPLE 5   Solve the following system by substitution.

$$\frac{1}{3}x - \frac{3}{4}y = -\frac{3}{4}$$

$$\frac{1}{6}x + \frac{1}{2}y = \frac{13}{12}$$

Solution

Step 1   *To clear the fractions, multiply both equations by* 12.

$$\frac{1}{3}x - \frac{3}{4}y = -\frac{3}{4} \qquad\qquad \frac{1}{6}x + \frac{1}{2}y = \frac{13}{12}$$

$$12\left(\frac{1}{3}x - \frac{3}{4}y\right) = 12\left(-\frac{3}{4}\right) \qquad 12\left(\frac{1}{6}x + \frac{1}{2}y\right) = 12\left(\frac{13}{12}\right)$$

$$4x - 9y = -9 \qquad\qquad 2x + 6y = 13$$

Step 2   *Solve the equation* $2x + 6y = 13$ *for* x. *In this case we cannot avoid fractions.*

$$\begin{aligned}
2x + 6y &= 13 &&\text{\textit{Second equation from Step 1}}\\
2x &= 13 - 6y &&\text{\textit{Subtract} 6y}\\
x &= \frac{13 - 6y}{2} &&\text{\textit{Divide by} 2}\\
x &= \frac{13}{2} - 3y &&\text{\textit{Simplify the right side}}
\end{aligned}$$

Step 3   *Substitute* $x = 13/2 - 3y$ *into* $4x - 9y = -9$ *and solve the resulting equation in one variable.*

$$4x - 9y = -9 \quad \text{\textit{First equation from Step 1}}$$

$$4\left(\frac{13}{2} - 3y\right) - 9y = -9 \quad \text{\textit{Replace x with 13/2 - 3y}}$$

$$26 - 12y - 9y = -9 \quad \text{\textit{Distributive property}}$$

$$26 - 21y = -9 \quad \text{\textit{Combine like terms}}$$

$$-21y = -35 \quad \text{\textit{Subtract 26}}$$

$$y = \frac{-35}{-21} \quad \text{\textit{Divide by -21}}$$

$$y = \frac{5}{3} \quad \text{\textit{Write in lowest terms}}$$

Step 4 *To find x, substitute y = 5/3 into the equation resulting from Step 2.*

$$x = \frac{13}{2} - 3y \quad \text{\textit{Equation from Step 2}}$$

$$x = \frac{13}{2} - 3\left(\frac{5}{3}\right) \quad \text{\textit{Replace y with 5/3}}$$

$$x = \frac{13}{2} - 5 = \frac{13}{2} - \frac{10}{2} = \frac{3}{2} \quad \text{\textit{Simplify}}$$

Try Problem 33 >   **Step 5** *Check the solution (3/2, 5/3) in both of the original equations.* ■

PROBLEM SOLVING

EXAMPLE 6   A demand equation for a product gives the quantity, D, demanded at price p. A supply equation gives the quantity, S, that firms are willing to supply at price p. The point at which supply equals demand is called the *equilibrium point*. Find the equilibrium point for the following system of supply and demand equations. Assume p is in dollars.

$$D = 253 - 6p$$
$$S = 16p$$

Solution   The equilibrium point occurs when supply equals demand. Therefore write

$$S = D.$$

Now replace S with $16p$ and D with $253 - 6p$.

$$16p = 253 - 6p$$

Solve for p.

$$22p = 253 \quad \text{\textit{Add 6p}}$$
$$p = 11.5 \quad \text{\textit{Divide by 22}}$$

To find S, substitute $p = 11.5$ into $S = 16p$.

$$S = 16p$$
$$S = 16(11.5) = 184$$

Try Problem 37 >

Therefore the equilibrium price is $11.50. Supply (as well as demand) at that price is 184 units, as shown in Fig. 7.5. Check in the original system.

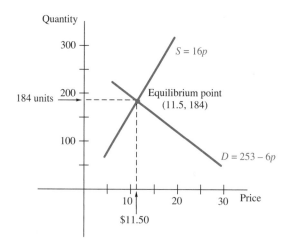

FIGURE 7.5

7.3   Problem Set

LEARNING THROUGH WRITING

☐ Describe the steps in solving a linear system of two equations by substitution.

Solve each system by the substitution method.

1. $3x + 2y = 22$
$\quad\quad y = 4x$

2. $4x + 3y = 50$
$\quad\quad y = 2x$

3. $x + y = 14$
$\quad\quad y = x + 2$

4. $x + y = 11$
$\quad\quad y = x + 3$

5. $x = 11 - 3y$
$\quad 5x + 2y = 3$

6. $x = 13 - 4y$
$\quad 2x + 3y = 6$

7. $10x - 2y = 0$
$\quad\quad x = \dfrac{1}{2}y$

8. $12x - 3y = 0$
$\quad\quad x = \dfrac{1}{2}y$

9. $8x - 5y = 11$
$\quad\quad y + 6 = 0$

10. $6x - 4y = 15$
$\quad\quad y + 8 = 0$

11. $11x - 4y = -6$
$\quad\quad y = \dfrac{5}{4} + 3x$

12. $5x - 3y = -9$
$\quad\quad y = \dfrac{7}{3} + 2x$

Solve each system by the substitution method.

13. $x - 3y = 10$
$\quad\ 2x + y = 6$

14. $x - 4y = 9$
$\quad\ 3x + y = 14$

15. $\quad 2x + y = 5$
$\quad\ 3x - 4y = 13$

16. $\quad 4x + y = 10$
$\quad\ 2x - 3y = 12$

17. $8x + 4y = 7$
$\quad\ 2x + y = 3$

18. $3x + 9y = 5$
$\quad\ x + 3y = 2$

19. $5x - 2y = -9$
$\quad\ 4x - y = -3$

20. $5x - 3y = -7$
$\quad\ 6x - y = 2$

21. $3x + 6y = -3$
$x + 2y = -1$

22. $8x - 4y = -12$
$-2x + y = 3$

23. $-3x + 5y = 6$
$-x + 4y = 2$

24. $-4x + 3y = 12$
$-x + 5y = 3$

Solve each system by the substitution method.

25. $4x + 3y = 7$
$2x - 9y = 0$

26. $2x + 6y = 5$
$4x - 3y = 0$

27. $5x + 2y = 9$
$3x - 4y = -5$

28. $2x + 3y = 7$
$4x - 5y = 3$

29. $5x + 3y = 2$
$3x - 4y = 4$

30. $4x - 5y = 7$
$3x + 3y = 2$

31. $\dfrac{x}{2} + \dfrac{y}{3} = 1$

$\dfrac{x}{4} - y = 4$

32. $\dfrac{x}{4} + \dfrac{y}{3} = \dfrac{1}{4}$

$x - \dfrac{y}{3} = 6$

33. $\dfrac{1}{3}x - \dfrac{1}{2}y = -\dfrac{11}{12}$

$\dfrac{1}{4}x + \dfrac{1}{2}y = \dfrac{5}{8}$

34. $\dfrac{2}{3}x - \dfrac{1}{4}y = \dfrac{5}{6}$

$\dfrac{1}{4}x + \dfrac{3}{4}y = \dfrac{7}{8}$

35. $-\dfrac{2}{9}x + \dfrac{5}{18}y = \dfrac{1}{3}$

$\dfrac{1}{3}x - \dfrac{5}{12}y = \dfrac{3}{8}$

36. $-\dfrac{1}{4}x + \dfrac{1}{3}y = \dfrac{2}{3}$

$\dfrac{1}{3}x - \dfrac{4}{9}y = \dfrac{1}{2}$

Find the equilibrium point for each system of supply and demand equations. Assume p is in dollars.

37. $D = 216 - 6p$
$S = 10p$

38. $D = 225 - 4p$
$S = 14p$

39. $D = 1750 - 35p$
$S = 100 + 15p$

40. $D = 1500 - 25p$
$S = 150 + 5p$

Write a system of equations that describes each word problem. Then solve the system by the substitution method.

41. Two numbers, x and y, are such that the sum of twice x and y is 68, and y is six times x. Find the numbers.

42. Two numbers, x and y, are such that the sum of three times x and y is 76, and y is nine times x. Find the numbers.

43. The difference of two numbers, x and y, is 13, and x is 5 less than four times y. Find the numbers.

44. The difference of two numbers, x and y, is 8, and x is 3 less than twice y. Find the numbers.

45. Two consecutive even integers, x and y, have a sum of 54. Find the numbers.

46. Two consecutive odd integers, x and y, have a sum of 88. Find the integers.

7.4   Problem Solving with Systems of Equations

Many word problems with two unknown quantities are easier to solve using two variables rather than one. However, when we use two variables, we must write a system of two equations in order to solve the problem.

> **TO SOLVE A WORD PROBLEM USING A SYSTEM OF EQUATIONS**
>
> 1. Write down the two unknown quantities and represent each quantity by a different variable.
> 2. Write a system of two equations involving the variables. Sometimes a chart or a diagram is helpful here.
> 3. Solve the system.
> 4. Check the solution in the words of the original problem.

Geometry Problems

EXAMPLE 1   The perimeter of a rectangle is 82 centimeters. The length is 5 centimeters more than three times the width. Find the width and the length.

Solution

Step 1   *Write down the two unknown quantities and represent each quantity by a different variable.*

x = width of rectangle
y = length of rectangle

Step 2   *Write a system of two equations involving the variables. A diagram is helpful here* (see Fig. 7.6). For the first equation, write

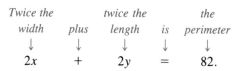

Twice the width	plus	twice the length	is	the perimeter
↓	↓	↓	↓	↓
$2x$	$+$	$2y$	$=$	$82.$

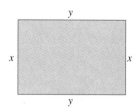

y

x x

y

FIGURE 7.6

Simplify this equation by dividing both sides by 2.

$$x + y = 41$$

For the second equation, write

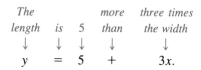

The length	is	5	more than	three times the width
↓	↓	↓	↓	↓
y	$=$	5	$+$	$3x.$

Therefore the system that describes the original problem is

$$x + y = 41$$
$$y = 5 + 3x.$$

Step 3   *Solve the system.* Since the second equation is solved for y, solve by substitution.

$$
\begin{aligned}
x + y &= 41 && \textit{First equation} \\
x + (5 + 3x) &= 41 && \textit{Replace } y \textit{ with } 5 + 3x \\
5 + 4x &= 41 && \textit{Combine like terms} \\
4x &= 36 && \textit{Subtract 5} \\
x &= 9 && \textit{Divide by 4}
\end{aligned}
$$

To find y, substitute $x = 9$ into $y = 5 + 3x$ and get $y = 5 + 3(9) = 32$. Therefore the width is 9 cm and the length is 32 cm.

Step 4   *Check in the words of the original problem.* Twice the width is 18 cm, and twice the length is 64 cm, giving a perimeter of 82 cm. Also, 5 cm more than three times the width is 32 cm, which is the length.   ■

Try Problem 1 >

Value Problems

EXAMPLE 2   Two pencils and three pens cost $14. Four pencils and one
pen cost $8. Find the cost of each pencil and each pen.

Solution

x = cost of each pencil
y = cost of each pen

For the first equation, write

Value of		*value of*		
two pencils	*plus*	*three pens*	*is*	14
↓	↓	↓	↓	↓
$2x$	$+$	$3y$	$=$	$14.$

For the second equation, write

Value of		*value of*		
four pencils	*plus*	*one pen*	*is*	8
↓	↓	↓	↓	↓
$4x$	$+$	y	$=$	$8.$

Therefore the system that describes the original problem is

$$2x + 3y = 14$$
$$4x + y = 8.$$

Solve by addition.

$$
\begin{array}{ll}
2x + 3y = 14 & \textit{First equation} \\
\underline{-12x - 3y = -24} & \textit{Second equation multiplied by } -3 \\
-10x = -10 & \textit{Add} \\
x = 1 & \textit{Divide by } -10
\end{array}
$$

To find y, substitute $x = 1$ into either of the original equations. This gives
$y = 4$. Therefore each pencil costs $1, and each pen costs $4. Check in the
words of the original problem.   ■

Try Problem 7 >

EXAMPLE 3   The total receipts for a basketball game were $450. Adult
tickets were $3, and student tickets were $2. A total of 170 tickets was sold.
How many adults and how many students attended the game?

Solution

x = number of adults
y = number of students

Since a total of 170 tickets was sold, the first equation is

$$x + y = 170.$$

To write the second equation, construct the following chart.

	Number of Tickets	Cost per Ticket	Value of Tickets
Adult tickets	x	3	$3x$
Student tickets	y	2	$2y$

⌐ *Sum is*
⌐ *total receipts*

Since total receipts were $450, the second equation is

$$3x + 2y = 450.$$

Therefore the system that describes the original problem is

$$x + y = 170$$
$$3x + 2y = 450.$$

Solve by addition.

$-2x - 2y =$	-340	*First equation multiplied by* -2
$3x + 2y =$	450	*Second equation*
$x \quad\quad =$	110	*Add*

Try Problem 13 >

Substitute $x = 110$ into $x + y = 170$ to get $y = 60$. Therefore 110 adults and 60 students attended the game. Check in the words of the original problem. ■

Mixture Problems

EXAMPLE 4   One solution contains 20% alcohol, and a second solution contains 70% alcohol. How many kilograms of each solution are needed to make 100 kilograms of 50% alcohol solution?

Solution

x = number of kilograms of 20% solution
y = number of kilograms of 70% solution

Since the final mixture contains 100 kilograms, the first equation is

$$x + y = 100.$$

To write the second equation, construct the following chart.

	kg of Solution	kg of Alcohol
20% solution	x	$0.20x$
70% solution	y	$0.70y$
50% solution	100	$0.50(100)$

⌐ *Sum equals*

Since no alcohol is gained or lost during mixing, the second equation is

Alcohol in *alcohol in* *alcohol in*
20% solution *plus* *70% solution* *equals* *50% solution*
↓ ↓ ↓ ↓ ↓
0.20x + 0.70y = 0.50(100).

Therefore the system is

$$x + y = 100$$
$$0.2x + 0.7y = 50.$$

Solve by addition.

$$-2x - 2y = -200 \quad \textit{First equation multiplied by } -2$$
$$\underline{2x + 7y = 500} \quad \textit{Second equation multiplied by } 10$$
$$5y = 300 \quad \textit{Add}$$
$$y = 60 \quad \textit{Divide by } 5$$

Substitute $y = 60$ into $x + y = 100$ to get $x = 40$. Therefore 40 kilograms of 20% solution and 60 kilograms of 70% solution are needed. Check in the words of the original problem. ∎

Try Problem 15 >

Motion Problems

To solve motion problems we use the formula

$$d = rt,$$

where d is distance, r is rate, and t is time.

EXAMPLE 5 A jogger and a cyclist are 56 miles apart. They start toward each other, with the cyclist traveling 3 times as fast as the jogger. If they meet in 2 hours, what is the speed of each?

— 56 mi —

Solution

x = speed of jogger
y = speed of cyclist

Since the cyclist travels 3 times as fast as the jogger, the first equation is

$$y = 3x.$$

To write the second equation, construct the following chart.

	Rate	Time	Distance
Jogger	x	2	$2x$
Cyclist	y	2	$2y$

Since $d = rt$

$$
\begin{array}{ccccc}
\textit{Distance} & & \textit{distance} & & \\
\textit{traveled} & & \textit{traveled} & & \\
\textit{by jogger} & \textit{plus} & \textit{by cyclist} & \textit{is} & 56 \\
\downarrow & \downarrow & \downarrow & \downarrow & \downarrow \\
2x & + & 2y & = & 56
\end{array}
$$

Simplify this equation by dividing both sides by 2.

$x + y = 28$

Therefore the system is

$$y = 3x$$
$$x + y = 28.$$

Solve by substitution.

$x + y = 28$	*Second equation*
$x + 3x = 28$	*Replace y with 3x*
$4x = 28$	*Combine like terms*
$x = 7$	*Divide by 4*

Try Problem 27 >

Substitute $x = 7$ into $y = 3x$ to get $y = 21$. Therefore the jogger's speed is 7 mph and the cyclist's speed is 21 mph. Check in the words of the original problem. ■

7.4 Problem Set

LEARNING THROUGH WRITING

☐ Describe the steps in solving a word problem using a system of equations.

Write a system of equations for each geometry problem. Then solve the system.

1. The perimeter of a rectangle is 124 centimeters. The length is 7 centimeters more than four times the width. Find the width and the length.

2. The perimeter of a rectangle is 138 centimeters. The length is 3 centimeters less than five times the width. Find the width and the length.

3. An isosceles triangle has two equal sides. The perimeter of the isosceles triangle in Fig. 7.7 is 64 feet, and the base, y, is 2/3 of x. Find x and y.

4. An isosceles triangle has two equal sides. The perimeter of the isosceles triangle in Fig. 7.7 is 72 feet, and the base, y, is 2/5 of x. Find x and y.

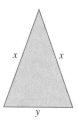

FIGURE 7.7

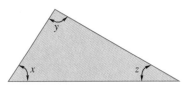

FIGURE 7.8

5. The sum of the angles of any triangle is 180°. Find angles x and y in Fig. 7.8 if x is one-half of y, and z is 27°.

6. The sum of the angles of any triangle is 180°. Find angles x and y in Fig. 7.8 if x is one-third of y, and z is 32°.

Write a system of equations for each value problem. Then solve the system.

7. Three basketballs and two footballs cost $41. One basketball and four footballs cost $47. Find the cost of each basketball and each football.

8. Two belts and five scarfs cost $11. Six belts and one scarf cost $19. Find the cost of each belt and each scarf.

9. A coin changer contains $10.45 in dimes and quarters. If there are 4 fewer dimes than quarters, how many dimes and how many quarters are in the changer?

10. A cash register contains $13.90 in dimes and quarters. If there are 6 more dimes than quarters, how many dimes and how many quarters are in the register?

11. A collection of 24 nickels and dimes is worth $1.75. How many nickels and how many dimes are in the collection?

12. A collection of 28 nickels and dimes is worth $1.95. How many nickels and how many dimes are in the collection?

13. The total receipts for a play were $645. Adult tickets were $5 each, and student tickets were $3 each. A total of 145 tickets was sold. How many adults and how many students attended the play?

14. The total receipts for a football game were $545. Adult tickets were $4 each, and student tickets were $3 each. A total of 165 tickets was sold. How many adults and how many students attended the game?

Write a system of equations for each mixture problem. Then solve the system.

15. One solution contains 20% acid, and a second solution contains 60% acid. How many kilograms of each solution are needed to make 40 kilograms of 35% acid solution?

16. One solution contains 15% formaldehyde, and a second solution contains 40% formaldehyde. How many kilograms of each solution are needed to make 25 kilograms of 20% formaldehyde solution?

17. A grocer wants to mix nuts worth $0.85 per pound with nuts worth $1.35 per pound to make 20 pounds of nuts worth $1.00 per pound. How many pounds of each should she use?

18. A candystore owner wants to mix candy worth $0.75 per pound with candy worth $1.15 per pound to make 40 pounds of candy worth $1.00 per pound. How many pounds of each should he use?

19. How many grams of pure silver and how many grams of an alloy that is 15% silver should be melted together to produce 34 grams of an alloy that is 50% silver?

20. How many grams of pure gold and how many grams of an alloy that is 45% gold should be melted together to produce 33 grams of an alloy that is 75% gold?

Write a system of equations for each interest problem. Then solve the system.

21. A total of $25,000 is invested, part at 5% and the rest at 7%. How much is invested at each rate if the total first year's interest is $1390?

22. A total of $10,000 is invested, part at 7% and the rest at 12%. How much is invested at each rate if the total first year's interest is $1000?

	Amount	Interest
5% investment	x	0.05x
7% investment	y	

	Amount	Interest
7% investment	x	
12% investment	y	0.12y

23. A total of $6300 is invested, part at 8% and the rest at 12%. How much is invested at each rate if the first year's interest on the two investments is the same?

24. A total of $4200 is invested, part at 6% and the rest at 9%. How much is invested at each rate if the first year's interest on the two investments is the same?

25. A financial planner invested twice as much of a client's money at a lower-risk 9 1/2% than at a higher-risk 14 1/2%. If the total first year's interest on the two investments was $4355, how much was invested at each rate?

26. A stockbroker invested three times as much of a client's money at a lower-risk 8 1/2% than at a higher-risk 13 1/2%. If the total first year's interest on the two investments was $6630, how much was invested at each rate?

Write a system of equations for each motion problem. Then solve the system.

27. A walker and a runner are 36 miles apart. They start toward each other, with the runner traveling twice as fast as the walker. If they meet in 3 hours, what is the speed of each?

28. Two trains, 147 miles apart, travel toward each other. One train travels 5 mph faster than the other. If they meet in 3 hours, what is the speed of each?

29. An enemy missile is sighted by radar to be 5500 miles from a friendly missile base and approaching the base at 7000 mph. Immediately, an antimissile missile whose speed is 8400 mph is launched from the base. How far does each missile travel before they meet?

30. Two runners who live 7 miles apart leave their respective homes simultaneously and run toward each other, one at 9 mph and the other at 12 mph. How far does each run before they meet?

	r	t	d
Enemy missile	7000		x
Antimissile missile	8400	$\dfrac{y}{8400}$	y

	r	t	d
Slower runner	9	$\dfrac{x}{9}$	x
Faster runner	12		y

31. A tour boat takes 2 hours to travel 16 miles upstream to a picnic area but only 1 hour and 20 minutes to make the return trip downstream. Find the speed of the current, c, and the speed of the boat in still water, b.

32. A small plane takes 2 hours to travel 240 miles against the wind but only 1 hour and 30 minutes to make the return trip with the wind. Find the speed of the wind, w, and the speed of the plane in still air, p.

	r	t	d
Upstream	$b - c$	2	$2(b - c)$
Downstream	$b + c$	$1\dfrac{1}{3}$	

	r	t	d
Against the wind	$p - w$	2	
With the wind	$p + w$	$1\dfrac{1}{2}$	$1\dfrac{1}{2}(p + w)$

33. A helicopter can fly 102.5 mph with the wind but only 87.5 mph against the wind. Find the speed of the wind and the speed of the helicopter in still air.

34. A motorboat can travel 16.5 mph with the current but only 9.5 mph against the current. Find the speed of the current and the speed of the motorboat in still water.

7.5   Systems of Linear Inequalities

A **system of linear inequalities** consists of two or more linear inequalities. Recall that the solution of a linear inequality such as

$$x > 2, \qquad y \le x + 2, \qquad \text{or} \qquad 3x + 5y \ge 15$$

is represented by a half-plane. Therefore the solution of a system of two linear inequalities is represented by the intersection of two half-planes.

EXAMPLE 1   Graph the solution of the system

$$x > 2$$
$$y < 3.$$

Solution   First graph $x > 2$. This is the half-plane to the right of the vertical line $x = 2$. Then on the same coordinate axes, graph $y < 3$. This is the half-plane below the horizontal line $y = 3$. The solution of the system is represented by the doubly shaded region in Fig. 7.9.   ■

Try Problem 1 >

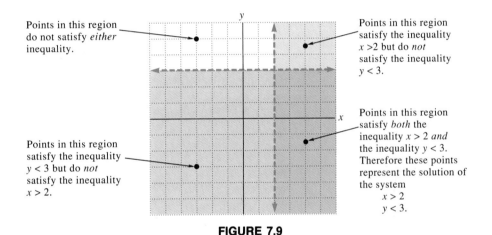

Points in this region do not satisfy *either* inequality.

Points in this region satisfy the inequality $x > 2$ but do *not* satisfy the inequality $y < 3$.

Points in this region satisfy the inequality $y < 3$ but do *not* satisfy the inequality $x > 2$.

Points in this region satisfy *both* the inequality $x > 2$ *and* the inequality $y < 3$. Therefore these points represent the solution of the system
$$x > 2$$
$$y < 3.$$

FIGURE 7.9

EXAMPLE 2   Graph the solution of the system

$$x + y > 2$$
$$y \le x + 2.$$

Solution   First graph $x + y > 2$. To do this, graph the boundary line $x + y = 2$. Make the line dashed, since the inequality symbol is $>$ and not $\ge$. Then choose a test point not on the boundary line, say $(0, 0)$. Substitute $(0, 0)$ into $x + y > 2$.

$$x + y > 2 \quad \textit{First inequality}$$
$$0 + 0 > 2 \quad \textit{Let } x = 0 \textit{ and } y = 0$$
$$0 > 2 \quad \textit{False}$$

Since $(0, 0)$ is not a solution of $x + y > 2$, shade the half-plane that does not contain $(0, 0)$, as shown in Fig. 7.10.

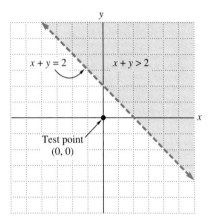

FIGURE 7.10

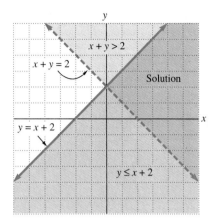

FIGURE 7.11

Now graph $y \leq x + 2$ on the same coordinate axes. Make the boundary line $y = x + 2$ solid, since the inequality symbol is $\leq$ and not $<$. The solution of the system is represented by the doubly shaded region in Fig. 7.11. The solution includes part of the boundary line $y = x + 2$. ∎

Try Problem 13 >

EXAMPLE 3   Graph the solution of the system

$$y \geq 2x$$
$$3x + 5y \geq 15.$$

Solution   First graph $y \geq 2x$. Then on the same coordinate axes, graph $3x + 5y \geq 15$. The solution of the system is represented by the doubly shaded region in Fig. 7.12. The solution includes part of both boundary lines. ∎

Try Problem 19 >

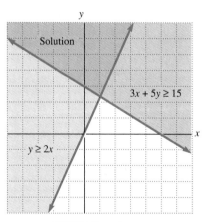

FIGURE 7.12

7.5 Problem Set

Graph the solution of each system of inequalities.

1. $x > 3$
$y < 2$

2. $x > 1$
$y < 4$

3. $x \leq -1$
$y \leq -4$

4. $x \leq -2$
$y \geq 3$

5. $x \geq 0$
$y \geq 0$

6. $x \leq 0$
$y \leq 0$

7. $y \geq x$
$y > 2$

8. $y \leq x$
$y < 1$

9. $x + y < 5$
$x \geq 1$

10. $x - y > 5$
$x \leq 2$

11. $5x - 3y < 10$
$x \leq 0$

12. $4x + 3y > 8$
$y \geq 0$

Graph the solution of each system of inequalities.

13. $x + y > 3$
$y \leq x + 3$

14. $x + y > 4$
$y \leq x + 4$

15. $3x + y \geq 6$
$x - 2y > 2$

16. $2x + y \leq 6$
$3x - y < -3$

17. $x + y < 4$
$2x - y \geq -4$

18. $x - y > 5$
$2x + y \leq 4$

19. $y \geq 3x$
$3x + 4y \geq 12$

20. $y \geq 4x$
$4x + 5y \geq 20$

21. $y \leq x + 2$
$y \geq x$

22. $y \leq -x + 3$
$y \geq -x$

23. $y \geq x + 2$
$y \leq x$

24. $y \geq -x + 3$
$y \leq -x$

*For Problems 25 and 26, (**a**) graph the solution of the system, (**b**) list three ordered pairs that lie in the graphed region.*

25. A neighborhood-theater owner wants to be able to admit a family of 2 adults and 1 child for no more than $10. Also, the owner wants the price of a child's ticket, x, to be no more than half the price of an adult's ticket, y. A system of inequalities that describes this situation is

$$x + 2y \leq 10$$
$$x \leq \frac{1}{2}y$$
$$x \geq 0$$
$$y \geq 0.$$

26. The storeroom of a shoe store will hold at most 300 pairs of shoes, and the owner wants to order at least twice as many women's shoes as men's shoes. If x and y are the number of pairs of women's shoes and men's shoes, respectively, then a system of inequalities that describes this situation is

$$x + y \leq 300$$
$$x \geq 2y$$
$$x \geq 0$$
$$y \geq 0.$$

CHAPTER 7 SUMMARY

Key Terms

Consistent system, p. 328
Dependent system, p. 328
Inconsistent system, p. 328
Independent system, p. 328

Solution of a system, p. 326
System of linear equations, p. 326
System of linear inequalities, p. 350

C H A P T E R 7 R E V I E W P R O B L E M S

[7.1] *Determine whether the given ordered pair is a solution of the given system.*

1. $(4, -1)$

$$y = 2x - 9$$
$$3x - 2y = 14$$

2. $\left(-\dfrac{1}{3}, \dfrac{1}{4}\right)$

$$6x - 4y = -3$$
$$9x + 8y = 5$$

Solve each system by the graphing method. Classify each system as dependent or independent and as consistent or inconsistent.

3. $x - y = 5$
    $x + 2y = 2$

4. $y = x - 3$
    $y = x + 1$

5. $y = 2x + 6$
    $x + y = 0$

6. $x + 3y = -6$
    $2x + 6y = -12$

Without graphing, classify each system as dependent or independent and as consistent or inconsistent, and then determine the number of solutions.

7. $y = 5x - 7$
    $y = 10x - 7$

8. $2x - 6y = 9$
    $-4x + 12y = -18$

9. $x + \dfrac{1}{3}y = 1$

$$\dfrac{x}{2} + \dfrac{y}{6} = 1$$

[7.2] *Solve each system by the addition method.*

10. $3x - y = 7$
     $x + y = 9$

11. $5x + y = 7$
     $2x + y = 1$

12. $4x + 5y = 7$
     $2x + 3y = 1$

13. $4x - 5y = 0$
     $3x - 2y = -14$

14. $8x - 2y = 1$
     $-5x + y = -1$

15. $x - 2y = 4$
     $-3x + 6y = -12$

16. $9x + 6y = 5$
     $3x + 2y = 0$

17. $y = 2 - x$
     $4x - 5y - 8 = 0$

18. $\dfrac{x}{4} + \dfrac{y}{3} = -\dfrac{5}{6}$

$$\dfrac{x}{6} - \dfrac{y}{5} = -\dfrac{2}{15}$$

19. Write a system of equations that describes the following conditions: Two numbers, x and y, are such that the sum of twice x and y is 57, and the difference of x and three times y is 4. Then solve the system by addition.

[7.3] *Solve each system by the substitution method.*

20. $3x + y = 15$
     $y = 2x$

21. $2x - 5y = 6$
     $x = 4y$

22. $5x - 2y = 1$
     $2x + y = 4$

23. $x - 2y = 5$
     $4x - 8y = 7$

24. $6x - y = 1$
     $9x + 2y = 5$

25. $x + 2y = 4$
     $5x + 3y = 6$

26. $2x = 6y - 2$
     $-x + 3y - 1 = 0$

27. $4x - 5y = 9$
     $3x + 2y = 1$

28. $\dfrac{x}{2} + \dfrac{y}{3} = -\dfrac{3}{2}$

$$x - \dfrac{y}{2} = 4$$

29. Find the equilibrium point for the following system of supply and demand equations. Assume p is in dollars.

$$D = 374 - 4p$$
$$S = 7p$$

30. Write a system of equations that describes the following conditions: Two consecutive integers have a sum of 35. Then solve the system by substitution.

[7.4] *Write a system of equations for each word problem. Then solve the system.*

31. The perimeter of the isosceles triangle in Fig. 7.13 is 72 feet. The base, *y*, is 1/4 of *x*. Find *x* and *y*.

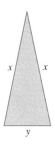

FIGURE 7.13

32. Two shovels and 3 rakes cost $36. Four shovels and 5 rakes cost $64. Find the cost of each shovel and each rake.

33. The total receipts for a basketball game attended by 315 people were $725. Reserved seat tickets were $3 each and general admission tickets were $2 each. How many of each kind of ticket were sold?

34. A candystore owner wants to mix candy worth $.65 per pound with candy worth $1.15 per pound to make 30 pounds of candy worth $1.10 per pound. How many pounds of each should the owner use?

35. A total of $4000 is invested, part at 6% and the rest at 8%. How much is invested at each rate if the total first year's interest is $272?

36. Two riverboats start 110 miles apart and travel toward each other, one at 6 mph faster than the other. If they meet in 5 hours, find the speed of each.

[7.5] *Graph the solution of each system of inequalities.*

37. $x > 2$
$y < -3$

38. $y \geq 2x$
$y \geq 2$

39. $x + y \geq 5$
$x < 5$

40. $3x + y < 6$
$3x - y > -6$

41. $3x - 4y \leq 12$
$y > 4x + 4$

42. $x + y \leq 0$
$x + y \geq -4$

C H A P T E R 7 T E S T

Solve each system by the graphing method. Classify each system as dependent or independent and as consistent or inconsistent.

1. $x + y = 6$
$y = 2x$

2. $2x + 4y = -8$
$3x + 6y = -12$

3. $x - y = 5$
$y = x$

Solve each system by the addition method.

4. $2x + y = 7$
$x - y = 5$

5. $3x + 2y = 2$
$3x + 5y = 5$

6. $5x + 6y = 45$
$4x - 3y = -3$

7. $2x - 5y = 12$
$3x - 4y = 25$

Solve each system by the substitution method.

8. $7x - y = 24$
$y = 3x$

9. $2x + 3y = 9$
$x = 8 - 2y$

10. $4x + y = -11$
$x - 2y = 4$

11. $6x - 2y = 1$
$3x - y = 5$

Solve each system by any method.

12. $9x = 8y + 12$
$3x + 4y + 1 = 0$

13. $\dfrac{x}{3} + \dfrac{y}{2} = 1$
$\dfrac{x}{6} + \dfrac{y}{4} = \dfrac{1}{2}$

Write a system of equations for each word problem. Then solve the system.

14. Two consecutive odd integers have a sum of 68. Find the integers.

15. A collection of 20 nickels and dimes is worth $1.45. How many nickels and how many dimes are in the collection?

16. A total of $5400 is invested, part at 7% and the rest at 11%. How much is invested at each rate if the first year's interest on the two investments is the same?

17. A car and a cyclist are 128 miles apart. They start toward each other, the car traveling three times as fast as the cyclist. If they meet in 2 hours, what is the speed of each?

Graph the solution of each system of inequalities.

18. $x \le -1$
$y \ge 0$

19. $y > x$
$x + y < 2$

20. $x - 3y \ge 6$
$x + 2y > -4$

CHAPTER 8

Roots and Radicals

S ections of railroad track are laid with a small space between them to allow for expansion when the metal becomes hot. In Section 8.3 we show, by using the Pythagorean theorem and square roots, that even a small amount of overexpansion can cause serious buckling problems.

8.1 **Finding Roots**

The reverse of squaring a number is finding the *square root* of a number. For example, to square 5 we write

$$5^2 = 5 \cdot 5 = 25.$$

To find the square root of a number, we reverse the procedure. That is, given 25 we find the number whose square is 25. Actually, there are two numbers whose square is 25, namely, 5 and -5.

$$5^2 = 5 \cdot 5 = 25$$
$$(-5)^2 = (-5)(-5) = 25$$

DEFINITION OF SQUARE ROOT

The number b is a **square root** of the number a if $b^2 = a$.

EXAMPLE 1   Find all square roots of 64.

Try Problem 1 >

Solution   Since $8^2 = 64$ and $(-8)^2 = 64$, the square roots of 64 are 8 and -8. ∎

Caution! ∎

Do not confuse the phrase *square of a number* with the phrase *square root of a number.*

The square of 4 is 16.
The square roots of 4 are 2 and -2.

The symbol $\sqrt{}$ is a distortion of the letter *r*, from the Latin word *radix* (meaning "root").

Every positive real number has two square roots, one positive and one negative. However, in many applied problems we are interested only in the positive square root of the number, called the *principal square root*. To denote the principal square root of 4, we write $\sqrt{4}$. The symbol $\sqrt{}$ is called a **radical sign,** the number 4 is called the **radicand,** and $\sqrt{4}$ is called a **radical.** The expression $\sqrt{4}$ is read "the principal square root of 4" or "radical 4."

EXAMPLE 2   Find each square root.

a. $\sqrt{9}$ b. $-\sqrt{9}$ c. $\pm\sqrt{9}$

Solution

  a. The expression $\sqrt{9}$ denotes the positive (principal) square root of 9. Therefore $\sqrt{9} = 3$.

Try Problem 13 >

b. The expression $-\sqrt{9}$ denotes the negative square root of 9. Therefore $-\sqrt{9} = -3$.

c. The expression $\pm\sqrt{9}$ denotes both the positive and the negative square roots of 9. Therefore $\pm\sqrt{9} = \pm3$.   ■

Note that the expression ±3 represents the two numbers 3 and -3.

EXAMPLE 3   Find each square root.

a. $\sqrt{0}$ b. $\sqrt{\dfrac{4}{9}}$ c. $\sqrt{-4}$

Solution

a. $\sqrt{0} = 0$ *Since $0^2 = 0$*

b. $\sqrt{\dfrac{4}{9}} = \dfrac{2}{3}$ *Since $(2/3)^2 = 4/9$*

Try Problem 29 >

c. There is no real number we can square to get -4. Note that $2^2 = 4$ and $(-2)^2 = 4$. Therefore $\sqrt{-4}$ is not a real number.   ■

The square root of a negative number is not a real number—it is called an **imaginary number.** We will study imaginary numbers in Section 9.5.

Caution! ■
■
■

Do not confuse the expressions $-\sqrt{100}$ and $\sqrt{-100}$.

$-\sqrt{100} = -10$

$\sqrt{-100}$ is not a real number

Some square roots are rational numbers and others are irrational numbers. For example, $\sqrt{4}$ and $\sqrt{25}$ are rational numbers and $\sqrt{2}$ and $\sqrt{10}$ are irrational numbers. **The square root of a positive integer that is not a perfect-square integer is an irrational number.** A **perfect-square integer** is an integer that is the square of an integer. The first 12 perfect-square integers are

1, 4, 9, 16, 25, 36, 49, 64, 81, 100, 121, and 144.

Rational numbers have decimal representations that either terminate or repeat. For example, the decimal representations for the rational numbers 8, 3/4, and 1/3 are

$$8 = 8, \qquad \frac{3}{4} = 0.75, \qquad \text{and} \qquad \frac{1}{3} = 0.33\overline{3}.$$

The bar over the 3 in $0.33\overline{3}$ means that the 3's repeat indefinitely.

Irrational numbers have decimal representations that neither terminate nor repeat. Therefore the exact value of an irrational number cannot be written in decimal form. The decimal approximations for the irrational numbers $\sqrt{2}$, $\sqrt{10}$, and π are

$$\sqrt{2} \approx 1.4142, \qquad \sqrt{10} \approx 3.1622, \qquad \text{and} \qquad \pi \approx 3.1416.$$

Square root tables written on clay tablets by the early Babylonians date back as far as 350 B.C.

We can find square roots using a calculator with a square root key. Also, there is a square root table on the inside back cover that gives square roots of whole numbers from 1 through 200.

EXAMPLE 4   Determine whether each number is rational or irrational. If the number is rational, give its exact value; if the number is irrational, give its value to the nearest hundredth.

a. $\sqrt{11}$ b. $\sqrt{196}$

Solution

a. Since 11 is not a perfect-square integer, $\sqrt{11}$ is an irrational number. To find $\sqrt{11}$ on your calculator, press

| Clear | 11 | $\sqrt{x}$ | 3.31662479 |

To find $\sqrt{11}$ from the table on the inside back cover, find 11 under the n column and then find $\sqrt{11}$ under the $\sqrt{n}$ column. Either method gives

$$\sqrt{11} \approx 3.32.$$

b. Since 196 is a perfect-square integer, $\sqrt{196}$ is a rational number. Using either a calculator or the table on the inside back cover, we have

Try Problem 39 >

$$\sqrt{196} = 14. \qquad \blacksquare$$

We have seen that finding the square root of a number is the reverse of squaring a number. Finding the **cube root** of a number is the reverse of cubing a number. For example, 5 is the cube root of 125 since $5^3 = 125$. The symbol $\sqrt[3]{a}$ is read "the principal cube root of a." The number 3 is called the **index of the radical.**

EXAMPLE 5   Find each cube root.

a. $\sqrt[3]{8} = 2$ *Since $2^3 = 8$*

Try Problem 49 >

b. $\sqrt[3]{-8} = -2$ *Since $(-2)^3 = -8$* $\blacksquare$

Note that the cube root of a positive number is a positive number and the cube root of a negative number is a negative number.

In addition to square roots and cube roots, we can find fourth roots, fifth roots, and so on.

DEFINITION OF THE PRINCIPAL nTH ROOT

If a is a real number and n is a positive integer greater than 1, then $\sqrt[n]{a}$ is read "the principal nth root of a" and

$$\sqrt[n]{a} = b \quad \text{if} \quad b^n = a.$$

Suppose n is an even integer.

   a. If a is positive, then $\sqrt[n]{a}$ is positive.
   b. If a is negative, then $\sqrt[n]{a}$ is not a real number.

Suppose n is an odd integer.

   a. If a is positive, then $\sqrt[n]{a}$ is positive.
   b. If a is negative, then $\sqrt[n]{a}$ is negative.

For any n, $\sqrt[n]{0} = 0$.

EXAMPLE 6   Find each root.

   a. $\sqrt[4]{81}$ b. $\sqrt[4]{-81}$ c. $\sqrt[5]{-32}$ d. $-\sqrt[5]{-32}$

Solution

   a. Both 3^4 and $(-3)^4$ equal 81. But $\sqrt[4]{81}$ denotes the principal fourth root of 81. Therefore $\sqrt[4]{81} = 3$.
   b. $\sqrt[4]{-81}$ is not a real number.
   c. The only real number that equals -32 when raised to the fifth power is -2. Therefore $\sqrt[5]{-32} = -2$.

Try Problem 59 >   d. $-\sqrt[5]{-32} = -(-2) = 2$ ■

Here is a table of some commonly used roots.

Square Roots		Cube Roots	Fourth Roots
$\sqrt{1} = 1$	$\sqrt{121} = 11$	$\sqrt[3]{1} = 1$	$\sqrt[4]{1} = 1$
$\sqrt{4} = 2$	$\sqrt{144} = 12$	$\sqrt[3]{8} = 2$	$\sqrt[4]{16} = 2$
$\sqrt{9} = 3$	$\sqrt{169} = 13$	$\sqrt[3]{27} = 3$	$\sqrt[4]{81} = 3$
$\sqrt{16} = 4$	$\sqrt{196} = 14$	$\sqrt[3]{64} = 4$	$\sqrt[4]{256} = 4$
$\sqrt{25} = 5$	$\sqrt{225} = 15$	$\sqrt[3]{125} = 5$	$\sqrt[4]{625} = 5$
$\sqrt{36} = 6$	$\sqrt{256} = 16$	$\sqrt[3]{216} = 6$	$\sqrt[4]{1296} = 6$
$\sqrt{49} = 7$	$\sqrt{289} = 17$	$\sqrt[3]{343} = 7$	$\sqrt[4]{2401} = 7$
$\sqrt{64} = 8$	$\sqrt{324} = 18$	$\sqrt[3]{512} = 8$	$\sqrt[4]{4096} = 8$
$\sqrt{81} = 9$	$\sqrt{361} = 19$	$\sqrt[3]{729} = 9$	$\sqrt[4]{6561} = 9$
$\sqrt{100} = 10$	$\sqrt{400} = 20$	$\sqrt[3]{1000} = 10$	$\sqrt[4]{10,000} = 10$

To solve the next example we use the Pythagorean theorem, which was first stated in Section 4.8.

$$c^2 = a^2 + b^2$$

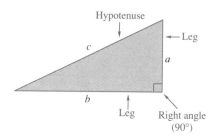

Since c must be a positive number, c must be the principal square root of $a^2 + b^2$. That is,

$$c = \sqrt{a^2 + b^2}.$$

PROBLEM SOLVING

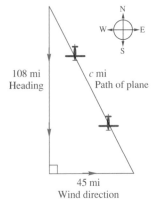

FIGURE 8.1

Try Problem 81 >

EXAMPLE 7 A plane with an airspeed of 108 mph flies on a due-south heading for 1 hour. During this time, a 45-mph wind blowing from west to east causes the plane to travel in a southeasterly direction, as shown in Fig. 8.1. Find the total distance traveled by the plane.

Solution The path of the plane is the hypotenuse of a right triangle with legs of length 108 miles and 45 miles. Therefore use the Pythagorean theorem.

$$c = \sqrt{a^2 + b^2} \qquad \textit{Pythagorean theorem}$$
$$c = \sqrt{108^2 + 45^2} \qquad \textit{Substitute } a = 108 \textit{ and } b = 45$$
$$\qquad\qquad\qquad (b = 108 \textit{ and } a = 45 \textit{ gives the same answer})$$
$$c = \sqrt{11{,}664 + 2025} \qquad \textit{Square each number}$$
$$c = \sqrt{13{,}689} \qquad \textit{Add before taking the square root}$$
$$c = 117 \qquad \textit{Take the square root}$$

The plane travels a total of 117 miles.

8.1 | Problem Set

LEARNING THROUGH WRITING

☐ Write the equation $\sqrt{36} = 6$ in words.

☐ Write the equation $\sqrt[3]{8} = 2$ in words.

☐ Define the term *square root*.

☐ Define the term *principal nth root*.

☐ Define the terms *radicand* and *index of a radical*.

☐ Define the term *perfect-square integer*.

☐ Describe the decimal representation of a rational number.

☐ Describe the decimal representation of an irrational number.

Find all square roots of each number.

1. 16   **2.** 36   **3.** 121   **4.** 144

5. $\dfrac{1}{9}$ **6.** $\dfrac{1}{4}$ **7.** $\dfrac{4}{25}$ **8.** $\dfrac{9}{64}$

9. 0.49   **10.** 0.81   **11.** 2809   **12.** 5041

Find the following square roots.

13. $\sqrt{4}$ **14.** $\sqrt{25}$ **15.** $-\sqrt{4}$ **16.** $-\sqrt{25}$

17. $\pm\sqrt{4}$ **18.** $\pm\sqrt{25}$ **19.** $\sqrt{900}$ **20.** $\sqrt{400}$

21. $-\sqrt{1}$ **22.** $-\sqrt{0}$ **23.** $\pm\sqrt{0}$ **24.** $\pm\sqrt{1}$

25. $\sqrt{\dfrac{1}{81}}$ **26.** $\sqrt{\dfrac{1}{100}}$ **27.** $\sqrt{\dfrac{25}{144}}$ **28.** $\sqrt{\dfrac{4}{121}}$

29. $\sqrt{-9}$ **30.** $\sqrt{-16}$ **31.** $\sqrt{4^2}$ **32.** $\sqrt{9^2}$

33. $\sqrt{(-3)^2}$ **34.** $\sqrt{(-2)^2}$ **35.** $-\sqrt{-81}$ **36.** $-\sqrt{-100}$

Determine whether each number is rational or irrational. If the number is rational, give its exact value; if the number is irrational, give its value to the nearest hundredth.

37. $\sqrt{2}$ **38.** $\sqrt{3}$ **39.** $\sqrt{23}$ **40.** $\sqrt{24}$

41. $\sqrt{169}$ **42.** $\sqrt{225}$ **43.** $\sqrt{48}$ **44.** $\sqrt{68}$

45. $\sqrt{177}$ **46.** $\sqrt{185}$ **47.** $\sqrt{361}$ **48.** $\sqrt{441}$

Find the following roots.

49. $\sqrt[3]{27}$ **50.** $\sqrt[3]{64}$ **51.** $\sqrt[3]{-27}$ **52.** $\sqrt[3]{-64}$

53. $-\sqrt[3]{125}$ **54.** $-\sqrt[3]{1000}$ **55.** $-\sqrt[3]{-125}$ **56.** $-\sqrt[3]{-1000}$

57. $\sqrt[3]{343}$ **58.** $\sqrt[3]{216}$ **59.** $\sqrt[4]{16}$ **60.** $\sqrt[4]{625}$

61. $\sqrt[4]{-16}$ **62.** $\sqrt[4]{-625}$ **63.** $\sqrt[5]{32}$ **64.** $\sqrt[5]{243}$

65. $\sqrt[5]{-1}$ **66.** $\sqrt[7]{-1}$ **67.** $\sqrt[3]{4^3}$ **68.** $\sqrt[3]{5^3}$

69. $\sqrt[6]{0}$ **70.** $\sqrt[6]{1}$ **71.** $\sqrt[4]{(-3)^4}$ **72.** $\sqrt[4]{(-2)^4}$

Solve each problem.

73. Simplify $\sqrt{16 + 9}$ and $\sqrt{16} + \sqrt{9}$ and compare the results. What conclusion can you make?

74. Simplify $\sqrt{64 + 36}$ and $\sqrt{64} + \sqrt{36}$ and compare the results. What conclusion can you make?

75. Simplify $\sqrt{625 - 49}$ and $\sqrt{625} - \sqrt{49}$ and compare the results. What conclusion can you make?

76. Simplify $\sqrt{169 - 144}$ and $\sqrt{169} - \sqrt{144}$ and compare the results. What conclusion can you make?

77. For the car in Fig. 8.2 to negotiate the circular loop successfully, its minimum velocity, v, in feet per second, at the top of the loop must be

$$v = \sqrt{32r},$$

where r is the radius of the loop, in feet. Determine the minimum velocity required to negotiate the loop if its radius is 50 feet.

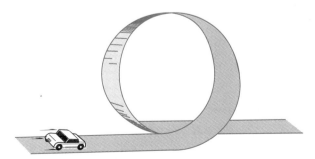

FIGURE 8.2

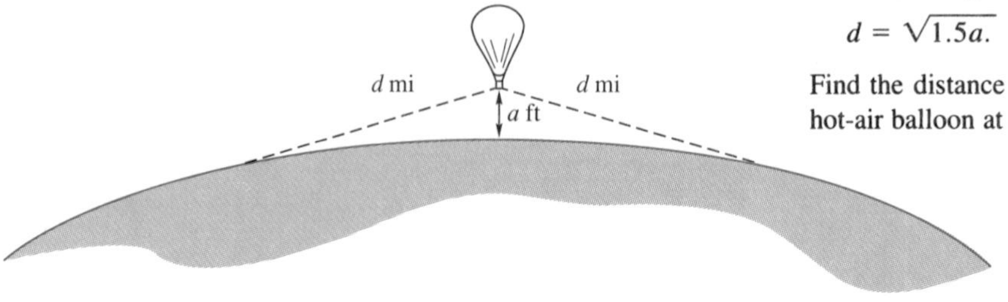

78. The distance, d, in miles to the horizon from an altitude of a feet (see Fig. 8.3) is given by the formula

$$d = \sqrt{1.5a}.$$

Find the distance to the horizon from an observer in a hot-air balloon at an altitude of 1350 feet.

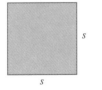

d mi d mi

a ft

FIGURE 8.3

79. The area, A, of a square is related to the length of its side, s, by the formula $A = s^2$. Find the length of one side of a square whose area is 100 square centimeters.

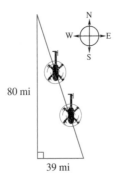

s

s

80. The volume, V, of a cube is related to the length of its side, s, by the formula $V = s^3$. Find the length of one side of a cube whose volume is 125 cubic centimeters.

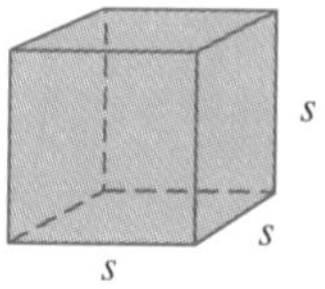

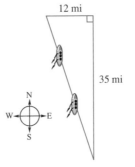

s

s

s

81. A helicopter flies with an airspeed of 80 mph on a due-south heading for 1 hour. During this time, a 39-mph wind blowing from west to east causes the copter to travel in a southeasterly direction, as shown in Fig. 8.4. Find the total distance traveled by the copter.

N

W — E

S

80 mi

39 mi

FIGURE 8.4

82. A ship with a speed of 35 mph sails on a due-north heading for 1 hour. During this time, a 12-mph current flowing from east to west causes the ship to travel in a north-westerly direction, as shown in Fig. 8.5. Find the total distance traveled by the ship.

12 mi

35 mi

N

W — E

S

FIGURE 8.5

83. Consider two forces of magnitude F_1 and F_2, exerted at right angles to one another as shown in Fig. 8.6. The magnitude, F, of the resultant force is given by the formula

$$F = \sqrt{F_1^2 + F_2^2}.$$

84. Determine the slant height, s, of a cone if the height is 15 feet and the diameter of the base is 16 feet (see Fig. 8.8).

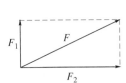

F_1 F F_2

FIGURE 8.6

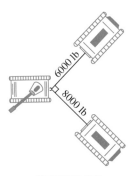

6000 lb
8000 lb

FIGURE 8.7

s 15 ft

16 ft

FIGURE 8.8

Suppose two recovery vehicles pull at right angles on a tank stuck in the mud (see Fig. 8.7). If one vehicle exerts a force of 6000 pounds and the other a force of 8000 pounds, what is the magnitude of the resultant force on the tank?

The area, A, of a triangle can be determined from the lengths of its sides, a, b, and c, by using Heron's formula,
$A = \sqrt{s(s - a)(s - b)(s - c)}$, *where s is one-half the perimeter of the triangle (see Fig. 8.9).*

85. Find the area of a triangle with sides of length 10 inches, 17 inches, and 21 inches.

86. Find the area of a triangle with sides of length 13 inches, 14 inches, and 15 inches.

$s = \frac{1}{2}(a + b + c)$

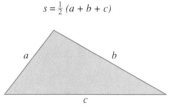

a b

c

FIGURE 8.9

Heron's formula is named after Heron of Alexandria (ca. 75 A.D.), who probably was born in Egypt but trained in Greece, and who helped lay the foundation for modern engineering and surveying. In his writings we find descriptions of such things as a surveyor's transit, mirrors for observing the back of one's head, and a device for opening temple doors using a fire on the altar.

▦ CALCULATOR PROBLEMS

The procedure for finding cube roots, fourth roots, and so on varies on different calculators, so check your owner's manual. On many calculators you can find $\sqrt[3]{2744}$ by pressing the following keys:

| Clear | 2744 | INV | y^x | 3 | = | 14 |

Find the following roots. Round approximate answers to the nearest hundredth.

87. $\sqrt[3]{4913}$ **88.** $\sqrt[3]{-729}$ **89.** $\sqrt[3]{100}$ **90.** $\sqrt[4]{2401}$

91. $\sqrt[4]{-4096}$ **92.** $\sqrt[4]{8488}$ **93.** $\sqrt[5]{7776}$ **94.** $\sqrt[5]{-65.2}$

8.2	**Simplifying Radicals**

Two important rules that radicals obey are the *product rule* and the *quotient rule*. In this section we use these rules to simplify radicals. To illustrate the first rule, note that

$$\sqrt{4 \cdot 9} = \sqrt{36} = 6 \quad \text{and} \quad \sqrt{4} \cdot \sqrt{9} = 2 \cdot 3 = 6,$$

which means that

$$\sqrt{4 \cdot 9} = \sqrt{4} \cdot \sqrt{9}.$$

This suggests the following rule.

PRODUCT RULE FOR RADICALS

If a and b are nonnegative real numbers, then

$$\sqrt{a \cdot b} = \sqrt{a} \cdot \sqrt{b}.$$

In words, the product rule for radicals states that the square root of a product equals the product of the square roots.

Caution! The expressions $\sqrt{a + b}$ and $\sqrt{a} + \sqrt{b}$ are not equal. Also, the expressions $\sqrt{a - b}$ and $\sqrt{a} - \sqrt{b}$ are not equal.

Correct

$$\sqrt{4 \cdot 100} = \sqrt{4} \cdot \sqrt{100}$$

Wrong

$$\sqrt{16 + 9} = \sqrt{16} + \sqrt{9}$$

Although we cannot write $\sqrt{12}$ as an integer, we can use the product rule to simplify $\sqrt{12}$, that is, to write the radical so the radicand contains no perfect-square factor (except 1).

EXAMPLE 1   Simplify $\sqrt{12}$.

Solution   The radicand 12 has the perfect-square factor 4. Therefore factor 4 from 12 and apply the product rule.

$$\begin{aligned}
\sqrt{12} &= \sqrt{4 \cdot 3} & \textit{Factor out the perfect-square 4} \\
&= \sqrt{4} \cdot \sqrt{3} & \textit{Apply the product rule} \\
&= 2 \cdot \sqrt{3} & \textit{Since } \sqrt{4} = 2 \\
&= 2\sqrt{3} & \textit{Omit the multiplication symbol} \qquad ■
\end{aligned}$$

Try Problem 1 >

We often omit the multiplication symbol when multiplying a number and a radical, or when multiplying two radicals. That is, we write $2 \cdot \sqrt{3}$ as $2\sqrt{3}$, and $\sqrt{3} \cdot \sqrt{7}$ as $\sqrt{3}\sqrt{7}$.

An algebraic expression that contains one or more radicals is called a **radical expression,** for example, $6\sqrt{10}$ and $1 + \sqrt{5}$.

EXAMPLE 2   Simplify each radical expression.

a. $\sqrt{72}$ b. $5\sqrt{99}$ c. $\sqrt{30}$

Solution

a. Although 4 and 9 are both perfect-square factors of 72, the largest perfect-square factor is 36. Therefore write

$$\sqrt{72} = \sqrt{36 \cdot 2} = \sqrt{36}\sqrt{2} = 6\sqrt{2}.$$

b. The largest perfect-square factor of 99 is 9. Therefore write

$$5\sqrt{99} = 5 \cdot \sqrt{9 \cdot 11} = 5\sqrt{9}\sqrt{11} = 5 \cdot 3\sqrt{11} = 15\sqrt{11}.$$

c. The largest perfect-square factor of 30 is 1. Therefore $\sqrt{30}$ cannot be simplified further.   ■

Try Problem 9 >

If you did not recognize that 36 was the largest perfect-square factor of 72 in Example 2a, you could have proceeded in stages as follows.

$$\sqrt{72} = \sqrt{9 \cdot 8} = \sqrt{9}\sqrt{8} = 3\sqrt{8} = 3\sqrt{4 \cdot 2} = 3\sqrt{4}\sqrt{2} = 3 \cdot 2\sqrt{2} = 6\sqrt{2}$$

Just as we can distribute a radical sign over a product, so can we distribute a radical sign over a quotient. Note that

$$\sqrt{\frac{64}{16}} = \sqrt{4} = 2 \quad \text{and} \quad \frac{\sqrt{64}}{\sqrt{16}} = \frac{8}{4} = 2,$$

which means that

$$\sqrt{\frac{64}{16}} = \frac{\sqrt{64}}{\sqrt{16}}.$$

This suggests the following rule.

QUOTIENT RULE FOR RADICALS

If a and b are nonnegative real numbers ($b \neq 0$), then

$$\sqrt{\frac{a}{b}} = \frac{\sqrt{a}}{\sqrt{b}}.$$

In words, the quotient rule for radicals states that the square root of a quotient equals the quotient of the square roots.

EXAMPLE 3   Simplify each radical expression.

a. $\sqrt{\dfrac{49}{144}} = \dfrac{\sqrt{49}}{\sqrt{144}}$ *Apply the quotient rule*

$\qquad\quad = \dfrac{7}{12}$ *Find each square root*

b. $\sqrt{\dfrac{5}{9}} = \dfrac{\sqrt{5}}{\sqrt{9}}$ *Quotient rule*

$\qquad\ = \dfrac{\sqrt{5}}{3}$ *Since* $\sqrt{9} = 3$

c. $\sqrt{\dfrac{75}{16}} = \dfrac{\sqrt{75}}{\sqrt{16}}$ *Quotient rule*

$\qquad\quad = \dfrac{\sqrt{25 \cdot 3}}{4}$ *Since* $75 = 25 \cdot 3$ *and* $\sqrt{16} = 4$

$\qquad\quad = \dfrac{\sqrt{25}\sqrt{3}}{4}$ *Product rule*

Try Problem 21 > $\qquad\quad = \dfrac{5\sqrt{3}}{4}$ *Since* $\sqrt{25} = 5$ ∎

Caution! ∎   You must be careful when the radicand contains variables. That is because $\sqrt{x^2}$
∎   is not necessarily x. Thus, $\sqrt{3^2} = 3$ but $\sqrt{(-3)^2} \neq -3$. In other words,
∎
∎ $\sqrt{x^2} = x$ only if x is nonnegative.

EXAMPLE 4   Simplify each expression. Assume $x > 0$.

a. $\sqrt{x^6} = x^3$ *Since* $(x^3)^2 = x^6$
b. $\sqrt{81x^2y^4} = \sqrt{81}\sqrt{x^2}\sqrt{y^4}$ *Product rule*

Try Problem 37 > $\qquad\qquad\ = 9xy^2$ *Find each square root*   ∎

EXAMPLE 5   Simplify each expression. Assume all variables represent positive numbers.

a. $\sqrt{m^{11}} = \sqrt{m^{10} \cdot m}$ *Since m^{10} is a perfect square*
      $= \sqrt{m^{10}}\sqrt{m}$ *Product rule*
      $= m^5\sqrt{m}$ *Since $\sqrt{m^{10}} = m^5$*

b. $\sqrt{48p^3} = \sqrt{16p^2 \cdot 3p}$ *Since $16p^2$ is a perfect square*
      $= \sqrt{16p^2}\sqrt{3p}$ *Product rule*
      $= 4p\sqrt{3p}$ *Since $\sqrt{16p^2} = 4p$*

c. $-2a\sqrt{98a^8b^3} = -2a\sqrt{49a^8b^2} \cdot \sqrt{2b}$ *Product rule*
      $= -2a \cdot 7a^4b\sqrt{2b}$ *Since $\sqrt{49a^8b^2} = 7a^4b$*
      $= -14a^5b\sqrt{2b}$ *Multiply*   ■

Try Problem 47 >

EXAMPLE 6   Simplify each expression. Assume all variables represent positive numbers.

a. $\sqrt{\dfrac{7}{r^2}} = \dfrac{\sqrt{7}}{\sqrt{r^2}}$ *Quotient rule*
     $= \dfrac{\sqrt{7}}{r}$ *Since $\sqrt{r^2} = r$*

b. $\sqrt{\dfrac{24x^4}{8}} = \sqrt{3x^4}$ *Simplify the radicand*
     $= \sqrt{x^4}\sqrt{3}$ *Product rule*
     $= x^2\sqrt{3}$ *Since $\sqrt{x^4} = x^2$*

c. $\sqrt{\dfrac{44x^3}{16xy^2}} = \sqrt{\dfrac{11x^2}{4y^2}}$ *Simplify the radicand*
     $= \dfrac{\sqrt{11x^2}}{\sqrt{4y^2}}$ *Quotient rule*
     $= \dfrac{\sqrt{x^2}\sqrt{11}}{2y}$ *Product rule and $\sqrt{4y^2} = 2y$*
     $= \dfrac{x\sqrt{11}}{2y}$ *Since $\sqrt{x^2} = x$*   ■

Try Problem 65 >

The product rule and the quotient rule also apply to cube roots, fourth roots, and so on.

PRODUCT AND QUOTIENT RULES FOR RADICALS

If the indicated roots exist and no denominator is 0, then

$$\sqrt[n]{ab} = \sqrt[n]{a}\,\sqrt[n]{b} \qquad \text{and} \qquad \sqrt[n]{\dfrac{a}{b}} = \dfrac{\sqrt[n]{a}}{\sqrt[n]{b}}.$$

To help you identify perfect-cube factors and perfect-fourth-power factors, here is a list of some commonly used perfect powers.

Perfect Cubes: 1, 8, 27, 64, 125, 216, 343, 512, 729, 1000
Perfect Fourth Powers: 1, 16, 81, 256, 625, 1296, 2401, 4096, 6561, 10,000

EXAMPLE 7   Simplify.

a. $\sqrt[3]{54}$ b. $\sqrt[4]{80}$

Solution

a. The largest perfect-cube factor of 54 is 27.

$$\begin{aligned}
\sqrt[3]{54} &= \sqrt[3]{27 \cdot 2} && \textit{Factor out the perfect-cube 27} \\
&= \sqrt[3]{27}\,\sqrt[3]{2} && \textit{Apply the product rule} \\
&= 3\sqrt[3]{2} && \textit{Since } \sqrt[3]{27} = 3
\end{aligned}$$

b. The largest perfect-fourth-power factor of 80 is 16.

$$\begin{aligned}
\sqrt[4]{80} &= \sqrt[4]{16}\,\sqrt[4]{5} && \textit{Product rule} \\
&= 2\sqrt[4]{5} && \textit{Since } \sqrt[4]{16} = 2
\end{aligned}$$

Try Problem 73 >

EXAMPLE 8   Simplify each expression.

a. $\sqrt[3]{216y^4} = \sqrt[3]{216y^3}\,\sqrt[3]{y}$ *Product rule*

$\qquad\qquad\quad = 6y\sqrt[3]{y}$ *Since $\sqrt[3]{216y^3} = 6y$*

b. $\sqrt[3]{\dfrac{4r^3s^5}{125t^6}} = \dfrac{\sqrt[3]{4r^3s^5}}{\sqrt[3]{125t^6}}$ *Quotient rule*

$\qquad\qquad = \dfrac{\sqrt[3]{r^3s^3}\sqrt[3]{4s^2}}{5t^2}$ *Product rule and $\sqrt[3]{125t^6} = 5t^2$*

Try Problem 87 >

$\qquad\qquad = \dfrac{rs\sqrt[3]{4s^2}}{5t^2}$ *Since $\sqrt[3]{r^3s^3} = rs$*

PROBLEM SOLVING

EXAMPLE 9   A baseball infield is a square 90 feet on a side (see Fig. 8.10). Find the distance of a throw from home plate to second base.

Solution   A throw from home plate to second base travels along the hypotenuse of a right triangle whose legs are 90 feet. Therefore use the Pythagorean theorem.

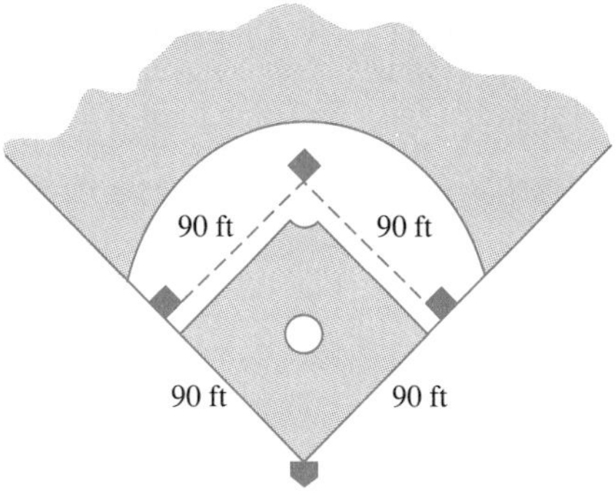

FIGURE 8.10

$$c = \sqrt{a^2 + b^2} \qquad \textit{Pythagorean theorem}$$
$$c = \sqrt{90^2 + 90^2} \qquad \textit{Substitute } a = 90 \textit{ and } b = 90$$
$$c = \sqrt{90^2 \cdot 2} \qquad \textit{Since } 90^2 + 90^2 = 90^2(1 + 1) = 90^2 \cdot 2$$
$$c = \sqrt{90^2}\sqrt{2} \qquad \textit{Product rule}$$
$$c = 90\sqrt{2} \qquad \textit{Since } \sqrt{90^2} = 90$$

Try Problem 101 >   The throw covers a distance of $90\sqrt{2}$ feet.

8.2 Problem Set

LEARNING THROUGH WRITING

☐ Write the equation $\sqrt{4 \cdot 25} = \sqrt{4} \cdot \sqrt{25}$ in words.

☐ Write the equation $\sqrt[4]{\dfrac{81}{16}} = \dfrac{\sqrt[4]{81}}{\sqrt[4]{16}}$ in words.

☐ State the *product rule for radicals* in words.

☐ State the *quotient rule for radicals* in words.

☐ Define the term *radical expression*.

☐ Under what condition does $\sqrt{x^2} = x$?

Use the product rule to simplify each radical expression.

1. $\sqrt{20}$

2. $\sqrt{28}$

3. $\sqrt{18}$

4. $\sqrt{45}$

5. $\sqrt{300}$

6. $\sqrt{200}$

7. $\sqrt{48}$

8. $\sqrt{32}$

9. $3\sqrt{50}$

10. $2\sqrt{75}$

11. $5\sqrt{76}$

12. $4\sqrt{117}$

13. $\sqrt{42}$

14. $\sqrt{70}$

15. $-4\sqrt{432}$

16. $-5\sqrt{288}$

Use the quotient rule and/or the product rule to simplify each radical expression.

17. $\sqrt{\dfrac{64}{121}}$

18. $\sqrt{\dfrac{49}{81}}$

19. $\sqrt{\dfrac{1}{100}}$

20. $\sqrt{\dfrac{1}{144}}$

21. $\sqrt{\dfrac{3}{4}}$ **22.** $\sqrt{\dfrac{7}{16}}$ **23.** $\sqrt{\dfrac{6}{49}}$ **24.** $\sqrt{\dfrac{10}{81}}$

25. $\sqrt{\dfrac{8}{9}}$ **26.** $\sqrt{\dfrac{27}{25}}$ **27.** $\dfrac{5\sqrt{63}}{3}$ **28.** $\dfrac{7\sqrt{44}}{2}$

29. $\sqrt{\dfrac{245}{64}}$ **30.** $\sqrt{\dfrac{405}{36}}$ **31.** $-6\sqrt{\dfrac{156}{144}}$ **32.** $-5\sqrt{\dfrac{132}{100}}$

Simplify each expression. Assume all variables represent positive numbers.

33. $\sqrt{x^4}$ **34.** $\sqrt{x^8}$ **35.** $\sqrt{4x^2}$ **36.** $\sqrt{9x^2}$

37. $\sqrt{25x^2y^6}$ **38.** $\sqrt{49x^2y^{10}}$ **39.** $\sqrt{169z^{16}}$ **40.** $\sqrt{196z^{36}}$

41. $\sqrt{m^7}$ **42.** $\sqrt{m^9}$ **43.** $\sqrt{r^2s}$ **44.** $\sqrt{rs^2}$

45. $\sqrt{9k^3}$ **46.** $\sqrt{16k^3}$ **47.** $\sqrt{80p^5}$ **48.** $\sqrt{54p^{11}}$

49. $2\sqrt{500t^{13}}$ **50.** $3\sqrt{700t^{15}}$ **51.** $10\sqrt{81x^6y^3}$ **52.** $9\sqrt{25x^3y^4}$

53. $-4a\sqrt{125a^{10}b^3}$ **54.** $-6b\sqrt{27a^{12}b^7}$ **55.** $\dfrac{2}{3}rs\sqrt{36r^3st^2}$ **56.** $\dfrac{4}{5}rs\sqrt{100rs^3t^4}$

Simplify each expression. Assume all variables represent positive numbers.

57. $\sqrt{\dfrac{y^6}{9}}$ **58.** $\sqrt{\dfrac{y^4}{25}}$ **59.** $\sqrt{\dfrac{16}{x^4}}$ **60.** $\sqrt{\dfrac{64}{x^6}}$

61. $\sqrt{\dfrac{3}{r^2}}$ **62.** $\sqrt{\dfrac{5}{r^2}}$ **63.** $\dfrac{\sqrt{24k}}{6}$ **64.** $\dfrac{\sqrt{54k}}{6}$

65. $\sqrt{\dfrac{60x^6}{12}}$ **66.** $\sqrt{\dfrac{90x^4}{18}}$ **67.** $\sqrt{\dfrac{27p^3}{q^2}}$ **68.** $\sqrt{\dfrac{8p^3}{q^2}}$

69. $\sqrt{\dfrac{5ab^2c}{20abc^3}}$ **70.** $\sqrt{\dfrac{7a^2b^2c}{63ab^4c}}$ **71.** $\sqrt{\dfrac{68x^5}{36x^3y^4}}$ **72.** $\sqrt{\dfrac{76x^5y^6}{64x^7}}$

Simplify each expression.

73. $\sqrt[3]{24}$ **74.** $\sqrt[3]{40}$ **75.** $\sqrt[3]{625}$ **76.** $\sqrt[3]{81}$

77. $\sqrt[3]{250}$ **78.** $\sqrt[3]{128}$ **79.** $\sqrt[4]{32}$ **80.** $\sqrt[4]{162}$

81. $\sqrt[3]{\dfrac{9}{64}}$ **82.** $\sqrt[3]{\dfrac{4}{27}}$ **83.** $\sqrt[4]{\dfrac{80}{81}}$ **84.** $\sqrt[4]{\dfrac{405}{16}}$

85. $\sqrt[3]{-8x^3}$ **86.** $\sqrt[3]{-27x^3}$ **87.** $\sqrt[3]{64y^4}$ **88.** $\sqrt[3]{125y^5}$

89. $\sqrt[3]{\dfrac{9r^3s^2}{1000t^6}}$ **90.** $\sqrt[3]{\dfrac{4r^2s^6}{343t^3}}$ **91.** $\sqrt[3]{\dfrac{16m^9n^2}{27mn^5}}$ **92.** $\sqrt[3]{\dfrac{81m^8n}{8mn^7}}$

Simplify each expression. Assume $x > 0$ and $y > 0$.

93. $\sqrt{(x+3)^2}$ **94.** $\sqrt{(x+5)^2}$ **95.** $\sqrt{x^2+4x+4}$

96. $\sqrt{x^2+8x+16}$ **97.** $\sqrt{9x^2+30xy+25y^2}$ **98.** $\sqrt{4x^2+40xy+100y^2}$

Solve each word problem.

99. The speed, s_a, of a car that was involved in an accident can be estimated as follows: A police officer drives a car (the same car if possible) under similar conditions at some test speed, s_t, and then skids to a stop. Then s_a is given by the formula

$$s_a = s_t \sqrt{\frac{l_a}{l_t}},$$

where l_a and l_t are the lengths of the skid marks from the accident and from the test, respectively. Determine s_a if $s_t = 40$ mph, $l_a = 90$ feet, and $l_t = 40$ feet.

100. The time, t, in seconds that it takes a pendulum l feet long to complete a cycle (see Fig. 8.11) is given by the formula

$$t = 2\pi \sqrt{\frac{l}{32}}.$$

How long does it take a pendulum that is 2 feet long to complete a cycle?

FIGURE 8.11

101. A softball infield is a square 65 feet on a side. Find the distance of a throw from home plate to second base.

102. Determine the distance from one corner to the opposite corner of a boxing ring that is 20 feet by 20 feet square.

103. The area, A, of a square is related to the length of its side, s, by the formula $A = s^2$. Find the length of one side of a square whose area is 160 square meters.

104. The volume, V, of a cube is related to the length of its side, s, by the formula $V = s^3$. Find the length of one side of a cube whose volume is 256 cubic meters.

8.3 | **Multiplying and Dividing Radicals**

If we turn the product and the quotient rules for radicals around, we can use them to multiply and divide radicals that have the same index.

PRODUCT AND QUOTIENT RULES FOR RADICALS

If the indicated roots exist and no denominator is 0, then

$$\sqrt[n]{a}\,\sqrt[n]{b} = \sqrt[n]{ab} \qquad \text{and} \qquad \frac{\sqrt[n]{a}}{\sqrt[n]{b}} = \sqrt[n]{\frac{a}{b}}.$$

In words, these rules state that we can multiply or divide two radicals having the same index by multiplying or dividing their radicands.

EXAMPLE 1   Find each product. Assume $m > 0$.

a. $\sqrt{2}\sqrt{7} = \sqrt{2 \cdot 7}$ *Product rule*
$\quad\quad\quad = \sqrt{14}$ *Simplify the radicand*

Try Problem 1 >   b. $\sqrt{6}\sqrt{m} = \sqrt{6m}$ *Product rule*   ■

EXAMPLE 2   Multiply and simplify.

a. $\sqrt{10}\sqrt{15} = \sqrt{10 \cdot 15}$ *Product rule*
$\quad\quad\quad = \sqrt{150}$ *Simplify the radicand*
$\quad\quad\quad = \sqrt{25}\sqrt{6}$ *Product rule*
$\quad\quad\quad = 5\sqrt{6}$ *Simplify*

Try Problem 11 >   b. $(\sqrt{3})^2 = \sqrt{3}\sqrt{3} = \sqrt{9} = 3$ ■

Example 2b illustrates the following rule.

SQUARING A RADICAL

If a is a nonnegative number, then

$$(\sqrt{a})^2 = \sqrt{a}\sqrt{a} = a.$$

Here are some more examples of the rule for squaring a radical.

$$(\sqrt{9})^2 = 9 \quad\quad (\sqrt{k})^2 = k \quad\quad (\sqrt{2x + 5})^2 = 2x + 5$$

EXAMPLE 3   Multiply and simplify. Assume $x > 0$ and $y > 0$.

a. $(3\sqrt{5x})(2\sqrt{11x}) = (3 \cdot 2)(\sqrt{5x}\sqrt{11x})$ *Group the whole numbers, group the radicals*

$\quad\quad\quad\quad\quad\quad = 6\sqrt{55x^2}$ *Multiply the whole numbers, multiply the radicals*

$\quad\quad\quad\quad\quad\quad = 6\sqrt{x^2}\sqrt{55}$
$\quad\quad\quad\quad\quad\quad = 6x\sqrt{55}$ $\Big\}$ *Simplify the radical*

b. $\sqrt{6x^2y}\sqrt{8xy^5} = \sqrt{48x^3y^6}$ *Product rule*

$\quad\quad\quad\quad\quad = \sqrt{16x^2y^6}\sqrt{3x}$ *Product rule*

Try Problem 35 > $\quad\quad\quad\quad\quad = 4xy^3\sqrt{3x}$ *Simplify*   ■

EXAMPLE 4   Find each quotient. Assume $m > 0$.

a. $\dfrac{\sqrt{21}}{\sqrt{3}} = \sqrt{\dfrac{21}{3}}$ *Quotient rule*

$\quad\quad = \sqrt{7}$ *Simplify the radicand*

b. $\dfrac{\sqrt{15m}}{\sqrt{5}} = \sqrt{\dfrac{15m}{5}}$ *Quotient rule*

Try Problem 53 > $= \sqrt{3m}$ *Simplify the radicand*   ■

EXAMPLE 5   Divide and simplify. Assume $r > 0$.

a. $\dfrac{\sqrt{32r}}{\sqrt{2r}} = \sqrt{\dfrac{32r}{2r}}$ *Quotient rule*

$= \sqrt{16}$ *Simplify the radicand*

$= 4$ *Simplify*

b. $\dfrac{\sqrt{200}}{\sqrt{10}} = \sqrt{\dfrac{200}{10}}$ *Quotient rule*

$= \sqrt{20}$ *Simplify the radicand*

$= \sqrt{4}\sqrt{5}$ *Product rule*

Try Problem 61 > $= 2\sqrt{5}$ *Simplify*   ■

EXAMPLE 6   Divide and simplify. Assume $x > 0$.

a. $\dfrac{6\sqrt{9}}{3\sqrt{3}} = \dfrac{6}{3} \cdot \dfrac{\sqrt{9}}{\sqrt{3}}$ *Write as a product of two fractions*

$= 2 \cdot \sqrt{\dfrac{9}{3}}$ *Simplify 6/3, apply the quotient rule*

$= 2\sqrt{3}$ *Simplify the radicand*

b. $\dfrac{12\sqrt{28x^4}}{4\sqrt{7x}} = \dfrac{12}{4} \cdot \dfrac{\sqrt{28x^4}}{\sqrt{7x}}$ *Write as a product of two fractions*

$= 3 \cdot \sqrt{4x^3}$ *Simplify 12/4, apply the quotient rule*

$= 3 \cdot \sqrt{4x^2}\sqrt{x}$ *Product rule*

$= 3 \cdot 2x\sqrt{x}$ *Since $\sqrt{4x^2} = 2x$*

Try Problem 67 > $= 6x\sqrt{x}$ *Simplify*   ■

EXAMPLE 7   Perform the indicated operation and simplify.

a. $\sqrt[3]{2x^2}\sqrt[3]{4x} = \sqrt[3]{8x^3}$ *Product rule*

$= 2x$ *Simplify*

b. $\dfrac{\sqrt[4]{405x^{10}}}{\sqrt[4]{5x^2}} = \sqrt[4]{\dfrac{405x^{10}}{5x^2}}$ *Quotient rule*

$= \sqrt[4]{81x^8}$ *Simplify the radicand*

Try Problem 79 > $= 3x^2$ *Simplify*   ■

Caution! ■   To apply the product or the quotient rule for radicals, the indexes must be the
■   same.
■
■   *Wrong*   *Wrong*   *Wrong*
■ $\sqrt{2}\sqrt[3]{2} = \sqrt{4}$ $\sqrt{2}\sqrt[3]{2} = \sqrt[3]{4}$ $\sqrt{2}\sqrt[3]{2} = \sqrt[6]{4}$

Sometimes the Pythagorean theorem is more useful when it is solved for one of the legs rather than solved for the hypotenuse.

$$a^2 + b^2 = c^2$$
$$a^2 = c^2 - b^2$$
$$a = \sqrt{c^2 - b^2}$$

PROBLEM SOLVING

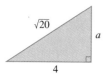

FIGURE 8.12

EXAMPLE 8   If the hypotenuse of a right triangle is $\sqrt{20}$ and one leg is 4, what is the other leg (see Fig. 8.12)?

Solution   Since the hypotenuse and one leg of a right triangle are given, use the Pythagorean theorem solved for one leg.

$a = \sqrt{c^2 - b^2}$ *Pythagorean theorem*
$a = \sqrt{(\sqrt{20})^2 - 4^2}$ *Substitute $c = \sqrt{20}$ and $b = 4$*
$a = \sqrt{20 - 16}$ *Since $(\sqrt{20})^2 = 20$ and $4^2 = 16$*
$a = \sqrt{4}$ *Subtract before taking the square root*
$a = 2$ *Take the square root*

Try Problem 89 >   The length of the other leg is 2.

8.3 Problem Set

LEARNING THROUGH WRITING

☐ Write the equation $\sqrt[n]{a}\,\sqrt[n]{b} = \sqrt[n]{ab}$ in words.

☐ Write the equation $\dfrac{\sqrt[n]{a}}{\sqrt[n]{b}} = \sqrt[n]{\dfrac{a}{b}}$ in words.

☐ Write the equation $(\sqrt{a})^2 = a$ in words.

Multiply and simplify. Assume all variables represent positive numbers.

1. $\sqrt{2}\sqrt{3}$	2. $\sqrt{3}\sqrt{5}$	3. $\sqrt{6}\sqrt{7}$	4. $\sqrt{10}\sqrt{11}$
5. $\sqrt{14}\sqrt{m}$	6. $\sqrt{21}\sqrt{m}$	7. $\sqrt{5}\sqrt{10}$	8. $\sqrt{2}\sqrt{6}$
9. $\sqrt{6}\sqrt{10}$	10. $\sqrt{6}\sqrt{15}$	11. $\sqrt{12}\sqrt{15}$	12. $\sqrt{27}\sqrt{45}$
13. $\sqrt{2}\sqrt{2}$	14. $\sqrt{5}\sqrt{5}$	15. $(\sqrt{7})^2$	16. $(\sqrt{11})^2$
17. $\sqrt{x}\sqrt{x}$	18. $\sqrt{y}\sqrt{y}$	19. $(3\sqrt{2})(5\sqrt{11})$	20. $(2\sqrt{3})(7\sqrt{13})$
21. $(2\sqrt{3})(4\sqrt{27})$	22. $(3\sqrt{2})(5\sqrt{8})$	23. $\sqrt{4}\sqrt{18}$	24. $\sqrt{25}\sqrt{20}$
25. $\sqrt{x}\sqrt{x^3}$	26. $\sqrt{x^3}\sqrt{x^3}$	27. $\sqrt{3z}\sqrt{5z}$	28. $\sqrt{2z}\sqrt{7z}$
29. $(-2\sqrt{p})^2$	30. $(-3\sqrt{p})^2$	31. $(6\sqrt{m})(-3\sqrt{m})$	32. $(5\sqrt{m})(-7\sqrt{m})$
33. $(5\sqrt{2t})^2$	34. $(2\sqrt{6t})^2$	35. $(4\sqrt{7x})(5\sqrt{11x})$	36. $(3\sqrt{5x})(4\sqrt{13x})$
37. $\sqrt{8x^2y^2}\sqrt{2x^3y}$	38. $\sqrt{3xy}\sqrt{12x^4y^4}$	39. $-\sqrt{12x^5}\sqrt{4x^5}$	40. $-\sqrt{8x^3}\sqrt{4x^3}$

41. $2\sqrt{15x^{11}y^7}\sqrt{10x^5y^7}$ **42.** $5\sqrt{10x^{13}y^5}\sqrt{20x^7y^9}$ **43.** $\sqrt{3}\sqrt{2x+5}$ **44.** $\sqrt{2}\sqrt{3x+7}$

45. $(\sqrt{y}+1)^2$ **46.** $(\sqrt{y}+4)^2$ **47.** $(2\sqrt{4p}+9)^2$ **48.** $(3\sqrt{9p}+1)^2$

Divide and simplify. Assume all variables represent positive numbers.

49. $\dfrac{\sqrt{20}}{\sqrt{5}}$ **50.** $\dfrac{\sqrt{63}}{\sqrt{7}}$ **51.** $\dfrac{\sqrt{288}}{\sqrt{2}}$ **52.** $\dfrac{\sqrt{242}}{\sqrt{2}}$

53. $\dfrac{\sqrt{15}}{\sqrt{3}}$ **54.** $\dfrac{\sqrt{35}}{\sqrt{5}}$ **55.** $\dfrac{\sqrt{21m}}{\sqrt{7}}$ **56.** $\dfrac{\sqrt{33m}}{\sqrt{3}}$

57. $\dfrac{\sqrt{98r}}{\sqrt{2r}}$ **58.** $\dfrac{\sqrt{200r}}{\sqrt{2r}}$ **59.** $\dfrac{\sqrt{75a}}{\sqrt{3}}$ **60.** $\dfrac{\sqrt{48a}}{\sqrt{3}}$

61. $\dfrac{\sqrt{120}}{\sqrt{10}}$ **62.** $\dfrac{\sqrt{180}}{\sqrt{10}}$ **63.** $\dfrac{\sqrt{162k}}{\sqrt{6}}$ **64.** $\dfrac{\sqrt{48k}}{\sqrt{6}}$

65. $\dfrac{12\sqrt{17}}{\sqrt{16}}$ **66.** $\dfrac{14\sqrt{19}}{\sqrt{49}}$ **67.** $\dfrac{6\sqrt{4}}{2\sqrt{2}}$ **68.** $\dfrac{10\sqrt{25}}{5\sqrt{5}}$

69. $\dfrac{8\sqrt{45x^4}}{4\sqrt{5x}}$ **70.** $\dfrac{18\sqrt{108x^6}}{6\sqrt{3x}}$ **71.** $\dfrac{9\sqrt{50y^5z^6}}{18\sqrt{2yz}}$ **72.** $\dfrac{4\sqrt{80y^5z^4}}{12\sqrt{5yz}}$

73. $\dfrac{\sqrt{21x^5y}}{\sqrt{28xy}}$ **74.** $\dfrac{\sqrt{35x^3y}}{\sqrt{45xy^3}}$ **75.** $\dfrac{\sqrt{12x^2}\sqrt{18xy}}{\sqrt{6x^3y^3}}$ **76.** $\dfrac{\sqrt{32x}\sqrt{8x^2y^2}}{\sqrt{4x^5y^2}}$

Perform the indicated operation and simplify.

77. $\sqrt[3]{9}\sqrt[3]{3}$ **78.** $\sqrt[3]{4}\sqrt[3]{2}$ **79.** $\sqrt[3]{4x^2}\sqrt[3]{16x}$ **80.** $\sqrt[3]{3x}\sqrt[3]{9x^2}$

81. $\sqrt[3]{12y^4}\sqrt[3]{2y^2}$ **82.** $\sqrt[3]{32y^5}\sqrt[3]{4y}$ **83.** $\dfrac{\sqrt[3]{250}}{\sqrt[3]{2}}$ **84.** $\dfrac{\sqrt[3]{375}}{\sqrt[3]{3}}$

85. $\dfrac{\sqrt[4]{48}}{\sqrt[4]{3}}$ **86.** $\dfrac{\sqrt[4]{162}}{\sqrt[4]{2}}$ **87.** $\dfrac{\sqrt[4]{2500x^{10}}}{\sqrt[4]{4x^2}}$ **88.** $\dfrac{\sqrt[4]{160x^{18}}}{\sqrt[4]{10x^6}}$

Find a in Problems 89–92.

89.

90.

91.

92.

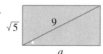

Solve each word problem.

93. Find the perimeter of a square whose side is $5\sqrt{7}$ yards.

94. Find the perimeter of an equilateral triangle whose side is $10\sqrt{6}$ yards.

95. Determine the longest umbrella that will fit in a rectangular carton 8 inches wide, 24 inches long, and 6 inches deep (see Fig. 8.13).

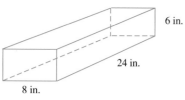

FIGURE 8.13

96. Sections of railroad track are laid with a small space between them to allow for expansion when the metal becomes hot. Suppose two 40-foot sections are laid so that the outer ends are fixed. If each section expands 1 inch and no space is allowed for this expansion, by how much would the junction be raised? See Fig. 8.14.

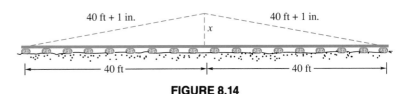

FIGURE 8.14

8.4   Adding and Subtracting Radicals

Recall that we add like terms by adding their coefficients.

$$2x + 5x = (2 + 5)x \quad \text{\textit{Distributive property}}$$
$$= 7x \quad \text{\textit{Add the coefficients}}$$

In much the same way, we add **like radicals,** that is, radical expressions that have the same index and the same radicand.

Like Radicals	*Unlike Radicals*	
$2\sqrt{5}, 7\sqrt{5}$	$2\sqrt{5}, 7\sqrt[3]{5}$	(different indexes)
$-4\sqrt{11x}, \sqrt{11x}$	$-4\sqrt{11x}, \sqrt{11y}$	(different radicands)

EXAMPLE 1   Add like radicals.

a. $2\sqrt{3} + 5\sqrt{3} = (2 + 5)\sqrt{3}$ *Distributive property*
           $= 7\sqrt{3}$ *Add the coefficients*

Try Problem 1 >   b. $\sqrt{2} + \sqrt{3}$ cannot be simplified because $\sqrt{2}$ and $\sqrt{3}$ are unlike radicals. ■

EXAMPLE 2   Subtract like radicals.

a. $8\sqrt{10} - 6\sqrt{10} = (8 - 6)\sqrt{10}$ *Distributive property*
            $= 2\sqrt{10}$ *Subtract the coefficients*

b. $\sqrt{7} - 4\sqrt{7} = 1\sqrt{7} - 4\sqrt{7}$ *Since $\sqrt{7} = 1 \cdot \sqrt{7}$*
          $= (1 - 4)\sqrt{7}$ *Distributive property*

Try Problem 9 > $= -3\sqrt{7}$ *Subtract the coefficients*   ■

Sometimes we must simplify the radicals before we can add or subtract them.

EXAMPLE 3   Add or subtract as indicated.

a. $\sqrt{12} + 9\sqrt{3} = \sqrt{4}\sqrt{3} + 9\sqrt{3}$ *Product rule*

$\qquad\qquad\quad = 2\sqrt{3} + 9\sqrt{3}$ *Simplify*

$\qquad\qquad\quad = 11\sqrt{3}$ *Combine like radicals*

b. $2\sqrt{50} + \sqrt{18} - 3\sqrt{5} = 2\sqrt{25}\sqrt{2} + \sqrt{9}\sqrt{2} - 3\sqrt{5}$ *Product rule*

$\qquad\qquad\qquad\quad = 2 \cdot 5\sqrt{2} + 3\sqrt{2} - 3\sqrt{5}$

$\qquad\qquad\qquad\quad = 10\sqrt{2} + 3\sqrt{2} - 3\sqrt{5}$ $\Big\}$*Simplify*

Try Problem 23 > $\qquad\qquad\qquad\quad = 13\sqrt{2} - 3\sqrt{5}$ *Combine like radicals* ■

EXAMPLE 4   Simplify each expression. Assume all variables represent positive numbers.

a. $\sqrt{20m} + \sqrt{5m} = \sqrt{4}\sqrt{5m} + \sqrt{5m}$ *Product rule*

$\qquad\qquad\qquad = 2\sqrt{5m} + \sqrt{5m}$ *Simplify*

$\qquad\qquad\qquad = 3\sqrt{5m}$ *Combine like radicals*

b. $4\sqrt{27x^2y} - 2\sqrt{3x^2y} = 4\sqrt{9x^2}\sqrt{3y} - 2\sqrt{x^2}\sqrt{3y}$ *Product rule*

$\qquad\qquad\qquad\quad = 4 \cdot 3x\sqrt{3y} - 2 \cdot x\sqrt{3y}$ $\Big\}$*Simplify*

$\qquad\qquad\qquad\quad = 12x\sqrt{3y} - 2x\sqrt{3y}$

Try Problem 51 > $\qquad\qquad\qquad\quad = 10x\sqrt{3y}$ *Combine like radicals* ■

EXAMPLE 5   Simplify $\sqrt{6x} + \sqrt{8y} - \sqrt{150x} + \sqrt{98y}$. Assume $x > 0$ and $y > 0$.

Solution

$\sqrt{6x} + \sqrt{8y} - \sqrt{150x} + \sqrt{98y}$ *Original expression*

$= \sqrt{6x} + \sqrt{4}\sqrt{2y} - \sqrt{25}\sqrt{6x} + \sqrt{49}\sqrt{2y}$ *Product rule*

$= \sqrt{6x} + 2\sqrt{2y} - 5\sqrt{6x} + 7\sqrt{2y}$ *Simplify*

$= -4\sqrt{6x} + 9\sqrt{2y}$ *Combine like*

Try Problem 55 >   *radicals* ■

EXAMPLE 6   Simplify each expression.

a. $10\sqrt[3]{7} + 3\sqrt[3]{7} + 5\sqrt{7} = 13\sqrt[3]{7} + 5\sqrt{7}$

b. $5\sqrt[3]{16x^3} - \sqrt[3]{54x^3} + \sqrt[3]{2x^3}$ *Original expression*

$= 5\sqrt[3]{8x^3}\sqrt[3]{2} - \sqrt[3]{27x^3}\sqrt[3]{2} + \sqrt[3]{x^3}\sqrt[3]{2}$ *Product rule*

$= 5 \cdot 2x\sqrt[3]{2} - 3x\sqrt[3]{2} + x\sqrt[3]{2}$

$= 10x\sqrt[3]{2} - 3x\sqrt[3]{2} + x\sqrt[3]{2}$ $\Big\}$*Simplify*

$= 8x\sqrt[3]{2}$ *Combine like*

Try Problem 61 >   *radicals* ■

EXAMPLE 7   The voltage V required to operate an electrical appliance is given by the formula

$$V = \sqrt{WR},$$

where W is the wattage and R is the resistance, in ohms. Determine the total voltage needed to operate two appliances connected in series, one with a wattage of 100 and a resistance of 12 ohms, and the other with a wattage of 450 and a resistance of 6 ohms.

Solution   The first appliance requires a voltage of

$$V = \sqrt{WR} = \sqrt{100 \cdot 12} = \sqrt{1200} = \sqrt{400}\sqrt{3} = 20\sqrt{3}.$$

The second appliance requires a voltage of

$$V = \sqrt{WR} = \sqrt{450 \cdot 6} = \sqrt{2700} = \sqrt{900}\sqrt{3} = 30\sqrt{3}.$$

The total voltage is the sum of the two voltages.

Try Problem 75 >   Total voltage $= 20\sqrt{3} + 30\sqrt{3} = 50\sqrt{3}$ volts

8.4 Problem Set

LEARNING THROUGH WRITING   ☐ Describe how to add or subtract like radicals.

☐ Define the term *like radicals*.

Add or subtract as indicated.

1. $3\sqrt{5} + 4\sqrt{5}$
2. $5\sqrt{7} + 3\sqrt{7}$
3. $2\sqrt{11} + \sqrt{11}$
4. $4\sqrt{13} + \sqrt{13}$
5. $\sqrt{3} + \sqrt{7}$
6. $\sqrt{2} + \sqrt{5}$
7. $9\sqrt{15} - 4\sqrt{15}$
8. $7\sqrt{14} - 2\sqrt{14}$
9. $\sqrt{2} - 5\sqrt{2}$
10. $\sqrt{3} - 6\sqrt{3}$
11. $4\sqrt{5} - 10\sqrt{5} + \sqrt{5}$
12. $5\sqrt{2} - 8\sqrt{2} + \sqrt{2}$
13. $3\sqrt{2} - 4\sqrt{5} + 2\sqrt{2}$
14. $5\sqrt{3} - 2\sqrt{7} + 2\sqrt{3}$
15. $4.2\sqrt{17} + 3.6\sqrt{17}$
16. $5.1\sqrt{19} + 2.7\sqrt{19}$
17. $-\dfrac{2}{3}\sqrt{15} - \dfrac{3}{4}\sqrt{15}$
18. $-\dfrac{3}{4}\sqrt{26} - \dfrac{5}{6}\sqrt{26}$

Add or subtract as indicated.

19. $\sqrt{20} + \sqrt{5}$
20. $\sqrt{28} + \sqrt{7}$
21. $\sqrt{8} + \sqrt{50}$
22. $\sqrt{12} + \sqrt{27}$
23. $\sqrt{18} + 7\sqrt{2}$
24. $\sqrt{45} + 9\sqrt{5}$
25. $2\sqrt{63} - \sqrt{700}$
26. $2\sqrt{80} - \sqrt{500}$
27. $\dfrac{2}{3}\sqrt{486} + \sqrt{294}$
28. $\dfrac{3}{2}\sqrt{540} + \sqrt{960}$
29. $\sqrt{24} + \sqrt{6} - \sqrt{54}$
30. $\sqrt{40} + \sqrt{10} - \sqrt{90}$

31. $3\sqrt{32} + \sqrt{8} - 5\sqrt{3}$ **32.** $2\sqrt{75} + \sqrt{12} - 7\sqrt{2}$ **33.** $2\sqrt{2}\sqrt{5} - 3\sqrt{10} + \sqrt{40}$
34. $3\sqrt{3}\sqrt{7} - 4\sqrt{21} + \sqrt{84}$ **35.** $\sqrt{3}\sqrt{15} + \sqrt{50} - 4\sqrt{2}\sqrt{10}$ **36.** $\sqrt{2}\sqrt{6} + \sqrt{18} - \sqrt{5}\sqrt{15}$

Simplify each expression. Assume all variables represent positive numbers.

37. $\sqrt{3a} + \sqrt{3a}$

38. $\sqrt{5a} + \sqrt{5a}$

39. $2\sqrt{6r} - 5\sqrt{6r} + 7\sqrt{6r}$

40. $3\sqrt{7r} - 6\sqrt{7r} + 8\sqrt{7r}$

41. $6\sqrt{x} + x - \sqrt{x} + 2x$

42. $9x - \sqrt{x} + x + 4\sqrt{x}$

43. $3z\sqrt{z} + 5z\sqrt{z}$

44. $2z\sqrt{z} + 8z\sqrt{z}$

45. $\sqrt{12m} + \sqrt{3m}$

46. $\sqrt{45m} + \sqrt{5m}$

47. $5\sqrt{32y} - 4\sqrt{18y}$

48. $4\sqrt{50y} - 3\sqrt{8y}$

49. $p\sqrt{28} + \sqrt{7p^2}$

50. $p\sqrt{40} + \sqrt{10p^2}$

51. $3\sqrt{8x^2y} - 2\sqrt{2x^2y}$

52. $2\sqrt{125x^2y} - 3\sqrt{5x^2y}$

53. $\sqrt{98k^3} - \sqrt{288k^3}$

54. $\sqrt{128k^3} - \sqrt{242k^3}$

55. $\sqrt{22x} + \sqrt{12y} - \sqrt{198x} + \sqrt{108y}$

56. $\sqrt{10x} + \sqrt{18y} - \sqrt{160x} + \sqrt{162y}$

57. $4a\sqrt{5b} + \sqrt{5a^2b} - \sqrt{20a^2b}$

58. $5a\sqrt{3b} + \sqrt{3a^2b} - \sqrt{12a^2b}$

59. $2\sqrt{ab^3} + 3a\sqrt{ab} - 5b\sqrt{4ab}$

60. $3\sqrt{a^3b} + 7b\sqrt{ab} - 4a\sqrt{9ab}$

Simplify each expression. Assume $y > 0$.

61. $11\sqrt[3]{2} + 2\sqrt[3]{2} + 3\sqrt{2}$ **62.** $13\sqrt[3]{5} + 4\sqrt[3]{5} + 2\sqrt{5}$ **63.** $\sqrt[4]{7} - \sqrt[3]{7} + 6\sqrt[4]{7}$
64. $\sqrt[4]{3} - \sqrt[3]{3} + 2\sqrt[4]{3}$ **65.** $\sqrt[3]{81} + 4\sqrt[3]{3}$ **66.** $\sqrt[3]{16} + 5\sqrt[3]{2}$
67. $7\sqrt[3]{40x^3} - \sqrt[3]{135x^3} + \sqrt[3]{5x^3}$ **68.** $5\sqrt[3]{192x^3} - \sqrt[3]{24x^3} + \sqrt[3]{3x^3}$ **69.** $\sqrt[4]{32y^3} + \sqrt[4]{162y^3}$
70. $\sqrt[4]{48y^3} + \sqrt[4]{243y^3}$ **71.** $5\sqrt[3]{4a^4b^8} - a\sqrt[3]{4ab^8}$ **72.** $10\sqrt[3]{9a^5b^7} - a\sqrt[3]{9a^2b^7}$

Solve each word problem.

73. Find the perimeter of a rectangle with width $\sqrt{128}$ and length $\sqrt{242}$.

74. Find the perimeter of a triangle whose sides are $\sqrt{75}$, $\sqrt{147}$, and $\sqrt{363}$.

75. Determine the total voltage needed to operate two electrical appliances connected in series, one with a wattage of 300 and a resistance of 18 ohms, and the other with a wattage of 196 and a resistance of 6 ohms. Use $V = \sqrt{WR}$.

76. Determine the total voltage needed to operate two electrical appliances connected in series, one with a wattage of 256 and a resistance of 20 ohms, and the other with a wattage of 300 and a resistance of 15 ohms. Use $V = \sqrt{WR}$.

8.5 Combinations of Operations

We now know how to add, subtract, multiply, and divide radicals. In this section we discuss how to perform combinations of these operations. Recall how we used the product rule to multiply radical expressions that contained one term.

$$\sqrt{3}\sqrt{7} = \sqrt{3 \cdot 7} = \sqrt{21}$$
$$(\sqrt{2})^2 = \sqrt{2}\sqrt{2} = 2$$
$$(4\sqrt{5})(3\sqrt{6}) = (4 \cdot 3)(\sqrt{5}\sqrt{6}) = 12\sqrt{30}$$

To multiply a radical expression containing two terms by a radical expression containing one term, use the distributive property.

EXAMPLE 1   Multiply and simplify.

a. $\sqrt{5}(\sqrt{2} + \sqrt{5}) = \sqrt{5}\sqrt{2} + \sqrt{5}\sqrt{5}$ *Distributive property*
$\qquad\qquad\qquad = \sqrt{10} + 5$ *Product rule*

b. $3\sqrt{2}(\sqrt{5} + 4\sqrt{7}) = 3\sqrt{2}\cdot\sqrt{5} + 3\sqrt{2}\cdot 4\sqrt{7}$ *Distributive property*
$\qquad\qquad\qquad\quad = 3\sqrt{10} + 12\sqrt{14}$ *Product rule*   ∎

Try Problem 3 >

To multiply two radical expressions that both contain two terms, use the FOIL method.

EXAMPLE 2   Multiply and simplify.

$$
\begin{array}{cccc}
\text{F} & \text{O} & \text{I} & \text{L} \\
\downarrow & \downarrow & \downarrow & \downarrow
\end{array}
$$

a. $(\sqrt{3} + 4)(\sqrt{3} + 2) = \sqrt{3}\sqrt{3} + 2\sqrt{3} + 4\sqrt{3} + 4\cdot 2$
$\qquad\qquad\qquad\quad = 3 + 2\sqrt{3} + 4\sqrt{3} + 8$
$\qquad\qquad\qquad\quad = 11 + 6\sqrt{3}$

$$
\begin{array}{cccc}
\text{F} & \text{O} & \text{I} & \text{L} \\
\downarrow & \downarrow & \downarrow & \downarrow
\end{array}
$$

b. $(\sqrt{6} + 4\sqrt{3})(\sqrt{2} - \sqrt{3}) = \sqrt{6}\sqrt{2} - \sqrt{6}\sqrt{3} + 4\sqrt{3}\sqrt{2} - 4\sqrt{3}\sqrt{3}$
$\qquad\qquad\qquad\qquad\qquad = \sqrt{12} - \sqrt{18} + 4\sqrt{6} - 4\cdot 3$
$\qquad\qquad\qquad\qquad\qquad = \sqrt{4}\sqrt{3} - \sqrt{9}\sqrt{2} + 4\sqrt{6} - 12$
$\qquad\qquad\qquad\qquad\qquad = 2\sqrt{3} - 3\sqrt{2} + 4\sqrt{6} - 12$

Try Problem 19 >

This answer cannot be simplified further.   ∎

Recall the rules for squaring a binomial and multiplying the sum and difference of two terms.

Squaring a binomial $\begin{cases} (a + b)^2 = a^2 + 2ab + b^2 \\ (a - b)^2 = a^2 - 2ab + b^2 \end{cases}$

Sum and difference of two terms $\quad (a + b)(a - b) = a^2 - b^2$

EXAMPLE 3   Multiply and simplify.

a. $(\sqrt{10} - 1)^2$ $\qquad\qquad\qquad$ b. $(\sqrt{7} + \sqrt{3})(\sqrt{7} - \sqrt{3})$

Solution

a. Use the rule for squaring a binomial.

$(\sqrt{10} - 1)^2 = (\sqrt{10})^2 - 2\sqrt{10}\cdot 1 + 1^2$
$\qquad\qquad\quad = 10 - 2\sqrt{10} + 1$
$\qquad\qquad\quad = 11 - 2\sqrt{10}$

b. Use the rule for multiplying a sum and difference of two terms.

Try Problem 33 > $(\sqrt{7} + \sqrt{3})(\sqrt{7} - \sqrt{3}) = (\sqrt{7})^2 - (\sqrt{3})^2 = 7 - 3 = 4$ ■

EXAMPLE 4   Multiply and simplify. Assume $x > 0$ and $y > 0$.

a. $(\sqrt{3x} + 5)^2 = (\sqrt{3x})^2 + 2\sqrt{3x} \cdot 5 + 5^2$ *Square of a binomial*

$\qquad\qquad = 3x + 10\sqrt{3x} + 25$ *Simplify*

b. $(2\sqrt{x} + \sqrt{y})(2\sqrt{x} - \sqrt{y}) = (2\sqrt{x})^2 - (\sqrt{y})^2$ *Sum and difference of*

two terms

Try Problem 35 > $\qquad\qquad\qquad\qquad\qquad = 4x - y$ *Simplify*   ■

EXAMPLE 5   Simplify each expression.

a. $\dfrac{2 + 8\sqrt{5}}{2} = \dfrac{2(1 + 4\sqrt{5})}{2}$ *Factor the numerator*

$\qquad = 1 + 4\sqrt{5}$ *Divide out the common factor, 2*

b. $\dfrac{3 - \sqrt{63}}{12} = \dfrac{3 - \sqrt{9}\sqrt{7}}{12}$ *Product rule*

$\qquad = \dfrac{3 - 3\sqrt{7}}{12}$ *Simplify*

$\qquad = \dfrac{3(1 - \sqrt{7})}{12}$ *Factor the numerator*

Try Problem 59 > $\qquad = \dfrac{1 - \sqrt{7}}{4}$ *Divide out the common factor, 3*   ■

8.5 | Problem Set

LEARNING THROUGH WRITING

☐ How do you square a binomial?

☐ Describe the FOIL method for multiplying two binomials.

☐ How do you multiply a sum and difference of two terms?

Multiply and simplify. Assume all variables represent positive numbers.

1. $2(4\sqrt{5} - 1)$

2. $3(2\sqrt{7} - 1)$

3. $\sqrt{3}(\sqrt{2} + \sqrt{3})$

4. $\sqrt{2}(\sqrt{3} + \sqrt{2})$

5. $4\sqrt{5}(\sqrt{3} + 2\sqrt{7})$

6. $5\sqrt{7}(\sqrt{2} + 3\sqrt{5})$

7. $5\sqrt{2}(\sqrt{8} - 2\sqrt{6})$

8. $4\sqrt{3}(\sqrt{12} - 2\sqrt{6})$

9. $\sqrt{x}(\sqrt{x} + \sqrt{y})$

10. $\sqrt{y}(\sqrt{x} - \sqrt{y})$

11. $\sqrt{3p}(\sqrt{27p} - \sqrt{15p})$

12. $\sqrt{2p}(\sqrt{8p} + \sqrt{10p})$

13. $6\sqrt{2m}(\sqrt{14} + 7\sqrt{m})$

14. $8\sqrt{3m}(\sqrt{15} - 9\sqrt{m})$

15. $\sqrt{x + 1}(\sqrt{x + 1} - \sqrt{x})$

16. $\sqrt{x + 1}(\sqrt{x + 1} + \sqrt{x})$

17. $9(2\sqrt{x} + \sqrt{y} - 4)$

18. $7(3\sqrt{x} - \sqrt{y} + 5)$

Multiply and simplify. Assume all variables represent positive numbers.

19. $(\sqrt{2} + 1)(\sqrt{2} + 3)$
20. $(\sqrt{5} + 2)(\sqrt{5} + 1)$
21. $(\sqrt{3} + 2)(\sqrt{5} - 4)$

22. $(\sqrt{2} + 3)(\sqrt{7} - 5)$
23. $(\sqrt{5} + \sqrt{2})(\sqrt{3} + \sqrt{2})$
24. $(\sqrt{7} + \sqrt{2})(\sqrt{3} + \sqrt{2})$

25. $(\sqrt{6} + 5\sqrt{2})(\sqrt{3} - \sqrt{2})$
26. $(\sqrt{15} + 4\sqrt{3})(\sqrt{5} - \sqrt{3})$
27. $(\sqrt{14} - 1)^2$

28. $(\sqrt{15} - 1)^2$
29. $(2\sqrt{10} + 3)^2$
30. $(3\sqrt{6} + 2)^2$

31. $(\sqrt{7} - 3)(\sqrt{7} + 3)$
32. $(\sqrt{5} - 3)(\sqrt{5} + 3)$
33. $(\sqrt{11} + \sqrt{5})(\sqrt{11} - \sqrt{5})$

34. $(\sqrt{10} + \sqrt{3})(\sqrt{10} - \sqrt{3})$
35. $(\sqrt{2x} + 4)^2$
36. $(\sqrt{5x} - 6)^2$

37. $(2\sqrt{x} + 5)(3\sqrt{x} - 8)$
38. $(3\sqrt{x} + 8)(2\sqrt{x} - 3)$
39. $(4\sqrt{m} - \sqrt{n})^2$

40. $(5\sqrt{m} + \sqrt{n})^2$
41. $(z - 2\sqrt{7})(z + 2\sqrt{7})$
42. $(z - 3\sqrt{10})(z + 3\sqrt{10})$

43. $(\sqrt{3x} + \sqrt{8y})(\sqrt{2x} - \sqrt{2y})$
44. $(\sqrt{2x} + \sqrt{27y})(\sqrt{3x} - \sqrt{3y})$
45. $(4\sqrt{r} + 3\sqrt{6})^2$

46. $(6\sqrt{r} - 2\sqrt{10})^2$
47. $(\sqrt{20k} + \sqrt{10})(\sqrt{2k} + \sqrt{3})$
48. $(\sqrt{15k} + \sqrt{24})(\sqrt{3k} + \sqrt{5})$

49. $(4\sqrt{t} - \sqrt{8})(3\sqrt{t} + \sqrt{2})$
50. $(2\sqrt{t} - \sqrt{27})(5\sqrt{t} + \sqrt{3})$
51. $(\sqrt{x} - \sqrt{x + 3})^2$

52. $(\sqrt{x} - \sqrt{x + 1})^2$
53. $(\sqrt{y + 8} + 6)^2$
54. $(\sqrt{y + 5} + 7)^2$

Simplify each expression.

55. $\dfrac{5 - 5\sqrt{7}}{5}$
56. $\dfrac{3 - 3\sqrt{5}}{3}$
57. $\dfrac{2 + 6\sqrt{5}}{2}$
58. $\dfrac{5 + 10\sqrt{7}}{5}$

59. $\dfrac{3 - \sqrt{45}}{18}$
60. $\dfrac{2 - \sqrt{40}}{16}$
61. $\dfrac{10 + 2\sqrt{12}}{6}$
62. $\dfrac{12 + 3\sqrt{28}}{9}$

63. $\dfrac{8 \pm \sqrt{176}}{12}$
64. $\dfrac{15 \pm \sqrt{175}}{20}$
65. $\dfrac{-14 \pm \sqrt{245}}{28}$
66. $\dfrac{-18 \pm \sqrt{252}}{24}$

Multiply and simplify.

67. $\sqrt[3]{2}(\sqrt[3]{4} - 5)$
68. $\sqrt[3]{3}(\sqrt[3]{9} - 6)$
69. $3\sqrt[4]{9}(\sqrt[4]{9} + \sqrt[4]{3})$

70. $2\sqrt[4]{4}(\sqrt[4]{4} + \sqrt[4]{2})$
71. $(\sqrt[3]{5} + 7)(\sqrt[3]{25} - 2)$
72. $(\sqrt[3]{10} - 3)(\sqrt[3]{100} + 5)$

73. $(3\sqrt[3]{9} + 1)^2$
74. $(2\sqrt[4]{4} + 1)^2$
75. $(\sqrt[3]{12} - \sqrt[3]{2})(\sqrt[3]{12} + \sqrt[3]{2})$

76. $(\sqrt[3]{18} + \sqrt[3]{3})(\sqrt[3]{18} - \sqrt[3]{3})$

Find the perimeter and the area of each rectangle.

77.
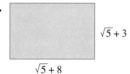
$\sqrt{5} + 3$
$\sqrt{5} + 8$

78.
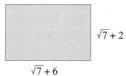
$\sqrt{7} + 2$
$\sqrt{7} + 6$

Find the unknown side of each triangle.

79.
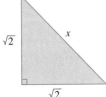
$\sqrt{2}$ x $\sqrt{2}$

80.
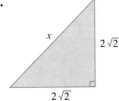
x $2\sqrt{2}$ $2\sqrt{2}$

81.
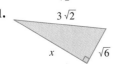
$3\sqrt{2}$ x $\sqrt{6}$

82.
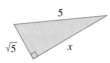
5 $\sqrt{5}$ x

8.6 Rationalizing the Denominator

There are three conditions that must be met before a radical expression is in simplest form. We state these conditions here for square roots, but they apply to other roots as well.

A RADICAL EXPRESSION IS IN SIMPLEST FORM WHEN ALL THREE OF THE FOLLOWING CONDITIONS ARE MET

1. The radicand contains no perfect-square factors.

   Example: $\sqrt{12}$ is not in simplest form, because 12 contains the perfect-square factor 4.

2. The radicand contains no fractions.

   Example: $\sqrt{\dfrac{7}{3}}$ is not in simplest form.

3. No denominator contains a radical.

   Example: $\dfrac{1}{\sqrt{5}}$ is not in simplest form.

EXAMPLE 1   Simplify $\dfrac{1}{\sqrt{2}}$.

Solution   Remove the radical from the denominator by multiplying the fraction by 1 in the form $\sqrt{2}/\sqrt{2}$.

$$\frac{1}{\sqrt{2}} = \frac{1}{\sqrt{2}} \cdot \frac{\sqrt{2}}{\sqrt{2}} \qquad \textit{Multiply numerator and denominator by } \sqrt{2}$$

Try Problem 1 >
$$= \frac{\sqrt{2}}{2} \qquad \textit{Since } 1 \cdot \sqrt{2} = \sqrt{2} \textit{ and } \sqrt{2} \cdot \sqrt{2} = 2 \qquad \blacksquare$$

Note that the denominator in Example 1 was changed from the irrational number $\sqrt{2}$ to the rational number 2. For this reason the process of removing radicals from the denominator of a fraction is called **rationalizing the denominator.**

EXAMPLE 2   Simplify $\dfrac{9}{\sqrt{6}}$.

Solution

$$\frac{9}{\sqrt{6}} = \frac{9}{\sqrt{6}} \cdot \frac{\sqrt{6}}{\sqrt{6}} \qquad \textit{Rationalize the denominator}$$

$$= \frac{9\sqrt{6}}{6} \qquad \textit{Product rule}$$

Try Problem 3 > $= \dfrac{3\sqrt{6}}{2} \qquad \textit{Simplify}$

■

EXAMPLE 3   Simplify $\sqrt{\dfrac{28}{5}}$.

Solution

$$\sqrt{\frac{28}{5}} = \frac{\sqrt{28}}{\sqrt{5}} \qquad \textit{Quotient rule}$$

$$= \frac{\sqrt{4}\sqrt{7}}{\sqrt{5}} \qquad \textit{Product rule}$$

$$= \frac{2\sqrt{7}}{\sqrt{5}} \qquad \textit{Simplify}$$

$$= \frac{2\sqrt{7}}{\sqrt{5}} \cdot \frac{\sqrt{5}}{\sqrt{5}} \qquad \textit{Rationalize the denominator}$$

Try Problem 13 > $= \dfrac{2\sqrt{35}}{5} \qquad \textit{Product rule}$

■

EXAMPLE 4   Simplify $\dfrac{\sqrt{6x^7}}{\sqrt{30xy}}$. Assume $x > 0$ and $y > 0$.

Solution

$$\frac{\sqrt{6x^7}}{\sqrt{30xy}} = \sqrt{\frac{6x^7}{30xy}} \qquad \textit{Quotient rule}$$

$$= \sqrt{\frac{x^6}{5y}} \qquad \textit{Simplify}$$

$$= \frac{\sqrt{x^6}}{\sqrt{5y}} \qquad \textit{Quotient rule}$$

$$= \frac{x^3}{\sqrt{5y}} \qquad \textit{Since } \sqrt{x^6} = x^3$$

$$= \frac{x^3}{\sqrt{5y}} \cdot \frac{\sqrt{5y}}{\sqrt{5y}} \qquad \textit{Rationalize the denominator}$$

Try Problem 31 > $= \dfrac{x^3\sqrt{5y}}{5y} \qquad \textit{Product rule}$

■

EXAMPLE 5   Simplify $\sqrt{\dfrac{7}{8}}\,\sqrt{\dfrac{1}{10}}$.

Solution

$$\sqrt{\frac{7}{8}}\,\sqrt{\frac{1}{10}} = \sqrt{\frac{7}{8}\cdot\frac{1}{10}} = \sqrt{\frac{7}{80}}$$ *Use the product rule to multiply the two radicals*

$$= \frac{\sqrt{7}}{\sqrt{80}} = \frac{\sqrt{7}}{\sqrt{16}\sqrt{5}} = \frac{\sqrt{7}}{4\sqrt{5}}$$ *Quotient rule and product rule*

Try Problem 35 >

$$= \frac{\sqrt{7}}{4\sqrt{5}}\cdot\frac{\sqrt{5}}{\sqrt{5}} = \frac{\sqrt{35}}{4\cdot 5} = \frac{\sqrt{35}}{20}$$ *Rationalize the denominator*   ■

The next example illustrates how to rationalize a denominator that is a cube root.

EXAMPLE 6   Simplify $\dfrac{10}{\sqrt[3]{2}}$.

Solution   Multiply numerator and denominator by $\sqrt[3]{4}$ to make the radicand in the denominator a perfect cube.

$$\frac{10}{\sqrt[3]{2}} = \frac{10}{\sqrt[3]{2}}\cdot\frac{\sqrt[3]{4}}{\sqrt[3]{4}}$$ *Rationalize the denominator*

$$= \frac{10\sqrt[3]{4}}{\sqrt[3]{8}}$$ *Product rule*

$$= \frac{10\sqrt[3]{4}}{2}$$ *Since $\sqrt[3]{8} = 2$*

Try Problem 39 >

$$= 5\sqrt[3]{4}$$ *Simplify*   ■

Caution! ■
■
■
■
■
■
■

You cannot rationalize the denominator of $10/\sqrt[3]{2}$ by multiplying numerator and denominator by $\sqrt[3]{2}$. You must obtain a perfect *cube* in the radicand.

Correct   Wrong

$$\frac{10}{\sqrt[3]{2}} = \frac{10}{\sqrt[3]{2}}\cdot\frac{\sqrt[3]{4}}{\sqrt[3]{4}} \qquad \frac{10}{\sqrt[3]{2}} = \frac{10}{\sqrt[3]{2}}\cdot\frac{\sqrt[3]{2}}{\sqrt[3]{2}}$$

EXAMPLE 7   Simplify $\sqrt[3]{\dfrac{5}{9}}$.

Solution

$$\sqrt[3]{\frac{5}{9}} = \frac{\sqrt[3]{5}}{\sqrt[3]{9}} \qquad \text{\textit{Quotient rule}}$$

$$= \frac{\sqrt[3]{5}}{\sqrt[3]{9}} \cdot \frac{\sqrt[3]{3}}{\sqrt[3]{3}} \qquad \text{\textit{Rationalize the denominator}}$$

$$= \frac{\sqrt[3]{15}}{\sqrt[3]{27}} \qquad \text{\textit{Product rule}}$$

Try Problem 41 > $\qquad = \frac{\sqrt[3]{15}}{3} \qquad \text{\textit{Since }} \sqrt[3]{27} = 3$ ∎

The expressions $\sqrt{7} + 2$ and $\sqrt{7} - 2$ are called **conjugates** of each other. These two conjugates form a sum and difference of two terms, and their product does not contain a radical.

$$(\sqrt{7} + 2)(\sqrt{7} - 2) = (\sqrt{7})^2 - 2^2 = 7 - 4 = 3$$

Thus, **to rationalize a denominator involving square roots and two terms, multiply numerator and denominator by the conjugate of the denominator.**

EXAMPLE 8   Simplify $\dfrac{1}{\sqrt{7} - 2}$.

Solution   Since the denominator contains two terms, multiply numerator and denominator by the conjugate of the denominator.

$$\frac{1}{\sqrt{7} - 2} = \frac{1}{\sqrt{7} - 2} \cdot \frac{\sqrt{7} + 2}{\sqrt{7} + 2} \qquad \text{\textit{The conjugate of }} \sqrt{7} - 2 \text{ \textit{is} } \sqrt{7} + 2$$

$$= \frac{1(\sqrt{7} + 2)}{(\sqrt{7})^2 - 2^2} \qquad \text{\textit{Multiply numerators, multiply denominators}}$$

$$= \frac{\sqrt{7} + 2}{7 - 4}$$

Try Problem 49 > $\qquad = \dfrac{\sqrt{7} + 2}{3}$ $\left.\begin{array}{c} \\ \\ \end{array}\right\}$ *Simplify*   ∎

EXAMPLE 9   Simplify $\dfrac{2}{3 + \sqrt{5}}$.

Solution

$$\frac{2}{3 + \sqrt{5}} = \frac{2}{3 + \sqrt{5}} \cdot \frac{3 - \sqrt{5}}{3 - \sqrt{5}} \qquad \textit{The conjugate of } 3 + \sqrt{5} \textit{ is } 3 - \sqrt{5}$$

$$= \frac{2(3 - \sqrt{5})}{3^2 - (\sqrt{5})^2} \qquad \textit{Multiply numerators, multiply denominators}$$

$$= \frac{2(3 - \sqrt{5})}{9 - 5}$$

$$= \frac{2(3 - \sqrt{5})}{4} \qquad \left.\begin{array}{l} \\ \\ \end{array}\right\} \textit{Simplify the denominator, leave the numerator in factored form}$$

Try Problem 53 >
$$= \frac{3 - \sqrt{5}}{2} \qquad \textit{Divide out the common factor, 2} \qquad ■$$

Recall the rules for squaring a binomial.

$$(a + b)^2 = a^2 + 2ab + b^2 \qquad \text{and} \qquad (a - b)^2 = a^2 - 2ab + b^2$$

We use the second rule in the next example.

EXAMPLE 10   Simplify $\dfrac{\sqrt{2} - \sqrt{3}}{\sqrt{2} + \sqrt{3}}$.

Solution

$$\frac{\sqrt{2} - \sqrt{3}}{\sqrt{2} + \sqrt{3}} = \frac{\sqrt{2} - \sqrt{3}}{\sqrt{2} + \sqrt{3}} \cdot \frac{\sqrt{2} - \sqrt{3}}{\sqrt{2} - \sqrt{3}} \qquad \textit{The conjugate of } \sqrt{2} + \sqrt{3} \textit{ is } \sqrt{2} - \sqrt{3}$$

$$= \frac{(\sqrt{2})^2 - 2\sqrt{2}\sqrt{3} + (\sqrt{3})^2}{(\sqrt{2})^2 - (\sqrt{3})^2} \qquad \textit{Multiply numerators, multiply denominators}$$

$$= \frac{2 - 2\sqrt{6} + 3}{2 - 3} \qquad \textit{Product rule}$$

$$= \frac{5 - 2\sqrt{6}}{-1} \qquad \textit{Combine like terms}$$

Try Problem 59 >
$$= -5 + 2\sqrt{6} \qquad \textit{Divide each term by } -1 \qquad ■$$

8.6 Problem Set

LEARNING THROUGH WRITING

☐ When is a radical expression in simplest form?

☐ What is meant by the phrase *rationalizing the denominator?*

☐ What are *conjugates?*

☐ How do you rationalize a denominator that involves square roots and two terms?

Simplify each radical expression. Rationalize all denominators. Assume all variables represent positive numbers.

1. $\dfrac{1}{\sqrt{3}}$

2. $\dfrac{1}{\sqrt{5}}$

3. $\dfrac{15}{\sqrt{6}}$

4. $\dfrac{15}{\sqrt{10}}$

5. $\dfrac{2}{\sqrt{2}}$

6. $\dfrac{3}{\sqrt{3}}$

7. $\sqrt{\dfrac{5}{3}}$

8. $\sqrt{\dfrac{7}{2}}$

9. $\dfrac{\sqrt{10}}{\sqrt{2}}$

10. $\dfrac{\sqrt{6}}{\sqrt{3}}$

11. $\dfrac{\sqrt{27}}{\sqrt{3}}$

12. $\dfrac{\sqrt{8}}{\sqrt{2}}$

13. $\sqrt{\dfrac{20}{7}}$

14. $\sqrt{\dfrac{12}{5}}$

15. $\dfrac{15}{2\sqrt{10}}$

16. $\dfrac{14}{3\sqrt{6}}$

17. $\sqrt{\dfrac{1}{8}}$

18. $\sqrt{\dfrac{1}{27}}$

19. $\dfrac{12\sqrt{3}}{8\sqrt{11}}$

20. $\dfrac{20\sqrt{2}}{12\sqrt{13}}$

21. $\dfrac{10}{\sqrt{75}}$

22. $\dfrac{16}{\sqrt{48}}$

23. $\dfrac{\sqrt{4x}}{\sqrt{y}}$

24. $\dfrac{\sqrt{9x}}{\sqrt{y}}$

25. $\dfrac{4}{\sqrt{6x}}$

26. $\dfrac{25}{\sqrt{10x}}$

27. $\sqrt{\dfrac{a^3}{9b}}$

28. $\sqrt{\dfrac{a^3}{4b}}$

29. $\dfrac{14\sqrt{5x}}{\sqrt{32y^2}}$

30. $\dfrac{15\sqrt{7x}}{\sqrt{72y^2}}$

31. $\dfrac{\sqrt{11x^7}}{\sqrt{77xy}}$

32. $\dfrac{\sqrt{5x^9}}{\sqrt{25xy}}$

33. $\sqrt{\dfrac{2}{5}} \cdot \sqrt{\dfrac{2}{9}}$

34. $\sqrt{\dfrac{3}{5}} \cdot \sqrt{\dfrac{3}{4}}$

35. $\sqrt{\dfrac{7}{12}} \cdot \sqrt{\dfrac{1}{6}}$

36. $\sqrt{\dfrac{5}{8}} \cdot \sqrt{\dfrac{1}{6}}$

Simplify each radical expression. Rationalize all denominators.

37. $\dfrac{1}{\sqrt[3]{3}}$

38. $\dfrac{1}{\sqrt[3]{5}}$

39. $\dfrac{6}{\sqrt[3]{2}}$

40. $\dfrac{8}{\sqrt[3]{2}}$

41. $\sqrt[3]{\dfrac{3}{4}}$

42. $\sqrt[3]{\dfrac{7}{9}}$

43. $\sqrt[3]{\dfrac{8}{25}}$

44. $\sqrt[3]{\dfrac{27}{16}}$

45. $\sqrt[3]{\dfrac{1}{72}}$

46. $\sqrt[3]{\dfrac{1}{108}}$

47. $\sqrt[3]{\dfrac{5}{6x^2}}$

48. $\sqrt[3]{\dfrac{3}{7x^2}}$

Simplify each radical expression. Rationalize all denominators. Assume $x > 0$ and $y > 0$.

49. $\dfrac{1}{\sqrt{7} - 1}$

50. $\dfrac{1}{\sqrt{10} - 2}$

51. $\dfrac{2}{-3 - \sqrt{7}}$

52. $\dfrac{4}{-3 - \sqrt{5}}$

53. $\dfrac{3}{3 + \sqrt{3}}$

54. $\dfrac{2}{3 - \sqrt{3}}$

55. $\dfrac{\sqrt{5}}{\sqrt{5} - \sqrt{2}}$

56. $\dfrac{\sqrt{7}}{\sqrt{7} - \sqrt{3}}$

57. $\dfrac{4\sqrt{3}}{\sqrt{7} + \sqrt{5}}$

58. $\dfrac{4\sqrt{2}}{\sqrt{5} + \sqrt{3}}$

59. $\dfrac{\sqrt{5} - \sqrt{6}}{\sqrt{5} + \sqrt{6}}$

60. $\dfrac{\sqrt{6} - \sqrt{7}}{\sqrt{6} + \sqrt{7}}$

61. $\dfrac{\sqrt{2} + 1}{-\sqrt{5} + \sqrt{3}}$

62. $\dfrac{\sqrt{3} + 1}{-\sqrt{5} + \sqrt{2}}$

63. $\dfrac{4 + \sqrt{6}}{\sqrt{3} - \sqrt{2}}$

64. $\dfrac{2 + \sqrt{30}}{\sqrt{6} - \sqrt{5}}$

65. $\dfrac{5\sqrt{14} - 3\sqrt{10}}{2\sqrt{2}}$

66. $\dfrac{4\sqrt{15} - 2\sqrt{21}}{3\sqrt{3}}$

67. $\dfrac{\sqrt{2}}{3\sqrt{3} - 2\sqrt{2}}$

68. $\dfrac{\sqrt{3}}{3\sqrt{3} + 2\sqrt{2}}$

69. $\dfrac{\sqrt{x} + \sqrt{y}}{\sqrt{x} - \sqrt{y}}$

70. $\dfrac{\sqrt{x} - \sqrt{y}}{\sqrt{x} + \sqrt{y}}$

71. $\dfrac{\sqrt{2x}}{\sqrt{2x} + 3}$

72. $\dfrac{\sqrt{3x}}{\sqrt{3x} - 4}$

The current, A, in amperes of an electrical appliance is given by the formula

$$A = \sqrt{\dfrac{W}{R}},$$

where W is the wattage of the appliance and R is the resistance of the appliance, in ohms.

73. Determine the current in a hair dryer that uses 1100 watts of power and has a resistance of 24 ohms.

74. Determine the current in a contact lens disinfecting unit that uses 27 watts of power and has a resistance of 540 ohms.

8.7 Radical Equations

In previous chapters we learned how to solve linear equations, quadratic equations, and equations with rational expressions. In this section we learn to how to solve equations like

$$\sqrt{x + 2} = 3, \qquad \sqrt{3m - 2} = m - 2, \qquad \text{and} \qquad \sqrt{x + 9} - \sqrt{x} = 1.$$

Such equations are called **radical equations,** because they contain a variable in a radicand.

To solve a radical equation, we use the *squaring property of equality.*

SQUARING PROPERTY OF EQUALITY

If $a = b$, then $a^2 = b^2$.

You will never lose solutions when you square both sides of an equation, but you may gain solutions. For example, the equation $x = 3$ has only the single solution 3. But if you square both sides, you get the equation $x^2 = 9$, which has two solutions, namely, 3 and -3.

Caution! ▪ Whenever you square both sides of an equation, you must check all solutions in the original equation. A solution obtained in the solving process that does not check in the original equation is called an **extraneous solution** and must be discarded.

EXAMPLE 1 Solve $\sqrt{x + 2} = 3$.

Solution Square both sides to remove the radical.

$$\begin{aligned}
\sqrt{x + 2} &= 3 && \textit{Original equation} \\
(\sqrt{x + 2})^2 &= 3^2 && \textit{Squaring property of equality} \\
x + 2 &= 9 && \textit{Simplify} \\
x &= 7 && \textit{Subtract 2}
\end{aligned}$$

Since we squared both sides, we must check our solution in the original equation.

$$\begin{aligned}
\sqrt{x + 2} &= 3 && \textit{Original equation} \\
\sqrt{7 + 2} &= 3 && \textit{Replace x with 7} \\
\sqrt{9} &= 3 && \textit{Simplify the radicand} \\
3 &= 3 && \textit{True}
\end{aligned}$$

Try Problem 3 >   The number 7 checks, so the solution is 7.   ∎

Solve $\sqrt{2p - 1} + 6 = 3$.

First isolate the radical on one side of the equation.

$$\begin{aligned}
\sqrt{2p - 1} + 6 &= 3 && \textit{Original equation} \\
\sqrt{2p - 1} &= -3 && \textit{Subtract 6} \\
(\sqrt{2p - 1})^2 &= (-3)^2 && \textit{Square both sides} \\
2p - 1 &= 9 && \textit{Simplify} \\
2p &= 10 && \textit{Add 1} \\
p &= 5 && \textit{Divide by 2}
\end{aligned}$$

Check in the original equation.

$$\begin{aligned}
\sqrt{2p - 1} + 6 &= 3 && \textit{Original equation} \\
\sqrt{2(5) - 1} + 6 &= 3 && \textit{Replace p with 5} \\
\sqrt{9} + 6 &= 3 \\
3 + 6 &= 3 && \Big\}\textit{Simplify} \\
9 &= 3 && \textit{False}
\end{aligned}$$

Try Problem 9 >   Since 5 does not check, it is an extraneous solution and must be discarded. Therefore there is no solution to the original equation.   ∎

Caution! ∎   Make sure you square each *side* of a radical equation. Do not square each *term*.

Wrong

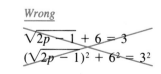

EXAMPLE 3 Solve $2\sqrt{y} = \sqrt{y + 6}$.

Solution
$$(2\sqrt{y})^2 = (\sqrt{y + 6})^2 \quad \textit{Square both sides}$$
$$4y = y + 6 \qquad \textit{Simplify}$$
$$3y = 6 \qquad \textit{Subtract } y$$
$$y = 2 \qquad \textit{Divide by } 3$$

Try Problem 19 > The number 2 checks, so the solution is 2. ■

EXAMPLE 4 Solve $\sqrt{3m - 2} = m - 2$.

Solution Square both sides. Remember that you are squaring a binomial on the right side.

$$(\sqrt{3m - 2})^2 = (m - 2)^2 \qquad \textit{Square both sides}$$
$$3m - 2 = m^2 - 4m + 4 \qquad \textit{Simplify}$$

This is a quadratic equation. Collect terms on the right side, then factor.

$$0 = m^2 - 7m + 6 \qquad \textit{Subtract } 3m, \textit{ add } 2$$
$$0 = (m - 1)(m - 6) \qquad \textit{Factor}$$

Set each factor equal to zero and solve.

$$m - 1 = 0 \quad \text{or} \quad m - 6 = 0$$
$$m = 1 \quad \text{or} \quad m = 6$$

Check both solutions in the original equation.

Check m = 1	*Check m = 6*
$\sqrt{3m - 2} = m - 2$	$\sqrt{3m - 2} = m - 2$
$\sqrt{3(1) - 2} = 1 - 2$	$\sqrt{3(6) - 2} = 6 - 2$
$\sqrt{1} = -1$	$\sqrt{16} = 4$
$1 = -1 \quad \textit{False}$	$4 = 4 \quad \textit{True}$

Try Problem 35 > The number 1 is an extraneous solution. Therefore the only solution is 6. ■

TO SOLVE A RADICAL EQUATION

1. Isolate a radical on one side of the equation.
2. Square both sides of the equation.
3. If the equation still contains a radical, simplify and repeat Steps 1 and 2.
4. Solve the resulting equation.
5. Check all solutions in the original equation and discard any extraneous solutions.

EXAMPLE 5 Solve $\sqrt{x + 9} - \sqrt{x} = 1$.

Solution

Step 1 *Isolate a radical on one side of the equation.*

$$\sqrt{x + 9} - \sqrt{x} = 1 \qquad \textit{Original equation}$$
$$\sqrt{x + 9} = 1 + \sqrt{x} \qquad \textit{Add } \sqrt{x} \textit{ to both sides}$$

Step 2 *Square both sides of the equation.*

$$(\sqrt{x + 9})^2 = (1 + \sqrt{x})^2$$
$$x + 9 = 1 + 2\sqrt{x} + x$$

Step 3 *Since the equation still contains a radical, simplify the equation, isolate a radical, and square again.*

$$8 = 2\sqrt{x} \qquad \textit{Subtract } x, \textit{ subtract } 1$$
$$4 = \sqrt{x} \qquad \textit{Divide by } 2$$
$$4^2 = (\sqrt{x})^2 \qquad \textit{Square both sides}$$
$$16 = x \qquad \textit{Simplify}$$

Step 4 *Solve the resulting equation.* This equation is already solved for x.

Step 5 *Check in the original equation.*

$$\sqrt{x + 9} - \sqrt{x} = 1 \quad \textit{Original equation}$$
$$\sqrt{16 + 9} - \sqrt{16} = 1 \quad \textit{Replace } x \textit{ with } 16$$
$$5 - 4 = 1 \quad \textit{Simplify}$$
$$1 = 1 \quad \textit{True}$$

Try Problem 57 >

The number 16 checks, so the solution is 16.   ■

P R O B L E M   S O L V I N G

EXAMPLE 6 Ignoring air resistance, the time, t, in seconds that it takes an object to fall a distance of d feet is given by the formula

$$t = \frac{\sqrt{d}}{4}.$$

A coin dropped into a well splashes into the water at the bottom of the well 2 seconds later. How deep is the well?

Solution

$$t = \frac{\sqrt{d}}{4} \qquad \textit{Write down the formula that fits the problem}$$
$$2 = \frac{\sqrt{d}}{4} \qquad \textit{Replace } t \textit{ with } 2$$
$$8 = \sqrt{d} \qquad \textit{Multiply by } 4$$
$$8^2 = (\sqrt{d})^2 \qquad \textit{Square both sides}$$
$$64 = d \qquad \textit{Simplify}$$

Try Problem 61 >

The number 64 checks, so the well is 64 feet deep.

8.7 Problem Set

Solve each equation.

1. $\sqrt{x} = 2$
2. $\sqrt{x} = 3$
3. $\sqrt{x + 1} = 3$
4. $\sqrt{x + 3} = 4$
5. $\sqrt{2y - 1} = 0$
6. $\sqrt{2y - 5} = 0$
7. $\sqrt{m - 1} = 5$
8. $\sqrt{m - 1} = 8$
9. $\sqrt{3p - 5} + 7 = 3$
10. $\sqrt{3p - 2} + 8 = 6$
11. $\sqrt{5r + 1} + 3 = 9$
12. $\sqrt{4r + 1} + 2 = 7$
13. $\sqrt{3t - 1} = \sqrt{t + 3}$
14. $\sqrt{3t - 2} = \sqrt{t + 6}$
15. $\sqrt{4x + 5} = \sqrt{3x + 4}$
16. $\sqrt{5x + 6} = \sqrt{4x + 5}$
17. $3\sqrt{m} = \sqrt{m + 8}$
18. $2\sqrt{m} = \sqrt{m + 3}$
19. $2\sqrt{y} = \sqrt{y + 9}$
20. $3\sqrt{y} = \sqrt{y + 16}$
21. $\sqrt{p + 2} = p$
22. $\sqrt{p + 6} = p$
23. $\sqrt{r^2 - 3} - 1 = 0$
24. $\sqrt{r^2 - 8} - 1 = 0$
25. $\sqrt{x^2 - 8x + 19} = 2$
26. $\sqrt{x^2 - 9x + 23} = 3$
27. $\sqrt{y^2 + 9y + 45} = y$
28. $\sqrt{y^2 + 6y + 54} = y$
29. $\sqrt{4z^2 + 2z - 1} = z$
30. $\sqrt{5z^2 + 3z - 1} = z$

Solve each equation.

31. $\sqrt{x^2 + 5} = x + 5$
32. $\sqrt{x^2 - 8} = x + 4$
33. $\sqrt{y + 4} = y + 2$
34. $\sqrt{y + 9} = y + 3$
35. $\sqrt{2m - 3} = m - 3$
36. $\sqrt{4m - 3} = m - 2$
37. $\sqrt{r + 2} = r$
38. $\sqrt{r + 6} = r$
39. $\sqrt{p^2 + 9} + 1 = p$
40. $\sqrt{p^2 + 7} + 1 = p$
41. $2\sqrt{r + 3} = r + 4$
42. $2\sqrt{r + 4} = r + 5$
43. $\sqrt{x - 17} = \sqrt{17 - x}$
44. $\sqrt{x - 19} = \sqrt{19 - x}$
45. $x + 1 = \sqrt{x + 1}$
46. $x + 2 = \sqrt{x + 4}$
47. $3 = \sqrt{y - 3} + y$
48. $1 = \sqrt{y - 1} + y$
49. $\sqrt{4z + 5} - 5 = 2z - 10$
50. $\sqrt{6z - 2} - 7 = 3z - 12$
51. $\sqrt{t^2 - 7t - 14} = t - 6$
52. $\sqrt{t^2 - 8t - 17} = t - 7$
53. $\sqrt{10k^2 + 2k - 7} = 3k + 2$
54. $\sqrt{5k^2 + 8k - 12} = 2k + 3$

Solve each equation.

55. $\sqrt{4 + 3\sqrt{x}} = 5$
56. $\sqrt{7 + 2\sqrt{x}} = 5$
57. $\sqrt{x + 7} - \sqrt{x} = 1$
58. $\sqrt{x + 8} - \sqrt{x} = 2$
59. $\sqrt{3y + 4} - \sqrt{y} = 2$
60. $\sqrt{3y + 1} - \sqrt{y} = 1$

Solve each word problem.

61. A marble dropped from a bridge hits the water below in 4 seconds (see Fig. 8.15). How high is the bridge? Use $t = \sqrt{d}/4$.

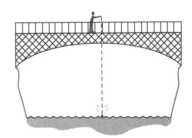

FIGURE 8.15

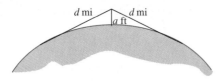

FIGURE 8.16

62. The distance d, in miles, to the horizon from an altitude of a feet is given by $d = \sqrt{1.5a}$ (see Fig. 8.16). How high above the water must the periscope of a submarine be to see a ship 3 miles away?

63. The principal square root of the sum of a number and 4 is 3. Find the number.

64. The principal square root of the difference of a number and 5 is 2. Find the number.

65. Twice the principal square root of a number equals the difference of the number and 3. Find the number.

66. Four times the principal square root of a number equals the sum of the number and 3. Find the number.

67. Solve the formula $V = \sqrt{WR}$ for R.

68. Solve the formula $A = \sqrt{W/R}$ for W.

8.8   Fractional Exponents

We have already defined exponents that are integers. Recall that

$$5^2 = 25, \qquad 5^0 = 1, \qquad \text{and} \qquad 5^{-2} = \frac{1}{25}.$$

In this section we define exponents that are fractions.

Consider the expression $5^{1/2}$. We would like to define $5^{1/2}$ so that the rules for exponents we studied earlier hold for fractional exponents as well. For example, if we square $5^{1/2}$ and apply the power-to-a-power rule, we get

$$(5^{1/2})^2 = 5^{(1/2)2} = 5^{2/2} = 5^1 = 5.$$

But by the product rule for radicals,

$$(\sqrt{5})^2 = 5.$$

Since squaring $5^{1/2}$ and squaring $\sqrt{5}$ produce the same number, 5, these expressions should be equal. That is,

$$5^{1/2} = \sqrt{5}.$$

By the same argument,

$$(5^{1/3})^3 = 5^{3/3} = 5 \qquad \text{and} \qquad (\sqrt[3]{5})^3 = \sqrt[3]{5}\ \sqrt[3]{5}\ \sqrt[3]{5} = \sqrt[3]{125} = 5.$$

Therefore

$$5^{1/3} = \sqrt[3]{5}.$$

These examples suggest the following definition.

DEFINITION OF THE EXPONENT 1/n

If n is a positive integer greater than 1 and a is a real number such that $\sqrt[n]{a}$ exists, then

$$a^{1/n} = \sqrt[n]{a}.$$

EXAMPLE 1   Simplify.

a. $9^{1/2}$

b. $125^{1/3}$

c. $16^{1/4}$

Solution

a. The exponent 1/2 tells us to take the principal square root of 9.

$9^{1/2} = \sqrt{9} = 3$

b. The exponent 1/3 tells us to take the principal cube root of 125.

$125^{1/3} = \sqrt[3]{125} = 5$

c. The exponent 1/4 tells us to take the principal fourth root of 16.

Try Problem 1 > $16^{1/4} = \sqrt[4]{16} = 2$ ■

Now let's consider the more general fractional exponent m/n. If we apply the power-to-a-power rule to $5^{2/3}$, we get

$$5^{2/3} = 5^{(1/3)2} = (5^{1/3})^2 = (\sqrt[3]{5})^2.$$

We can also apply the power-to-a-power rule in a different way and get

$$5^{2/3} = 5^{2(1/3)} = (5^2)^{1/3} = \sqrt[3]{5^2}.$$

These examples suggest the following definition.

DEFINITION OF THE EXPONENT m/n

If m and n are integers ($n > 1$) and a is a real number such that the indicated roots exist, then

$$a^{m/n} = (\sqrt[n]{a})^m = \sqrt[n]{a^m}.$$

You can think of the fractional exponent m/n as follows: **The numerator m indicates the power, and the denominator n indicates the root.**

EXAMPLE 2   Simplify.

a. $64^{2/3}$

b. $64^{3/2}$

c. $32^{2/5}$

The first known use of fractional exponents appeared in a tract written by the French mathematician Nicole Oresme (1323–1382), the best mathematician of his day. However, the English mathematician John Wallis (1616–1703) was the first to fully explain the meaning of fractional exponents.

Solution

a. The exponent 2/3 tells us to take the cube root of 64 and square the result.

$$64^{2/3} = (\sqrt[3]{64})^2 = (4)^2 = 16$$

We can also square first and then take the cube root.

$$64^{2/3} = \sqrt[3]{64^2} = \sqrt[3]{4096} = 16$$

In this case it was easier to take the cube root first.

b. The exponent 3/2 tells us to take the square root of 64 and cube the result.

$$64^{3/2} = (\sqrt{64})^3 = 8^3 = 512$$

c. The exponent 2/5 tells us to take the fifth root of 32 and square the result.

Try Problem 11 >

$$32^{2/5} = (\sqrt[5]{32})^2 = 2^2 = 4$$

Recall that we defined negative integer exponents as follows.

$$a^{-n} = \frac{1}{a^n}$$

We define negative fractional exponents in the same way.

DEFINITION OF THE EXPONENT $-m/n$

If $a^{m/n}$ exists and is not zero, then

$$a^{-m/n} = \frac{1}{a^{m/n}} \, .$$

EXAMPLE 3   Write with a positive exponent and simplify.

a. $100^{-1/2} = \dfrac{1}{100^{1/2}}$ *Since $a^{-m/n} = 1/a^{m/n}$*

$$= \frac{1}{\sqrt{100}}$$ *Since $a^{1/n} = \sqrt[n]{a}$*

$$= \frac{1}{10}$$ *Since $\sqrt{100} = 10$*

b. $81^{-3/4} = \dfrac{1}{81^{3/4}} = \dfrac{1}{(\sqrt[4]{81})^3} = \dfrac{1}{3^3} = \dfrac{1}{27}$

Try Problem 17 >

c. $(-8)^{-2/3} = \dfrac{1}{(-8)^{2/3}} = \dfrac{1}{(\sqrt[3]{-8})^2} = \dfrac{1}{(-2)^2} = \dfrac{1}{4}$

Since we defined fractional exponents with the rules of exponents in mind, those rules are true for fractional exponents as well as integer exponents. You may want to review the rules of exponents, which are summarized in Section 3.2.

EXAMPLE 4   Simplify each expression. Write your answers in exponential form.

a. $2^{3/5} \cdot 2^{4/5} = 2^{3/5+4/5}$ *Product rule for exponents*
   $= 2$ *Add the exponents*

b. $\dfrac{7^{5/3}}{7^{1/3}} = 7^{5/3-1/3}$ *Quotient rule for exponents*

   $= 7^{4/3}$ *Subtract the exponents*

c. $(6^{1/4})^2 = 6^{(1/4)2}$ *Power-to-a-power rule*

Try Problem 25 > $= 6^{1/2}$ *Multiply the exponents*   ∎

EXAMPLE 5   Simplify each expression. Write your answers in exponential form with positive exponents. Assume all variables represent positive numbers.

a. $x^{1/2} \cdot x^{-1/2} = x^{1/2+(-1/2)} = x^0 = 1$

b. $\dfrac{y^{1/4}}{y^{3/4}} = y^{1/4-3/4} = y^{-1/2} = \dfrac{1}{y^{1/2}}$

c. $(p^6)^{1/3} = p^{6(1/3)} = p^2$

d. $(8m^{12})^{1/3} = 8^{1/3}(m^{12})^{1/3} = \sqrt[3]{8}\,m^{12(1/3)} = 2m^4$

Try Problem 51 >   e. $\left(\dfrac{c^2}{d^2}\right)^{5/2} = \dfrac{(c^2)^{5/2}}{(d^2)^{5/2}} = \dfrac{c^{2(5/2)}}{d^{2(5/2)}} = \dfrac{c^5}{d^5}$ ∎

Sometimes we can simplify a radical by first writing it in exponential form with a fractional exponent.

EXAMPLE 6   Simplify each expression.

a. $\sqrt[4]{25} = \sqrt[4]{5^2} = 5^{2/4} = 5^{1/2} = \sqrt{5}$
b. $\sqrt[9]{r^3} = r^{3/9} = r^{1/3} = \sqrt[3]{r}$

Try Problem 69 >   c. $\sqrt{\sqrt{3}} = \sqrt{3^{1/2}} = (3^{1/2})^{1/2} = 3^{(1/2)(1/2)} = 3^{1/4} = \sqrt[4]{3}$ ∎

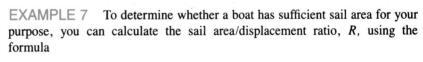

PROBLEM SOLVING

EXAMPLE 7   To determine whether a boat has sufficient sail area for your purpose, you can calculate the sail area/displacement ratio, R, using the formula

$$R = \dfrac{A}{D^{2/3}},$$

where A is the area of the sail in square feet and D is the displacement in cubic feet. (Boats that rely primarily on engines for power, but carry some sail, have R values between 8 and 14. Cruising sailboats have R values between 14 and 16, and racing sailboats have R values over 16.) Calculate the sail area/displacement ratio for a boat with a sail area of 375 square feet and a displacement of 125 cubic feet.

Solution

$$R = \frac{A}{D^{2/3}}$$ *Write down the formula that fits the problem*

$$R = \frac{375}{125^{2/3}}$$ *Substitute $A = 375$ and $D = 125$*

$$R = \frac{375}{25}$$ *Since $125^{2/3} = (\sqrt[3]{125})^2 = 5^2 = 25$*

$$R = 15$$ *Divide*

Try Problem 81 >   The sail area/displacement ratio is 15.

8.8 Problem Set

LEARNING THROUGH WRITING

☐ Explain how to calculate $a^{1/n}$ in words.

☐ Explain how to calculate $a^{m/n}$ in words.

☐ Explain how to calculate $a^{-m/n}$ in words.

Write each expression in radical form and simplify.

1. $16^{1/2}$
2. $36^{1/2}$
3. $25^{1/2}$
4. $49^{1/2}$
5. $8^{1/3}$
6. $27^{1/3}$
7. $64^{1/3}$
8. $1000^{1/3}$
9. $81^{1/4}$
10. $625^{1/4}$
11. $27^{2/3}$
12. $8^{2/3}$
13. $9^{3/2}$
14. $4^{3/2}$
15. $32^{3/5}$
16. $32^{4/5}$
17. $121^{-1/2}$
18. $144^{-1/2}$
19. $16^{-5/4}$
20. $81^{-5/4}$
21. $(-8)^{2/3}$
22. $(-27)^{2/3}$
23. $(-125)^{-1/3}$
24. $(-64)^{-1/3}$

Use the rules of exponents to simplify each expression. Write your answers in exponential form with positive exponents.

25. $2^{2/3} \cdot 2^{5/3}$
26. $6^{1/5} \cdot 6^{3/5}$
27. $5^{3/2} \cdot 5^{-1}$
28. $3^{4/3} \cdot 3^{-1}$
29. $\dfrac{11^{4/5}}{11^{1/5}}$
30. $\dfrac{15^{6/7}}{15^{1/7}}$
31. $\dfrac{12}{12^{1/3}}$
32. $\dfrac{14}{14^{1/2}}$
33. $(10^{1/4})^2$
34. $(20^{1/6})^3$
35. $(3^{2/5})^{10}$
36. $(2^{3/4})^8$
37. $(2^{1/3}6^{1/3})^3$
38. $(3^{1/2}5^{1/2})^2$
39. $(9^{2/5}3^{-1/5})^5$
40. $(4^{3/4}2^{-1/4})^4$
41. $\left(\dfrac{9}{16}\right)^{3/2}$
42. $\left(\dfrac{16}{25}\right)^{3/2}$
43. $\left(\dfrac{8}{27}\right)^{-1/3}$
44. $\left(\dfrac{64}{125}\right)^{-1/3}$

Use the rules of exponents to simplify each expression. Write your answers in exponential form with positive exponents. Assume all variables represent positive numbers.

45. $x^{1/3} \cdot x^{-1/3}$
46. $x^{1/4} \cdot x^{-1/4}$
47. $m^{1/2} \cdot m^{3/2}$
48. $m^{1/3} \cdot m^{5/3}$
49. $\dfrac{a^{5/2}}{a^{3/2}}$
50. $\dfrac{a^{7/3}}{a^{4/3}}$
51. $\dfrac{y^{1/6}}{y^{3/6}}$
52. $\dfrac{y^{1/6}}{y^{4/6}}$
53. $\dfrac{z^{-1/4}}{z^{3/4}}$
54. $\dfrac{z^{-1/5}}{z^{4/5}}$
55. $(p^6)^{1/2}$
56. $(p^{12})^{1/3}$
57. $(r^{2/3})^2$
58. $(r^{3/4})^3$
59. $(27m^6)^{1/3}$
60. $(16m^{12})^{1/2}$

61. $(a^{-2}b^{1/5})^5$

62. $(a^{1/4}b^{-2})^4$

63. $\left(\dfrac{c^2}{d^2}\right)^{3/2}$

64. $\left(\dfrac{c^3}{d^3}\right)^{4/3}$

65. $\left(\dfrac{x^{3/4}}{y^{3/2}}\right)^{2/3}$

66. $\left(\dfrac{x^{4/9}}{y^{4/3}}\right)^{3/4}$

67. $\dfrac{k \cdot k^{-5/2}}{k^{1/4} \cdot k^{-3/4}}$

68. $\dfrac{k \cdot k^{-8/3}}{k^{1/6} \cdot k^{-5/6}}$

Write each radical in exponential form and simplify. Write your answers in radical form. Assume all variables represent positive numbers.

69. $\sqrt[4]{4}$

70. $\sqrt[4]{9}$

71. $\sqrt[6]{36^3}$

72. $\sqrt[6]{64^2}$

73. $\sqrt[8]{r^2}$

74. $\sqrt[12]{r^4}$

75. $\sqrt[12]{x^8}$

76. $\sqrt[8]{x^6}$

77. $\sqrt{\sqrt{2}}$

78. $\sqrt{\sqrt{5}}$

79. $\sqrt[3]{\sqrt{y}}$

80. $\sqrt{\sqrt[3]{y}}$

Solve each word problem.

81. Calculate the sail area/displacement ratio, R, for a boat with a sail area of 320 square feet and a displacement of 64 cubic feet. Use $R = A/D^{2/3}$.

82. Calculate the sail area/displacement ratio, R, for a boat with a sail area of 468 square feet and a displacement of 216 cubic feet. Use $R = A/D^{2/3}$.

▦ CALCULATOR PROBLEMS

To find $8^{5/3}$ on most calculators, press

Clear	8	INV	y^x	3	y^x	5	=	32

Find each power on your calculator. Round approximate answers to the nearest hundredth.

83. $81^{1/2}$

84. $27^{1/3}$

85. $64^{2/3}$

86. $125^{4/3}$

87. $3^{1/4}$

88. $\sqrt{\sqrt{3}}$

89. $(-1024)^{1/5}$

90. $50^{4/5}$

The year of a planet in our solar system is the time it takes the planet to make one revolution around the sun. Kepler's third law of planetary motion states that the number of Earth days, y, in a planet's year is given approximately by the formula

$$y = 0.41d^{3/2},$$

where d is the mean distance between the planet and the sun, in millions of miles.

91. Determine the number of Earth days in the year of Mercury, whose mean distance from the sun is approximately 36,000,000 miles.

92. Determine the number of Earth days in the year of Venus, whose mean distance from the sun is approximately 67,000,000 miles.

93. Determine the number of Earth days in the year of Earth, whose mean distance from the sun is approximately 92,600,000 miles.

94. Determine the number of Earth days in the year of Mars, whose mean distance from the sun is approximately 141,000,000 miles.

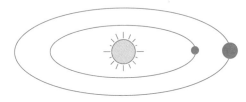

Kepler's third law of planetary motion is named after the German mathematician and astronomer Johann Kepler (1571–1630), who was the first to state the precise laws regarding the orbits of the planets. He based his lengthy calculations on the detailed observations of the Danish astronomer Tycho Brahe (1546–1601).

S U M M A R Y

Key Terms

Conjugate, p. 388
Cube root, p. 360
Extraneous solution, p. 391
Imaginary number, p. 359
Index of a radical, p. 360
Irrational number, p. 359

Like radicals, p. 378
Perfect cube, p. 370
Perfect fourth power, p. 370
Perfect-square integer, p. 359
Radical, p. 358
Radical equation, p. 391

Radical expression, p. 367
Radical sign, p. 358
Radicand, p. 358
Rational number, p. 359
Rationalizing the denominator, p. 385
Square root, p. 358

Key Rules

Principal nth Root
If a is a real number and n is a positive integer greater than 1, then

$$\sqrt[n]{a} = b \quad \text{if} \quad b^n = a.$$

Suppose n is an even integer.

a. If a is positive, then $\sqrt[n]{a}$ is positive.
b. If a is negative, then $\sqrt[n]{a}$ is not a real number.

Suppose n is an odd integer.

a. If a is positive, then $\sqrt[n]{a}$ is positive.
b. If a is negative, then $\sqrt[n]{a}$ is negative.
For any n, $\sqrt[n]{0} = 0$.

Pythagorean Theorem
$$c^2 = a^2 + b^2 \qquad c = \sqrt{a^2 + b^2} \qquad a = \sqrt{c^2 - b^2}$$

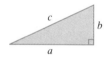

Product Rule for Radicals
If the indicated roots exist, then
$$\sqrt[n]{a}\sqrt[n]{b} = \sqrt[n]{ab}.$$

Quotient Rule for Radicals
If the indicated roots exist and no denominator is 0, then

$$\frac{\sqrt[n]{a}}{\sqrt[n]{b}} = \sqrt[n]{\frac{a}{b}}.$$

If $x \geq 0$, Then:
$$\sqrt{x^2} = x \qquad \text{and} \qquad (\sqrt{x})^2 = x.$$

A Radical Expression Is in Simplest Form When:
1. The radicand contains no perfect-square factors, and
2. The radicand contains no fractions, and
3. No denominator contains a radical.

Squaring Property of Equality
If $a = b$, then $a^2 = b^2$.

Fractional Exponents
Assume each root exists and no denominator is 0.

$$a^{1/n} = \sqrt[n]{a} \qquad a^{m/n} = (\sqrt[n]{a})^m = \sqrt[n]{a^m} \qquad a^{-m/n} = \frac{1}{a^{m/n}}$$

R E V I E W P R O B L E M S

[8.1] *Find all square roots of each number.*

1. 100

2. $\dfrac{16}{25}$

3. 1.69

Find each root that is a real number.

4. $\sqrt{36}$

5. $\sqrt{-49}$

6. $\pm\sqrt{9}$

7. $\sqrt[3]{125}$

8. $-\sqrt[3]{-8}$

9. $\sqrt[4]{256}$

Determine whether each number is rational or irrational. If the number is rational, give its exact value; if the number is irrational, give its value to the nearest hundredth.

10. $\sqrt{5}$ **11.** $\sqrt{196}$ **12.** $\sqrt{130}$

13. A motorboat with a speed of 20 mph motors on a due-east heading for 2 hours. During this time, a 4.5-mph current flowing from north to south causes the boat to travel in a southeasterly direction, as shown in Fig. 8.17. Find the total distance traveled by the boat.

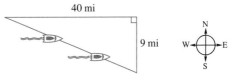

FIGURE 8.17

[8.2] *Use the product rule to simplify each radical expression.*

14. $\sqrt{44}$ **15.** $2\sqrt{108}$ **16.** $-5\sqrt{160}$

Use the quotient rule and/or the product rule to simplify each radical expression.

17. $\sqrt{\dfrac{25}{121}}$ **18.** $\sqrt{\dfrac{12}{49}}$ **19.** $\dfrac{4\sqrt{90}}{3}$

Simplify each expression. Assume all variables represent positive numbers.

20. $\sqrt{16x^{64}}$ **21.** $5\sqrt{300p^3}$ **22.** $-6a\sqrt{8a^5b^6}$ **23.** $\dfrac{3}{4}\sqrt{25r^2s^3t^4}$

24. $\sqrt{\dfrac{y^{10}}{64}}$ **25.** $\sqrt{\dfrac{11}{m^2}}$ **26.** $\dfrac{\sqrt{50r}}{10}$ **27.** $\sqrt{\dfrac{7xy^2}{28x^3z^4}}$

28. $\sqrt[3]{135}$ **29.** $\sqrt[4]{\dfrac{48}{625}}$ **30.** $\sqrt[3]{\dfrac{27m^7n^4}{64mn^2}}$ **31.** $\sqrt{x^2 + 12x + 36}$

32. Determine the distance from one corner to the opposite corner of a meeting room that is 30 feet by 30 feet square.

[8.3] *Multiply and simplify. Assume all variables represent positive numbers.*

33. $\sqrt{5}\sqrt{6y}$ **34.** $(4\sqrt{k})^2$ **35.** $(7\sqrt{2})(3\sqrt{8})$ **36.** $(-8\sqrt{6xy})(2\sqrt{30xy^7})$

Divide and simplify. Assume all variables represent positive numbers.

37. $\dfrac{\sqrt{30x}}{\sqrt{6}}$ **38.** $\dfrac{\sqrt{196r}}{\sqrt{2r}}$ **39.** $\dfrac{48\sqrt{20m^5}}{8\sqrt{5m}}$ **40.** $\dfrac{\sqrt{21a^5b}}{\sqrt{336ab^3}}$

Perform the indicated operation and simplify.

41. $\sqrt[3]{10x^2}\sqrt[3]{100x}$ **42.** $\dfrac{\sqrt[4]{405}}{\sqrt[4]{5}}$

43. Find x in Fig. 8.18

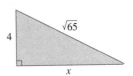

FIGURE 8.18

[8.4] *Combine like radicals. Assume all variables represent positive numbers.*

44. $\sqrt{10} + 5\sqrt{10}$

45. $4\sqrt{3} + 3\sqrt{2} - 7\sqrt{3}$

46. $\sqrt{45} + 8\sqrt{5}$

47. $5\sqrt{28} - \sqrt{3}\sqrt{21} + 2\sqrt{2}\sqrt{56}$

48. $\sqrt{18m} + \sqrt{8m}$

49. $\sqrt{96k^3} + \sqrt{150k^3}$

50. $\sqrt[3]{250} + \sqrt[3]{40} + \sqrt[3]{5}$

51. $4\sqrt[4]{48} - 2\sqrt[4]{3}$

[8.5] *Multiply and simplify. Assume all variables represent positive numbers.*

52. $\sqrt{2}(\sqrt{5} + \sqrt{8})$

53. $\sqrt{5p}(\sqrt{125p} - \sqrt{15p})$

54. $\sqrt{y+4}(\sqrt{y+4} + \sqrt{y})$

55. $(\sqrt{x} + 1)(\sqrt{x} - 1)$

56. $(\sqrt{3} + 4)(\sqrt{5} - 2)$

57. $(2\sqrt{7} + 3)^2$

58. $(2\sqrt{3} + 1)(3\sqrt{3} - 5)$

59. $(4\sqrt{m} + \sqrt{n})(4\sqrt{m} - \sqrt{n})$

Simplify each expression.

60. $\dfrac{2 + \sqrt{20}}{2}$

61. $\dfrac{-6 \pm \sqrt{80}}{6}$

Multiply and simplify.

62. $\sqrt[3]{5}(\sqrt[3]{25} - 2)$

63. $(\sqrt[3]{3} + 4)^2$

64. Find x in Fig. 8.19.

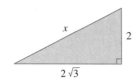

FIGURE 8.19

[8.6] *Simplify each radical expression. Rationalize all denominators. Assume all variables represent positive numbers.*

65. $\dfrac{7}{\sqrt{7}}$

66. $\sqrt{\dfrac{1}{12}}$

67. $\dfrac{\sqrt{6a^{13}}}{\sqrt{66a^7b}}$

68. $\sqrt{\dfrac{5}{8}} \cdot \sqrt{\dfrac{1}{3}}$

69. $\dfrac{6}{\sqrt[3]{4}}$

70. $\sqrt[3]{\dfrac{27}{5}}$

71. $\dfrac{1}{\sqrt{5} - 2}$

72. $\dfrac{3\sqrt{2}}{\sqrt{7} + \sqrt{2}}$

73. $\dfrac{\sqrt{3} + 1}{\sqrt{3} - 3}$

[8.7] *Solve each equation.*

74. $\sqrt{3x - 2} = 5$

75. $\sqrt{t} + 6 = 4$

76. $\sqrt{m + 12} = m$

77. $\sqrt{2y^2 - 9y - 10} = y$

78. $\sqrt{2p + 2} = p - 3$

79. $2\sqrt{r} - 1 = r$

80. $\sqrt{8k - 15} + 3 = 2k$

81. $\sqrt{y + 9} - \sqrt{y} = 1$

82. Three times the principal square root of a number equals the difference of the number and 4. Find the number.

[8.8] *Write each expression in radical form and simplify.*

83. $100^{1/2}$

84. $125^{1/3}$

85. $81^{3/4}$

86. $32^{-2/5}$

Use the rules of exponents to simplify each expression. Write your answers in exponential form with positive exponents. Assume all variables represent positive numbers.

87. $3^{1/2} \cdot 3^{5/2}$

88. $(64p^6)^{1/3}$

89. $(a^{3/4}b^{-1})^8$

90. $\left(\dfrac{x^{1/2}}{y^{1/3}}\right)^{1/2}$

91. $\dfrac{m^{3/8}}{m^{5/8}}$ **92.** $\dfrac{t^{2/3} \cdot t^{-2/3}}{t \cdot t^{-3/2}}$

Write each radical in exponential form and simplify. Write your answers in radical form.

93. $\sqrt[4]{36}$ **94.** $\sqrt[9]{x^3}$ **95.** $\sqrt{\sqrt{7}}$

C H A P T E R 8 TEST

Find each root that is a real number.

1. $\sqrt{81}$ **2.** $-\sqrt{1600}$ **3.** $\sqrt[3]{27}$ **4.** $\sqrt[4]{-16}$

Write each expression in radical form and simplify.

5. $8^{-1/3}$ **6.** $25^{3/2}$

Simplify each expression. Assume all variables represent positive numbers.

7. $2\sqrt{50}$ **8.** $\sqrt{24m^3}$ **9.** $\sqrt[4]{112}$ **10.** $(9x^6)^{1/2}$

11. $\sqrt{\dfrac{45}{49}}$ **12.** $\dfrac{7^{1/2} \cdot 7^{1/2}}{7^{3/4}}$

Multiply and simplify.

13. $2\sqrt{5}(3\sqrt{3} + \sqrt{15})$ **14.** $(\sqrt{6} - 1)^2$ **15.** $(\sqrt{2} + 5)(\sqrt{3} - 4)$

Divide and simplify. Assume y is a positive number.

16. $\dfrac{\sqrt{18y^2}}{\sqrt{2y}}$ **17.** $\dfrac{7\sqrt{60}}{14\sqrt{3}}$

Add or subtract as indicated. Assume p is a positive number.

18. $\sqrt{7} - 4\sqrt{7} + 7\sqrt{3}$ **19.** $2\sqrt{98} + 2\sqrt{6}\sqrt{3}$ **20.** $\sqrt{27p^2} + 4\sqrt{3p^2}$ **21.** $\sqrt[3]{40} - \sqrt[3]{5}$

Rationalize the denominator and simplify.

22. $\sqrt{\dfrac{3}{5}}$ **23.** $\dfrac{10}{\sqrt[3]{2}}$ **24.** $\dfrac{4}{\sqrt{6} + 2}$ **25.** $\dfrac{\sqrt{2} + 1}{\sqrt{5} - \sqrt{3}}$

Solve each equation.

26. $\sqrt{4x + 1} + 9 = 12$ **27.** $2\sqrt{r - 1} = \sqrt{r + 5}$ **28.** $\sqrt{3t + 1} = t - 3$

29. The principal square root of the difference of a number and 7 is 4. Find the number.

More Quadratic Equations

To collect the television signals from a satellite and bounce them to a receptor, called a feedhorn, a satellite dish must have a parabolic shape. In Section 9.6 we see that this parabolic shape can be produced by graphing a quadratic equation in two variables.

9.1 The Square Root Property

In Chapter 4 we solved quadratic equations by factoring. In this section we solve quadratic equations using the *square root property*.

SQUARE ROOT PROPERTY

Suppose k is a positive number.

If $x^2 = k$, then $x = \sqrt{k}$ or $x = -\sqrt{k}$.

We often write the two equations $x = \sqrt{k}$ and $x = -\sqrt{k}$ as the single equation $x = \pm\sqrt{k}$.

EXAMPLE 1   Solve $x^2 - 9 = 0$.

Solution
Method 1 *Factoring*

$$x^2 - 9 = 0 \quad \textit{Original equation}$$
$$(x - 3)(x + 3) = 0 \quad \textit{Factor the left side}$$

$$x - 3 = 0 \quad \text{or} \quad x + 3 = 0 \quad \textit{Set each factor equal to 0}$$
$$x = 3 \quad \text{or} \quad x = -3 \quad \textit{Solve each linear equation}$$

Method 2 *The Square Root Property*

$$x^2 - 9 = 0 \quad \textit{Original equation}$$
$$x^2 = 9 \quad \textit{Solve for } x^2$$
$$x = \pm\sqrt{9} \quad \textit{Take both square roots of 9}$$
$$x = \pm 3 \quad \textit{Simplify the radical}$$

Try Problem 3 >

Using either method, the solutions are 3 and -3. Check both solutions in the original equation. ∎

Caution! ■
■
■
■
■
■
■

When you use the square root property, be sure to take both the positive and the negative square root.

Correct	*Wrong*
$x^2 = 4$	$x^2 = 4$
$x = \pm 2$	$\cancel{x = 2}$

EXAMPLE 2   Solve $x^2 - 5 = 0$.

Solution

$$x^2 - 5 = 0 \qquad \textit{Original equation}$$
$$x^2 = 5 \qquad \textit{Solve for } x^2$$
$$x = \pm\sqrt{5} \qquad \textit{Square root property}$$

Try Problem 9 > The solutions are $\sqrt{5}$ and $-\sqrt{5}$. We could approximate these solutions as decimals, but normally we leave them in radical form.   ∎

EXAMPLE 3   Solve $2y^2 - 24 = 0$.

Solution

$$2y^2 - 24 = 0 \qquad \textit{Original equation}$$
$$2y^2 = 24$$
$$y^2 = 12 \qquad \textbig\} \textit{Solve for } y^2$$
$$y = \pm\sqrt{12} \qquad \textit{Square root property}$$
$$y = \pm 2\sqrt{3} \qquad \textit{Simplify the radical}$$

Try Problem 11 > The solutions are $2\sqrt{3}$ and $-2\sqrt{3}$.   ∎

EXAMPLE 4   Solve $p^2 + 4 = 0$.

Solution

$$p^2 = -4 \qquad \textit{Solve for } p^2$$
$$p = \pm\sqrt{-4} \qquad \textit{Square root property}$$

Try Problem 15 > Since neither $\sqrt{-4}$ nor $-\sqrt{-4}$ is a real number, this equation has no real solution.   ∎

We can also use the square root property to solve equations like

$$(x - 1)^2 = 25.$$

EXAMPLE 5   Solve $(x - 1)^2 = 25$.

Solution   Use the square root property and get

$$x - 1 = \pm\sqrt{25}$$
$$x - 1 = \pm 5.$$

Then solve for x by adding 1 to both sides.

$$x = 1 \pm 5$$

This equation means

$$x = 1 + 5 \quad \text{or} \quad x = 1 - 5$$
$$x = 6 \quad\quad \text{or} \quad x = -4.$$

Try Problem 19 >   The solutions are 6 and −4.

TO SOLVE A QUADRATIC EQUATION USING THE SQUARE ROOT PROPERTY

1. Write the equation in the form $x^2 = k$.
2. Take both square roots of k and get $x = \pm\sqrt{k}$.
3. Simplify the radical if possible.
4. Solve for the variable if necessary.
5. Check each solution in the original equation.

EXAMPLE 6   Solve $(m + 3)^2 = 24$.

Solution

Step 1   *The equation is already in the form $x^2 = k$.*

$$(m + 3)^2 = 24$$

Step 2   *Take both square roots of 24.*

$$m + 3 = \pm\sqrt{24}$$

Step 3   *Simplify the radical.*

$$m + 3 = \pm\sqrt{4}\sqrt{6} \quad\quad \textit{Product rule for radicals}$$
$$m + 3 = \pm2\sqrt{6} \quad\quad \textit{Since } \sqrt{4} = 2$$

Step 4   *Solve for m.*

$$m = -3 \pm 2\sqrt{6} \quad \textit{Subtract 3}$$

Step 5   *Check each solution in the original equation.*

Check $m = -3 + 2\sqrt{6}$	*Check $m = -3 - 2\sqrt{6}$*
$(m + 3)^2 = 24$	$(m + 3)^2 = 24$
$(-3 + 2\sqrt{6} + 3)^2 = 24$	$(-3 - 2\sqrt{6} + 3)^2 = 24$
$(2\sqrt{6})^2 = 24$	$(-2\sqrt{6})^2 = 24$
$24 = 24 \quad True$	$24 = 24 \quad True$

Try Problem 23 >   The solutions are $-3 + 2\sqrt{6}$ and $-3 - 2\sqrt{6}$.

EXAMPLE 7   Solve $(4r - 2)^2 = 8$.

Solution

$$4r - 2 = \pm\sqrt{8} \qquad \textit{Square root property}$$

$$4r - 2 = \pm2\sqrt{2} \qquad \textit{Simplify the radical}$$

$$4r = 2 \pm 2\sqrt{2} \qquad \textit{Add 2}$$

$$r = \frac{2 \pm 2\sqrt{2}}{4} \qquad \textit{Divide by 4}$$

$$r = \frac{2(1 \pm \sqrt{2})}{4} \qquad \textit{Factor the numerator}$$

$$r = \frac{1 \pm \sqrt{2}}{2} \qquad \textit{Divide out 2}$$

Try Problem 33 >   The solutions are $\dfrac{1 + \sqrt{2}}{2}$ and $\dfrac{1 - \sqrt{2}}{2}$.   ■

PROBLEM SOLVING

EXAMPLE 8   The speed of the current in a stream can be determined using an open-ended, L-shaped tube like the one shown in Fig. 9.1. The current speed, *s,* in feet per second, is given by Torricelli's law as

$$s^2 = 64h,$$

where *h* is the height, in feet, of the water in the tube. Find the current speed if $h = 6$ inches.

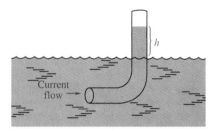

FIGURE 9.1

Solution   Since *h* must be in feet, write

$$h = 6 \text{ in.} = \frac{6}{12} \text{ ft} = \frac{1}{2} \text{ ft.}$$

Then substitute $h = 1/2$ into the formula $s^2 = 64h$.

$$s^2 = 64\left(\frac{1}{2}\right)$$

$$s^2 = 32$$

$$s = \pm\sqrt{32} \qquad \textit{Square root property}$$

$$s = \pm\sqrt{16}\sqrt{2}$$

$$s = \pm4\sqrt{2}$$

Try Problem 43 >

Since the speed cannot be negative, we reject the solution $-4\sqrt{2}$. Therefore the speed of the current is $4\sqrt{2}$ (about 5.7) feet per second.

9.1 Problem Set

LEARNING THROUGH WRITING

☐ State the *square root property* in words.

☐ Describe the steps in solving a quadratic equation using the square root property.

Solve each equation (a) by factoring, (b) using the square root property.

1. $x^2 = 25$ **2.** $x^2 = 36$ **3.** $x^2 - 16 = 0$ **4.** $x^2 - 64 = 0$
5. $9x^2 - 4 = 0$ **6.** $4x^2 - 9 = 0$ **7.** $x^2 - 2 = 0$ **8.** $x^2 - 3 = 0$

Solve each equation using the square root property. Simplify your answer.

9. $x^2 - 7 = 0$ **10.** $x^2 - 11 = 0$ **11.** $3y^2 - 60 = 0$ **12.** $2y^2 - 36 = 0$
13. $4m^2 - 45 = 0$ **14.** $9m^2 - 28 = 0$ **15.** $p^2 + 9 = 0$ **16.** $p^2 + 25 = 0$
17. $2r^2 - 1 = 0$ **18.** $3r^2 - 1 = 0$ **19.** $(x - 1)^2 = 49$ **20.** $(x - 1)^2 = 81$
21. $(p - 3)^2 = 3$ **22.** $(p - 2)^2 = 2$ **23.** $(m + 2)^2 = 18$ **24.** $(m + 5)^2 = 12$
25. $(x - 5)^2 = -4$ **26.** $(x - 3)^2 = -9$ **27.** $(2t + 7)^2 = 9$ **28.** $(2t + 9)^2 = 25$
29. $(2z - 2)^2 = 1$ **30.** $(3z - 4)^2 = 1$ **31.** $(5y + 4)^2 = 11$ **32.** $(5y + 3)^2 = 13$
33. $(6r - 3)^2 = 27$ **34.** $(6r - 2)^2 = 24$ **35.** $\left(x - \dfrac{1}{2}\right)^2 = \dfrac{9}{4}$ **36.** $\left(x - \dfrac{1}{2}\right)^2 = \dfrac{25}{4}$
37. $\left(y + \dfrac{3}{2}\right)^2 = \dfrac{5}{4}$ **38.** $\left(y + \dfrac{3}{2}\right)^2 = \dfrac{7}{4}$

Solve each word problem.

39. Eight less than five times the square of a number is 597. Find the number.

40. Seven more than six times the square of a number is 871. Find the number.

41. The length of a rectangle is twice the width. If the area is 200 square feet, what are the width and the length?

42. The length of a rectangle is three times the width. If the area is 507 square feet, what are the width and the length?

43. Find the current speed in Fig. 9.1 if $h = 9$ inches.

44. Find the current speed in Fig. 9.1 if $h = 15$ inches.

The value, V, of a savings account that compounds interest annually is given by the formula

$$V = P(1 + r)^t,$$

where P is the principal, r is the interest rate, in decimal form, and t is the time, in years.

45. What interest rate, r, compounded annually will make $100 grow to $121 in 2 years?

46. What interest rate, r, compounded annually will make $100 grow to $144 in 2 years?

9.2 Completing the Square

Many quadratic equations cannot be solved by factoring. However, every quadratic equation can be solved by writing the equation in the form

$$(x + d)^2 = k$$

and then using the square root property. To write the left side as $(x + d)^2$ requires that we first write the left side as the perfect-square trinomial

$$x^2 + 2dx + d^2.$$

Note that the coefficient of x^2 in the trinomial is 1 and that the last term is the square of half the coefficient of x.

$$x^2 \quad + \quad 2dx \quad + \quad d^2$$

Coefficient is 1 $\left(\dfrac{2d}{2}\right)^2 = d^2$

For example, to write

$$x^2 + 6x$$

as a perfect-square trinomial, first note that the coefficient of x^2 is 1. Then the coefficient of x is 6, half the coefficient of x is 3, and $3^2 = 9$. Therefore add 9 to $x^2 + 6x$ and get

$$x^2 + 6x + 9.$$

Since adding 9 to $x^2 + 6x$ produces a perfect-square trinomial, adding 9 is called **completing the square** on $x^2 + 6x$. Note that the trinomial can be factored as the square of a binomial.

$$x^2 + 6x + 9 = (x + 3)^2$$

EXAMPLE 1   Complete the square on each expression. Then factor the resulting perfect-square trinomial.

a. $x^2 - 4x$ b. $y^2 - y$ c. $z^2 + \dfrac{4}{3}z$

Solution   Note that the coefficient of the squared term in each expression is already 1.

a. Half of -4 is -2, and $(-2)^2 = 4$. Therefore add 4 and factor the result.

$$x^2 - 4x + 4 = (x - 2)^2$$

b. Half of -1 is $-1/2$, and $(-1/2)^2 = 1/4$. Therefore add 1/4 and factor the result.

$$y^2 - y + \frac{1}{4} = \left(y - \frac{1}{2}\right)^2$$

c. Half of 4/3 is $1/2 \cdot 4/3 = 2/3$, and $(2/3)^2 = 4/9$. Therefore add 4/9 and factor the result.

Try Problem 1 >
$$z^2 + \frac{4}{3}z + \frac{4}{9} = \left(z + \frac{2}{3}\right)^2$$ ∎

EXAMPLE 2   Solve $x^2 - 6x + 5 = 0$ by completing the square.

Solution

$$\begin{array}{lll} x^2 - 6x + 5 = 0 & \textit{Original equation} \\ x^2 - 6x \quad = -5 & \textit{Subtract 5} \end{array}$$

To make the left side a perfect-square trinomial, add the square of half the coefficient of x to both sides. Since the coefficient of x is -6, half the coefficient of x is -3, and the square of -3 is 9. Therefore add 9 to both sides.

$$\begin{array}{ll} x^2 - 6x + 9 = -5 + 9 & \textit{Add 9 to both sides} \\ (x - 3)^2 = 4 & \textit{Factor the left side, simplify the right side} \\ x - 3 = \pm\sqrt{4} & \textit{Square root property} \\ x - 3 = \pm 2 & \textit{Since } \sqrt{4} = 2 \\ x = 3 \pm 2 & \textit{Add 3} \end{array}$$

$$\left.\begin{array}{lll} x = 3 + 2 & \text{or} & x = 3 - 2 \\ x = 5 & \text{or} & x = 1 \end{array}\right\} \textit{Solve each linear equation}$$

Try Problem 13 >   Both numbers check, so the solutions are 5 and 1. ∎

The fact that the solutions of Example 2 were rational numbers means that we could have solved the equation by factoring. This is not the case in Example 3.

EXAMPLE 3   Solve $x^2 - 6x + 4 = 0$.

Solution

$$\begin{array}{ll} x^2 - 6x + 4 = 0 & \textit{Original equation} \\ x^2 - 6x = -4 & \textit{Subtract 4 from both sides} \\ x^2 - 6x + 9 = -4 + 9 & \textit{Add } (-6/2)^2 = 9 \textit{ to both sides} \\ (x - 3)^2 = 5 & \textit{Factor the left side, simplify the right side} \\ x - 3 = \pm\sqrt{5} & \textit{Square root property} \\ x = 3 \pm \sqrt{5} & \textit{Add 3} \end{array}$$

Try Problem 19 >   The solutions are $3 + \sqrt{5}$ and $3 - \sqrt{5}$. ∎

If the coefficient a in the quadratic equation $ax^2 + bx + c = 0$ is not 1, divide both sides by a before completing the square.

EXAMPLE 4   Solve $4x^2 + 8x = 1$.

Solution   To make the coefficient of x^2 equal 1, divide both sides by 4.

$$\frac{4x^2}{4} + \frac{8x}{4} = \frac{1}{4} \qquad \textit{Divide by 4}$$

$$x^2 + 2x = \frac{1}{4} \qquad \textit{Simplify}$$

$$x^2 + 2x + 1 = \frac{1}{4} + 1 \qquad \textit{Complete the square by adding } (2/2)^2 = 1 \textit{ to both sides}$$

$$(x + 1)^2 = \frac{5}{4} \qquad \textit{Factor the left side, simplify the right side}$$

$$x + 1 = \pm\sqrt{\frac{5}{4}} \qquad \textit{Square root property}$$

$$x = -1 \pm \frac{\sqrt{5}}{2} \qquad \textit{Subtract 1 and simplify the radical}$$

Try Problem 25 >   The solutions are $-1 + \dfrac{\sqrt{5}}{2}$ and $-1 - \dfrac{\sqrt{5}}{2}$.   ■

TO SOLVE A QUADRATIC EQUATION BY COMPLETING THE SQUARE

1. Write the equation in the form $ax^2 + bx = -c$.
2. If $a \neq 1$, divide both sides by a.
3. Add the square of half the coefficient of x to both sides.
4. Factor the left side and simplify the right side.
5. Solve the equation resulting from Step 4 using the square root property.

EXAMPLE 5   Solve $2x^2 + 2x - 3 = 0$.

Solution
Step 1   *Write the equation in the form $ax^2 + bx = -c$.*

$$2x^2 + 2x - 3 = 0 \qquad \textit{Original equation}$$
$$2x^2 + 2x \quad = 3 \qquad \textit{Add 3}$$

Step 2   *Since $a \neq 1$, divide both sides by a.*

$$\frac{2x^2}{2} + \frac{2x}{2} \quad = \frac{3}{2} \qquad \textit{Divide both sides by 2}$$

$$x^2 + \quad x \quad = \frac{3}{2} \qquad \textit{Simplify}$$

Step 3 *Add the square of half the coefficient of x to both sides.*

$$x^2 + x + \frac{1}{4} = \frac{3}{2} + \frac{1}{4} \qquad Add \left(\frac{1}{2}\right)^2 = \frac{1}{4} \; to \; both \; sides$$

Step 4 *Factor the left side and simplify the right side.*

$$\left(x + \frac{1}{2}\right)^2 = \frac{7}{4} \qquad Since \; \frac{3}{2} + \frac{1}{4} = \frac{6}{4} + \frac{1}{4} = \frac{7}{4}$$

Step 5 *Solve using the square root property.*

$$x + \frac{1}{2} = \pm\frac{\sqrt{7}}{2} \qquad Take \; both \; square \; roots \; of \; \frac{7}{4}$$

$$x = -\frac{1}{2} \pm \frac{\sqrt{7}}{2} \qquad Subtract \; \frac{1}{2} \; from \; both \; sides$$

Try Problem 33 > The solutions are $-\frac{1}{2} + \frac{\sqrt{7}}{2}$ and $-\frac{1}{2} - \frac{\sqrt{7}}{2}$. ■

9.2 Problem Set

LEARNING THROUGH WRITING ☐ Describe the steps in solving a quadratic equation by completing the square.

Complete the square on each expression. Then factor the resulting perfect-square trinomial.

1. $x^2 - 8x$ **2.** $x^2 + 10x$ **3.** $m^2 + 12m$ **4.** $m^2 - 14m$

5. $r^2 - 2r$ **6.** $r^2 + 2r$ **7.** $y^2 + y$ **8.** $y^2 - y$

9. $p^2 + 3p$ **10.** $p^2 - 5p$ **11.** $z^2 - \frac{4}{5}z$ **12.** $z^2 + \frac{6}{5}z$

Solve each equation (a) by completing the square, (b) by factoring.

13. $x^2 - 4x + 3 = 0$ **14.** $x^2 - 8x + 7 = 0$ **15.** $x^2 + 6x + 9 = 0$ **16.** $x^2 + 2x + 1 = 0$

17. $x^2 - 10x = 0$ **18.** $x^2 - 6x = 0$

Solve each equation by completing the square. Simplify your answer.

19. $x^2 - 4x + 2 = 0$ **20.** $x^2 - 8x + 9 = 0$ **21.** $y^2 + 2y - 6 = 0$ **22.** $y^2 + 4y - 1 = 0$

23. $m^2 + 10m + 13 = 0$ **24.** $m^2 + 10m + 7 = 0$ **25.** $4x^2 + 8x = 3$ **26.** $4x^2 + 8x = 7$

27. $2p^2 + 4p = 11$ **28.** $2p^2 + 4p = 15$ **29.** $3r^2 - 6r - 5 = 0$ **30.** $3r^2 + 6r - 5 = 0$

31. $k^2 + k - 1 = 0$ **32.** $k^2 + k - 3 = 0$ **33.** $2x^2 + 2x - 5 = 0$ **34.** $2x^2 + 2x - 7 = 0$

35. $3y^2 = 2y + 1$ **36.** $3y^2 = -2y + 1$ **37.** $m^2 + 6m + 13 = 0$ **38.** $m^2 + 4m + 29 = 0$

39. $4p = -5p^2 + 4$ **40.** $8p = -5p^2 + 8$ **41.** $3t^2 - 8t + 6 = 0$ **42.** $3t^2 - 4t + 3 = 0$

Solve each problem.

43. The solutions of $x^2 - 4x + 1 = 0$ are $2 + \sqrt{3}$ and $2 - \sqrt{3}$. Check these solutions by substituting them into the equation.

44. The solutions of $x^2 - 2x - 4 = 0$ are $1 + \sqrt{5}$ and $1 - \sqrt{5}$. Check these solutions by substituting them into the equation.

45. The square of a positive number equals the sum of twice the number and 26. Find the number.

46. The square of a positive number equals the sum of twice the number and 62. Find the number.

47. One positive number is 3 more than another positive number. If their product is 7, what are the numbers?

48. One positive number is 5 more than another positive number. If their product is 8, what are the numbers?

9.3 The Quadratic Formula

Every quadratic equation can be solved by completing the square, but the method of completing the square is sometimes tedious to perform. We discussed this method for two main reasons: First, the process of completing the square has applications in other areas of mathematics. Second, we can use the method of completing the square to develop a formula for solving any quadratic equation.

Consider the standard form of a quadratic equation.

$$ax^2 + bx + c = 0 \qquad (a \neq 0)$$

We use the method of completing the square to solve this equation for x.

$$ax^2 + bx = -c \qquad \qquad \text{\textit{Subtract } c}$$

$$x^2 + \frac{b}{a}x = -\frac{c}{a} \qquad \qquad \text{\textit{Divide both sides by } a}$$

$$x^2 + \frac{b}{a}x + \frac{b^2}{4a^2} = -\frac{c}{a} + \frac{b^2}{4a^2} \qquad \text{\textit{Add} } \left(\frac{1}{2} \cdot \frac{b}{a}\right)^2 = \left(\frac{b}{2a}\right)^2 = \frac{b^2}{4a^2}$$

$$\left(x + \frac{b}{2a}\right)^2 = -\frac{c}{a} + \frac{b^2}{4a^2} \qquad \text{\textit{Factor the left side}}$$

$$\left(x + \frac{b}{2a}\right)^2 = -\frac{c}{a} \cdot \frac{4a}{4a} + \frac{b^2}{4a^2}$$

$$\left(x + \frac{b}{2a}\right)^2 = \frac{-4ac}{4a^2} + \frac{b^2}{4a^2} \qquad \left.\begin{array}{c} \\ \\ \\ \end{array}\right\} \text{\textit{Simplify the right side}}$$

$$\left(x + \frac{b}{2a}\right)^2 = \frac{b^2 - 4ac}{4a^2}$$

$$x + \frac{b}{2a} = \pm\sqrt{\frac{b^2 - 4ac}{4a^2}} \qquad \text{\textit{Square root property}}$$

$$x + \frac{b}{2a} = \pm\frac{\sqrt{b^2 - 4ac}}{\sqrt{4a^2}} \qquad \text{\textit{Quotient rule for radicals}}$$

$$x + \frac{b}{2a} = \pm\frac{\sqrt{b^2 - 4ac}}{2a} \qquad \text{\textit{Simplify the denominator}}$$

$$x = -\frac{b}{2a} \pm \frac{\sqrt{b^2 - 4ac}}{2a} \qquad \text{\textit{Subtract b/2a from both sides}}$$

$$x = \frac{-b \pm \sqrt{b^2 - 4ac}}{2a} \qquad \text{\textit{Combine the fractions}}$$

Both the quadratic formula and the method of completing the square were known by the Babylonians, as early as 2000 B.C.

The last equation is called the **quadratic formula,** and you should memorize it.

THE QUADRATIC FORMULA

The solutions of the quadratic equation $ax^2 + bx + c = 0$ are

$$x = \frac{-b + \sqrt{b^2 - 4ac}}{2a} \quad \text{and} \quad x = \frac{-b - \sqrt{b^2 - 4ac}}{2a}$$

EXAMPLE 1   Use the quadratic formula to solve $3x^2 + 5x = 2$.

Solution   Write the equation in the standard form $ax^2 + bx + c = 0$.

$$3x^2 + 5x = 2 \quad \textit{Original equation}$$
$$3x^2 + 5x - 2 = 0 \quad \textit{Subtract 2}$$

Identify a, b, and c.

$$a = 3 \quad b = 5 \quad c = -2$$

Substitute the values for a, b, and c into the quadratic formula.

$$x = \frac{-b \pm \sqrt{b^2 - 4ac}}{2a} \quad \textit{Quadratic formula}$$

$$x = \frac{-5 \pm \sqrt{5^2 - 4(3)(-2)}}{2(3)} \quad \textit{Substitute } a = 3, b = 5, \textit{ and } c = -2$$

Simplify the right side.

$$x = \frac{-5 \pm \sqrt{25 + 24}}{6}$$

$$x = \frac{-5 \pm \sqrt{49}}{6}$$

$$x = \frac{-5 \pm 7}{6}$$

Separate into two equations and simplify the right side of each equation.

$$x = \frac{-5 + 7}{6} \quad \text{or} \quad x = \frac{-5 - 7}{6}$$

$$x = \frac{1}{3} \quad \text{or} \quad x = -2$$

Try Problem 13 >   Both numbers check, so the solutions are 1/3 and -2.   ∎

The fact that the solutions to Example 1 were rational numbers means that we could have solved the equation by factoring. This is not the case in Example 2.

EXAMPLE 2   Solve $x^2 = 3x - 1$.

Solution   Write the equation in standard form.

$$x^2 - 3x + 1 = 0 \quad \textit{Subtract 3x and add 1}$$

The left side cannot be factored, so substitute $a = 1$, $b = -3$, and $c = 1$ into the quadratic formula.

$$x = \frac{-b \pm \sqrt{b^2 - 4ac}}{2a} \qquad \textit{Quadratic formula}$$

$$x = \frac{-(-3) \pm \sqrt{(-3)^2 - 4(1)(1)}}{2(1)} \qquad \textit{Substitute } a = 1, b = -3, \textit{ and } c = 1$$

$$x = \frac{3 \pm \sqrt{9 - 4}}{2}$$

$$x = \frac{3 \pm \sqrt{5}}{2} \qquad \textit{Simplify the right side}$$

Try Problem 21 >   The solutions are $\dfrac{3 + \sqrt{5}}{2}$ and $\dfrac{3 - \sqrt{5}}{2}$. ∎

Caution!   Be sure to divide the *entire* numerator in the quadratic formula by $2a$.

Correct	*Wrong*
$x = \dfrac{-b \pm \sqrt{b^2 - 4ac}}{2a}$	$x = -b \pm \dfrac{\sqrt{b^2 - 4ac}}{2a}$

If the radicand, $b^2 - 4ac$, **in the quadratic formula equals 0, the quadratic equation has just one real solution.** This is demonstrated in the next example.

EXAMPLE 3   Solve $x^2 - 6x + 9 = 0$.

Solution   The equation is already in standard form. Therefore substitute $a = 1$, $b = -6$, and $c = 9$ into the quadratic formula.

$$x = \frac{-b \pm \sqrt{b^2 - 4ac}}{2a}$$

$$x = \frac{-(-6) \pm \sqrt{(-6)^2 - 4(1)(9)}}{2(1)}$$

$$x = \frac{6 \pm \sqrt{36 - 36}}{2}$$

$$x = \frac{6 \pm 0}{2}$$

$$x = 3$$

Try Problem 27 >   The solution is 3. ∎

> **TO SOLVE A QUADRATIC EQUATION USING THE QUADRATIC FORMULA**
>
> 1. Write the equation in the standard form $ax^2 + bx + c = 0$. Be sure to clear fractions.
> 2. Identify a, b, and c.
> 3. Substitute the values for a, b, and c into the quadratic formula
>
> $$x = \frac{-b \pm \sqrt{b^2 - 4ac}}{2a}.$$
>
> 4. Simplify the right side.

EXAMPLE 4   Solve $\dfrac{1}{6}x^2 - \dfrac{1}{3}x - \dfrac{1}{3} = 0$.

Solution

Step 1 *Write the equation in the standard form $ax^2 + bx + c = 0$. Be sure to clear fractions.* The equation is already in standard form. We could use $a = 1/6$, $b = -1/3$, and $c = -1/3$. However, our calculations will be simpler if we clear fractions by multiplying both sides by the LCD, 6.

$$\frac{1}{6}x^2 - \frac{1}{3}x - \frac{1}{3} = 0 \qquad \textit{Original equation}$$

$$6\left(\frac{1}{6}x^2 - \frac{1}{3}x - \frac{1}{3}\right) = 6(0) \qquad \textit{Multiply both sides by 6}$$

$$x^2 - 2x - 2 = 0 \qquad \textit{Simplify each side}$$

Step 2 *Identify a, b, and c.*

$$a = 1 \qquad b = -2 \qquad c = -2$$

Step 3 *Substitute the values for a, b, and c into the quadratic formula.*

$$x = \frac{-b \pm \sqrt{b^2 - 4ac}}{2a} \qquad \textit{Quadratic formula}$$

$$x = \frac{-(-2) \pm \sqrt{(-2)^2 - 4(1)(-2)}}{2(1)} \qquad \textit{Substitute } a = 1,\ b = -2,\ and$$
$$\textit{c} = -2$$

Step 4   *Simplify the right side.*

$$x = \frac{2 \pm \sqrt{4 + 8}}{2}$$

$$x = \frac{2 \pm \sqrt{12}}{2}$$

$$x = \frac{2 \pm 2\sqrt{3}}{2} \qquad \textit{Since } \sqrt{12} = \sqrt{4}\sqrt{3} = 2\sqrt{3}$$

$$x = \frac{2(1 \pm \sqrt{3})}{2} \qquad \textit{Factor the numerator}$$

$$x = 1 \pm \sqrt{3} \qquad \textit{Divide out the common factor 2}$$

Try Problem 47 >   The solutions are $1 + \sqrt{3}$ and $1 - \sqrt{3}$.   ■

Caution! ■   Be careful when you are simplifying your answer to a quadratic equation.

Correct

$$\frac{6 + \cancel{3}\sqrt{2}}{6} = \frac{3(2 + \sqrt{2})}{\cancel{3} \cdot 2}$$

Wrong

$$\frac{6 + 3\sqrt{2}}{6} \ \cancel{=} \ \frac{\cancel{6} + 3\sqrt{2}}{\cancel{6}}$$

If the radicand, $b^2 - 4ac$, in the quadratic formula is negative, the quadratic equation has no real solutions. This is demonstrated in the next example.

EXAMPLE 5   Solve $x^2 + 9 = 0$.

Solution   Substitute $a = 1$, $b = 0$, and $c = 9$ into the quadratic formula.

$$x = \frac{-0 \pm \sqrt{0^2 - 4(1)(9)}}{2(1)} = \frac{\pm\sqrt{-36}}{2}$$

Try Problem 55 >   But $\sqrt{-36}$ is not a real number. Therefore the equation has no real solutions.

■

P R O B L E M   S O L V I N G

EXAMPLE 6   A piece of metal 16 inches wide is to be made into a trough with a rectangular cross section by folding up its edges (see Fig. 9.2). What should the height, x, of the trough be if the area of the cross section is to be 10 square inches?

Solution   The length of the rectangular cross section is $16 - 2x$ and the width is x (see Fig. 9.2). Therefore we can write the following equation.

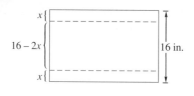
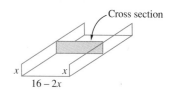

FIGURE 9.2

Area of cross section is 10

$$\overbrace{x(16 - 2x)}^{} = 10$$

Solve for x.

$$16x - 2x^2 = 10 \qquad \textit{Distribute } x$$
$$-2x^2 + 16x - 10 = 0 \qquad \textit{Subtract } 10$$
$$\frac{-2x^2}{-2} + \frac{16x}{-2} - \frac{10}{-2} = \frac{0}{-2} \qquad \textit{Divide by } -2$$
$$x^2 - 8x + 5 = 0 \qquad \textit{Simplify}$$

Substitute $a = 1$, $b = -8$, and $c = 5$ into the quadratic formula and simplify.

$$x = \frac{-(-8) \pm \sqrt{(-8)^2 - 4(1)(5)}}{2(1)}$$

$$x = \frac{8 \pm \sqrt{64 - 20}}{2} = \frac{8 \pm \sqrt{44}}{2}$$

But $\sqrt{44} = \sqrt{4}\sqrt{11} = 2\sqrt{11}$. Therefore

$$x = \frac{8 \pm 2\sqrt{11}}{2} = \frac{8}{2} \pm \frac{2\sqrt{11}}{2} = 4 \pm \sqrt{11}.$$

Try Problem 63 >

There are two possible heights for the trough, namely, $x = 4 + \sqrt{11}$ (approximately 7.32) in. and $x = 4 - \sqrt{11}$ (approximately 0.68) in.

9.3 Problem Set

LEARNING THROUGH WRITING

☐ What method was used to prove the quadratic formula?

☐ If $b^2 - 4ac$ is 0, what can be said about the solutions of $ax^2 + bx + c = 0$?

☐ If $b^2 - 4ac$ is negative, what can be said about the solutions of $ax^2 + bx + c = 0$?

☐ Describe the steps in using the quadratic formula to solve a quadratic equation.

Write each quadratic equation in standard form, and identify a, b, and c. Do not solve the equation.

1. $2x^2 + 9x = -4$

2. $3x^2 + 7x = -2$

3. $x^2 + 4 = 4x$

4. $x^2 + 9 = 6x$

5. $x^2 = x$

6. $x^2 = 1$

7. $9(x^2 + x) - 25 = 9x$

8. $4(x^2 - x) + 5 = 5(1 - x)$

9. $(2x + 3)^2 = 4(3x + 2)$

10. $(3x + 2)^2 = 2(5x + 2)$

11. $2(x^2 + 1) - x = 4x - 3 + x^2$

12. $4(x^2 + x) - 6 = 3x^2 + 4(x + 1)$

Solve each equation (a) using the quadratic formula, (b) by factoring.

13. $3x^2 + x = 2$

14. $3x^2 + 2x = 1$

15. $p^2 - 6p = 0$

16. $p^2 - 7p = 0$

17. $r^2 - 4 = 0$

18. $r^2 - 9 = 0$

Use the quadratic formula to solve each equation. Simplify your answer.

19. $x^2 + 3x + 1 = 0$

20. $x^2 + 5x + 3 = 0$

21. $x^2 = 5x - 1$

22. $x^2 = 5x - 5$

23. $2m^2 - 3m - 1 = 0$

24. $2m^2 - 5m - 1 = 0$

25. $3p^2 + p = 1$

26. $3p^2 + p = 3$

27. $x^2 - 4x + 4 = 0$

28. $x^2 - 10x + 25 = 0$

29. $r^2 - 2r - 7 = 0$

30. $r^2 - 2r - 11 = 0$

31. $2t^2 - 4t - 1 = 0$

32. $3t^2 - 2t - 2 = 0$

33. $5y^2 - 10y + 4 = 0$

34. $6y^2 - 12y + 5 = 0$

35. $m^2 - 18 = 0$

36. $m^2 - 45 = 0$

37. $4p^2 + 6p + 1 = 0$

38. $4p^2 + 10p + 3 = 0$

39. $5k = 4 - 6k^2$

40. $k = 2 - 6k^2$

41. $0 = 9z^2 - 6z - 1$

42. $0 = 9z^2 - 6z - 2$

Use the quadratic formula to solve each equation. Simplify your answer.

43. $4(x^2 + 2) = 7 - 7x$

44. $4(x^2 + 3) = 11 - 9x$

45. $(y + 4)(y - 3) = -(y + 3)$

46. $(y + 5)(y - 2) = -(y + 3)$

47. $\frac{1}{6}x^2 - \frac{1}{3}x - 1 = 0$

48. $\frac{1}{8}x^2 - \frac{1}{4}x - \frac{1}{2} = 0$

49. $\frac{1}{4}r^2 - \frac{1}{3}r - \frac{5}{12} = 0$

50. $\frac{2}{3}r^2 - \frac{4}{9}r - \frac{1}{3} = 0$

51. $\frac{p^2}{2} + p = \frac{5}{4}$

52. $\frac{3p^2}{2} - p = 2$

53. $6 + \frac{3}{t} = \frac{4}{t^2}$

54. $5 + \frac{3}{t} = \frac{3}{t^2}$

Use the quadratic formula to solve each equation.

55. $x^2 + 1 = 0$

56. $x^2 + 16 = 0$

57. $y^2 - 2y + 2 = 0$

58. $y^2 - 2y + 5 = 0$

59. $2m^2 + 3m + 5 = 0$

60. $3m^2 + 5m + 7 = 0$

Solve each word problem.

61. One number is 1 more than twice another. The sum of the squares of the two numbers is 5. Find the numbers.

62. One number is 3 more than twice another. The sum of the squares of the numbers is 7. Find the numbers.

63. A piece of metal 12 inches wide is to be made into a trough with a rectangular cross section by folding up its edges (see Fig. 9.3). What should the height, x, of the trough be if the area of the cross section is to be 8 square inches?

64. A piece of metal 12 inches wide is to be made into a trough with a rectangular cross section by folding up its edges (see Fig. 9.3). What should the height, x, of the trough be if the area of the cross section is to be 6 square inches?

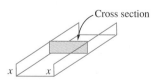

FIGURE 9.3

65. One computer can perform a job in 1 hour less than it takes another computer. If both computers working together can perform the job in 2 hours, how long would it take each computer working alone?

66. One pipe can fill a tank in 2 hours less than it takes another pipe. If both pipes are open, it takes 4 hours to fill the tank. How long would it take each pipe to fill the tank on its own?

67. The speed of a boat in still water is 6 mph. The boat travels 4 miles upstream and 7 miles downstream in a total time of 2 hours. Find the speed of the current.

68. The speed of a boat in still water is 9 mph. The boat travels 8 miles upstream and 11 miles downstream in a total time of 3 hours. Find the speed of the current.

69. A ball is thrown vertically upward with an initial velocity of 48 feet per second. The height h, in feet, of the ball after t seconds is given by the formula $h = -16t^2 + 48t$.
 a. When will the height, h, be 16 feet?
 b. When will the height, h, be 64 feet?

70. A stone is thrown vertically upward with an initial velocity of 40 feet per second. The height h, in feet, of the stone after t seconds is given by the formula $h = -16t^2 + 40t$.
 a. When will the height, h, be 20 feet?
 b. When will the height, h, be 32 feet?

9.4 Summary of Quadratic Equations

Here is a summary of the advantages and disadvantages of each method for solving a quadratic equation.

CHOOSING A METHOD TO SOLVE A QUADRATIC EQUATION

Method	Advantages	Disadvantages
Factoring	Easy and fast	Not all equations are factorable Some equations are difficult to factor because their coefficients are large
Square root property	Best method for solving equations of the form $x^2 = k$	Many equations are not of this form
Completing the square	Useful in other areas of mathematics	Sometimes tedious to use
Quadratic formula	Will solve any quadratic equation	Not as easy to use as factoring or the square root property

EXAMPLE 1   Solve $2y^2 + 11y = 21$.

Solution   If the equation is written in standard form, the left side is easily factored. Therefore solve by factoring.

$$2y^2 + 11y - 21 = 0 \quad \textit{Subtract 21}$$
$$(2y - 3)(y + 7) = 0 \quad \textit{Factor}$$

$$2y - 3 = 0 \quad \text{or} \quad y + 7 = 0 \quad \textit{Set each factor equal to 0}$$
$$2y = 3$$
$$y = \frac{3}{2} \quad \text{or} \quad y = -7 \quad \Big\} \textit{Solve each linear equation.}$$

Try Problem 11 >   The solutions are 3/2 and −7.   ■

EXAMPLE 2   Solve $4(p + 8)^2 = 100$.

Solution   If both sides are divided by 4, the equation takes the form $x^2 = k$. Therefore solve using the square root property.

$$(p + 8)^2 = 25 \quad \textit{Divide by 4}$$
$$p + 8 = \pm 5 \quad \textit{Take both square roots of 25}$$
$$p = -8 \pm 5 \quad \textit{Subtract 8}$$

$$p = -8 + 5 \quad \text{or} \quad p = -8 - 5 \quad \textit{Split into two equations}$$
$$p = -3 \quad \text{or} \quad p = -13 \quad \textit{Simplify}$$

Try Problem 17 >   The solutions are −3 and −13.   ■

EXAMPLE 3   Solve $3x^2 - 5x + 1 = 0$.

Solution   The left side cannot be factored using integers. Therefore use the quadratic formula with $a = 3$, $b = -5$, and $c = 1$.

$$x = \frac{-b \pm \sqrt{b^2 - 4ac}}{2a}$$

$$x = \frac{-(-5) \pm \sqrt{(-5)^2 - 4(3)(1)}}{2(3)}$$

$$x = \frac{5 \pm \sqrt{25 - 12}}{6} = \frac{-5 \pm \sqrt{13}}{6}$$

Try Problem 25 >   The solutions are $\dfrac{-5 + \sqrt{13}}{6}$ and $\dfrac{-5 - \sqrt{13}}{6}$.   ■

9.4   Problem Set

LEARNING THROUGH WRITING

☐ Discuss the advantages and disadvantages of the four methods for solving a quadratic equation.

Solve each quadratic equation. Simplify your answer.

1. $x^2 = 121$

2. $x^2 = 144$

3. $9y^2 = 36y$

4. $4y^2 = 100y$

5. $z^2 - 8z + 15 = 0$

6. $z^2 - 12z + 35 = 0$

7. $x^2 - x = 1$

8. $x^2 + x = 1$

9. $m^2 = 0$

10. $m^2 = 1$

11. $2y^2 + 9y = 35$

12. $3y^2 + 19y = 14$

13. $4r^2 - 81 = 0$

14. $9r^2 - 64 = 0$

15. $k^2 - 13 = 0$

16. $k^2 - 17 = 0$

17. $6(p + 6)^2 = 54$

18. $5(p + 7)^2 = 80$

19. $-t^2 + 32 = 0$

20. $-t^2 + 63 = 0$

21. $25m^2 = 40m - 16$

22. $16m^2 = 24m - 9$

23. $(6z - 2)^2 = 90$

24. $(6z - 3)^2 = 48$

25. $3x^2 - 7x + 3 = 0$

26. $2x^2 - 5x + 1 = 0$

27. $(y + 4)^2 = 8y$

28. $(y + 3)^2 = 6y$

29. $24k^2 + 70k - 75 = 0$

30. $36k^2 + 95k - 150 = 0$

31. $(3r + 2)^2 = r^2 + 11r + 4$

32. $(2r + 5)^2 = r^2 + 19r + 25$

33. $(2p + 1)(p - 2) = 2p - 6$

34. $(4p - 3)(p + 1) = 7p - 6$

35. $x^2 + \dfrac{2}{3}x - \dfrac{1}{2} = 0$

36. $x^2 + \dfrac{4}{3}x - \dfrac{1}{2} = 0$

9.5   Complex Solutions of Quadratic Equations

René Descartes (1596–1650) introduced the term *imaginary number,* thus giving such numbers a permanent stigma. Of course, these numbers really do exist and, in fact, have a wide variety of useful applications in physics and engineering. The first application of imaginary numbers was introduced by Charles Steinmetz (1865–1923), who used them to explain the behavior of electric circuits.

Earlier we noted that $\sqrt{-4}$ is not a real number. In this section we see that such numbers are called **imaginary numbers.**

DEFINITION OF THE IMAGINARY UNIT

The **imaginary unit** is denoted i, where

$$i = \sqrt{-1} \quad \text{and} \quad i^2 = -1.$$

If we extend the product rule for radicals so that it applies when one of the radicands is negative, we can write square roots of negative numbers in terms of i.

EXAMPLE 1   Write each square root in terms of i.

Try Problem 1 >

a. $\sqrt{-9} = \sqrt{9 \cdot (-1)} = \sqrt{9} \cdot \sqrt{-1} = 3i$

b. $\sqrt{-5} = \sqrt{5 \cdot (-1)} = \sqrt{5} \cdot \sqrt{-1} = \sqrt{5}i$

c. $\sqrt{-12} = \sqrt{12 \cdot (-1)} = \sqrt{12} \cdot \sqrt{-1} = 2\sqrt{3}i$ ■

Caution! ■

■ The number $\sqrt{5}i$ means $(\sqrt{5})i$ and not $\sqrt{5i}$. To avoid confusion we will write $\sqrt{5}i$ as $i\sqrt{5}$, and we will write $2\sqrt{3}i$ as $2i\sqrt{3}$.

The numbers $3i$, $i\sqrt{5}$, and $2i\sqrt{3}$ are all imaginary numbers. Other examples of imaginary numbers are $3 + 4i$ and $5 - 7i$. If we combine the set of imaginary numbers with the set of real numbers, we obtain the set of *complex numbers*.

DEFINITION OF A COMPLEX NUMBER

A **complex number** is a number of the form

   $a + bi,$

where a and b are real numbers and $i = \sqrt{-1}$.

Since every real number and every imaginary number is a complex number, all of the following numbers are complex numbers.

$$9 + 13i \quad 10 \quad i \quad i\sqrt{3} \quad \sqrt{7} \quad -2.8 \quad 0 \quad -1 - \frac{3}{5}i$$

Note that if $b = 0$, the complex number $a + bi$ is simply the real number a. For example, $8 + 0i$ is the real number 8. If $a = 0$, the complex number $a + bi$ becomes bi, which is called a **pure imaginary number** (so long as $b \neq 0$). For example, $0 + 6i$ is the pure imaginary number $6i$. Fig. 9.4 illustrates the relationships between the set of complex numbers and its subsets.

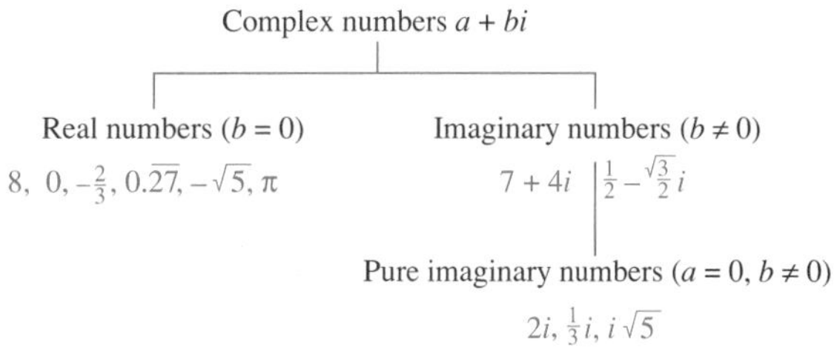

Complex numbers $a + bi$

Real numbers ($b = 0$)   Imaginary numbers ($b \neq 0$)

$8, \ 0, -\frac{2}{3}, 0.\overline{27}, -\sqrt{5}, \pi$ $7 + 4i \quad \frac{1}{2} - \frac{\sqrt{3}}{2}i$

Pure imaginary numbers ($a = 0, b \neq 0$)

$2i, \frac{1}{3}i, i\sqrt{5}$

FIGURE 9.4

We add, subtract, multiply, and divide complex numbers as if they were polynomials in i.

EXAMPLE 2   Add $5 + 3i$ and $2 + 6i$.

Solution

$$\begin{aligned}(5 + 3i) + (2 + 6i) &= 5 + 3i + 2 + 6i \quad \text{\textit{Remove parentheses}}\\ &= 7 + 9i \quad\quad\quad\quad\ \text{\textit{Combine like terms}}\end{aligned}$$

Try Problem 19 >

EXAMPLE 3   Add $-4 - i$ and $7i$.

Solution

$$\begin{aligned}(-4 - i) + 7i &= -4 - i + 7i \quad \text{\textit{Remove parentheses}}\\ &= -4 + 6i \quad\quad\ \ \text{\textit{Combine like terms}}\end{aligned}$$

Try Problem 23 >

EXAMPLE 4   Subtract $1 + 8i$ from $5 + 2i$.

Solution

Try Problem 25 >

$$(5 + 2i) - (1 + 8i) = 5 + 2i - 1 - 8i \quad \textit{Distribute} -1$$
$$= 4 - 6i \quad \textit{Combine like terms} \quad \blacksquare$$

EXAMPLE 5   Subtract $3 + 2i$ from 9.

Solution

Try Problem 29 >

$$9 - (3 + 2i) = 9 - 3 - 2i \quad \textit{Distribute} -1$$
$$= 6 - 2i \quad \textit{Combine like terms} \quad \blacksquare$$

When you multiply or divide complex numbers, make sure you always replace i^2 with -1.

EXAMPLE 6   Multiply $3i$ and $4 - 2i$.

Solution

Try Problem 31 >

$$3i(4 - 2i) = 3i \cdot 4 - 3i \cdot 2i \quad \textit{Distribute } 3i$$
$$= 12i - 6i^2 \quad \textit{Find each product}$$
$$= 12i - 6(-1) \quad \textit{Replace } i^2 \textit{ with } -1$$
$$= 6 + 12i \quad \textit{Simplify} \quad \blacksquare$$

EXAMPLE 7   Multiply $4 + 5i$ and $2 + 3i$.

Solution

Try Problem 33 >

$$(4 + 5i)(2 + 3i)$$
$$= 4 \cdot 2 + 4 \cdot 3i + 5i \cdot 2 + 5i \cdot 3i \quad \textit{FOIL method}$$
$$= 8 + 12i + 10i + 15i^2 \quad \textit{Find each product}$$
$$= 8 + 12i + 10i + 15(-1) \quad \textit{Replace } i^2 \textit{ with } -1$$
$$= -7 + 22i \quad \textit{Combine like terms} \quad \blacksquare$$

The complex numbers $a + bi$ and $a - bi$ are called **complex conjugates** of each other. The product of two complex conjugates is always a real number, because when you multiply a sum and a difference of two terms, the middle term drops out.

$$(a + bi)(a - bi) = a^2 - (bi)^2$$
$$= a^2 - b^2 i^2$$
$$= a^2 - b^2(-1)$$
$$= a^2 + b^2$$

Note that $a^2 + b^2$ is a real number, because a and b are real numbers.

The easiest way to find the quotient of two complex numbers, such as

$$\frac{7 - i}{3 + i},$$

is to multiply numerator and denominator by the conjugate of the denominator. This produces a real number in the denominator. From there it is easy to write the fraction in the form $a + bi$.

EXAMPLE 8   Divide $7 - i$ by $3 + i$.

Solution   Multiply numerator and denominator by the conjugate of the denominator.

$$\frac{7 - i}{3 + i} = \frac{7 - i}{3 + i} \cdot \frac{3 - i}{3 - i} \qquad \textit{The conjugate of } 3 + i \textit{ is } 3 - i$$

$$= \frac{21 - 7i - 3i + i^2}{3^2 - i^2} \qquad \textit{Multiply numerators, multiply denominators}$$

$$= \frac{21 - 7i - 3i + (-1)}{9 - (-1)} \qquad \textit{Replace } i^2 \textit{ with } -1$$

$$= \frac{20 - 10i}{10} \qquad \textit{Simplify}$$

The denominator is now a real number. Write the fraction in the form $a - bi$ as follows.

$$= \frac{20}{10} - \frac{10i}{10} \qquad \textit{Divide each term by } 10$$

Try Problem 45 >

$$= 2 - i \qquad \textit{Simplify} \qquad \blacksquare$$

Note the similarity between rationalizing denominators and dividing complex numbers. In one case, we remove radicals from the denominator; in the other we remove i, which is the radical $\sqrt{-1}$.

EXAMPLE 9   Divide $3 + 5i$ by i.

Solution

$$\frac{3 + 5i}{i} = \frac{3 + 5i}{i} \cdot \frac{-i}{-i} \qquad \textit{The conjugate of } i \textit{ is } -i.$$

$$= \frac{-3i - 5i^2}{-i^2} \qquad \textit{Multiply numerators, multiply denominators}$$

$$= \frac{-3i - 5(-1)}{-(-1)} \qquad \textit{Replace } i^2 \textit{ with } -1$$

$$= \frac{5 - 3i}{1} \quad \Bigg\} \textit{Simplify}$$

Try Problem 49 >

$$= 5 - 3i \qquad \blacksquare$$

We can now solve quadratic equations that have complex solutions.

EXAMPLE 10   Solve $x^2 + 49 = 0$.

Solution   Solve using the square root property.

$$x^2 = -49 \qquad \textit{Subtract } 49$$
$$x = \pm\sqrt{-49} \qquad \textit{Take both square roots of } -49$$
$$x = \pm 7i \qquad \textit{Simplify the radical}$$

Try Problem 51 >   The solutions are $7i$ and $-7i$. $\blacksquare$

EXAMPLE 11   Solve $(3y - 5)^2 = -54$.

Solution

$$3y - 5 = \pm\sqrt{-54} \qquad \textit{Square root property}$$
$$3y - 5 = \pm3i\sqrt{6} \qquad \textit{Since } \sqrt{-54} = \sqrt{9}\sqrt{6}\sqrt{-1} = 3\sqrt{6}i = 3i\sqrt{6}$$
$$3y = 5 \pm 3i\sqrt{6} \qquad \textit{Add 5}$$
$$y = \frac{5 \pm 3i\sqrt{6}}{3} \qquad \textit{Divide by 3}$$
$$y = \frac{5}{3} \pm i\sqrt{6} \qquad \textit{Simplify}$$

Try Problem 57 >   The solutions are $\dfrac{5}{3} + i\sqrt{6}$ and $\dfrac{5}{3} - i\sqrt{6}$.   ■

EXAMPLE 12   Solve $p^2 - 6p + 13 = 0$.

Solution   Use the quadratic formula with $a = 1$, $b = -6$, and $c = 13$.

$$p = \frac{-(-6) \pm \sqrt{(-6)^2 - 4(1)(13)}}{2(1)}$$
$$p = \frac{6 \pm \sqrt{36 - 52}}{2}$$
$$p = \frac{6 \pm \sqrt{-16}}{2}$$
$$p = \frac{6 \pm 4i}{2}$$
$$p = 3 \pm 2i$$

Try Problem 61 >   The solutions are $3 + 2i$ and $3 - 2i$.   ■

9.5 Problem Set

LEARNING THROUGH WRITING

☐ Tell everything you know about the number i.

☐ Why do we write $\sqrt{3}i$ as $i\sqrt{3}$?

☐ Define the term *complex number*.

☐ Define the term *imaginary number*.

☐ Define the term *pure imaginary number*.

☐ How do we treat complex numbers when we add, subtract, multiply, and divide them?

☐ Define the term *complex conjugates*.

☐ Explain how to divide two complex numbers.

Write each square root in terms of i.

1. $\sqrt{-4}$

2. $\sqrt{-25}$

3. $\sqrt{-3}$

4. $\sqrt{-7}$

5. $\sqrt{-20}$

6. $\sqrt{-18}$

7. $-\sqrt{-36}$

8. $-\sqrt{-64}$

9. $\sqrt{-\dfrac{1}{9}}$

10. $\sqrt{-\dfrac{1}{16}}$

11. $\sqrt{-\dfrac{3}{4}}$

12. $\sqrt{-\dfrac{5}{9}}$

True or false.

13. Every real number is also a complex number.

14. Every imaginary number is also a complex number.

15. No real number is also an imaginary number.

16. No imaginary number is also a real number.

17. Every pure imaginary number is also an imaginary number.

18. Some imaginary numbers are not pure imaginary numbers.

Add or subtract as indicated.

19. $(6 + 2i) + (4 + 5i)$

20. $(3 + 4i) + (7 + 2i)$

21. $(-8 + 3i) + (7 - 4i)$

22. $(5 - 6i) + (4 - 9i)$

23. $(-5 - i) + 6i$

24. $(-8 + i) + (-4i)$

25. $(10 + 4i) - (3 + 7i)$

26. $(12 + 3i) - (5 + 8i)$

27. $(6 - 5i) - (2 - 5i)$

28. $(7 + 2i) - (3 + 2i)$

29. $15 - (4 + 9i)$

30. $13 - (5 + 7i)$

Multiply.

31. $2i(6 - 3i)$

32. $4i(5 - 2i)$

33. $(2 + 7i)(3 + 4i)$

34. $(5 + 2i)(4 + 3i)$

35. $(5 + 2i)(6 - i)$

36. $(6 - 5i)(2 - 7i)$

37. $(3 - 4i)(3 + 4i)$

38. $(6 - 2i)(6 + 2i)$

39. i^3

40. i^4

41. i^5

42. i^6

Divide.

43. $\dfrac{4}{1 + i}$

44. $\dfrac{10}{1 - i}$

45. $\dfrac{9 + 2i}{2 + i}$

46. $\dfrac{9 - 2i}{4 + i}$

47. $\dfrac{4 - 5i}{3 - 2i}$

48. $\dfrac{1 + 6i}{4 - 3i}$

49. $\dfrac{3 + 4i}{5i}$

50. $\dfrac{5 - 3i}{4i}$

Solve each quadratic equation. Write your answer in terms of i and in simplest form.

51. $x^2 + 25 = 0$

52. $x^2 + 64 = 0$

53. $y^2 + 8 = 0$

54. $y^2 + 27 = 0$

55. $(z - 4)^2 = -7$

56. $(z - 6)^2 = -5$

57. $(3y - 8)^2 = -90$

58. $(4y - 9)^2 = -96$

59. $-2(t + 5)^2 = 72$

60. $-3(t + 2)^2 = 147$

61. $p^2 - 4p + 5 = 0$

62. $p^2 - 6p + 10 = 0$

63. $r^2 + 3r + 4 = 0$

64. $r^2 + 5r + 7 = 0$

65. $2m^2 - 4m + 5 = 0$

66. $3m^2 - 2m + 3 = 0$

67. $4k^2 + 3 = -2k$

68. $6k^2 + 5 = -2k$

9.6   Graphing Parabolas

In Chapter 6 we graphed equations in two variables of the form

$$y = mx + b.$$

For example, we graphed equations like $y = 2x + 6$ and $y = -3x$. The graphs of these equations were straight lines.

In this section we graph equations in two variables of the form

$$y = ax^2 + bx + c \qquad (a \neq 0).$$

For example, we graph the equations

$$y = x^2, \qquad y = -x^2 + 4, \qquad \text{and} \qquad y = x^2 - 2x - 3.$$

Each of these equations graphs into a curve called a **parabola.**

EXAMPLE 1   Graph $y = x^2$.

Solution   To construct a table of values, substitute any convenient values for x into $y = x^2$. Then compute the corresponding values for y.

x	y
3	9
2	4
1	1
0	0
-1	1
-2	4
-3	9

If $x = 3$,   then $y = 3^2 = 9$

If $x = 2$,   then $y = 2^2 = 4$

If $x = 1$,   then $y = 1^2 = 1$

If $x = 0$,   then $y = 0^2 = 0$

If $x = -1$, then $y = (-1)^2 = 1$

If $x = -2$, then $y = (-2)^2 = 4$

If $x = -3$, then $y = (-3)^2 = 9$

Try Problem 1 >

Graph the points $(3, 9)$, $(2, 4)$, $(1, 1)$, $(0, 0)$, $(-1, 1)$, $(-2, 4)$, and $(-3, 9)$. Then draw a smooth curve through them to get the parabola shown in Fig. 9.5. ∎

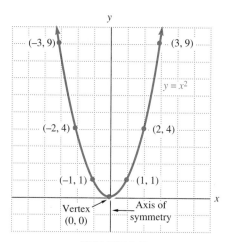

FIGURE 9.5

The lowest point on a parabola that opens upward is called the **vertex of the parabola.** Thus the vertex in Fig. 9.5 is $(0, 0)$. The vertical line through the vertex of a parabola that opens upward is called the **axis of symmetry of the**

parabola. Thus the axis of symmetry in Fig. 9.5 is the y-axis. Note that if we folded the page along the axis of symmetry in Fig. 9.5, the two halves of the parabola would coincide.

The next example illustrates that when a is a negative number, the parabola $y = ax^2 + bx + c$ opens downward.

EXAMPLE 2   Graph $y = -x^2 + 4$.

Solution   Construct the following table of values.

x	y
3	-5
2	0
1	3
0	4
-1	3
-2	0
-3	-5

If $x = 3$,   then $y = -3^2 + 4 = -9 + 4 = -5$

If $x = 2$,   then $y = -2^2 + 4 = -4 + 4 = 0$

If $x = 1$,   then $y = -1^2 + 4 = -1 + 4 = 3$

If $x = 0$,   then $y = -0^2 + 4 = -0 + 4 = 4$

If $x = -1$, then $y = -(-1)^2 + 4 = -1 + 4 = 3$

If $x = -2$, then $y = -(-2)^2 + 4 = -4 + 4 = 0$

If $x = -3$, then $y = -(-3)^2 + 4 = -9 + 4 = -5$

Plot these points and draw a smooth curve through them to produce the parabola shown in Fig. 9.6. In this case the vertex is $(0, 4)$, and it is the highest point on the parabola.   ∎

Try Problem 3 >

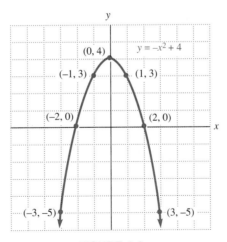

FIGURE 9.6

The most important points of the parabola $y = ax^2 + bx + c$ are the y-intercept, the x-intercepts, and the vertex. To find the y-intercept, set $x = 0$.

$$y = a(0)^2 + b(0) + c$$
$$y = c$$

Therefore there is one y-intercept, and it is c.

To find the x-intercept, set $y = 0$.

$$0 = ax^2 + bx + c$$

Since this is a quadratic equation, it will have 2, 1, or 0 real solutions. Therefore the parabola $y = ax^2 + bx + c$ will have 2, 1, or 0 x-intercepts, as shown in Fig. 9.7.

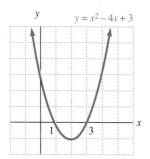

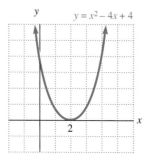

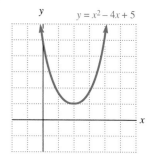

Two solutions to
$x^2 - 4x + 3 = 0$;
namely, $x = 1$ and $x = 3$

One solution to
$x^2 - 4x + 4 = 0$;
namely, $x = 2$

No real solution to
$x^2 - 4x + 5 = 0$

FIGURE 9.7

To find the x-value of the vertex, use the following formula.

VERTEX OF A PARABOLA

The vertex of the parabola $y = ax^2 + bx + c$ occurs at

$$x = \frac{-b}{2a}.$$

We could prove this formula by rewriting the right side of the equation $y = ax^2 + bx + c$, but we shall leave this proof to a more advanced course.

EXAMPLE 3   Graph $y = x^2 - 6x$. Label the y-intercept, the x-intercepts, and the vertex.

Solution   Since $c = 0$, the y-intercept is 0. To find the x-intercepts, set $y = 0$.

$$0 = x^2 - 6x \qquad \textit{Set } y = 0$$
$$0 = x(x - 6) \qquad \textit{Factor}$$

$$x = 0 \quad \text{or} \quad x - 6 = 0 \qquad \textit{Set each factor equal to 0}$$
$$x = 0 \quad \text{or} \quad x = 6 \qquad \textit{Two x-intercepts}$$

To find the x-value of the vertex, substitute $b = -6$ and $a = 1$ into the vertex formula.

$$x = \frac{-b}{2a} \qquad \textit{Vertex formula}$$

$$x = \frac{-(-6)}{2(1)} \qquad \textit{Substitute } b = -6 \textit{ and } a = 1$$

$$x = 3 \qquad \textit{Simplify}$$

To find the y-value of the vertex, substitute the x-value of the vertex, namely $x = 3$, into the original equation.

$$y = x^2 - 6x \qquad \textit{Original equation}$$
$$y = 3^2 - 6(3) \qquad \textit{Substitute } x = 3$$
$$\left.\begin{array}{l} y = 9 - 18 \\ y = -9 \end{array}\right\} \textit{Simplify}$$

Since $a = 1$ (a positive number), the parabola opens upward, as shown in

Try Problem 7 >

Fig. 9.8.   ▪

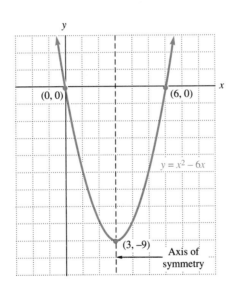

FIGURE 9.8

EXAMPLE 4   Graph $y = x^2 - 2x - 3$. Label the intercepts and the vertex.

Solution   The y-intercept is -3. To find the x-intercepts, set $y = 0$.

$$0 = x^2 - 2x - 3 \qquad \textit{Set } y = 0$$
$$0 = (x + 1)(x - 3) \qquad \textit{Factor}$$

$$x = -1 \quad \text{or} \quad x = 3 \qquad \textit{Two x-intercepts}$$

To find the x-value of the vertex, substitute $b = -2$ and $a = 1$ into the vertex formula.

$$x = \frac{-b}{2a} = \frac{-(-2)}{2(1)} = \frac{2}{2} = 1$$

To find the y-value of the vertex, substitute $x = 1$ into the original equation.

$$y = 1^2 - 2(1) - 3 = 1 - 2 - 3 = -4$$

Try Problem 13 >

Using symmetry, we conclude that the point $(2, -3)$ must be on the parabola since the point $(0, -3)$ is on the parabola (see Fig. 9.9). ∎

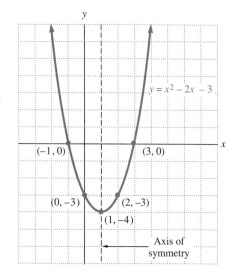

FIGURE 9.9

We can summarize the procedure for graphing a parabola as follows.

TO GRAPH THE PARABOLA $y = ax^2 + bx + c$

1. Note that the y-intercept is c.
2. Set $y = 0$ to find the x-intercepts. There will be 2, 1, or 0 x-intercepts.
3. Use the formula $x = -b/2a$ to find the x-value of the vertex.
4. Substitute the x-value found in Step 3 into the original equation to find the y-value of the vertex.
5. If $a > 0$, the parabola opens upward; if $a < 0$, the parabola opens downward.
6. Draw a smooth curve through the intercepts and the vertex. Plot additional points if necessary.

EXAMPLE 5   Graph $y = x^2 - 2x + 1$. Label the intercepts and the vertex.

Solution
Step 1   *Note that the y-intercept is 1.*

Step 2   *Set y = 0 to find the x-intercepts.*

$$0 = x^2 - 2x + 1 \qquad \textit{Set } y = 0$$
$$0 = (x - 1)(x - 1) \qquad \textit{Factor}$$
$$x = 1 \qquad\qquad \textit{One x-intercept}$$

Step 3   *Use the formula $x = -b/2a$ to find the x-value of the vertex.*

$$x = \frac{-(-2)}{2(1)} = 1 \qquad \textit{Substitute } b = -2 \textit{ and } a = 1$$

Step 4   *Substitute the x-value found in Step 3 into the original equation to find the y-value of the vertex.*

$$y = x^2 - 2x + 1 \qquad \textit{Original equation}$$
$$y = 1^2 - 2(1) + 1 \qquad \textit{Substitute } x = 1$$
$$y = 0 \qquad\qquad \textit{Simplify}$$

Step 5   *Since $a > 0$, the parabola opens upward.*

Step 6   *Draw a smooth curve through the intercepts and the vertex. Plot additional points if necessary.* Since the vertex and the x-intercept occur at the same point, (1, 0), find some additional points to make the graph more accurate.

If $x = -1$, then $y = (-1)^2 - 2(-1) + 1 = 4$.

We now know that the points $(-1, 4)$ and $(0, 1)$ and the vertex, $(1, 0)$, are on the parabola. Using symmetry we conclude that $(2, 1)$ and $(3, 4)$ must be on the parabola. This gives the graph shown in Fig. 9.10.   ■

Try Problem 17 >

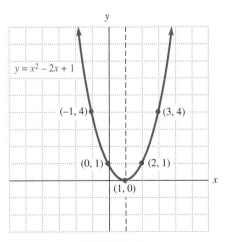

FIGURE 9.10

Caution! ■   Here are some common errors that students make when graphing parabolas.

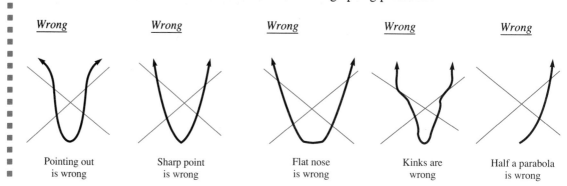

Wrong	*Wrong*	*Wrong*	*Wrong*	*Wrong*
Pointing out is wrong	Sharp point is wrong	Flat nose is wrong	Kinks are wrong	Half a parabola is wrong

Parabolas have many useful applications (see Fig. 9.11). The trajectory of an object that is projected upward is essentially a parabola. Solar furnaces use parabolas as an integral part of their design. The reflectors in spotlights and satellite dishes have parabolic cross sections, and the 200-inch mirror in the telescope at Mount Palomar Observatory uses its parabolic shape to reflect light to its focus 55 feet away.

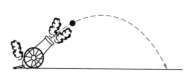

Ignoring air resistance, the path of this cannon-ball is a portion of a parabola.

When a light is placed at point F (the *focus*), the parabolic reflector will direct the rays into parallel beams.

Television signals from a satellite are collected by the parabolic dish and bounced to the "feedhorn."

FIGURE 9.11

9.6 Problem Set

LEARNING THROUGH WRITING

☐ Define the term *vertex of a parabola*.

☐ Define the term *axis of symmetry of a parabola*.

☐ How do you know whether the parabola $y = ax^2 + bx + c$ opens upward or downward?

☐ Describe the steps in graphing the parabola $y = ax^2 + bx + c$.

Complete each table of values using the given equation. Then plot the points and draw a smooth curve through them.

1. $y = x^2 + 1$

x	y
3	
2	
1	
0	
−1	
−2	
−3	

2. $y = x^2 + 2$

x	y
3	
2	
1	
0	
−1	
−2	
−3	

3. $y = -x^2 + 1$

x	y
3	
2	
1	
0	
−1	
−2	
−3	

4. $y = -x^2 + 9$

x	y
3	
2	
1	
0	
−1	
−2	
−3	

5. $y = 2x^2 - 8$

x	y
3	
2	
1	
0	
−1	
−2	
−3	

6. $y = 2x^2 - 2$

x	y
3	
2	
1	
0	
−1	
−2	
−3	

Graph each parabola. Label the intercepts and the vertex.

7. $y = x^2 - 4x$
8. $y = x^2 - 2x$
9. $y = x^2 + 6x$
10. $y = x^2 + 4x$
11. $y = -x^2 + 2x$
12. $y = -x^2 + 6x$
13. $y = x^2 - 2x - 8$
14. $y = x^2 - 4x - 5$
15. $y = -x^2 - 6x - 5$
16. $y = -x^2 - 4x - 3$
17. $y = x^2 - 4x + 4$
18. $y = x^2 - 6x + 9$
19. $y = x^2 - x - 6$
20. $y = x^2 - 3x - 4$
21. $y = x^2 - 6x + 10$
22. $y = x^2 - 4x + 5$
23. $y = 2x^2 + 3x - 2$
24. $y = 2x^2 + 5x - 3$
25. $y = x^2 - 5$
26. $y = x^2 - 7$
27. $y = -3x^2 - 6x$
28. $y = -3x^2 + 6x$
29. $y = \frac{1}{4}x^2$
30. $y = -\frac{1}{4}x^2$

Solve each problem.

31. Graph $y = x^2$, $y = 2x^2$, and $y = (1/2)x^2$ on the same coordinate axes. Then compare the graphs.

32. Graph $y = x^2$, $y = x^2 - 4$, and $y = x^2 + 4$ on the same coordinate axes. Then compare the graphs.

33. A rancher plans to use 8 miles of fencing to construct a rectangular pasture. One side of the rancher's property lies along an existing fence and needs no additional fencing (see Fig. 9.12). What should the width and the length of the pasture be to maximize its area?

34. The outside edges of a piece of sheet metal that is 16 inches wide are folded up to make a trough (see Fig. 9.13). What should x be to maximize the cross-sectional area of the trough?

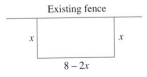

FIGURE 9.12

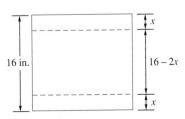

FIGURE 9.13

C H A P T E R 9   S U M M A R Y

Key Terms

Axis of symmetry of a parabola, p. 432
Completing the square, p. 413
Complex conjugates, p. 428
Complex number, p. 427

Imaginary number, p. 426
Imaginary unit, p. 426
Parabola, p. 432

Pure imaginary number, p. 427
Quadratic formula, p. 418
Vertex of a parabola, p. 432

Key Rules

Square Root Property
Suppose k is a positive number.
If $x^2 = k$, then $x = \sqrt{k}$ or $x = -\sqrt{k}$.

Vertex of the Parabola $y = ax^2 + bx + c$

$$x = \frac{-b}{2a}$$

Quadratic Formula
The solutions of the quadratic equation $ax^2 + bx + c = 0$
are

$$x = \frac{-b \pm \sqrt{b^2 - 4ac}}{2a}.$$

C H A P T E R 9   R E V I E W   P R O B L E M S

[9.1] *Solve each equation (a) by factoring, (b) using the square root property.*

1. $x^2 = 49$ **2.** $4x^2 - 25 = 0$

Solve using the square root property. Simplify your answer.

3. $9y^2 - 8 = 0$ **4.** $m^2 + 36 = 0$ **5.** $(p - 2)^2 = 81$ **6.** $(r + 4)^2 = 21$

7. $(10t - 5)^2 = 125$ **8.** $\left(z + \dfrac{1}{2}\right)^2 = \dfrac{3}{4}$

9. Seven more than twice the square of a number is 47.
Find the number.

[9.2] *Complete the square on each expression. Then factor the resulting perfect-square trinomial.*

10. $x^2 - 8x$ **11.** $m^2 + 3m$ **12.** $y^2 + y$ **13.** $r^2 - \dfrac{2}{5}r$

Solve each equation (a) by completing the square, (b) by factoring.

14. $p^2 - 6p + 8 = 0$ **15.** $r^2 + 4r = 0$

Solve by completing the square. Simplify your answer.

16. $x^2 - 2x - 6 = 0$ **17.** $y^2 + 10y - 2 = 0$ **18.** $2t^2 + 8t = 1$ **19.** $3m^2 = 4m + 1$

20. The square of a positive number added to twice the
number is 14. Find the number.

[9.3] *Write each quadratic equation in standard form, and identify a, b, and c. Do not solve the equation.*

21. $(2x - 5)(x + 3) = 6$ **22.** $(y + 4)^2 = 16$

Solve each equation (**a**) *using the quadratic formula*, (**b**) *by factoring.*

23. $x^2 - 6x + 9 = 0$ **24.** $2r^2 + 5r = 12$

Use the quadratic formula to solve each equation. Simplify your answer.

25. $x^2 - 3x + 1 = 0$ **26.** $y^2 = 5y - 3$ **27.** $p^2 + 4p + 2 = 0$ **28.** $4m^2 - 8m + 1 = 0$

29. $\dfrac{2}{9}k^2 + \dfrac{1}{3}k - \dfrac{1}{9} = 0$ **30.** $3r^2 + 1 = 2r$

31. One number is 2 more than three times another. The sum of the squares of the two numbers is 6. Find the numbers.

32. One bricklayer can build a wall in 1 hour less than it takes another bricklayer. If both bricklayers work together, they can build the wall in 4 hours. How long does it take each bricklayer to build the wall working alone?

[9.4] *Solve each quadratic equation. Simplify your answer.*

33. $x^2 - 8x = 9$ **34.** $y^2 = 100$ **35.** $3z^2 - 162 = 0$ **36.** $m^2 + m - 7 = 0$

37. $2(4p - 1)^2 = 98$ **38.** $(3k - 2)^2 = 3k + 4$ **39.** $\dfrac{r^2}{3} - \dfrac{2}{3}r - \dfrac{1}{2} = 0$ **40.** $-50t^2 = 180t - 80$

41. $(x + 7)(x - 3) = 4x$

[9.5] *Write each square root in terms of i.*

42. $\sqrt{-16}$ **43.** $\sqrt{-2}$ **44.** $-\sqrt{-1}$ **45.** $\sqrt{-\dfrac{1}{25}}$

Perform the indicated operations.

46. $(4 + 5i) + (3 - 2i)$ **47.** $-8 + (6 + i)$ **48.** $(11 + 7i) - (2 + 9i)$ **49.** $5i - (1 - 4i)$

50. $(3 + 2i)(4 - 5i)$ **51.** $6i(-1 + i)$ **52.** $(2 + 5i)(2 - 5i)$ **53.** $\dfrac{15}{2 - i}$

54. $\dfrac{1 + i}{3 + 4i}$ **55.** $\dfrac{-2 + 9i}{6i}$

Solve each equation. Write your answer in terms of i in simplest form.

56. $x^2 + 100 = 0$ **57.** $y^2 + 2y + 3 = 0$ **58.** $4p^2 - 5p + 2 = 0$

[9.6] *Complete each table of values using the given equation. Then plot the points and draw a smooth curve through them.*

59. $y = x^2 - 9$

x	y
3	
2	
1	
0	
-1	
-2	
-3	

60. $y = -2x^2$

x	y
3	
2	
1	
0	
-1	
-2	
-3	

Graph each parabola. Label the intercepts and the vertex.

61. $y = x^2 + 2x$ **62.** $y = -x^2 + 4x$ **63.** $y = x^2 - 6x + 5$ **64.** $y = x^2 + 3x - 4$

65. $y = -x^2 + 2x - 1$ **66.** $y = x^2 - 2x + 2$

C H A P T E R   9   T E S T

Solve using the square root property. Simplify your answer.

1. $x^2 = 81$
2. $2y^2 - 54 = 0$
3. $(3m + 2)^2 = 5$

Solve by completing the square. Simplify your answer.

4. $p^2 + 4p = 12$
5. $r^2 - 2r - 5 = 0$
6. $2x^2 + 2x - 1 = 0$

Solve using the quadratic formula. Simplify your answer.

7. $x^2 + 3x + 2 = 0$
8. $y^2 + 4y = 2$
9. $\dfrac{2}{3}m^2 - \dfrac{1}{6}m - \dfrac{1}{3} = 0$

Solve by any method. Simplify your answer.

10. $r^2 - 9r = 0$
11. $\left(z - \dfrac{1}{3}\right)^2 = \dfrac{4}{9}$
12. $5x^2 - 16 = 0$
13. $y^2 + 6y + 7 = 0$

14. $3p^2 + 11p = 4$
15. $t^2 + 7 = 0$
16. $m(2m + 1) = 9m - 5$
17. $x^2 - 4x + 8 = 0$

Perform the indicated operations.

18. $3i + (4 + i) - (5 - 2i)$
19. $(6 + 5i)(2 - 3i)$
20. $\dfrac{1 + i}{i}$

21. $\dfrac{3 - 2i}{4 + 4i}$

Graph each parabola. Label the intercepts and the vertex.

22. $y = \dfrac{1}{4}x^2$
23. $y = x^2 - 4$
24. $y = -x^2 - 2x$
25. $y = x^2 - 6x - 7$

Solve this word problem.

26. The speed of a boat in still water is 5 mph. The boat travels 6 miles upstream and 10 miles downstream in a total time of 4 hours. Find the speed of the current.

Appendixes

APPENDIX 1	**Final Exam**

1. Simplify $|3 - 8|$.

2. Write 140 in prime factored form.

3. Evaluate $\left(\dfrac{3}{4}\right)^{-2}$.

4. Solve $P = 2w + 2\ell$ for ℓ.

5. Write $64^{-1/3}$ in radical form and simplify.

6. Evaluate $4(2[15 - 5(6 - 4)])$ using the order of operations.

7. If $f(x) = 4x^2 - 9x - 11$, find $f(-2)$.

8. Find an equation of the line through $(-3, 5)$ and $(3, -4)$.

9. Divide $\dfrac{8.6 \times 10^3}{2 \times 10^6}$. Write your answer in scientific notation.

10. Determine the slope and the y-intercept of the line $2x + 4y - 12 = 0$.

11. Simplify the complex fraction $\dfrac{1 - \dfrac{3}{x}}{1 - \dfrac{9}{x^2}}$.

12. Find the domain of the function $y = \dfrac{3x}{x - 5}$.

Perform the indicated operations. Write your answer in lowest terms.

13. $-\dfrac{15}{8} \div 1\dfrac{1}{4}$

14. $-\dfrac{3}{4} - \left(-\dfrac{5}{6}\right)$

Solve each equation.

15. $5m - 3 = 17$

16. $2p - (p + 7) = 4p + 5$

17. $\dfrac{m}{2} - 5 = \dfrac{3m}{4}$

18. $\sqrt{2t - 1} = t - 2$

Perform the indicated operations.

19. $5xy^2(2xy^{-4})^2$

20. $(2a - 3)(2a^2 + 4a - 5)$

21. $\dfrac{16r^3 + 12r^2 - 4r}{4r}$

22. $\dfrac{6x^3 + 17x^2 - 3x - 13}{2x + 5}$

Solve each inequality. Then graph the solution.

23. $-6x < 12$

24. $3(2y - 5) \geq 4y + 7$

25. $-5 < 3m - 2 < 7$

Factor each polynomial.

26. $k^3 + 27$

27. $xy - 7y + 3x - 21$

Perform the indicated operations. Write your answer in simplest form.

28. $\dfrac{p^2 + 4p}{3p - 3} \div \dfrac{p^2 - 16}{p^2 - 5p + 4}$

29. $\dfrac{x}{x + 2} + \dfrac{1}{x - 3}$

Rationalize the denominator and simplify.

30. $\sqrt{\dfrac{2}{3}}$

31. $\dfrac{6}{3 - \sqrt{7}}$

Perform the indicated operations. Write your answer in simplest form.

32. $\dfrac{\sqrt{72y^2}}{\sqrt{2y}}$

33. $5\sqrt{28} + \sqrt{63}$

Perform each operation.

34. $(3 + 7i) - (4 - 5i)$

35. $\dfrac{9 + 3i}{4 - 2i}$

Solve each equation.

36. $p^2 - 36 = 0$

37. $y^2 - 4y = 5$

38. $4m^2 + 28m = 0$

39. $3x^2 = 5x - 1$

40. $t^2 + 4t + 5 = 0$

41. Solve the following system of equations:
$$3x - 2y = 8$$
$$4x + 3y = 5$$

Solve each word problem. Solve at least one problem by writing a system of equations.

42. Three out of every 180 fuses are defective. How many defective fuses can be expected in a shipment of 3600 fuses?

43. A collection of nickels and dimes is worth $1.65. There are 3 more dimes than nickels. How many of each kind of coin are in the collection?

44. One leg of a right triangle is 3 feet longer than three times the other leg. The hypotenuse is 3 feet less than four times the shorter leg. Find the length of each side.

45. One pipe can fill a swimming pool in 2 days, whereas another pipe takes 3 days. How long would it take both pipes together to fill the pool?

46. The sum of two numbers is 30. The larger number is 2 more than six times the smaller. Find the numbers.

Graph each equation or inequality.

47. $y = 2x - 6$

48. $3x - 4y < 12$

49. $y = x^2 + 1$

50. $y = x^2 - 4x - 5$

APPENDIX 2   Sets

Sets were introduced by the German mathematician Georg Cantor (1845–1918).

A **set** is a collection of objects. The objects are the **elements,** or **members,** of the set. We enclose the elements of a set in braces, { }, and we separate them with commas. Therefore if S is the set whose elements are the first three *natural numbers,* then

$S = \{1, 2, 3\}$.

The set $\{1, 2, 3\}$ is a **finite set** because it has a limited number of elements. The set of natural numbers, N, is an **infinite set,** since it has an unlimited number of elements.

$N = \{1, 2, 3, 4, 5, \ldots\}$

The three dots mean "and so on." The set that contains no elements is called the **empty set.** We use the symbol $\emptyset$ to represent the empty set.

Caution! ■   Write $\emptyset$ to represent the empty set. Do *not* write $\{\emptyset\}$.

To signify that 2 is an element of the set $S = \{1, 2, 3\}$, we write

$2 \in S$ or $2 \in \{1, 2, 3\}$.

To signify that 4 is not an element of the set $S = \{1, 2, 3\}$, we write

$4 \notin S$ or $4 \notin \{1, 2, 3\}$.

We describe a set either by listing its elements or by stating a rule that its elements obey. For example, using the listing method, we describe the set of natural numbers between 5 and 13 as

$\{6, 7, 8, 9, 10, 11, 12\}$.

Using the rule method, we describe the same set as

$\{x | x$ is a natural number between 5 and 13$\}$.

Read this last expression as "the set of all elements x such that x is a natural number between 5 and 13."

Two sets are **equal** if they have exactly the same elements. Therefore

$\{1, 2, 3\} = \{3, 1, 2\}$.

On the other hand,

$\{1, 2, 3\} \neq \{1, 2, 3, 4\}$,

where $\neq$ means "is not equal to."

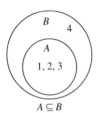

$A \subseteq B$

FIGURE A.1

Diagrams that depict sets as regions are called **Venn diagrams,** after the English logician John Venn (1834–1923).

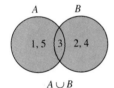

$A \cup B$

FIGURE A.2

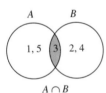

$A \cap B$

FIGURE A.3

Set A is a **subset** of set B, written $A \subseteq B$, if every element of A is also an element of B. Therefore

$$\{1, 2, 3\} \subseteq \{1, 2, 3, 4\},$$

since every element of $\{1, 2, 3\}$ is also an element of $\{1, 2, 3, 4\}$. A diagram of this relationship is shown in Figure A.1. On the other hand,

$$\{1, 2, 3, 4\} \nsubseteq \{1, 2, 3\},$$

where $\nsubseteq$ means "is not a subset of." Note that 4 is an element of $\{1, 2, 3, 4\}$, but 4 is not an element of $\{1, 2, 3\}$.

Since every element of set A is an element of A, set A is a subset of itself. Also, since the empty set has no elements, it cannot have any elements that are not elements of A. Therefore the empty set is a subset of A. We can summarize this discussion as follows.

For any set A,

$$A \subseteq A \quad \text{and} \quad \emptyset \subseteq A.$$

Caution! Do not confuse the symbols $\in$ and $\subseteq$. The symbol $\in$ is used between an element and a set. The symbol $\subseteq$ is used between two sets.

Correct	*Correct*	*Wrong*	*Wrong*
$2 \in \{1, 2, 3\}$	$\{2\} \subseteq \{1, 2, 3\}$	~~$2 \subseteq \{1, 2, 3\}$~~	~~$\{2\} \in \{1, 2, 3\}$~~

The **union** of set A and set B, written $A \cup B$, is the set of all elements that are either in A or in B, or in both A and B. For example,

$$\{1, 3, 5\} \cup \{2, 3, 4\} = \{1, 2, 3, 4, 5\}.$$

Even though 3 is an element of both sets, we do not list 3 twice in our answer. A Venn diagram of this operation is shown in Figure A.2.

The **intersection** of set A and set B, written $A \cap B$, is the set of all elements common to A and B. For example,

$$\{1, 3, 5\} \cap \{2, 3, 4\} = \{3\}.$$

A Venn diagram of this operation is shown in Figure A.3.

A.1 Problem Set

1. Is $\{2, 4, 6, 8\}$ a finite set or an infinite set?

2. Is $\{2, 4, 6, 8, \ldots\}$ a finite set or an infinite set?

True or false.

3. $5 \in \{5, 6, 7\}$

4. $8 \in \{5, 6, 7\}$

5. $4 \in \{x | x$ is an even natural number$\}$

6. $13 \in \{y | y$ is a multiple of 5$\}$

Write each set using the listing method.

7. $\{x | x$ is a natural number less than 5$\}$

8. $\{y | y$ is a natural number greater than 7$\}$

9. $\{t | t$ is a natural number between 1 and 6$\}$

10. $\{p | p$ is a natural number between 3 and 4$\}$

Write each set using the rule method.

11. $\{4, 5, 6, 7, 8\}$

12. $\{1, 2, 3, 4, 5\}$

13. $\{10, 11, 12, 13, \ldots\}$

14. $\{7, 9, 11, 13, \ldots\}$

True or false.

15. $\{3, 4, 7\} \subseteq \{1, 3, 4, 7\}$

16. $\{1, 3, 4, 7\} \subseteq \{3, 4, 7\}$

17. $\{5, 8, 9\} \subseteq \{8, 9, 5\}$

18. $\emptyset \subseteq \{2, 5, 6\}$

19. $\{x | x$ is an odd natural number$\} \subseteq \{x | x$ is an even natural number$\}$

20. $\{y | y$ is a multiple of 4$\} \subseteq \{y | y$ is a multiple of 2$\}$

21. If $A \subseteq B$ and $B \subseteq C$, then $A \subseteq C$.

22. If $A \subseteq B$ and $B \subseteq A$, then $A = B$.

Find all subsets of each set.

23. $\emptyset$

24. $\{1\}$

25. $\{1, 2\}$

26. $\{1, 2, 3\}$

If $A = \{1, 2, 4\}$, $B = \{2, 3, 5, 7\}$, and $C = \{6, 3, 5, 8\}$, find each of the following.

27. $A \cup B$

28. $B \cap C$

29. $(A \cap B) \cup C$

30. $B \cup (A \cap C)$

31. $A \cup A$

32. $A \cap A$

33. $\emptyset \cup A$

34. $\emptyset \cap A$

Answers

The following pages contain Answers to Odd-Numbered Problems, Chapter Review Problems, Chapter Tests, Final Exam (Appendix 1), and Appendix 2 Problems.

CHAPTER 1

Problem Set 1.1

1. 2   **3.** 4   **5.** 6   **7.** 1   **9.** 1/2   **11.** 2/3
13. 3/4   **15.** 5/9   **17.** 5/4   **19.** 3/10
21. 1/6   **23.** 1/4   **25.** 3/10   **27.** 10/21
29. 1/4   **31.** 16/27   **33.** 9   **35.** 3   **37.** 1/2
39. 3/4   **41.** 2/7   **43.** 3/10   **45.** 7/9
47. 7/10   **49.** 2/15   **51.** 1/12   **53.** 13/18
55. 1/12   **57.** 39/7   **59.** 19/20   **61.** 77/10
63. 9/5   **65.** 67/10   **67.** 13/3   **69.** 9/10
71. $99   **73.** $2 5/8   **75.** 9 glasses
77. 5 5/8 mi   **79.** 3 3/4 ton   **81.** 1/2 cup

Problem Set 1.2

1. 18°, −4°   **3.** +1 3/8, −3 1/8
5. 6 yd, −3 yd   **7.** False   **9.** True
11. False   **13.** True   **15.** False   **17.** True
19. True   **21.** True   **23.** True   **25.** True
27. True   **29.** −1, −2, −3
31. $\sqrt{5}$, $\sqrt{7}$, $-\sqrt{10}$ **33.** 4/7, 0, −3
35. a. 18, 0, $\sqrt{9}$ **b.** 18, −10, 0, $\sqrt{9}$
   c. 5/7, 18, 0.35, −10, 0, $\sqrt{9}$, −3 1/6
   d. $\sqrt{6}$, $-\sqrt{2}$ **e.** All of them
37. −2   **39.** 63   **41.** 5/6   **43.** −0.125
45. 9 1/4   **47.** 0   **49.** $-\sqrt{3}$ **51.** $\sqrt{15}$
53. 5   **55.** 4 2/5   **57.** 8.6   **59.** −17
61.

63. Positive number   **65.** −1   **67.** −0.375
69.

71.

73. Not a real number

Problem Set 1.3

1. 5 > 3   **3.** 7.07 < 7.1   **5.** −7 < 0
7. −4 < −2   **9.** 0.3 > −0.6

11. −1 3/5 < −1 2/5   **13.** 3/4 > 5/7
15. x = −17   **17.** z < 8   **19.** r ≥ −6
21. p ≤ 7   **23.** x > 0   **25.** y ≥ 0
27. a ≥ 21 yr   **29.** w ≤ 160 lb   **31.** 4 < x < 9
33. 12 ≥ y > −1   **35.** −3 < z < 6
37. 3 ≤ p < 10   **39.** −8° ≤ t ≤ 19°
41. 105 mi ≤ d ≤ 165 mi   **43.** $11.25 ≤ C ≤ $15
45. 6   **47.** 6   **49.** 1   **51.** 3/4   **53.** 7.2
55. $\sqrt{2}$ **57.** −10   **59.** −10   **61.** 5
63. −5   **65.** 7   **67.** 2   **69.** |8.1| > |5.96|
71. |−25| > |0| **73.** |1| = |−1| **75.** |3| < |−9|
77. |−14| < |18| **79.** |−1/2| < |−3/4|
81. 8 and −8   **83.** 4 and −8
85. False. Let a = −3.
87. False. Let a = −5 and b = 2.

Problem Set 1.4

1. 6   **3.** −7   **5.** −15   **7.** 4   **9.** −4
11. −4   **13.** 7   **15.** −14   **17.** 13
19. −15   **21.** −1   **23.** 4
25.   2 + 6 = 8   **27.**   24.1 + 9.2 = 33.3
   −2 + (−6) = −8   −24.1 + (−9.2) = −33.3
   2 + (−6) = −4   24.1 + (−9.2) = 14.9
   −2 + 6 = 4   −24.1 + 9.2 = −14.9
29. 0   **31.** −8   **33.** 0   **35.** −93
37. −5/7   **39.** 1/2   **41.** 0   **43.** −1/12
45. 5.3   **47.** −14.24   **49.** 0   **51.** −0.48
53. 0   **55.** −4   **57.** 9   **59.** 31   **61.** −10
63. 8   **65.** 13°   **67.** −2   **69.** up 6.11
71. −56   **73.** −1461

Problem Set 1.5

1. −4   **3.** −9   **5.** 15   **7.** −4   **9.** −6
11. 7   **13.** −15   **15.** −5   **17.** 23
19. −6   **21.** −17   **23.** 16   **25.** 6
27. −9   **29.** −5   **31.** 10   **33.** 44
35. 140   **37.** −172   **39.** 0   **41.** −52   **43.** 0
45.   432 − 167 = 265
   −432 − 167 = −599
   432 − (−167) = 599
   −432 − (−167) = −265
47.   5 1/2 − 3 3/4 = 1 3/4
   −5 1/2 − 3 3/4 = −9 1/4
   5 1/2 − (−3 3/4) = 9 1/4
   −5 1/2 − (−3 3/4) = −1 3/4
49. −1/6   **51.** −2/9   **53.** 1/12   **55.** −4 2/5

57. -8.8 **59.** -3.31 **61.** 12.04 **63.** 0.4
65. $5 - (-2) = 7$ **67.** $-4 - (-1) = -3$
         $5 - 7 = -2$ $-4 - (-3) = -1$
69. -6 **71.** 19 **73.** -37 **75.** $-11°$
77. $14{,}770$ ft   **79.** $\$-16.03$ **81.** -28 **83.** 153

Problem Set 1.6

1. $3 \times 10 = 30$
$2 \times 10 = 20$
$1 \times 10 = 10$
$0 \times 10 = 0$
$-1 \times 10 = -10$
$-2 \times 10 = -20$
3. -16 **5.** -20 **7.** 42 **9.** 6 **11.** 1
13. -16 **15.** 0 **17.** -36 **19.** -9
21. 144 **23.** 60 **25.** 0
27. $6(8) = 48$ **29.** $168(4.2) = 705.6$
$-6(-8) = 48$ $-168(-4.2) = 705.6$
$6(-8) = -48$ $168(-4.2) = -705.6$
$(-6)8 = -48$ $(-168)4.2 = -705.6$
31. $15/28$ **33.** $-5/9$ **35.** -5 **37.** -1
39. 1 **41.** 1.21 **43.** -93.13 **45.** 0.0016
47. -31.605 **49.** -70 **51.** 64 **53.** 24
55. -600 **57.** 0 **59.** $1/5$ **61.** -6
63. $-3/2$ **65.** 1 **67.** -10 **69.** $7/17$
71. -12 yd   **73.** -12 lb   **75.** $\$-2500$
77. -266 **79.** $118{,}846$ **81.** -0.4

Problem Set 1.7

1. $15 \div 5 = 3$
$10 \div 5 = 2$
$5 \div 5 = 1$
$0 \div 5 = 0$
$-5 \div 5 = -1$
$-10 \div 5 = -2$
3. 5 **5.** -4 **7.** 3 **9.** -4 **11.** -2
13. 3 **15.** 5 **17.** -6 **19.** -1
21. -40 **23.** -1 **25.** 56 **27.** -9 **29.** 1
31. $\dfrac{16}{2} = 8$ **33.** $6 \div \dfrac{2}{3} = 9$

$\dfrac{-16}{-2} = 8$ $-6 \div \left(-\dfrac{2}{3}\right) = 9$

$\dfrac{-16}{2} = -8$ $-6 \div \dfrac{2}{3} = -9$

$\dfrac{16}{-2} = -8$ $6 \div \left(-\dfrac{2}{3}\right) = -9$

35. $2/5$ **37.** $-2/5$ **39.** $3/8$ **41.** $-2/5$
43. $1/4$ **45.** $-3/4$ **47.** $-15/16$ **49.** $-1/4$
51. $9/2$ **53.** 20 **55.** -3.2 **57.** 15
59. -15.4 **61.** 0 **63.** Undefined   **65.** 0
67. Undefined
69. $-24 \div 4 = -6$ **71.** $40 \div (-5) = -8$
         $-24 \div (-6) = 4$ $40 \div (-8) = -5$
73. $-1/2$ **75.** Undefined   **77.** $-3°$
79. -2 yd   **81.** $0 \div 4 = 0$, since $4 \cdot 0 = 0$
83. 0 **85.** -13.8

Problem Set 1.8

1. 64 **3.** $10{,}000$ **5.** 25 **7.** -25
9. -125 **11.** -125 **13.** $81/256$ **15.** $1/4$
17. -16 **19.** 1 **21.** 50 **23.** 3 **25.** 11
27. 16 **29.** 4 **31.** 10 **33.** 17 **35.** 1
37. 19 **39.** 31 **41.** 36 **43.** $12\ 2/5$
45. -7 **47.** -15 **49.** 37 **51.** -8
53. -142 **55.** $3/2$ **57.** 10 **59.** -5
61. 2 **63.** -6 **65.** $11/14$ **67.** 9 **69.** 29
71. 24 **73.** 294 **75.** $-1/2$ **77.** $\$-4$
79. 114 lb   **81.** $\$30$ **83.** $\$1795$ **85.** 49
87. $1{,}048{,}576$ **89.** 12

Problem Set 1.9

1. $6 + (-2)$ **3.** $(-7)5$ **5.** $x + 3$
7. $1 + (2 + (-5))$ **9.** $-3(4 \cdot 5)$
11. $\left(\dfrac{1}{3} \cdot 3\right)y$ **13.** 5 **15.** x **17.** y
19. 0 **21.** 0 **23.** 1 **25.** $3 \cdot 5 + 3 \cdot x$
27. $2 \cdot 7 + 4 \cdot 7$ **29.** $2(8y) - 2(1)$
31. $(-1)x + (-1)y - (-1)6$ **33.** $10x$ **35.** x
37. x **39.** x **41.** $4x + 4$ **43.** $12y + 24$
45. $24x - 32$ **47.** $24t - 10$
49. $4x + 6y - 8$ **51.** $x + 4$ **53.** 5 **55.** 1
57. $x + 4$ **59.** x **61.** $y - 5$ **63.** $y - 1$
65. $-6x$ **67.** $-20x$ **69.** $-6y$ **71.** r
73. $-6x - 15$ **75.** $-20x + 5$ **77.** $-y + 7$
79. $-8y - 12$ **81.** $a + 3b - 5c$
83. $-2x + y - 12$ **85.** $-5x$ **87.** $-2x$
89. y **91.** $5 - 2 \neq 2 - 5$
93. $6 - (4 - 1) \neq (6 - 4) - 1$

Chapter 1 Review Problems

1. $2/3$ **2.** $1/5$ **3.** $12/25$ **4.** $1/10$ **5.** 3
6. $12/5$ **7.** $1/3$ **8.** $9/10$ **9.** $7/12$

10. 1 3/5 **11.** 7 1/2 in. **12.** 6 3/4 cu yd
13. 7 **14.** −3/5 **15.** 6 **16.** −23
17.

$-\frac{5}{3}$ $2\frac{1}{4}$

−4 −3 −2 −1 0 1 2 3 4 5

18. 14, $\sqrt{16}$, 0 **19.** −3, 14, $\sqrt{16}$, 0
20. 6.2, −3, 14, $\sqrt{16}$, −9/2, 0, 3 2/7 **21.** $\sqrt{7}$
22. 14, $\sqrt{16}$ **23.** All of them
24. −75 < −50 **25.** 4/9 > 7/16 **26.** $x = -6$
27. $y \neq 9$ **28.** $p \geq 4$ **29.** −1 < x < 1
30. −2 < r ≤ 5 **31.** 0 watts ≤ w ≤ 150 watts
32. 4 **33.** 13 **34.** −12 **35.** 5
36. |−6| > |4| **37.** |−9| = |9| **38.** 3
39. −5 **40.** 2 **41.** 4.48 **42.** −5/7
43. −3/8 **44.** 9° **45.** −5 **46.** −10
47. 11 **48.** 2.82 **49.** −4 3/5 **50.** 23/18
51. 47° **52.** −5 **53.** 84 **54.** −48
55. −2 **56.** −34.225 **57.** 1/4 **58.** 1/3
59. −5/12 **60.** −5.4 points **61.** 15
62. −10 **63.** 4 **64.** −1 **65.** −25/32
66. 20 **67.** 4/9 **68.** −1/2 **69.** 0
70. Undefined **71.** −2 yd **72.** 1000
73. −81 **74.** 1/16 **75.** −1 **76.** 24
77. 40 **78.** −6 **79.** −4 **80.** 75/2
81. −3/4 **82.** −19 **83.** 7 people **84.** $y \cdot x$
85. $y + (6 + 8)$ **86.** m **87.** 1
88. $5(4x) + 5(7)$ **89.** x **90.** x **91.** $9y - 8$
92. $y - 15$ **93.** $-z$ **94.** z **95.** $-2y$
96. $-6x - 8y + 2$ **97.** $t + 6$

Chapter 1 Test

1. 3/4 **2.** −1/5 **3.** 64 **4.** −25 **5.** −12
6. 6 **7.** −4.7 **8.** −20 **9.** 4 **10.** −3/5
11. −5/8 **12.** −3.4 **13.** −1 **14.** Undefined
15. −1 1/3 **16.** −17/18 **17.** −|−4| < |4|
18. |3 − 9| = |9 − 3| **19.** $x > -7$
20. 11 ≤ y < 14 **21.** 43 **22.** 90 **23.** 17
24. −31 **25.** $x - 4$ **26.** −3r **27.** 2/3
28. $4z - 3$ **29.** m **30.** $t - 1$ **31.** 13
32. 3 3/8
33.

$-\frac{4}{3}$ 2.5

−3 −2 −1 0 1 2 3 4

34. $x + 3$ **35.** y **36.** $(4 \cdot 5)m$
37. $7x + 7y$ **38.** 0

CHAPTER 2

Problem Set 2.1

1. x, 3 **3.** −3x, 4y, −10 **5.** x^2, 5xy, −y^2
7. 4 **9.** 6 **11.** −15 **13.** 1 **15.** 2/3
17. 2.9 **19.** Like **21.** Unlike **23.** Unlike
25. Like **27.** Like **29.** Unlike **31.** 9x
33. 41z − 1 **35.** 32m **37.** 13y^2 **39.** 6p
41. 8p^2 + p **43.** −2rs **45.** −5m
47. x − 3 **49.** −5y^2 **51.** −1 **53.** z^3
55. 7t^3 + 5t^2 **57.** 0 **59.** 11m + 15 **61.** 5r
63. 4p − 15 **65.** −5t − 10 **67.** −11x + 13y
69. −10r^2 + 2r + 6 **71.** 2x + 14
73. 5y − 5 **75.** −5y + 8 **77.** 13x − 26
79. 6x − 22 **81.** −18a + b **83.** −7x
85. −12x + 5y **87.** −7p + 10
89. −7m − 22 **91.** −3a − 2 **93.** 18k + 15
95. 10m − 18 **97.** −15

Problem Set 2.2

1. Yes **3.** No **5.** Yes **7.** Yes **9.** 7
11. −4 **13.** −6 **15.** 43 **17.** −13.1
19. 0 **21.** −23 **23.** 0 **25.** −2 **27.** 6
29. −2 **31.** 15 **33.** −10 **35.** −11
37. 11 **39.** −13 **41.** 4.5 **43.** 7/5
45. 9 **47.** 2 **49.** 7 **51.** 12 **53.** 24
55. −14 **57.** −38 **59.** −17 **61.** −27
63. −34 **65.** 0 **67.** −4/9

Problem Set 2.3

1. 2 **3.** 1/4 **5.** −5 **7.** −4 **9.** 2/3
11. 9 **13.** 6/5 **15.** 32 **17.** 0 **19.** −16
21. 1/9 **23.** −5/9 **25.** 0 **27.** −3/8
29. −1/3 **31.** −8/5 **33.** −8 **35.** 6.5
37. 2 **39.** 1 **41.** −2 **43.** −7 **45.** −1
47. 5 **49.** 0 **51.** 10 **53.** −1/2 **55.** −3
57. −4 **59.** 5 **61.** 12 **63.** 7/8

Problem Set 2.4

1. 3 **3.** −9 **5.** 0 **7.** −2.5 **9.** 16
11. −26/7 **13.** −6 **15.** −5 **17.** −4

19. 4   **21.** −3   **23.** 11   **25.** 9   **27.** 1
29. −2   **31.** 5/2   **33.** 13   **35.** 0   **37.** −1
39. −3   **41.** −2   **43.** 8   **45.** 3/4   **47.** 7
49. 5   **51.** −3   **53.** 6.4   **55.** 3/4   **57.** 22
59. 20/3

Problem Set 2.5

1. 22 yd   **3.** 25 ft   **5.** 12 sq m   **7.** 4.5 cm
9. 314 sq in.   **11.** 0.785 sq mi   **13.** 15.7 ft
15. 5 km   **17.** 990 cu in.   **19.** 12 ft   **21.** $45
23. $850   **25.** 75 mi   **27.** 20 mi
29. 52 sq cm   **31.** 20 yd   **33.** $t = d/r$ **a.** 14 hr
b. 12 hr   **c.** 10.5 hr   **35.** $\ell = A/w$
37. $r = I/Pt$ **39.** $w = (P - 2\ell)/2$
41. $t = (A - P)/Pr$ **43.** $h = 2A/b$
45. $a = 2s - b - c$ **47.** $b = (2A - hB)/h$
49. $a^2 = c^2 - b^2$ **51.** $r^2 = 3V/\pi h$
53. $F = \dfrac{9}{5}C + 32$ **a.** 167°   **b.** 32°   **c.** −4°
55. 9400 mph   **57.** 4400 ft
59. The 12-in. pizza   **61.** 150.72 cu ft
63. 432.7 yd   **65.** $750   **67.** 31.74 sq cm
69. 942 sq ft   **71.** 111.841 cm

Problem Set 2.6

1. $2x + 5$ **3.** $2(x + 5)$ **5.** $\dfrac{x}{3} - 1$

7. $6x^2$ **9.** $-8x$ **11.** $\dfrac{x}{2} - \dfrac{1}{2}$

13. $60t$ sec   **15.** $175(z + 6)$ cal
17. $5x + 25y$ cents   **19.** $0.11m$ dollars
21. $0.05(40 - p)\ \ell$ **23.** $\dfrac{60}{x}$ ft
25. $x, x + 1, x + 2$ **27.** $x, x + 2, x + 4, x + 6$
29. $\dfrac{2}{3}x, x$ **31.** $x, x + 6$
33. $x, x - 5, 2x, 2x - 5$ **35.** $x, 500 - x$
37. $3x + 16$ **39.** $-3x + 29$ **41.** $6x$
43. $0.92x$ **45.** $4x + 30$ hr   **47.** 11   **49.** 75
51. 55   **53.** 10   **55.** 2   **57.** −5
59. $38   **61.** 5500 people   **63.** 9.6 months
65. *Arithmetic solution:* 5; 5 + 7 = 12; 3 · 12 = 36;
36 − 9 = 27; 2 · 27 = 54; 54 ÷ 6 = 9; 9 − 5 = 4.
Algebraic solution: x; $x + 7$; $3(x + 7) = 3x + 21$;
$3x + 21 - 9 = 3x + 12$; $2(3x + 12) = 6x + 24$;
$(6x + 24) \div 6 = x + 4$; $x + 4 - x = 4$.

Problem Set 2.7

1. 11, 22   **3.** 26, 28   **5.** 5, 6   **7.** 7/8, 21/40
9. Stacy, 12 yr; Sean, 16 yr
11. Lisa, 1 yr; Nancy, 10 yr
13. Brother, 14 yr; Steve, 28 yr
15. Mother, 36 yr; Chris, 12 yr
17. Width, 8 m; length, 19 m
19. Width, 27 ft; length, 78 ft   **21.** 98 ft
23. 21 ft, 23 ft, 42 ft   **25.** 54°, 42°, 84°
27. 3 ft, 5 ft, 8 ft   **29.** 20 bundles   **31.** 250 mi

Problem Set 2.8

1. 20 nickels, 26 dimes
3. 12 nickels, 9 dimes, 24 quarters
5. 17 nickels, 23 dimes
7. 16 hr at $5 job, 12 hr at $4.50 job
9. $300 at 7%, $900 at 11%
11. $3780 at 8%, $2520 at 12%
13. $7250 at 9 1/2%, $4750 at 14 1/2%
15. $750,000   **17.** 20 g   **19.** 40 kg   **21.** 6 lb
23. 5.6 ton of $45.50 feed, 15.4 ton of $38 feed
25. 2.5 hr   **27.** 3 hr
29. Slow train, 35 mph; fast train, 40 mph
31. Slow runner, 6 mph; fast runner, 8 mph
33. 896 mi   **35.** 20 min

Problem Set 2.9

1. $x < 4$

3. $y \geq -6$

5. $t > 1$

7. $x > -2$

9. $p \leq 0$

11. $y \geq 8$

13. $r \leq 5$

15. $t < -7$

17. $p > 2$

19. $x > 0$

21. $y \le -2$

23. $x < 6$

25. $m \ge -25$ **27.** $z \ge -1/9$

29. $x < 5$ **31.** $p \le -4$

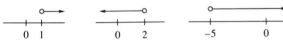

33. $x > 7$ **35.** $y \le 0$

37. $z < 4$ **39.** $r \le 12$

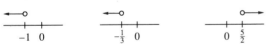

41. $p > 1$ **43.** $t < 2$ **45.** $p > -5$

47. $m < -1$ **49.** $t < -1/3$,   **51.** $x > 5/2$

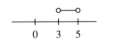

53. $3 < x < 5$ **55.** $-2 \le y \le 4$

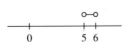

57. $-3 \le y < -1$ **59.** $5 < r < 6$

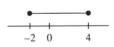

61. $-15/4 < z \le 3$ **63.** $-3 < t < 0$

65. $-9 \le p \le -6$ **67.** $-8 < m < 12$

69. $-5 \le x \le 2$

71. $x < -3$ **73.** $7 < x < 8$
75. Width ≥ 12.5 ft
77. More than \$1750 worth of goods
79. $49 \le$ Score < 99

Chapter 2 Review Problems

1. $2x$, 3   **2.** $4x^2$, $-5y$, 1   **3.** 8   **4.** 3/5
5. 1   **6.** -1 **7.** Like   **8.** Like
9. Unlike   **10.** Unlike   **11.** $-17mn$
12. $r^2 + 9r - 17$ **13.** $7k + 27$ **14.** $11x - 13y$
15. $21a - 2$ **16.** $14t + 13$ **17.** 3   **18.** -4
19. $-2/3$ **20.** 5   **21.** 0   **22.** 36   **23.** No
24. 3   **25.** -9 **26.** 50   **27.** -48
28. 3/5   **29.** 0   **30.** -13 **31.** 14   **32.** 3
33. 8   **34.** -1 **35.** 9   **36.** 13   **37.** 4
38. $-4/3$ **39.** 0   **40.** -2 **41.** 29/7
42. 7 ft   **43.** 5°   **44.** $P = I/rt$

45. $b = 2s - a - c$ **46.** $C = \dfrac{5}{9}(F - 32)$

47. 47 mph   **48.** 128 cu ft   **49.** 443 sq cm
50. $2x + 3$ **51.** $45x$ mi   **52.** $0.2y$ g
53. $5x + 24$ **54.** $15x + 20$ **55.** x, $x - 8$
56. x, $758 - x$ **57.** 48   **58.** -7
59. 2675 people   **60.** 4, 24   **61.** 9, 11
62. Peggy, 7 yr; Sandi, 12 yr
63. brother, 10 yr; Derek, 20 yr
64. width, 6 m; length, 22 m
65. 10 ft, 20 ft, 29 ft
66. 3 nickels, 6 dimes, 6 quarters
67. \$200 at 14%, \$350 at 8%   **68.** 5 g
69. 1.2 hr
70. 40 lb of \$0.12 coffee, 32 lb of \$0.30 coffee
71. Slow ship, 20 mph; fast ship, 30 mph
72. $r \ge 10$ **73.** $m > -3$

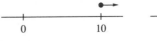

74. $p \geq -7$

75. $x > 0$

76. $t \geq 50$

77. $k < 5$

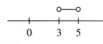
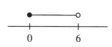

78. $p < 3$ **79.** $z \leq 2$ **80.** $m \leq 3/5$

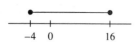

81. $3 < x < 5$ **82.** $0 \leq y < 6$

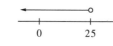

83. $-4 \leq k \leq 16$

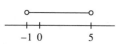

84. $x < 6$ **85.** More than \$2000 worth of goods
86. $-20° < C < -5°$

Chapter 2 Test

1. $8p^2 - 7p - 1$ **2.** $13x - 18y$ **3.** $10a - 2$
4. -16 **5.** -3 **6.** 6 **7.** 3 **8.** -3
9. 0 **10.** 1 **11.** -11 **12.** \$575   **13.** $10°$
14. $\ell = (P - 2w)/2$ **15.** $n = 3S - 1$
16. $p < -2$ **17.** $r < 25$ **18.** $t \geq 2$

19. $m \geq -3$ **20.** $y > 4$

21. $-1 < x < 5$

22. $9/2$ **23.** $28, 29$
24. Eric, 21 yr; Bryan, 23 yr   **25.** 8 ft, 17 ft, 24 ft
26. 31 nickels, 19 dimes   **27.** 7 hr

CHAPTER 3

Problem Set 3.1

1. base 5, exponent 4   **3.** base 3, exponent 2
5. base x, exponent 3   **7.** 9^2 **9.** $(-4x)^3$
11. $-t^6$ **13.** $(a^2)^3$ **15.** $\left(\dfrac{a}{b}\right)^3$ **17.** a^7
19. 3^7 **21.** y^{11} **23.** $6x^9$ **25.** $-20y^9$
27. $2p^{11}$ **29.** a^2 **31.** 9^8 **33.** $6x^7$ **35.** $2m^6$
37. $-4x^2y^{16}$ **39.** 1 **41.** 1 **43.** 1
45. 1 **47.** -5 **49.** $1/16$ **51.** $-1/121$
53. $3/32$ **55.** $-1/32$ **57.** $25/4$ **59.** 8
61. 81 **63.** 486 **65.** $3/4$ **67.** $14/3$ **69.** 9^4
71. $\dfrac{1}{5^6}$ **73.** $\dfrac{1}{x^2}$ **75.** $-15m^4$ **77.** $\dfrac{8}{k^4}$
79. $\dfrac{1}{6^3}$ **81.** $\dfrac{1}{r^2}$ **83.** 10^6 **85.** $\dfrac{b^{16}}{a^7}$
87. $-\dfrac{x^6y}{3}$ **89.** x^{n+1} **91.** x^{3n} **93.** x^{n-2}
95. z^{6m} **97. a.** 100 g **b.** 50 g **c.** 25 g
99. 0.0625 **101.** 1

Problem Set 3.2

1. x^6 **3.** 5^8 **5.** $\dfrac{1}{6^{10}}$ **7.** $64x^2$ **9.** $-27p^3q^3$
11. $80r^4s^4$ **13.** x^6y^{12} **15.** $\dfrac{p^{12}}{q^4}$ **17.** $\dfrac{t^6}{49}$
19. $-8m^{18}$ **21.** $\dfrac{1}{9x^2}$ **23.** $\dfrac{3}{x^2}$ **25.** $9/25$
27. $\dfrac{x^9}{y^{12}}$ **29.** $\dfrac{b^2}{a^2}$ **31.** r^6s^{15} **33.** a^{15}
35. x^{19} **37.** z^{16} **39.** $\dfrac{3^8}{x}$ **41.** y^9 **43.** $\dfrac{1}{t^5}$
45. $\dfrac{m^7}{4}$ **47.** $\dfrac{32}{a^2}$ **49.** $\dfrac{s^{14}}{r^7}$ **51.** $\dfrac{b^4}{a^8c^6}$
53. $\dfrac{2b^2}{3a}$ **55.** $\dfrac{y^5}{x^7}$ **57.** $\dfrac{16y^4}{x^4}$ **59.** $200x^{14}$
61. $48a^8b^7$ **63.** $-40r^6s^{15}$ **65.** $27p^9$ **67.** m^4
69. x^{7n+2} **71.** y^{7n} **73.** z^{6m} **75.** $r^{2m}s^{4m}$
77. $\dfrac{y^{6n}}{x^{3n}}$ **79.** x^{2m+4} **81.** 2^{14} **83.** \$1,047,518

Problem Set 3.3

1. 8.2×10^7 **3.** 3.03×10^9 **5.** 9.12×10^2
7. 10^5 **9.** 5×10^{-4} **11.** 7.4×10^{-1}

13. 6.18×10^{-7} **15.** 5.28×10^4 **17.** 9.3×10^{-5}
19. 700   **21.** 0.000064   **23.** 3.18
25. 0.0005   **27.** 271.3   **29.** 0.001
31. 2.6×10^{-5}, 1.94×10^{-2}, 5.3, 1.7×10^4
33. 8×10^3 **35.** 8.4×10^{-5} **37.** 1.35×10^9
39. 3×10^4 **41.** 2.6×10^5 **43.** 7×10^{-6}
45. 6×10^2 **47.** 4.4×10^{-10} **49.** 4.1×10^{10}
51. 4×10^{-8} **53.** 25,000,000,000,000 mi
55. 7.5×10^{-5} cm   **57.** 10^{15} **59.** 10^{-6} sec
61. 4 sec   **63.** 1.62×10^{10} **65.** 2.25×10^{10}
67. 6.25×10^{-11}

39. $2x^3 - 5x^2 - 4x + 3$
41. $a^4 + 4a^3 + 3a^2 + 7a - 20$
43. $y^4 - 3y^3 + 3y^2 - 1$
45. $20p^4 - p^3 - 8p^2 - 17p - 15$
47. $4x^4 + 3x^3 - 21x^2 + 17x - 3$
49. $p^2 - 3p - 40$ **51.** $4r^2 - 25$
53. $2x^3 + 11x^2 + 11x - 12$
55. $16p^4 - 2p^3 - 28p^2 + 5p - 30$
57. $15m^4 - 14m^3 - 43m^2 - 14m$ **59.** $x^3 - y^3$
61. $x^2 + 6x + 9$ **63.** $16x^2 - 40x + 25$
65. $m^3 + 12m^2 + 48m + 64$
67. $125a^3 - 150a^2b + 60ab^2 - 8b^3$ **69.** $n^2 + 2n$
71. $14x^2 + 13x - 12$ **73.** $4x^2 + 36x$ sq ft

Problem Set 3.4

1. x^5, monomial, degree 5
3. $3x^2 + 7x + 2$, trinomial, degree 2
5. $-2x^3y^5$, monomial, degree 8
7. $m^2 + 9m$, binomial, degree 2
9. $-t^8 + t^6 + 8t^4 - t^2$, polynomial, degree 8
11. 4, monomial, degree 0   **13.** 17   **15.** 17
17. 126.5   **19.** 7   **21.** -5 **23.** 8
25. $-17/25$ **27.** $8x^4$ **29.** $-4m^3$ **31.** $-9y^2$
33. $11t^2 + 3t$ **35.** $4x^3y$ **37.** $5p^2q^3 + 11p^3q^2$
39. $5x + 9$ **41.** $6x^2 + 2x - 2$ **43.** $8x^2 - 2y^2$
45. $2x + 4$ **47.** $6y^3 - 7y^2 - y + 10$
49. $-x^3 - 3x^2y + 15x - 1$
51. $11y^3 - 5y^2 + 3y - 6$ **53.** $2a^3 - 8a + 4$
55. $10x^2 + xy - 9y^2$ **57.** $4x^2 + 5x + 1$
59. $2a^3 + 3a^2 + a - 6$ **61.** $-2x^2 + 12y^3$
63. $20x^2 + x + 3$ **65.** $-2y^2 + 3y - 7$
67. $-4a^3 + 5a^2b - 5b^2$
69. $16m^3 - 5m^2 - m + 9$
71. $4r^3 - r^2 - 5r - 2$
73. $-x^3 + 3x^2 + 2x - 10$ **75.** $8x + 3$
77. a. 2 **b.** 35   **79. a.** 320 ft **b.** 0 ft

Problem Set 3.6

1. $x^2 + 8x + 15$ **3.** $x^2 + 2x - 8$
5. $x^2 - 7x + 6$ **7.** $9x^2 - 9x - 10$
9. $12y^2 + 4y - 21$ **11.** $2r^2 + 3rs + s^2$
13. $4p^2 - 27pq - 7q^2$ **15.** $40x^2 - 23xy + 3y^2$
17. $80a^2 - 4ab - 6b^2$ **19.** $10 + 3x - x^2$
21. $m^2 - 25$ **23.** $11.13x^2 + 5.6x - 8.68$
25. $t^2 - 16$ **27.** $p^2 - 64$ **29.** $36m^2 - 1$
31. $4x^2 - y^2$ **33.** $9r^2 - 49s^2$
35. $81x^2 - 9.61$ **37.** $x^2 + 4x + 4$
39. $z^2 - 10z + 25$ **41.** $4y^2 - 12y + 9$
43. $100a^2 + 20ab + b^2$ **45.** $25x^2 - 90xy + 81y^2$
47. $64k^2 + 8k + \dfrac{1}{4}$ **49.** $18y^2 + 9y - 20$
51. $1.21p^2 + 5.5p + 6.25$ **53.** $9k^2 - \dfrac{4}{9}$
55. $t^4 - 10t^2 + 9$ **57.** $z^4 - 9$
59. $25 - 10x^3 + x^6$ **61.** $-x + 19$
63. $20z - 136$ **65.** $-4xy$

Problem Set 3.5

1. $10x^4$ **3.** $-12m^9$ **5.** $45a^3b^2$ **7.** $-14pq^2$
9. $8r^5s^3$ **11.** $-24x^6y^6$ **13.** $y^2 + 5y$
15. $10x^3 + 30x$ **17.** $4r^3 - 8r^2 + 12r$
19. $-8y^4 + 16y^3 + 2y^2$
21. $-8p^3q^2 + 16p^2q^3 - 8pq^4$
23. $6t^8 - 48t^7 + 30t^6$ **25.** $x^2 + 6x + 8$
27. $t^2 - 9$ **29.** $2x^2 + 11x + 15$
31. $12x^2 - 7x - 10$ **33.** $6x^2 - 17xy + 7y^2$
35. $-24a^3 + 16a^2 + 30a$
37. $2m^3 - m^2 - 7m + 20$

Problem Set 3.7

1. $4x^5$ **3.** $-7y$ **5.** $2/m$ **7.** $-r^3s^3$ **9.** $\dfrac{10a^2}{b^2}$
11. $\dfrac{y^3}{2x}$ **13.** $x + 1$ **15.** $x + y$ **17.** $-3x + 2$
19. $y^2 - y + 1$ **21.** $2p^2 - 3p - 1$
23. $6y - 2x + 1$ **25.** $3a^3 + 5ab^2 - 2b^2$
27. $9m^3 + \dfrac{2}{3}m - 3$ **29.** $16x + \dfrac{3}{4} - \dfrac{1}{x}$
31. $\dfrac{a}{2} + b + \dfrac{b^2}{2a}$ **33.** $6k^2 - 2k + 3 - \dfrac{5}{k} + \dfrac{2}{3k^2}$

35. $3m^2 + 2m - 4$ **37.** $7x^5 - 10x^3 - 1$

39. $y + \dfrac{1}{3}$ **41.** $\dfrac{z}{3} + 3$ **43.** $5r^2 - 7r$

45. $3r^3 + 2r - 1$ **47.** $r^5s^4 - 3r^3s^2 - \dfrac{rs}{2} + \dfrac{2}{r}$

49. True   **51.** False

53. Ave $= \dfrac{n + (n + 1) + (n + 2)}{3} = \dfrac{3n + 3}{3} = n + 1$

Problem Set 3.8

1. $x + 7$ **3.** $4x + 3$ **5.** $3x + 4 + \dfrac{16}{3x - 2}$

7. $5y + 1 - \dfrac{10}{5y - 3}$ **9.** $p - 2 + \dfrac{9}{2p + 4}$

11. $2z - 1 + \dfrac{2}{4z + 1}$ **13.** $4x^2 - 8x + 5 + \dfrac{6}{2x + 3}$

15. $y^2 - 3y + 1$ **17.** $m^2 - 4m - 6 + \dfrac{9}{2m - 3}$

19. $2m^3 - 4m^2 + 3m - 7$

21. $3p^3 + 2p^2 + p + 7 + \dfrac{30}{6p - 5}$

23. $3x^3 - 2x^2 + 3x - 2$ **25.** $x^2 + 5x - 6$

27. $x^2 + 4x + 1 - \dfrac{3x - 2}{x^2 - 1}$

29. $2x^3 - 3x^2 - 4x - 1 + \dfrac{x}{2x^2 - x + 3}$

31. $2x^2 + x - 2 - \dfrac{2}{2x - 1}$ **33.** $m^2 - 3m + 9$

35. $y + \dfrac{2}{3} + \dfrac{5}{3y - 6}$ **37.** True   **39.** False

Chapter 3 Review Problems

1. Base 9, exponent 4   **2.** Base 4, exponent 2
3. Base 7x, exponent 3   **4.** $6x^5$ **5.** $(y + 5)^3$
6. -1 **7.** 1/9   **8.** $-1/16$ **9.** 1000
10. 25/16   **11.** -27 **12.** 2   **13.** 7/8

14. y^9 **15.** $\dfrac{1}{5^8}$ **16.** $-21x$ **17.** 4^6

18. $\dfrac{1}{t^6}$ **19.** $-6r^9s^8$ **20.** $\dfrac{6^7}{m^{14}}$ **21.** p^{3n-1}

22. x^{10} **23.** $-64m^{18}$ **24.** $\dfrac{x^8}{y^6}$ **25.** $\dfrac{1}{t^7}$

26. $\dfrac{p^4}{9}$ **27.** $\dfrac{a^{10}c^{20}}{b^{15}}$ **28.** $-32r^7s^{13}$ **29.** $\dfrac{49p^4}{q^{10}}$

30. z^{10n} **31.** 4.7×10^7 **32.** 3×10^{-6}

33. 9.08×10^{-3} **34.** 519,000   **35.** 0.0006062
36. 0.01   **37.** 8.2×10^5 **38.** 3×10^{-8}
39. 2.8×10^{-3} **40.** 1.2×10^5 **41.** 10^5 days
42. $3x + 8$, binomial, degree 1
43. $y^4 - 5y^2 + 6$, trinomial, degree 4
44. $9z^3$, monomial, degree 3
45. $-m^5 + m^3 + m + 1$, polynomial, degree 5
46. -30 **47.** $8x^2 + 5x - 4$ **48.** $8x^2 + 2y^2$
49. $2y^2 - 8y + 7$ **50.** $2a^3 - 2a^2 - 7a - 11$
51. $14m^3 - 8m^2 + 1$ **52.** $-4a^2 - 15ab + 6b^2$
53. $p^4 + 3p^3 - 2p^2 + 9p + 17$
54. a. \$400 **b.** \$650   **55.** $-30x^3y^{11}$
56. $-m^5 + 4m^4 - 7m^3$ **57.** $2p^4q - 4p^3q^2 + 6p^2q^3$
58. $12y^2 + 13y - 35$ **59.** $-6m^2n + 6n^3$
60. $4x^3 - 9x^2 + 5x - 6$
61. $3a^4 + a^3 - 21a^2 - a + 2$
62. $10p^4 + 17p^3 - p - 12$ **63.** $8k^3 - 12k^2 + 6k - 1$
64. $12m^4 + 16m^3 + 11m^2 + 21m$
65. $3x^4 + 7x^3 - 21x^2 + 13x - 2$ **66.** $10x^2 + 18x$
67. $8x^2 - 14x - 15$ **68.** $8a^2 + 19ab - 15b^2$
69. $m^2 + 14m + 49$ **70.** $9t^2 - 100$
71. $r^4 + 10r^2 + 25$ **72.** $36x^2 - 24xy + 4y^2$

73. $2xy - 2y^2$ **74.** $\dfrac{-8}{m^2}$ **75.** $-\dfrac{y^3}{x}$

76. $3r^2 + 5r - 1$ **77.** $2ab^3 - b^2 + \dfrac{3b}{a}$

78. $-2p^3 + 3p^2 - \dfrac{p}{2} - 1$ **79.** $x + 5$

80. $2y^2 - 3y + 1 + \dfrac{6}{y - 3}$ **81.** $4m^2 + 2m - 1$

82. $p^3 + 2p + 3 - \dfrac{3}{3p - 4}$

83. $3x^2 - x + 2 + \dfrac{6x + 11}{2x^2 + 2x - 1}$ **84.** $k^2 + 2k + 4$

Chapter 3 Test

1. 6,300,000   **2.** 7.12×10^{-5} **3.** 6   **4.** 49/9
5. 9/8   **6.** $7x^2 - 5x + 1$ **7.** $a^3 + 9a^2 - 5a$
8. 31   **9.** 4.5×10^4 **10.** 2.1×10^4 **11.** $-40x^7y$

12. $-20x^4$ **13.** $4a^5b^8$ **14.** $\dfrac{3^6}{t^{10}}$ **15.** $\dfrac{1}{8p^4}$

16. $4p^4 - 12p^3 + 24p^2$ **17.** $x^2 - 6xy + 9y^2$
18. $p^2 - 9$ **19.** $12t^2 + 13t - 35$
20. $4a^3 - 4a^2 + 5a + 4$ **21.** $2m^3 + 9m^2 - m + 8$

22. $3x^2 + 2x - 1$ **23.** $r^2 - 3r + \dfrac{1}{3} + \dfrac{1}{r}$

24. $p + 3$ **25.** $2m^2 + 4m + 6 - \dfrac{2}{2m - 3}$

CHAPTER 4

Problem Set 4.1

1. $2^2 \cdot 3$ **3.** $2 \cdot 3^2 \cdot 7$ **5.** prime
7. $2^3 \cdot 3^2 \cdot 5 \cdot 7$ **9.** 4   **11.** 18   **13.** 1
15. 84   **17.** 7   **19.** x^3 **21.** $25x^3$ **23.** $4x^7y^6$
25. $3a - 4$ **27.** $m + 5$ **29.** $2(m + 3)$
31. $3a(2b - 5c)$ **33.** $4x(3x + 5)$ **35.** $k(k^2 + 1)$
37. $12m^8(3m^4 - 2)$ **39.** prime   **41.** $-(x + 2y)$
43. $-(-r - s + t)$ **45.** $-(4a^2 + 9a - 10)$
47. $3(x^2 + 2x + 3)$ **49.** prime
51. $-6y(2y^2 - 3y + 1)$ **53.** $8z^{25}(z^{50} - 4z^{25} - 2)$
55. $12x^2y^2(2x^3 - 3xy + 4y^3)$
57. $6r^5s^5(5r^3t^3 + 12s^2t - 3rs^4)$
59. $abc(2a + 5b + 9c)$
61. $-11m^{17}p(2m^{36} - 5m^{20}p + 3m^7p^2 - p^3)$
63. $(a + 2b)(x + y)$ **65.** $(x + 8)(x - 3)$
67. $(y^2 + 9)(x - 2)$ **69.** $(4r - 5s)(x + 1)$
71. $(p - 7)(p - 6)$ **73.** $(r + 1)^2$ **75.** $\pi r(\ell + r)$

Problem Set 4.2

1. $(x + y)(a + b)$ **3.** $(x + 3)(y + 2)$
5. $(s - 8)(r + 2)$ **7.** $(x + y)(3x + 2)$
9. $(t - 6)(t^2 + 6)$ **11.** $(x - 1)(x + 7)$
13. $(m + 2)(4m - 3)$ **15.** $(2y - 9)(y - 2)$
17. $(5r + 3s)(2r + s)$ **19.** $(3x - 7a)(2x + 5a)$
21. $(k + 5)(k^2 + 1)$ **23.** $(t + 2)(t + 1)$
25. $(p - 8)(p - 1)$ **27.** $(m + 1)^2$ **29.** $(4x - 1)^2$
31. $(xy - a)(x - 1)$ **33.** $(3p - q)(4p - q)$
35. $(k - 3)(25k^2 - 6)$ **37.** $2(x - y)(a + b)$
39. $5(a + 4)(b + 2)$ **41.** $12(p - 2)(3p^2 + 4)$
43. $r^2s(r + 7s)(9r - 2s)$ **45.** $4y(x - 1)(y - 1)$
47. $(x - y + 1)(x + 3)$ **49.** $P(1 + r)^2$

Problem Set 4.3

1. $(x + 3)(x + 5)$ **3.** $(x + 2)^2$
5. $(x - 2)(x - 3)$ **7.** $(y - 1)(y - 4)$
9. $(y - 6)(y - 9)$ **11.** $(m + 6)(m - 2)$
13. $(m - 4)(m + 3)$ **15.** prime
17. $(z - 24)(z + 1)$ **19.** $(x - 1)(x - 14)$
21. $(t - 3)(t + 17)$ **23.** $(y - 10)(y + 2)$
25. $(x + 5y)(x + 7y)$ **27.** $(m - 5n)^2$
29. $(x + 7y)(x - 4y)$ **31.** $(r - 6s)(r + s)$
33. prime   **35.** $(p - 4q)(p - 9q)$
37. $-(x - 1)(x - 10)$ **39.** $-(z - 9)(z + 5)$
41. $-(r + 5s)(r + 6s)$ **43.** $4(x + 2)^2$

45. $a^2(a + 1)^2$ **47.** $m(m + 9)(m - 3)$
49. $5r^2(r - 1)(r - 11)$
51. $-10pq(p + 9q)(p - 4q)$
53. $6a^2x^3(x^2 - 8x - 12)$ **55.** $(t^2 + 2)(t^2 + 3)$
57. $(k^3 + 5)(k^3 - 2)$ **59.** $(x^2 + 3y^2)(x^2 + y^2)$
61. $2x^2 + 7x - 15$

Problem Set 4.4

1. $(2x + 1)(x + 5)$ **3.** $(2z - 5)(z - 1)$
5. $(7p - 2)(p - 2)$ **7.** $(5m - 3)(m + 1)$
9. $(6r - 1)(r + 2)$ **11.** $(2y + 1)(3y - 5)$
13. $(3t + 2)(2t + 5)$ **15.** $(4x + 3)(x + 2)$
17. $(2y - 3)^2$ **19.** $(4k + 1)(2k - 3)$
21. $(2z + 5)(10z - 1)$ **23.** $(4m - 7)(m + 2)$
25. $(4p - 5)(5p + 4)$ **27.** prime
29. $(4r + 3)(9r - 8)$ **31.** $(2x + 3y)(x + y)$
33. $(2p - 3q)(2p - q)$ **35.** $(5a - 9b)(2a - b)$
37. $(3r - s)(r + 5s)$ **39.** $(4m - 7n)(2m + 3n)$
41. $(4c - 3d)(3c + 4d)$ **43.** prime
45. $(5p - 3q)^2$ **47.** $(4m - 5n)(3m - 2n)$
49. $2(5x + 3)(x + 1)$ **51.** $4(3y - 2)(2y - 1)$
53. $-(4x + 1)(x + 3)$ **55.** $-2(3r + 1)(2r - 5)$
57. $z^3(3z + 1)^2$ **59.** $10p(2p + 3)(5p - 7)$
61. $m^2n(8m + 3n)(3m - 2n)$
63. $3p^4q(4p^2 - 5p + 10)$
65. $-3ab(3a - 7b)(2a + 5b)$
67. $(2x^2 - 3y^2)(x^2 + y^2)$
69. $(5x^3 + 3y)(x^3 + y)$ **71.** $9x^2 - 16$

Problem Set 4.5

1. $(x + 2)(x - 2)$ **3.** $(m + n)(m - n)$
5. $(3r + 5)(3r - 5)$ **7.** prime
9. $\left(y + \dfrac{4}{9}\right)\left(y - \dfrac{4}{9}\right)$
11. $(6 + z)(6 - z)$ **13.** $(2p + q)(2p - q)$
15. prime   **17.** $(11x + 9y)(11x - 9y)$
19. $(rs + 13)(rs - 13)$ **21.** $(m^2 + 3)(m^2 - 3)$
23. $7(x^2 + 1)(x + 1)(x - 1)$
25. $-3t^2(t^2 + 4)(t + 2)(t - 2)$
27. $4x(9x^2 + 4y^2)(3x + 2y)(3x - 2y)$ **29.** $(x + 5)^2$
31. $(y - 11)^2$ **33.** $(3r + 1)^2$ **35.** $(2m - 3)^2$
37. $(x + 2)(x + 8)$ **39.** prime   **41.** $(5a + 2b)^2$
43. $2(p - 10q)^2$ **45.** $5x(x + 3y)^2$
47. $(x + 3)(x^2 - 3x + 9)$
49. $(m - 2)(m^2 + 2m + 4)$
51. $(5r + 1)(25r^2 - 5r + 1)$
53. $(10r + s)(100r^2 - 10rs + s^2)$

55. $(2y - 5)(4y^2 + 10y + 25)$

57. $(3a + 4b)(9a^2 - 12ab + 16b^2)$

59. $(x^2 + 7y)(x^4 - 7x^2y + 49y^2)$

61. $-3k(k + 6)(k^2 - 6k + 36)$

63. $5(4p^2 - 5q)(16p^4 + 20p^2q + 25q^2)$

65. $(2x^3 - 5y)(4x^6 + 10x^3y + 25y^2)$

67. $(x + y + 3)(x - y - 3)$ **69.** $(10x^2 - 7y)^2$

71. $(x + 2 + y)(x + 2 - y)$

73. $(x + 1 - y)[(x + 1)^2 + y(x + 1) + y^2]$

Problem Set 4.6

1. $(x - 7)(x + 2)$ **3.** $(y + 8)(y - 8)$

5. $3(2z^2 + 6z - 1)$ **7.** $4(p^2 + 1)$

9. $(x - 7)(y + 2)$ **11.** $(k + 9)(k^2 + 1)$

13. $(t - 6)^2$ **15.** $9(2m - 5)$

17. $(c + 2d)(c^2 - 2cd + 4d^2)$ **19.** $-5r(3r^2 - 2r + 1)$

21. $a^2(a - 1)$ **23.** $(4p - 5q)^2$ **25.** prime

27. $(z - 1)(z^2 + z + 1)$ **29.** $(2y - 5)(y + 4)$

31. $(3c - 2d)(4c + 3d)$ **33.** $(1 + 7k)(1 - 7k)$

35. $(2x - 5)(y - 1)$ **37.** $x^4y^3z^5(x^7 + z^2 - x^4z^4)$

39. $2(2m - 7n)(m + 5n)$ **41.** $(b - 12)(b + 1)$

43. $(rs - 3)(r^2s^2 + 3rs + 9)$

45. $6(4a + 5b)(4a - 5b)$ **47.** $-t(4t - 5)(t + 6)$

49. $4\pi(R + r)(R - r)$

51. $p(2p + 5q)(4p^2 - 10pq + 25q^2)$

53. $6x^3(x^2 + 9)(x + 3)(x - 3)$

55. $-(7m + 4)(2m + 3)$ **57.** $(x + 3)(x + 2)(x - 2)$

59. $4(a + 2)(3ab - 5)$ **61.** $(11x^2 - 7y^2)^2$

63. $(3x^3 - 4y)(2x^3 + 5y)$

65. $(m - n - 3)[m^2 + m(n + 3) + (n + 3)^2]$

67. $4(p + 1)(p^2 - p + 1)(p - 1)(p^2 + p + 1)$

69. $(x + y + 1)(x - y - 1)$ **71.** $(a + b)(a - b + 5)$

Problem Set 4.7

1. $1, -3$ **3.** 9 **5.** $0, 4/7$ **7.** $1, 2$ **9.** $7, -5$

11. $-1, 1/3$ **13.** $-6, 1/2$ **15.** $4, -2/5$

17. 3 **19.** $9, -9$ **21.** $0, -8$ **23.** $5/2, -5/2$

25. $2/3$ **27.** 0 **29.** $-4, -3/5$ **31.** $0, 1/2$

33. $-1/6$ **35.** $-0, 4$ **37.** $1, -2$ **39.** $5, -3$

41. $2, -2$ **43.** $4, -5$ **45.** $4, -2/3$

47. $2, -7, 3/4$ **49.** $4, 1, -8$ **51.** $0, 7, -7$

53. $0, 13$ **55.** $0, 1, -6$ **57.** $0, 5, -4$

59. 3 or -7 **61.** 4 or -1

Problem Set 4.8

1. 7 and 9 or -9 and -7 **3.** 4 and 5   **5.** 17 and 34

7. -11 and -10 **9.** width, 3 m; length, 10 m

11. 1 mi by 4 mi or 2 mi by 2 mi

13. width, 2 cm; length, 5 cm   **15.** 40 ft   **17.** 25 ft

19. 3 in., 4 in., 5 in.   **21.** width, 8 yd; length, 15 yd

23. 12 in. by 12 in.   **25.** 3 sec

Chapter 4 Review Problems

1. $2^3 \cdot 5$ **2.** $3^2 \cdot 5^2 \cdot 11$ **3.** 18   **4.** 1   **5.** x^2y^5

6. $12m^{11}$ **7.** $7(a - 5b)$

8. $4r^{10}s^5(2r^{20}s^{10} - 3r^{10}s^5 - 1)$

9. $(p^2 + 9)(q - 4)$

10. $-10k(2k^3 + 3k^2 - 5k - 1)$ **11.** $(x + 5)(y + 3)$

12. $(m + 7)(5m - 2)$ **13.** $(t - 8)(t^2 + 1)$

14. $3(2r - s)(2r + 3s)$ **15.** $2ab(3a + 5b)(a - 2b)$

16. $(x + 3)(x + 7)$ **17.** $(m + 7)(m - 5)$

18. $(p - 9)(p + 4)$ **19.** $(r + 6s)(r - 4s)$

20. $(a - 8b)(a - b)$ **21.** $-(z + 6)(z + 7)$

22. $2x(x - 6)(x + 5)$ **23.** $5y^2a(y + 4a)^2$

24. $(3x - 2)(x + 4)$ **25.** prime

26. $(2p - 9)(2p + 1)$ **27.** $(6m - 5)(m + 4)$

28. $(5r - s)(r - 5s)$ **29.** $-(4k + 5)(2k - 3)$

30. $6(3x + 1)(x + 2)$ **31.** $mn(8m + 3n)(3m - 2n)$

32. $(5r + 4s)(5r - 4s)$ **33.** $(1 + xy)(1 - xy)$

34. $(m^2 + 9)(m + 3)(m - 3)$ **35.** $(x - 10)^2$

36. $(2p + 3q)^2$ **37.** $a(3a - 4b)^2$

38. $(a + 2)(a^2 - 2a + 4)$

39. $(b - 10)(b^2 + 10b + 100)$

40. $mn(2m + 3n)(4m^2 - 6mn + 9n^2)$

41. $4(z^2 + 3z - 2)$

42. $(c + 4d)(c^2 - 4cd + 16d^2)$

43. $a^2(a + 2)(a - 2)$ **44.** $b(b - 1)(b^2 + b + 1)$

45. $(x - 9)(y + 2)$ **46.** $2r(2r - 7)(2r + 3)$

47. $8(3m - 5n)(m + 4n)$ **48.** $(z + 5)(z - 5)(a + 1)$

49. $-(k - 8)^2$ **50.** $2/5, -3$ **51.** $4, -1/3$

52. $0, -9$ **53.** 4   **54.** $5/3, -5/3$ **55.** $0, 7$

56. $3, -4/3$ **57.** $5, -2$ **58.** $0, 6, -6$

59. 6 and 8 or -2 and 0   **60.** width, 4 m; length, 7 m

61. width, 6 yd; length, 12 yd   **62.** 13 ft

Chapter 4 Test

1. $2^2 \cdot 5$ **2.** $40x^4y$ **3.** $(x + 7)(x - 7)$

4. $(y + 1)^2$ **5.** $(m - 6)(m + 2)$

6. $(q + 5)(p + 2)$ **7.** $(k + 2)(k^2 - 2k + 4)$

8. $(3a - 5)(2a + 7)$ **9.** $4xy(3x + 4 - y)$

10. $(3x + 8y)(3x - 8y)$ **11.** $(3t - s)(9t^2 + 3ts + s^2)$

12. $10r^4s^3(10r^4s^3 - 1)$ **13.** $(2x - 5a)^2$

14. $(m - 6)(m + 2)(m - 2)$

15. $2c(4c + 7d)(3c - 4d)$

16. $5(p^2 + 4)(p + 2)(p - 2)$ **17.** $-(k + 4)(k + 6)$
18. $4, -2$ **19.** $-5, 2/3$ **20.** $4/5, -4/5$
21. $0, -6$ **22.** 9 **23.** $0, 1, -1$ **24.** 8 and 16
25. 8 in., 15 in., 17 in.   **26.** at $t = 3$ sec and $t = 4$ sec

CHAPTER 5

Problem Set 5.1

1. 0 **3.** 6 **5.** $5, -5$ **7.** $7, -3$ **9.** none
11. none   **13.** $4x^2$ **15.** $-2/7m$ **17.** $2/9$
19. $\dfrac{-5b^3}{4a}$ **21.** $2x + 3$ **23.** $2/5$ **25.** $1/3$

27. $\dfrac{2y}{5y - 1}$ **29.** $\dfrac{x}{8}$ **31.** $\dfrac{1}{t + 4}$ **33.** $\dfrac{x + 5}{x + 7}$

35. $\dfrac{1}{(r + s)^4}$ **37.** $\dfrac{c + d}{c - d}$ **39.** $\dfrac{z - 3}{z - 1}$

41. $\dfrac{2m + n}{m + 5n}$ **43.** $\dfrac{2(x + 1)}{x + 2}$ **45.** 1 **47.** -1

49. -1 **51.** $-\dfrac{a + b}{a + 3b}$ **53.** $-\dfrac{t + 5}{t + 7}$

55. $\dfrac{1}{x + 3}$ **57.** $\dfrac{p - 2}{p + 1}$ **59.** $\dfrac{3}{m + 2}$

61. $x^2 - 3x + 9$ **63.** $\dfrac{m^2 + 4}{m - 3}$ **65.** $120°$

67. 60

Problem Set 5.2

1. $5m/7$ **3.** $3a^2/b^2$ **5.** $y^2/9$ **7.** $-5/6k$
9. $3/c^2$ **11.** $r/10$ **13.** $-27y/2xz^2$ **15.** $2y/3x^2$

17. $7a/2$ **19.** $\dfrac{x + 3}{x}$ **21.** $-m^2$

23. $\dfrac{2}{3(t + 1)}$ **25.** y **27.** $\dfrac{p}{p + 1}$ **29.** $\dfrac{m + 3}{8m}$

31. $\dfrac{3(c + d)}{c - d}$ **33.** $\dfrac{x^2}{(y - 2)(y - 6)}$

35. $(t + 2)(t + 1)$ **37.** 1 **39.** $\dfrac{y - 2}{y + 2}$

41. $\dfrac{7(a - b)}{a(a + b)}$ **43.** $\dfrac{(c + 3)^2}{(c + 4)(c - 2)}$ **45.** $-\dfrac{1}{2r}$

47. $\dfrac{36}{x + 3}$ **49.** $\dfrac{5}{2x - 1}$ **51.** $\dfrac{x(3x + 1)}{3(x + 2)}$

53. $\dfrac{p - 3}{12p}$

Problem Set 5.3

1. $2a/3$ **3.** $3x/4$ **5.** $2/p$ **7.** $1/y$ **9.** $1/5r$

11. 2 **13.** 1 **15.** $\dfrac{2m + 1}{7x}$ **17.** $\dfrac{r + 7}{r^2}$

19. $\dfrac{x + 2}{x^2}$ **21.** $t + 3$ **23.** $\dfrac{3}{m - 1}$ **25.** $\dfrac{3}{p + 7}$

27. $a + b$ **29.** $4/y$ **31.** $\dfrac{x + 4}{x - 4}$

33. $\dfrac{x^2 + 25}{(x - 5)(x + 5)}$ **35.** $\dfrac{-3x + 11}{(x - 5)(x + 3)}$

37. $\dfrac{2(m + 1)(m + 2)}{(m + 4)(m + 3)}$ **39.** $\dfrac{3}{y + 2}$ **41.** $\dfrac{5}{m - 2}$

43. $\dfrac{9}{x - y}$ **45.** $\dfrac{-7(r - 1)}{r - 3}$ **47.** $\dfrac{1}{x - 1}$

Problem Set 5.4

1. y^6 **3.** $9z$ **5.** $3k$ **7.** $45p$ **9.** $18m^2$
11. a^3b^2 **13.** $180x^3y^4$ **15.** $3(m + 4)$
17. $6(r - 3)$ **19.** $k(k + 1)$ **21.** $x(x - 1)$
23. $t(t - 4)(t + 5)$ **25.** $18(3z + 2)$
27. $(y + 3)(y + 5)$ **29.** $(5m - 3)(10m + 9)$
31. $12(r + 2)(r - 2)$ **33.** $a + 7$
35. $(x + 2)(x - 2)$ **37.** $3(x + 6)(x - 6)$
39. $(x - y)(x + y)^2$ **41.** $10p(p + 10)$
43. $2(x + 4)(x - 1)$ **45.** $(r + 5)(r - 5)^2$
47. $(m - 9)(m + 1)(m - 6)$
49. $(3a + 2)(2a - 5)(a - 2)$ **51.** 72 oranges

Problem Set 5.5

1. $\dfrac{3x}{10}$ **3.** $\dfrac{a^2 - 4}{2a}$ **5.** $\dfrac{11}{18x}$ **7.** $\dfrac{7}{24m}$

9. $\dfrac{1 + 3r}{r^2}$ **11.** $\dfrac{4y - 2}{y^2}$ **13.** $\dfrac{8b + 6a}{a^2b}$

15. $\dfrac{9y - 10}{36x^2y^5}$ **17.** $\dfrac{2x - 3y + xy}{x^2y^2}$ **19.** $\dfrac{7x + 1}{x}$

21. $\dfrac{1 + 4t^2}{4t}$ **23.** $\dfrac{4a}{a + 4}$ **25.** $\dfrac{-4}{x(x - 4)}$

27. $\dfrac{m^2 + m + 6}{m(m + 6)}$ **29.** $\dfrac{11a + 4}{(a + 2)(a - 4)}$

31. $\dfrac{x^2 + 2x + 3}{(x - 3)(x + 3)}$ **33.** $\dfrac{-15t}{(t + 8)(t - 2)}$

35. $\dfrac{13}{3(m + 4)}$ **37.** $\dfrac{3}{r - 1}$ **39.** $\dfrac{11}{2(p - 2)}$

41. $\dfrac{3t + 1}{5t(t - 3)}$ **43.** $\dfrac{6k^2 + 4k + 2}{(k - 1)^2(k + 1)}$

45. $\dfrac{-4r - 6}{(r + 2)^2(r + 1)}$ **47.** $\dfrac{2m^2 - 16}{(m + 5)(m - 1)(m + 6)}$

49. $\dfrac{3x - 4}{(x + 4)(x + 2)}$ **51.** $\dfrac{3}{x + 3}$ **53.** $\dfrac{2y + 1}{y - 6}$

55. $\dfrac{-8}{z(z + 4)}$ **57.** $\dfrac{(x + 1)(x^2 + 2x + 4)}{(x - 2)(x^2 + 4)}$

59. $\dfrac{a}{b} + \dfrac{c}{d} = \dfrac{a}{b} \cdot \dfrac{d}{d} + \dfrac{c}{d} \cdot \dfrac{b}{b} = \dfrac{ad + bc}{bd}$

Problem Set 5.6

1. 3/5   **3.** 6/13   **5.** $\dfrac{x + 1}{x - 1}$ **7.** $\dfrac{s}{3}$

9. $\dfrac{1}{m - 4}$ **11.** $\dfrac{a}{b}$ **13.** $\dfrac{1}{a}$ **15.** $\dfrac{y}{y + x}$

17. $\dfrac{x(1 + xy)}{y(x - y)}$ **19.** -1 **21.** $\dfrac{4x}{x - 2}$

23. $t(t + 1)$ **25.** $\dfrac{9z - 8}{2(3z + 5)}$ **27.** $\dfrac{p + 3}{p + 2}$

29. $\dfrac{2x - 3}{3x - 1}$ **31.** $\dfrac{x + 1}{x + 2}$ **33.** $\dfrac{m + 7}{m - 3}$

35. $\dfrac{k - 6}{k - 2}$ **37.** $\dfrac{1}{y + 1}$ **39.** 3   **41.** $\dfrac{b^2}{a}$

43. $\dfrac{x + 1}{x}$ **45.** $\dfrac{-m^2}{m^2 + 2m + 4}$ **47.** 3/10

49. 3 mph   **51.** 6 2/3 mph

Problem Set 5.7

1. 4   **3.** 8   **5.** 24   **7.** -4 **9.** -2
11. 5   **13.** 10   **15.** 1   **17.** 2, -3 **19.** -22
21. no solution   **23.** 3   **25.** 3   **27.** 8
29. -1 **31.** -6 **33.** 6   **35.** no solution
37. 2   **39.** -3 **41.** -14 **43.** 0, -3
45. 1/2   **47.** no solution   **49.** -8 **51.** 1

53. 3   **55.** $n = 4T - 160$ **57.** $P = \dfrac{pvT}{tV}$

59. $T = \dfrac{PVt}{pv}$ **61.** $r = \dfrac{E - IR}{I}$ **63.** $x = \dfrac{y + 1}{y - 1}$

65. $x = \dfrac{yz}{y - z}$

Problem Set 5.8

1. 10   **3.** 3/4   **5.** 2, 6   **7.** 1   **9.** \$2152
11. 1 1/3 mph   **13.** 100 mph

15. slow racer, 30 mph; fast racer, 40 mph
17. 4 1/3 mph   **19.** 1 1/5 hr
21. fast typist, 6 days; slow typist, 12 days
23. new press, 10 hr; old press, 15 hr   **25.** 7 1/2 hr
27. 4 ohm   **29.** 35.2 ohm

Problem Set 5.9

1. 1/5   **3.** 5/1   **5.** 2/3   **7.** 6/1   **9.** 4/15

11. 5/12   **13.** $\dfrac{9 \text{ males}}{5 \text{ females}}$ **15.** 54¢/oz

17. 53 mi/hr   **19.** $\dfrac{1 \text{ oz shampoo}}{1 \text{ oz water}}$ **21.** 3/2

23. 12   **25.** 28   **27.** 12/5   **29.** 3   **31.** 9/5
33. 42   **35.** 1/2   **37.** 9.75   **39.** 5/3
41. 8, -2 **43.** 35 ft   **45.** 1170 males
47. 12.5 in.   **49.** 18 bulbs   **51.** 4400 ft^2
53. 11 hr   **55.** 465 deer   **57.** \$2550 and \$3570
59. 5 in.

Chapter 5 Review Problems

1. 3   **2.** 4, -1 **3.** none   **4.** $\dfrac{-7a^2}{b^2}$

5. 5/3   **6.** $\dfrac{k - 2}{k + 2}$ **7.** $\dfrac{m + 4}{m + 6}$ **8.** $s - r$

9. $\dfrac{4}{x + 2}$ **10.** 20%   **11.** $\dfrac{5m}{8}$ **12.** $\dfrac{b(a - b)}{a(a + b)}$

13. $\dfrac{6(p - 2)}{p + 3}$ **14.** $-\dfrac{1}{x}$ **15.** $y(y + 1)$

16. $\dfrac{3}{3r + 5}$ **17.** $\dfrac{a}{2}$ **18.** $\dfrac{1}{5k}$ **19.** $\dfrac{-8}{x + 8}$

20. $\dfrac{2}{y + 4}$ **21.** $\dfrac{5}{p - 5}$ **22.** 1   **23.** $84x^3y$

24. r **25.** $(y + 2)(y + 3)$ **26.** $m(m + 6)$
27. $(p + 1)(p + 4)(p - 1)$ **28.** $4k(k - 4)$

29. $\dfrac{3y}{10}$ **30.** $\dfrac{5r - 16}{2r^2}$ **31.** $\dfrac{a^3 + 1}{a^2}$

32. $\dfrac{4x + 8}{21}$ **33.** $\dfrac{p + 3}{p(p + 1)}$ **34.** $\dfrac{10m}{(m - 2)(m + 3)}$

35. $\dfrac{11}{2x + 8}$ **36.** $\dfrac{r^2 + 4r + 2}{(r + 1)^2(r + 2)}$ **37.** $\dfrac{3}{x + 2}$

38. $\dfrac{14}{17}$ **39.** $\dfrac{x + 5}{x - 5}$ **40.** $\dfrac{1}{a}$ **41.** $\dfrac{3 - x}{3x}$

42. $\dfrac{r + 2}{r + 3}$ **43.** $\dfrac{p + 10}{p - 2}$ **44.** $\dfrac{x + 1}{x - 1}$ **45.** 3

46. 12   **47.** -3 **48.** 7   **49.** 4, -1 **50.** 11

51. no solution   **52.** $-1/2$ **53.** $-6, 2$

54. $d = \dfrac{km}{a}$ **55.** $x = \dfrac{3y}{1-y}$ **56.** 20

57. 6, 18   **58.** Diane, 8 mph; Jack, 10 mph
59. 1 1/5 mph   **60.** 1 7/8 hr
61. new copier, 9 hr; old copier, 18 hr   **62.** 1/3
63. 6/25   **64.** $\dfrac{5 \text{ females}}{2 \text{ males}}$ **65.** 4.5   **66.** 2
67. 20   **68.** 3, -2 **69.** 32 ft   **70.** 204 mi
71. 16 qt   **72.** 128 fish

Chapter 5 Test

1. 3/2   **2.** 4, -4 **3.** 30   **4.** -5

5. $\dfrac{2m}{3m+4}$ **6.** $\dfrac{a-b}{a+b}$ **7.** $72r^3$

8. $5(y-3)(y+4)$ **9.** $\dfrac{r+7}{r-1}$ **10.** $\dfrac{x}{x-1}$

11. 8   **12.** 5, -2 **13.** 1   **14.** -2 **15.** $\dfrac{2}{5x}$

16. $\dfrac{5}{m-6}$ **17.** $\dfrac{3}{b^2}$ **18.** $\dfrac{y+5}{y+4}$ **19.** $\dfrac{1}{2}$

20. $\dfrac{a}{a+1}$ **21.** $\dfrac{m^2+3m+15}{4m(m+5)}$ **22.** $\dfrac{2}{x-6}$

23. $\dfrac{-1}{2x-1}$ **24.** $\dfrac{3}{4}$ **25.** 2 2/9 days

26. 54 parts   **27.** bus, 42 mph; car, 57 mph

CHAPTER 6

Problem Set 6.1

1. quadrant I

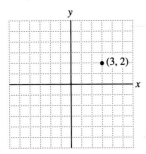

3. quadrant IV

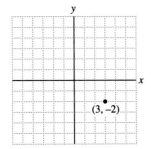

5. quadrant II

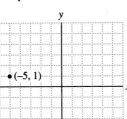

7. quadrant III

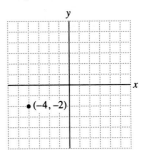

9. not in any quadrant; on the negative part of the y-axis

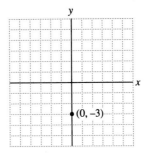

11. not in any quadrant; on the positive part of the x-axis

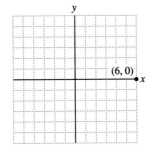

13. not in any quadrant

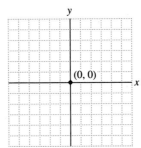

15. quadrant IV

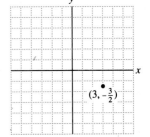

17. 16   **19.** $A(5, 2)$, $C(-3, 2)$, $E(-5, 0)$, $G(0, 0)$

21. and 23.

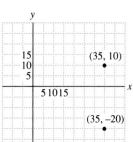

25. and 27.

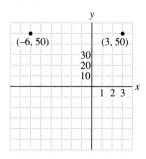

29. quadrant IV   **31.** quadrant I
33. quadrant I, quadrant II, or the positive part of the y-axis
35. Both coordinates are negative.
37. The x-coordinate is negative and the y-coordinate is positive.
39. The x-coordinate is positive and the y-coordinate is 0.
41. quadrant IV   **43.** quadrant I   **45.** quadrant IV

47.

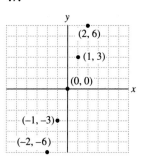

49.

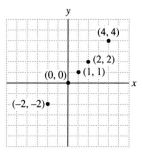

51.

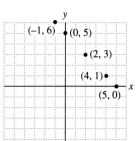

53.

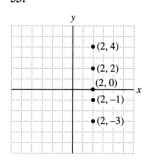

55.

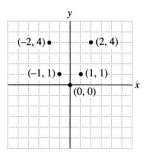

57.

Ordered Pair	Interpretation
(0, 0)	It costs \$0 to park 0 hr
(1, 10)	It costs \$10 to park 1 hr
(2, 10)	It costs \$10 to park 2 hr
(3, 15)	It costs \$15 to park 3 hr

59.

Ordered Pair	Interpretation
(0, 70)	0 min after mixing, the temperature is 70°
(5, 20)	5 min after mixing, the temperature is 20°
(20, −20)	20 min after mixing, the temperature is −20°

61. (1, 4), (2, 3), (3, 2), (4, 1)
63. (1, 6), (2, 5), (3, 4), (4, 3), (5, 2), (6, 1), (2, 6), (3, 5), (4, 4), (5, 3), (6, 2)

Problem Set 6.2

1. a. yes **b.** no **c.** yes   **3. a.** no **b.** yes **c.** yes
5. a. no **b.** yes **c.** no   **7. a.** no **b.** yes **c.** yes

9.

x	y
0	1
1	2
2	3
−1	0

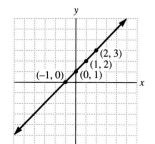

11.

x	y
0	3
6	0
2	2

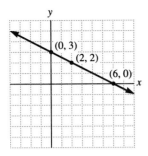

13.

x	y
0	0
4	3
−4	−3

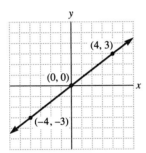

15.

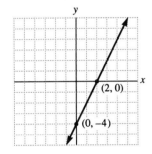

17.

19.

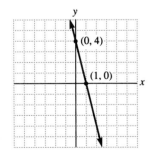

21.

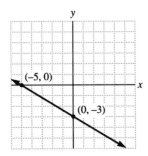

23.

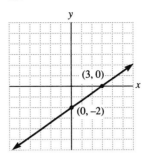

25.

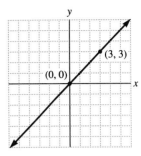

27.

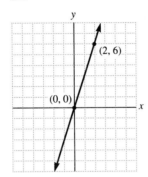

29.

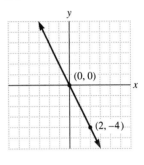

31.

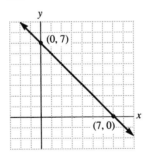

33.

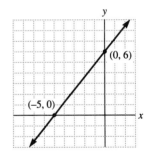

35.

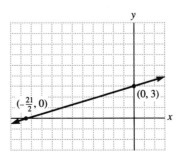

37.

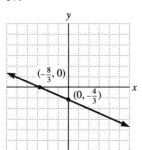

39.

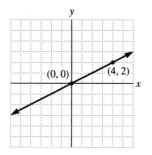

47.

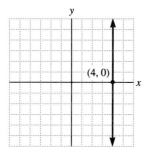

49.

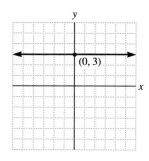

41.

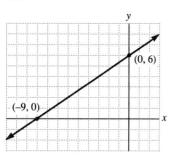

51.

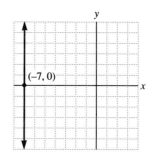

53.

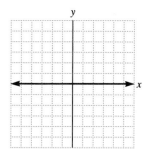

43.

x	y
0	2
4	2
-4	2

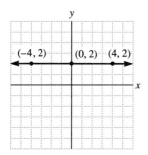

55.

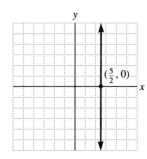

57.

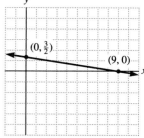

45.

x	y
-3	0
-3	5
-3	-3

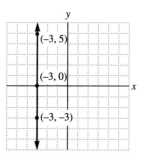

59. $y = 2x + 5$

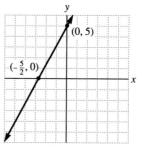

61. $x + 6y = 9$

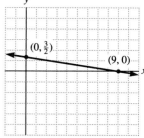

63. $y = 5$

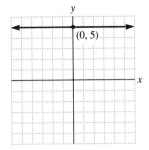

65. a. $100 **b.** $150 **c.** 30 calculators

67. a.

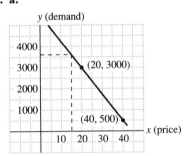

b. 3625 watches

Problem Set 6.3

1. 5/6 **3.** 1/3 **5.** −3/7 **7.** −2 **9.** −9/4
11. 0 **13.** undefined **15.** −3/7 **17.** −13/19

19.

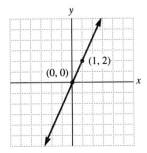

21.

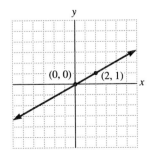

23.

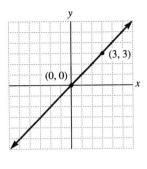

25.

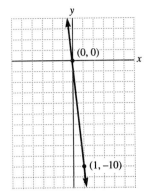

27.

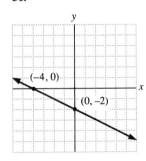

29.

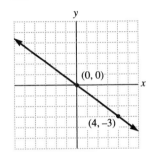

31.

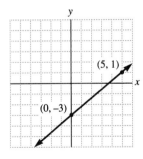

33.

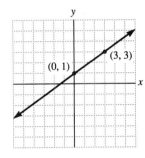

35.

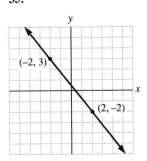

37.

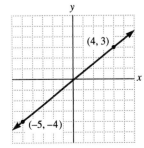

39.

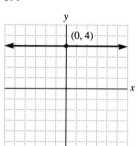

41.

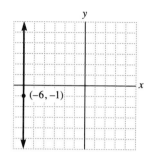

49. $m = 3$, $b = -6$

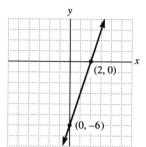

51. $m = 2/5$, $b = -2$

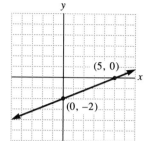

43. 3   **45.** $-1/2$ **47.** 0
49. The slope of the line through A and B equals the slope of the line through B and C.
51. 7/12   **53.** 1430 ft

53. parallel   **55.** perpendicular   **57.** parallel
59. parallel   **61.** neither   **63.** perpendicular
65. m is undefined, no y-intercept   **67.** $x = -1$
69. $4x - y = 1$ **71.** $x + 3y = -10$
73. a. $y = -200x + 11,000$ **b.** 7000 sunglasses

Problem Set 6.4

1. $3x - y = 1$ **3.** $4x - y = -11$
5. $x - 2y = 14$ **7.** $7x - 3y = -15$
9. $x + y = 9$ **11.** $2x + 5y = -16$
13. $2x - y = 5$ **15.** $x - 2y = -11$
17. $x + y = -1$ **19.** $5x + 2y = -13$
21. $4x - 5y = 0$ **23.** $y = 7$ **25.** $y = 5x + 3$

27. $y = x - 12$ **29.** $y = -\dfrac{1}{2}x + 1$ **31.** $y = \dfrac{4}{7}x$

33. $y = -8x - \dfrac{2}{3}$ **35.** $y = -5$

37. $m = 4$, $b = 8$ **39.** $m = -5/3$, $b = 4$
41. $m = 2/3$, $b = 0$ **43.** $m = 0$, $b = 9$

45. $m = 1$, $b = 3$ **47.** $m = -3$, $b = 0$

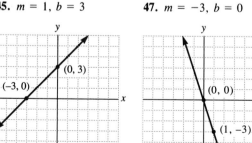

Problem Set 6.5

1.

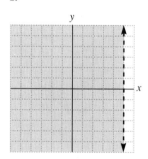

3.

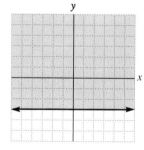

5.

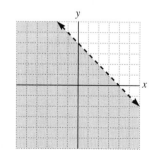

7.

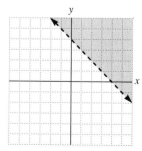

9.

11.

25.

27.

13.

15.

29.

31.

17.

19.

33.

35.

21.

23.

37.

39.

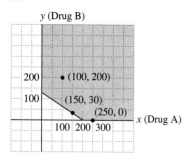

Problem Set 6.6

1. Domain is $\{2, -6, 0, 9\}$.
Range is $\{5, 4, 3\}$.
Is a function.

3. Domain is $\{3, 1\}$.
Range is $\{9, 7, -8\}$.
Not a function.

5. Domain is $\{1, 2, 3\}$.
Range is $\{1, 2, 3\}$.
Is a function.

7. Domain is $\{-5, -6, -7\}$.
Range is $\{0\}$.
Is a function.

9. Domain is $\{1, 2, 3\}$.
Range is $\{100\}$.
Is a function.

11. Domain is $\{7, -2, 11\}$.
Range is $\{-8, 6, 9\}$.
Not a function.

13. yes   **15.** yes   **17.** no   **19.** yes   **21.** no
23. no   **25.** all real numbers   **27.** $x \neq 3$
29. $x \neq 1, -1$ **31.** $x \neq 0, -8$ **33.** all real numbers
35. all real numbers   **37.** $y \geq 0$ **39.** $y \geq 1$
41. yes   **43.** no   **45.** yes   **47.** no
49. a. 3   **b.** 1   **c.** 0   **51. a.** -12 **b.** 0   **c.** 6
53. a. 11   **b.** 3   **c.** -1 **55. a.** 0   **b.** 2   **c.** 3
57. a. 2   **b.** 0   **c.** 6   **59. a.** 6   **b.** 9   **c.** 42
61. a. 9   **b.** 4   **c.** -23 **63. a.** -1 **b.** -4 **c.** -97
65. 18 yr   **67.** 100 lb   **69.** 64 in.   **71.** 18 yr
73. yes   **75.** no
77. $A = x^2$
Domain is $x > 0$.
Range is $A > 0$.
79. $R = 220 - a$
Domain is $18 \leq a \leq 55$.
Range is $165 \leq R \leq 202$.
81. $E(x) = 0.25x + 100$
  a. $E(0) = 100$ means he earns $100 if his sales are $0.
  b. $E(700) = 275$ means he earns $275 if his sales are
  $700.

Chapter 6 Review Problems

1. quadrant I

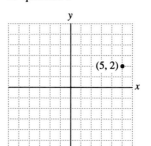

2. quadrant II

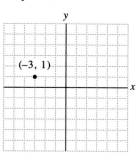

3. not in any quadrant; on the negative part of the y-axis

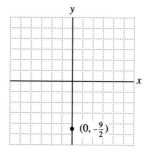

4. quadrant III

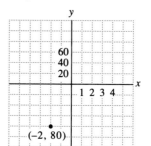

5.

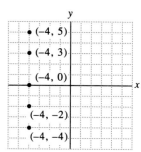

6.

Ordered Pair	Interpretation
(1, 70)	Your score on the first test was 70.
(2, 75)	Your score on the second test was 75.
(3, 80)	Your score on the third test was 80.
(4, 95)	Your score on the fourth test was 95.

7. a. yes   **b.** no   **8. a.** no   **b.** yes

9.

x	y
0	0
4	1
−4	−1

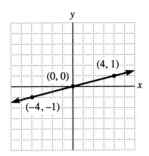

10.

x	y
0	6
2	0
1	3

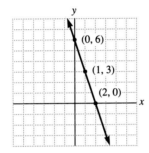

11.

x	y
0	6
−2	6
3	6

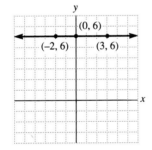

12.

x	y
−2	0
−2	−2
−2	5

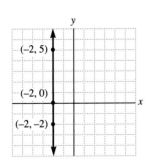

13.

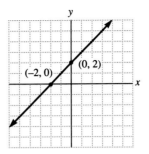

14.

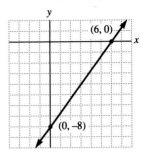

15.

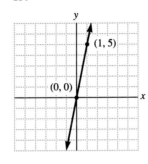

16.

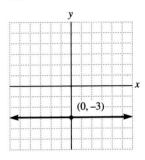

17.

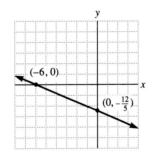

18.

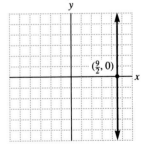

19. $y = -x - 3$

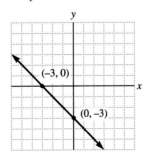

20. 5   **21.** $-3/4$ **22.** 0   **23.** undefined

24.

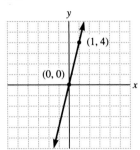

25.

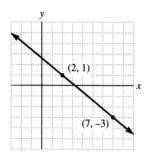

26.

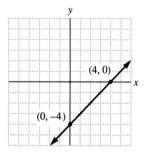

27.

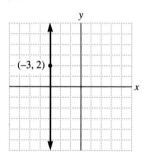

28. $2/3$ **29.** 0   **30.** $2x + y = 16$

31. $3x - 7y = -22$ **32.** $2x + y = 8$

33. $5x + 4y = -11$ **34.** $y = 10$ **35.** $y = 7x - 2$

36. $y = -\dfrac{1}{3}x$

37. $m = 2, b = 0$

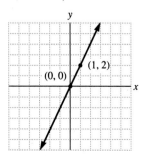

38. $m = \dfrac{2}{3}$, $b = -2$

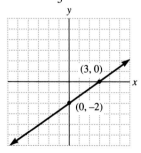

39. $m = 0, b = -7$

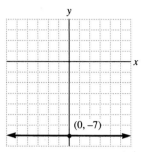

40. parallel   **41.** neither   **42.** perpendicular

43. $x + 3y = 13$

44.

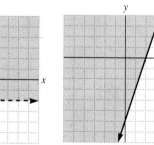

45.

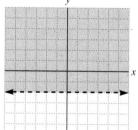

46.

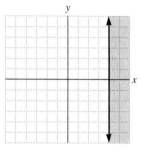

47.

48.

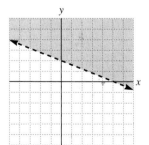

49.

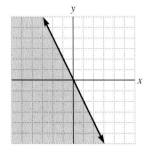

50. Domain is {7, −3}.
Range is {1, 8, −4}.
Not a function.
51. Domain is {1, 3, 5}.
Range is {2, 4, 6}.
Is a function.
52. Domain is {9, −2, 4}.
Range is {0, 4}.
Is a function.
53. Domain is {−8, −1, 6}.
Range is {3, 10}.
Not a function.
54. yes **55.** no **56.** yes **57.** all real numbers
58. $x \neq 3, -3$ **59.** all real numbers
60. all real numbers **61.** $y \geq 0$ **62.** $y \geq -2$
63. no **64.** yes **65. a.** 5 **b.** 14 **c.** −1
66. a. 1 **b.** −8 **c.** −3 **67. a.** 3 **b.** 1 **c.** 51
68. a. −1 **b.** −2 **c.** 3 **69.** $C = 3x + 25$

Chapter 6 Test

1. a. yes **b.** no **2. a.** yes **b.** no
3. a. yes **b.** no **4. a.** −3 **b.** 27
5. a. {−2, 5, 1} **b.** $x \neq -6$
6. a. {−6, 4, −1} **b.** all real numbers
7. $y = \dfrac{1}{3}x + 9$ **8.** $y = -x - \dfrac{4}{5}$
9. $m = -5, b = 0$ **10.** $m = 3/2, b = -3$
11. −1 **12.** −2/7 **13.** $6x - y = 31$
14. $x + 2y = 16$ **15.** $x + 2y = 19$ **16.** $x = 2$

17.

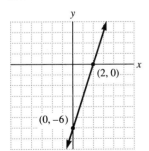

18.

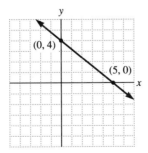

19.

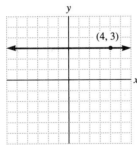

20.

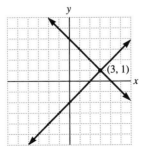

21.

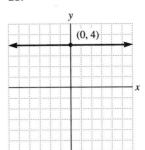

22.

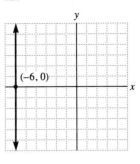

23.

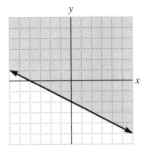

24.

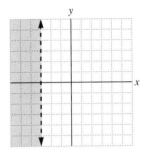

25. $y = 4.75x$
Domain is $0 \leq x \leq 24$.
Range is $0 \leq y \leq 114$.

CHAPTER 7

Problem Set 7.1

1. yes **3.** no **5.** no **7.** yes **9.** yes
11. yes
13. independent & consistent

15. independent & consistent

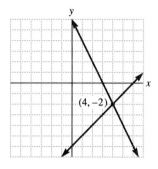

17. independent & consistent

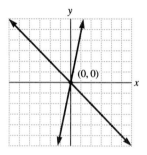

19. independent & consistent

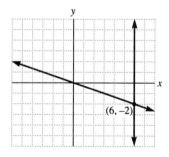

21. independent & consistent

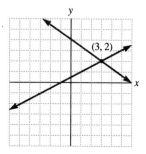

23. independent & inconsistent

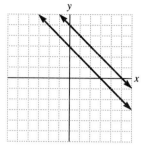

25. independent & consistent

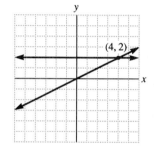

27. dependent & consistent

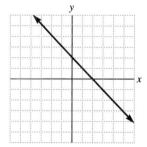

29. independent & consistent

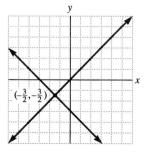

31. independent & consistent

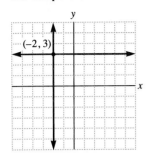

33. independent & consistent

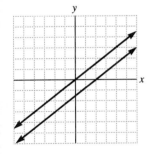

35. independent & inconsistent

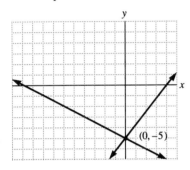

37. independent, inconsistent, no solution
39. independent, consistent, one solution
41. dependent, consistent, infinite number of solutions
43. independent, consistent, one solution
45. independent, inconsistent, no solution
47. dependent, consistent, infinite number of solutions

Problem Set 7.2

1. (3, 1)   **3.** (2, 3)   **5.** (1, −1)   **7.** (4, −1)
9. (−5, −4)   **11.** (8/3, 0)   **13.** (1, 3)
15. (−2, −4)   **17.** (5, −1)   **19.** (6, 9)

21. (−5, 0)   **23.** (−3/2, 4/3)   **25.** (2, −2)
27. (0, 1)   **29.** no solution   **31.** (0, 0)
33. infinite number of solutions   **35.** (−7/4, −7/4)
37. (−2, 5)   **39.** (47/31, 9/31)   **41.** no solution
43. $x = 64°, y = 26°$ **45.** $x = 10, y = -14$
47. $x = 8, y = 12$

Problem Set 7.3

1. (2, 8)   **3.** (6, 8)   **5.** (−1, 4)   **7.** (0, 0)
9. (−19/8, −6)   **11.** (1, 17/4)   **13.** (4, −2)
15. (3, −1)   **17.** no solution   **19.** (1, 7)
21. infinite number of solutions   **23.** (−2, 0)
25. (3/2, 1/3)   **27.** (1, 2)   **29.** (20/29, −14/29)
31. (4, −3)   **33.** (−1/2, 3/2)   **35.** no solution
37. $p = \$13.50, S = 135$ units
39. $p = \$33, S = 595$ units   **41.** $x = 17/2, y = 51$
43. $x = 19, y = 6$ **45.** $x = 26, y = 28$

Problem Set 7.4

1. width, 11 cm; length, 51 cm
3. $x = 24$ ft, $y = 16$ ft   **5.** $x = 51°, y = 102°$
7. basketball, \$7; football, \$10
9. 27 dimes, 31 quarters   **11.** 13 nickels, 11 dimes
13. 105 adults, 40 students
15. 25 kg of 20% solution,   **17.** 14 lb of \$0.85 nuts,
    15 kg of 60% solution   6 lb of \$1.35 nuts
19. 14 g pure silver,   **21.** \$18,000 at 5%,
    20 g of 15% alloy   \$7000 at 7%
23. \$3780 at 8%,   **25.** \$13,000 at 14 1/2%,
    \$2520 at 12%   \$26,000 at 9 1/2%
27. walker, 4 mph; runner, 8 mph
29. enemy missile, 2500 mi; antimissile missile, 3000 mi
31. current, 2 mph; boat, 10 mph
33. wind, 7.5 mph; helicopter, 95 mph

Problem Set 7.5

1.

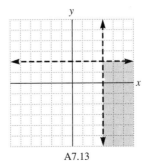

A7.13

3.

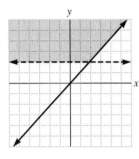

5.

15.

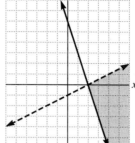

7.

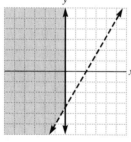

9.

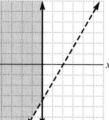

17.

19.

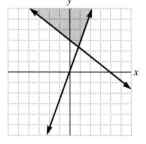

11.

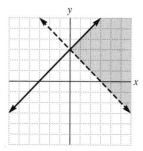

21.

23. no solution

13.

25.

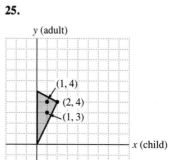

Chapter 7 Review Problems

1. yes   **2.** no

3. independent & consistent

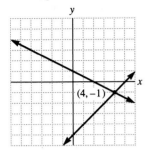

(4, −1)

4. independent & inconsistent

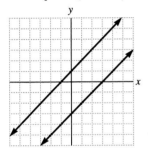

5. independent & consistent

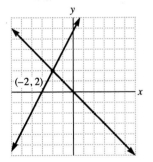

(−2, 2)

6. dependent & consistent

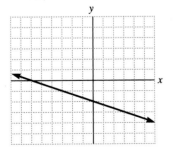

7. independent, consistent, one solution
8. dependent, consistent, infinite number of solutions
9. independent, inconsistent, no solution   **10.** (4, 5)
11. (2, −3)   **12.** (8, −5)   **13.** (−10, −8)
14. (1/2, 3/2)   **15.** infinite number of solutions
16. no solution   **17.** (2, 0)   **18.** (−2, −1)
19. $x = 25, y = 7$ **20.** (3, 6)   **21.** (8, 2)
22. (1, 2)   **23.** no solution   **24.** (1/3, 1)
25. (0, 2)   **26.** infinite number of solutions
27. (1, −1)   **28.** (1, −6)
29. $p = \$34, S = 238$ units   **30.** 17, 18
31. $x = 32$ ft, $y = 8$ ft   **32.** shovel, \$6; rake, \$8
33. 95 reserved seats, 220 general admission
34. 3 lb of \$0.65 candy, 27 lb of \$1.15 candy
35. \$2400 at 6%, \$1600 at 8%   **36.** 8 mph, 14 mph
37.

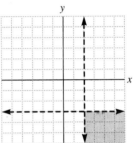

38.

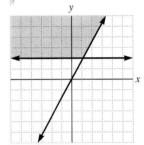

39.

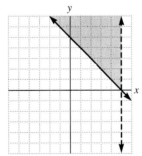

40.

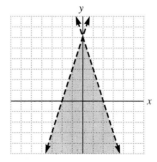

41. 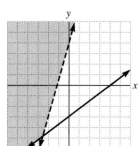 **42.**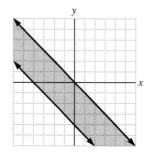

18. 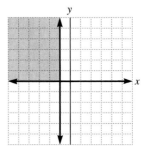 **19.**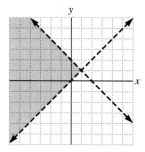

20.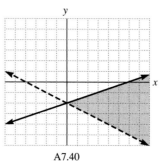

A7.40

Chapter 7 Test

1. independent & consistent **2.** dependent & consistent

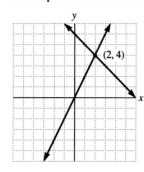 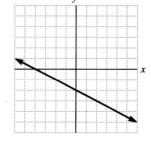

(2, 4)

3. independent & inconsistent

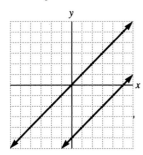

4. $(4, -1)$ **5.** $(0, 1)$ **6.** $(3, 5)$ **7.** $(11, 2)$
8. $(6, 18)$ **9.** $(-6, 7)$ **10.** $(-2, -3)$
11. no solution **12.** $(2/3, -3/4)$
13. infinite number of solutions **14.** 33, 35
15. 11 nickels, 9 dimes **16.** \$3300 at 7%, \$2100 at 11%
17. cyclist, 16 mph; car, 48 mph

CHAPTER 8

Problem Set 8.1

1. $4, -4$ **3.** $11, -11$ **5.** $1/3, -1/3$
7. $2/5, -2/5$ **9.** $0.7, -0.7$ **11.** $53, -53$
13. 2 **15.** -2 **17.** ± 2 **19.** 30 **21.** -1
23. 0 **25.** $1/9$ **27.** $5/12$
29. not a real number **31.** 4 **33.** 3
35. not a real number **37.** irrational, 1.41
39. irrational, 4.80 **41.** rational, 13
43. irrational, 6.93 **45.** irrational, 13.30
47. rational, 19 **49.** 3 **51.** -3 **53.** -5
55. 5 **57.** 7 **59.** 2 **61.** not a real number
63. 2 **65.** -1 **67.** 4 **69.** 0 **71.** 3
73. $\sqrt{16 + 9} = 5$, $\sqrt{16} + \sqrt{9} = 7$,
$\sqrt{a + b} \neq \sqrt{a} + \sqrt{b}$
75. $\sqrt{625 - 49} = 24$, $\sqrt{625} - \sqrt{49} = 18$,
$\sqrt{a - b} \neq \sqrt{a} - \sqrt{b}$
77. 40 ft/sec **79.** 10 cm **81.** 89 mi
83. 10,000 lb **85.** 84 sq in. **87.** 17
89. 4.64 **91.** not a real number **93.** 6

Problem Set 8.2

1. $2\sqrt{5}$ **3.** $3\sqrt{2}$ **5.** $10\sqrt{3}$ **7.** $4\sqrt{3}$
9. $15\sqrt{2}$ **11.** $10\sqrt{19}$ **13.** cannot be simplified
15. $-48\sqrt{3}$ **17.** $\dfrac{8}{11}$ **19.** $\dfrac{1}{10}$ **21.** $\dfrac{\sqrt{3}}{2}$
23. $\dfrac{\sqrt{6}}{7}$ **25.** $\dfrac{2\sqrt{2}}{3}$ **27.** $5\sqrt{7}$ **29.** $\dfrac{7\sqrt{5}}{8}$
31. $-\sqrt{39}$ **33.** x^2 **35.** $2x$ **37.** $5xy^3$
39. $13z^8$ **41.** $m^3\sqrt{m}$ **43.** $r\sqrt{s}$ **45.** $3k\sqrt{k}$
47. $4p^2\sqrt{5p}$ **49.** $20t^6\sqrt{5t}$ **51.** $90x^3y\sqrt{y}$
53. $-20a^6b\sqrt{5b}$ **55.** $4r^2st\sqrt{rs}$ **57.** $\dfrac{y^3}{3}$
59. $\dfrac{4}{x^2}$ **61.** $\dfrac{\sqrt{3}}{r}$ **63.** $\dfrac{\sqrt{6k}}{3}$ **65.** $x^3\sqrt{5}$
67. $\dfrac{3p\sqrt{3p}}{q}$ **69.** $\dfrac{\sqrt{b}}{2c}$ **71.** $\dfrac{x\sqrt{17}}{3y^2}$
73. $2\sqrt[3]{3}$ **75.** $5\sqrt[3]{5}$ **77.** $5\sqrt[3]{2}$ **79.** $2\sqrt[4]{2}$
81. $\dfrac{\sqrt[3]{9}}{4}$ **83.** $\dfrac{2\sqrt[4]{5}}{3}$ **85.** $-2x$ **87.** $4y\sqrt[3]{y}$
89. $\dfrac{r\sqrt[3]{9s^2}}{10t^2}$ **91.** $\dfrac{2m^2\sqrt[3]{2m^2}}{3n}$ **93.** $x + 3$
95. $x + 2$ **97.** $3x + 5y$ **99.** 60 mph
101. $65\sqrt{2}$ ft   **103.** $4\sqrt{10}$ m

Problem Set 8.3

1. $\sqrt{6}$ **3.** $\sqrt{42}$ **5.** $\sqrt{14m}$ **7.** $5\sqrt{2}$
9. $2\sqrt{15}$ **11.** $6\sqrt{5}$ **13.** 2   **15.** 7   **17.** x
19. $15\sqrt{22}$ **21.** 72   **23.** $6\sqrt{2}$ **25.** x^2
27. $z\sqrt{15}$ **29.** $4p$ **31.** $-18m$ **33.** $50t$
35. $20x\sqrt{77}$ **37.** $4x^2y\sqrt{xy}$ **39.** $-4x^5\sqrt{3}$
41. $10x^8y^7\sqrt{6}$ **43.** $\sqrt{6x} + 15$ **45.** $y + 1$
47. $16p + 36$ **49.** 2   **51.** 12   **53.** $\sqrt{5}$
55. $\sqrt{3m}$ **57.** 7   **59.** $5\sqrt{a}$ **61.** $2\sqrt{3}$
63. $3\sqrt{3k}$ **65.** $3\sqrt{17}$ **67.** $3\sqrt{2}$ **69.** $6x\sqrt{x}$
71. $\dfrac{5y^2z^2\sqrt{z}}{2}$ **73.** $\dfrac{x^2\sqrt{3}}{2}$ **75.** $\dfrac{6}{y}$ **77.** 3
79. $4x$ **81.** $2y^2\sqrt[3]{3}$ **83.** 5   **85.** 2   **87.** $5x^2$
89. 2   **91.** $3\sqrt{2}$ **93.** $20\sqrt{7}$ yd   **95.** 26 in.

Problem Set 8.4

1. $7\sqrt{5}$ **3.** $3\sqrt{11}$ **5.** cannot be simplified
7. $5\sqrt{15}$ **9.** $-4\sqrt{2}$ **11.** $-5\sqrt{5}$

13. $5\sqrt{2} - 4\sqrt{5}$ **15.** $7.8\sqrt{17}$ **17.** $-\dfrac{17}{12}\sqrt{15}$
19. $3\sqrt{5}$ **21.** $7\sqrt{2}$ **23.** $10\sqrt{2}$ **25.** $-4\sqrt{7}$
27. $13\sqrt{6}$ **29.** 0   **31.** $14\sqrt{2} - 5\sqrt{3}$ **33.** $\sqrt{10}$
35. $5\sqrt{2} - 5\sqrt{5}$ **37.** $2\sqrt{3a}$ **39.** $4\sqrt{6r}$
41. $5\sqrt{x} + 3x$ **43.** $8z\sqrt{z}$ **45.** $3\sqrt{3m}$
47. $8\sqrt{2y}$ **49.** $3p\sqrt{7}$ **51.** $4x\sqrt{2y}$
53. $-5k\sqrt{2k}$ **55.** $-2\sqrt{22x} + 8\sqrt{3y}$ **57.** $3a\sqrt{5b}$
59. $3a\sqrt{ab} - 8b\sqrt{ab}$ **61.** $13\sqrt[3]{2} + 3\sqrt{2}$
63. $7\sqrt[4]{7} - \sqrt[3]{7}$ **65.** $7\sqrt[3]{3}$ **67.** $12x\sqrt[3]{5}$
69. $5\sqrt[4]{2y^3}$ **71.** $4ab^2\sqrt[3]{4ab^2}$ **73.** $38\sqrt{2}$
75. $44\sqrt{6}$ volts

Problem Set 8.5

1. $8\sqrt{5} - 2$ **3.** $\sqrt{6} + 3$ **5.** $4\sqrt{15} + 8\sqrt{35}$
7. $20 - 20\sqrt{3}$ **9.** $x + \sqrt{xy}$ **11.** $9p - 3p\sqrt{5}$
13. $12\sqrt{7m} + 42m\sqrt{2}$ **15.** $x + 1 - \sqrt{x^2 + x}$
17. $18\sqrt{x} + 9\sqrt{y} - 36$ **19.** $5 + 4\sqrt{2}$
21. $\sqrt{15} - 4\sqrt{3} + 2\sqrt{5} - 8$
23. $\sqrt{15} + \sqrt{10} + \sqrt{6} + 2$
25. $3\sqrt{2} - 2\sqrt{3} + 5\sqrt{6} - 10$ **27.** $15 - 2\sqrt{14}$
29. $49 + 12\sqrt{10}$ **31.** -2 **33.** 6
35. $2x + 8\sqrt{2x} + 16$ **37.** $6x - \sqrt{x} - 40$
39. $16m - 8\sqrt{mn} + n$ **41.** $z^2 - 28$
43. $x\sqrt{6} - \sqrt{6xy} + 4\sqrt{xy} - 4y$
45. $16r + 24\sqrt{6r} + 54$
47. $2k\sqrt{10} + 2\sqrt{15k} + 2\sqrt{5k} + \sqrt{30}$
49. $12t - 2\sqrt{2t} - 4$ **51.** $2x - 2\sqrt{x^2 + 3x} + 3$
53. $y + 44 + 12\sqrt{y + 8}$ **55.** $1 - \sqrt{7}$
57. $1 + 3\sqrt{5}$ **59.** $\dfrac{1 - \sqrt{5}}{6}$ **61.** $\dfrac{5 + 2\sqrt{3}}{3}$
63. $\dfrac{2 \pm \sqrt{11}}{3}$ **65.** $\dfrac{-2 \pm \sqrt{5}}{4}$ **67.** $2 - 5\sqrt[3]{2}$
69. $9 + 3\sqrt[4]{27}$ **71.** $-9 - 2\sqrt[3]{5} + 7\sqrt[3]{25}$
73. $27\sqrt[3]{3} + 6\sqrt[3]{9} + 1$ **75.** $2\sqrt[3]{18} - \sqrt[3]{4}$
77. Perimeter is $4\sqrt{5} + 22$; area is $29 + 11\sqrt{5}$.
79. 2   **81.** $2\sqrt{3}$

Problem Set 8.6

1. $\dfrac{\sqrt{3}}{3}$ **3.** $\dfrac{5\sqrt{6}}{2}$ **5.** $\sqrt{2}$ **7.** $\dfrac{\sqrt{15}}{3}$
9. $\sqrt{5}$ **11.** 3   **13.** $\dfrac{2\sqrt{35}}{7}$ **15.** $\dfrac{3\sqrt{10}}{4}$
17. $\dfrac{\sqrt{2}}{4}$ **19.** $\dfrac{3\sqrt{33}}{22}$ **21.** $\dfrac{2\sqrt{3}}{3}$ **23.** $\dfrac{2\sqrt{xy}}{y}$

25. $\dfrac{2\sqrt{6x}}{3x}$ **27.** $\dfrac{a\sqrt{ab}}{3b}$ **29.** $\dfrac{7\sqrt{10x}}{4y}$

31. $\dfrac{x^3\sqrt{7y}}{7y}$ **33.** $\dfrac{2\sqrt{5}}{15}$ **35.** $\dfrac{\sqrt{14}}{12}$ **37.** $\dfrac{\sqrt[3]{9}}{3}$

39. $3\sqrt[3]{4}$ **41.** $\dfrac{\sqrt[3]{6}}{2}$ **43.** $\dfrac{2\sqrt[3]{5}}{5}$ **45.** $\dfrac{\sqrt[3]{3}}{6}$

47. $\dfrac{\sqrt[3]{180x}}{6x}$ **49.** $\dfrac{\sqrt{7}+1}{6}$ **51.** $-3+\sqrt{7}$

53. $\dfrac{3-\sqrt{3}}{2}$ **55.** $\dfrac{5+\sqrt{10}}{3}$ **57.** $2\sqrt{21}-2\sqrt{15}$

59. $-11+2\sqrt{30}$ **61.** $-\dfrac{\sqrt{10}+\sqrt{6}+\sqrt{5}+\sqrt{3}}{2}$

63. $6\sqrt{3}+7\sqrt{2}$ **65.** $\dfrac{5\sqrt{7}-3\sqrt{5}}{2}$

67. $\dfrac{3\sqrt{6}+4}{19}$ **69.** $\dfrac{x+2\sqrt{xy}+y}{x-y}$

71. $\dfrac{2x-3\sqrt{2x}}{2x-9}$ **73.** $\dfrac{5\sqrt{66}}{6}$ amps

Problem Set 8.7

1. 4   **3.** 8   **5.** 1/2   **7.** 36   **9.** no solution
11. 7   **13.** 2   **15.** -1 **17.** 1   **19.** 3
21. 2   **23.** 2, -2 **25.** 3, 5   **27.** no solution
29. 1/3   **31.** -2 **33.** 0   **35.** 6   **37.** 4
39. no solution   **41.** -2 **43.** 17   **45.** 0, -1
47. 3   **49.** 5   **51.** 10   **53.** 11   **55.** 49
57. 9   **59.** 0, 4   **61.** 256 ft   **63.** 5   **65.** 9
67. $R=\dfrac{V^2}{W}$

Problem Set 8.8

1. 4   **3.** 5   **5.** 2   **7.** 4   **9.** 3   **11.** 9
13. 27   **15.** 8   **17.** 1/11   **19.** 1/32   **21.** 4
23. $-1/5$ **25.** $2^{7/3}$ **27.** $5^{1/2}$ **29.** $11^{3/5}$
31. $12^{2/3}$ **33.** $10^{1/2}$ **35.** 3^4 **37.** 12   **39.** 27
41. 27/64   **43.** 3/2   **45.** 1   **47.** m^2 **49.** a
51. $\dfrac{1}{y^{1/3}}$ **53.** $\dfrac{1}{z}$ **55.** p^3 **57.** $r^{4/3}$ **59.** $3m^2$
61. $\dfrac{b}{a^{10}}$ **63.** $\dfrac{c^3}{d^3}$ **65.** $\dfrac{x^{1/2}}{y}$ **67.** $\dfrac{1}{k}$
69. $\sqrt{2}$ **71.** 6   **73.** $\sqrt[4]{r}$ **75.** $\sqrt[3]{x^2}$ **77.** $\sqrt[4]{2}$
79. $\sqrt[6]{y}$ **81.** 20   **83.** 9   **85.** 16   **87.** 1.32
89. -4 **91.** 89 days   **93.** 365 days

Chapter 8 Review Problems

1. 10, -10 **2.** 4/5, $-4/5$ **3.** 1.3, -1.3 **4.** 6
5. not a real number   **6.** ±3 **7.** 5   **8.** 2
9. 4   **10.** irrational, 2.24   **11.** rational, 14
12. irrational, 11.40   **13.** 41 mi   **14.** $2\sqrt{11}$
15. $12\sqrt{3}$ **16.** $-20\sqrt{10}$ **17.** $\dfrac{5}{11}$ **18.** $\dfrac{2\sqrt{3}}{7}$
19. $4\sqrt{10}$ **20.** $4x^{32}$ **21.** $50p\sqrt{3p}$
22. $-12a^3b^3\sqrt{2a}$ **23.** $\dfrac{15}{4}rst^2\sqrt{s}$ **24.** $\dfrac{y^5}{8}$
25. $\dfrac{\sqrt{11}}{m}$ **26.** $\dfrac{\sqrt{2r}}{2}$ **27.** $\dfrac{y}{2xz^2}$ **28.** $3\sqrt[3]{5}$
29. $\dfrac{2\sqrt[3]{3}}{5}$ **30.** $\dfrac{3m^2\sqrt[3]{n^2}}{4}$ **31.** $x+6$
32. $30\sqrt{2}$ ft   **33.** $\sqrt{30y}$ **34.** $16k$ **35.** 84
36. $-96xy^4\sqrt{5}$ **37.** $\sqrt{5x}$ **38.** $7\sqrt{2}$ **39.** $12m^2$
40. $\dfrac{a^2}{4b}$ **41.** $10x$ **42.** 3   **43.** 7   **44.** $6\sqrt{10}$
45. $3\sqrt{2}-3\sqrt{3}$ **46.** $11\sqrt{5}$ **47.** $15\sqrt{7}$
48. $5\sqrt{2m}$ **49.** $9k\sqrt{6k}$ **50.** $5\sqrt[3]{2}+3\sqrt[3]{5}$
51. $6\sqrt[4]{3}$ **52.** $\sqrt{10}+4$ **53.** $25p-5p\sqrt{3}$
54. $y+4+\sqrt{y^2+4y}$ **55.** $x-1$
56. $\sqrt{15}-2\sqrt{3}+4\sqrt{5}-8$ **57.** $37+12\sqrt{7}$
58. $13-7\sqrt{3}$ **59.** $16m-n$ **60.** $1+\sqrt{5}$
61. $\dfrac{-3\pm2\sqrt{5}}{3}$ **62.** $5-2\sqrt[3]{5}$
63. $\sqrt[3]{9}+8\sqrt[3]{3}+16$ **64.** 4   **65.** $\sqrt{7}$
66. $\dfrac{\sqrt{3}}{6}$ **67.** $\dfrac{a^3\sqrt{11b}}{11b}$ **68.** $\dfrac{\sqrt{30}}{12}$ **69.** $3\sqrt[3]{2}$
70. $\dfrac{3\sqrt[3]{25}}{5}$ **71.** $\sqrt{5}+2$ **72.** $\dfrac{3\sqrt{14}-6}{5}$
73. $\dfrac{-3-2\sqrt{3}}{3}$ **74.** 9   **75.** no solution   **76.** 4
77. 10   **78.** 7   **79.** 1   **80.** 2, 3   **81.** 16
82. 16   **83.** 10   **84.** 5   **85.** 27   **86.** 1/4
87. 27   **88.** $4p^2$ **89.** $\dfrac{a^6}{b^8}$ **90.** $\dfrac{x^{1/4}}{y^{1/6}}$
91. $\dfrac{1}{m^{1/4}}$ **92.** $t^{1/2}$ **93.** $\sqrt{6}$
94. $\sqrt[3]{x}$ **95.** $\sqrt[4]{7}$

Chapter 8 Test

1. 9   **2.** -40 **3.** 3   **4.** not a real number
5. 1/2   **6.** 125   **7.** $10\sqrt{2}$ **8.** $2m\sqrt{6m}$

9. $2\sqrt[4]{7}$ **10.** $3x^3$ **11.** $\dfrac{3\sqrt{5}}{7}$ **12.** $7^{1/4}$

13. $6\sqrt{15} + 10\sqrt{3}$ **14.** $7 - 2\sqrt{6}$

15. $\sqrt{6} - 4\sqrt{2} + 5\sqrt{3} - 20$ **16.** $3\sqrt{y}$ **17.** $\sqrt{5}$

18. $-3\sqrt{7} + 7\sqrt{3}$ **19.** $20\sqrt{2}$ **20.** $7p\sqrt{3}$

21. $\sqrt[3]{5}$ **22.** $\dfrac{\sqrt{15}}{5}$ **23.** $5\sqrt[3]{4}$ **24.** $2\sqrt{6} - 4$

25. $\dfrac{\sqrt{10} + \sqrt{6} + \sqrt{5} + \sqrt{3}}{2}$ **26.** 2 **27.** 3

28. 8 **29.** 23

CHAPTER 9

Problem Set 9.1

1. ± 5 **3.** ± 4 **5.** $\pm 2/3$ **7.** $\pm\sqrt{2}$

9. $\pm\sqrt{7}$ **11.** $\pm 2\sqrt{5}$ **13.** $\pm\dfrac{3\sqrt{5}}{2}$

15. no real solution **17.** $\pm\dfrac{\sqrt{2}}{2}$ **19.** $8, -6$

21. $3 \pm \sqrt{3}$ **23.** $-2 \pm 3\sqrt{2}$ **25.** no real solution

27. $-2, -5$ **29.** $\dfrac{3}{2}, \dfrac{1}{2}$ **31.** $\dfrac{-4 \pm \sqrt{11}}{5}$

33. $\dfrac{1 \pm \sqrt{3}}{2}$ **35.** $2, -1$ **37.** $\dfrac{-3 \pm \sqrt{5}}{2}$

39. 11 or -11 **41.** 10 ft, 20 ft **43.** $4\sqrt{3}$ ft/sec

45. 10%

Problem Set 9.2

1. $x^2 - 8x + 16 = (x - 4)^2$

3. $m^2 + 12m + 36 = (m + 6)^2$

5. $r^2 - 2r + 1 = (r - 1)^2$

7. $y^2 + y + \dfrac{1}{4} = \left(y + \dfrac{1}{2}\right)^2$

9. $p^2 + 3p + \dfrac{9}{4} = \left(p + \dfrac{3}{2}\right)^2$

11. $z^2 - \dfrac{4}{5}z + \dfrac{4}{25} = \left(z - \dfrac{2}{5}\right)^2$

13. $1, 3$ **15.** -3 **17.** $0, 10$ **19.** $2 \pm \sqrt{2}$

21. $-1 \pm \sqrt{7}$ **23.** $-5 \pm 2\sqrt{3}$ **25.** $-1 \pm \dfrac{\sqrt{7}}{2}$

27. $-1 \pm \dfrac{\sqrt{26}}{2}$ **29.** $1 \pm \dfrac{2\sqrt{6}}{3}$

31. $-\dfrac{1}{2} \pm \dfrac{\sqrt{5}}{2}$ **33.** $-\dfrac{1}{2} \pm \dfrac{\sqrt{11}}{2}$ **35.** $1, -\dfrac{1}{3}$

37. no real solution **39.** $-\dfrac{2}{5} \pm \dfrac{2\sqrt{6}}{5}$

41. no real solution

43. $(2 + \sqrt{3})^2 - 4(2 + \sqrt{3}) + 1 = 7 + 4\sqrt{3} - 8 - 4\sqrt{3} + 1 = 0$
$(2 - \sqrt{3})^2 - 4(2 - \sqrt{3}) + 1 = 7 - 4\sqrt{3} - 8 + 4\sqrt{3} + 1 = 0$

45. $1 + 3\sqrt{3}$ **47.** $-\dfrac{3}{2} + \dfrac{\sqrt{37}}{2}, \dfrac{3}{2} + \dfrac{\sqrt{37}}{2}$

Problem Set 9.3

1. $a = 2, b = 9, c = 4$ **3.** $a = 1, b = -4, c = 4$

5. $a = 1, b = -1, c = 0$ **7.** $a = 9, b = 0, c = -25$

9. $a = 4, b = 0, c = 1$ **11.** $a = 1, b = -5, c = 5$

13. $2/3, -1$ **15.** $0, 6$ **17.** $2, -2$ **19.** $\dfrac{-3 \pm \sqrt{5}}{2}$

21. $\dfrac{5 \pm \sqrt{21}}{2}$ **23.** $\dfrac{3 \pm \sqrt{17}}{4}$ **25.** $\dfrac{-1 \pm \sqrt{13}}{6}$

27. 2 **29.** $1 \pm 2\sqrt{2}$ **31.** $\dfrac{2 \pm \sqrt{6}}{2}$

33. $\dfrac{5 \pm \sqrt{5}}{5}$ **35.** $\pm 3\sqrt{2}$ **37.** $\dfrac{-3 \pm \sqrt{5}}{4}$

39. $1/2, -4/3$ **41.** $\dfrac{1 \pm \sqrt{2}}{3}$ **43.** $\dfrac{-7 \pm \sqrt{33}}{8}$

45. $-1 \pm \sqrt{10}$ **47.** $1 \pm \sqrt{7}$ **49.** $\dfrac{2 \pm \sqrt{19}}{3}$

51. $\dfrac{-2 \pm \sqrt{14}}{2}$ **53.** $\dfrac{-3 \pm \sqrt{105}}{12}$

55. no real solution **57.** no real solution

59. no real solution

61. $\dfrac{-2 + 2\sqrt{6}}{5}$ and $\dfrac{1 + 4\sqrt{6}}{5}$ or
$\dfrac{-2 - 2\sqrt{6}}{5}$ and $\dfrac{1 - 4\sqrt{6}}{5}$

63. $3 + \sqrt{5}$ in. or $3 - \sqrt{5}$ in.

65. slow computer, $\dfrac{5 + \sqrt{17}}{2}$ hr;
fast computer, $\dfrac{3 + \sqrt{17}}{2}$ hr

67. $\dfrac{3 + \sqrt{57}}{4}$ mph

69. a. $\dfrac{3 - \sqrt{5}}{2}$ sec and $\dfrac{3 + \sqrt{5}}{2}$ sec **b.** never

Problem Set 9.4

1. ± 11 **3.** 0, 4   **5.** 3, 5   **7.** $\dfrac{1 \pm \sqrt{5}}{2}$

9. 0   **11.** $-7, 5/2$ **13.** $\pm 9/2$ **15.** $\pm\sqrt{13}$

17. $-3, -9$ **19.** $\pm 4\sqrt{2}$ **21.** 4/5

23. $\dfrac{2 \pm 3\sqrt{10}}{6}$ **25.** $\dfrac{7 \pm \sqrt{13}}{6}$

27. no real solution   **29.** 5/6, $-15/4$ **31.** 0, $-1/8$

33. no real solution   **35.** $\dfrac{-2 \pm \sqrt{22}}{6}$

3.

x	y
3	-8
2	-3
1	0
0	1
-1	0
-2	-3
-3	-8

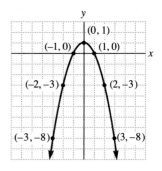

Problem Set 9.5

1. $2i$ **3.** $i\sqrt{3}$ **5.** $2i\sqrt{5}$ **7.** $-6i$ **9.** $\dfrac{1}{3}i$

11. $\dfrac{\sqrt{3}}{2}i$ **13.** true   **15.** true   **17.** true

19. $10 + 7i$ **21.** $-1 - i$ **23.** $-5 + 5i$

25. $7 - 3i$ **27.** 4   **29.** $11 - 9i$ **31.** $6 + 12i$

33. $-22 + 29i$ **35.** $32 + 7i$ **37.** 25   **39.** $-i$

41. i **43.** $2 - 2i$ **45.** $4 - i$ **47.** $\dfrac{22}{13} - \dfrac{7}{13}i$

49. $\dfrac{4}{5} - \dfrac{3}{5}i$ **51.** $\pm 5i$ **53.** $\pm 2i\sqrt{2}$

55. $4 \pm i\sqrt{7}$ **57.** $\dfrac{8}{3} \pm i\sqrt{10}$ **59.** $-5 \pm 6i$

61. $2 \pm i$ **63.** $-\dfrac{3}{2} \pm \dfrac{\sqrt{7}}{2}i$ **65.** $1 \pm \dfrac{\sqrt{6}}{2}i$

67. $-\dfrac{1}{4} \pm \dfrac{\sqrt{11}}{4}i$

5.

x	y
3	10
2	0
1	-6
0	-8
-1	-6
-2	0
-3	10

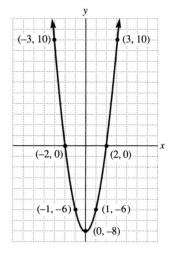

Problem Set 9.6

1.

x	y
3	10
2	5
1	2
0	1
-1	2
-2	5
-3	10

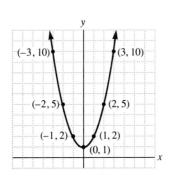

7.

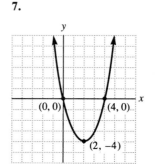

9.

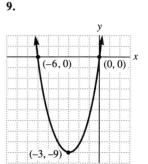

11.

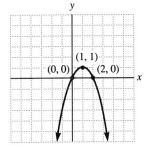

13.

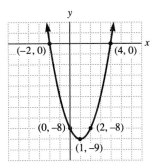

15.

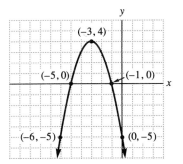

17.

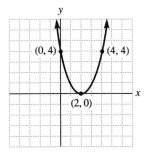

19.

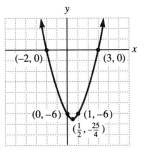

21.

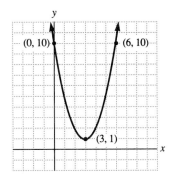

23.

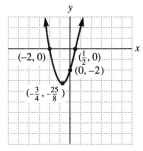

25.

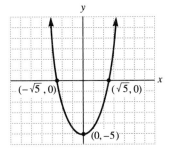

27.

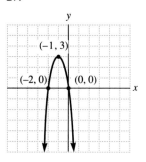

29.

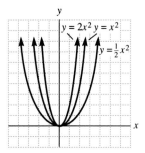

31.

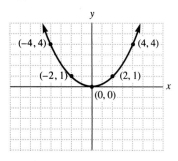

33. width, 2 mi; length, 4 mi

Chapter 9 Review Problems

1. ± 7 **2.** $\pm 5/2$ **3.** $\pm \dfrac{2\sqrt{2}}{3}$ **4.** no real solution

5. 11, -7 **6.** $-4 \pm \sqrt{21}$ **7.** $\dfrac{1 \pm \sqrt{5}}{2}$

8. $-\dfrac{1}{2} \pm \dfrac{\sqrt{3}}{2}$ **9.** $2\sqrt{5}$ or $-2\sqrt{5}$

10. $x^2 - 8x + 16 = (x - 4)^2$

11. $m^2 + 3m + \dfrac{9}{4} = \left(m + \dfrac{3}{2} \right)^2$

12. $y^2 + y + \dfrac{1}{4} = \left(y + \dfrac{1}{2} \right)^2$

13. $r^2 - \dfrac{2}{5}r + \dfrac{1}{25} = \left(r - \dfrac{1}{5} \right)^2$

14. 2, 4   **15.** 0, -4 **16.** $1 \pm \sqrt{7}$

17. $-5 \pm 3\sqrt{3}$ **18.** $-2 \pm \dfrac{3\sqrt{2}}{2}$ **19.** $\dfrac{2}{3} \pm \dfrac{\sqrt{7}}{3}$

20. $-1 + \sqrt{15}$ **21.** $a = 2, b = 1, c = -21$

22. $a = 1, b = 8, c = 0$ **23.** 3   **24.** -4, 3/2

25. $\dfrac{3 \pm \sqrt{5}}{2}$ **26.** $\dfrac{5 \pm \sqrt{13}}{2}$ **27.** $-2 \pm \sqrt{2}$

28. $\dfrac{2 \pm \sqrt{3}}{2}$ **29.** $\dfrac{-3 \pm \sqrt{17}}{4}$ **30.** no real solution

31. $\dfrac{-3 + \sqrt{14}}{5}$ and $\dfrac{1 + 3\sqrt{14}}{5}$, or

$\dfrac{-3 - \sqrt{14}}{5}$ and $\dfrac{1 - 3\sqrt{14}}{5}$

32. slow bricklayer, $\dfrac{9 + \sqrt{65}}{2}$ hr;

fast bricklayer, $\dfrac{7 + \sqrt{65}}{2}$ hr

33. 9, -1 **34.** ± 10 **35.** $\pm 3\sqrt{6}$

36. $\dfrac{-1 \pm \sqrt{29}}{2}$ **37.** 2, $-\dfrac{3}{2}$ **38.** 0, $\dfrac{5}{3}$

39. $\dfrac{2 \pm \sqrt{10}}{2}$ **40.** -4, $\dfrac{2}{5}$ **41.** $\pm \sqrt{21}$ **42.** $4i$

43. $i\sqrt{2}$ **44.** $-i$ **45.** $\dfrac{1}{5}i$ **46.** $7 + 3i$

47. $-2 + i$ **48.** $9 - 2i$ **49.** $-1 + 9i$

50. $22 - 7i$ **51.** $-6 - 6i$ **52.** 29   **53.** $6 + 3i$

54. $\dfrac{7}{25} - \dfrac{1}{25}i$ **55.** $\dfrac{3}{2} + \dfrac{1}{3}i$ **56.** $\pm 10i$

57. $-1 \pm i\sqrt{2}$ **58.** $\dfrac{5}{8} \pm \dfrac{\sqrt{7}}{8}i$

59.

x	y
3	0
2	-5
1	-8
0	-9
-1	-8
-2	-5
-3	0

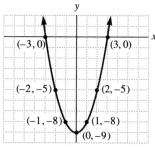

60.

x	y
3	-18
2	-8
1	-2
0	0
-1	-2
-2	-8
-3	-18

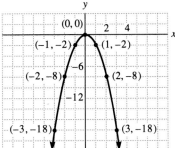

61.

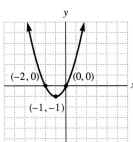

62.

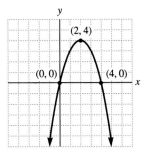

63.

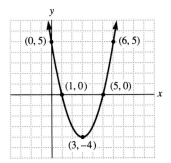

64.

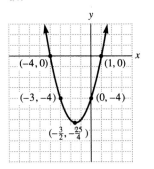

65.

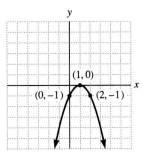

66.

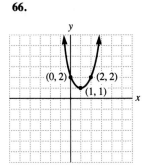

Chapter 9 Test

1. ± 9 **2.** $\pm 3\sqrt{3}$ **3.** $\dfrac{-2 \pm \sqrt{5}}{3}$ **4.** $2, -6$

5. $1 \pm \sqrt{6}$ **6.** $-\dfrac{1}{2} \pm \dfrac{\sqrt{3}}{2}$ **7.** $-1, -2$

8. $-2 \pm \sqrt{6}$ **9.** $\dfrac{1 \pm \sqrt{33}}{8}$ **10.** $0, 9$

11. $1, -\dfrac{1}{3}$ **12.** $\pm \dfrac{4\sqrt{5}}{5}$ **13.** $-3 \pm \sqrt{2}$

14. $-4, \dfrac{1}{3}$ **15.** $\pm i\sqrt{7}$ **16.** $\dfrac{4 \pm \sqrt{6}}{2}$

17. $2 \pm 2i$ **18.** $-1 + 6i$ **19.** $27 - 8i$

20. $1 - i$ **21.** $\dfrac{1}{8} - \dfrac{5}{8}i$

22.

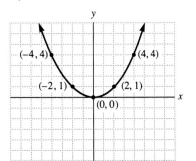

23.

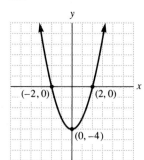

24.

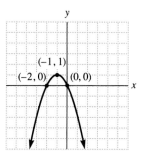

25. $-1 < m < 3$

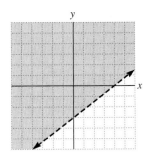

26. $(k + 3)(k^2 - 3k + 9)$ **27.** $(x - 7)(y + 3)$

28. $\dfrac{p}{3}$ **29.** $\dfrac{x^2 - 2x + 2}{(x + 2)(x - 3)}$ **30.** $\dfrac{\sqrt{6}}{3}$

31. $9 + 3\sqrt{7}$ **32.** $6\sqrt{y}$ **33.** $13\sqrt{7}$

34. $-1 + 12i$ **35.** $\dfrac{3}{2} + \dfrac{3}{2}i$ **36.** ± 6

37. $5, -1$ **38.** $0, -7$ **39.** $\dfrac{5 \pm \sqrt{13}}{6}$

40. $-2 \pm i$ **41.** $(2, -1)$ **42.** 60 defective fuses

43. 9 nickels, 12 dimes   **44.** 7 ft, 24 ft, 25 ft

45. 1 1/5 days   **46.** 4 and 26

25.

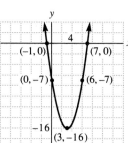

26. $\dfrac{1 + \sqrt{21}}{2}$ mph

47.

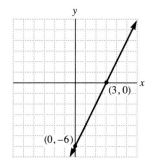

48.

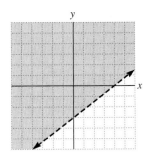

APPENDIX 1: FINAL EXAM

1. 5   **2.** $2^2 \cdot 5 \cdot 7$ **3.** 16/9   **4.** $\ell = \dfrac{P - 2w}{2}$

5. 1/4   **6.** 40   **7.** 23   **8.** $3x + 2y = 1$

9. 4.3×10^{-3} **10.** $m = -1/2, b = 3$ **11.** $\dfrac{x}{x + 3}$

12. $x \neq 5$ **13.** $-3/2$ **14.** 1/12   **15.** 4

16. -4 **17.** -20 **18.** 5   **19.** $\dfrac{20x^3}{y^6}$

20. $4a^3 + 2a^2 - 22a + 15$ **21.** $4r^2 + 3r - 1$

22. $3x^2 + x - 4 + \dfrac{7}{2x + 5}$

23. $x > -2$ **24.** $y \geq 11$

49.

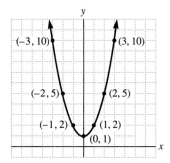

50.

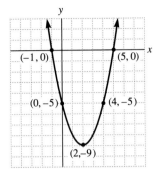

APPENDIX 2: SETS

Problem Set A.1

1. finite   **2.** infinite   **3.** true   **4.** false
5. true   **6.** false   **7.** {1, 2, 3, 4}
8. {8, 9, 10, 11, . . .}   **9.** {2, 3, 4, 5}   **10.** Ø
11. {x|x is a natural number between 3 and 9}
12. {y|y is a natural number less than 6}
13. {t|t is a natural number greater than 9}
14. {p|p is an odd natural number greater than 6}
15. true   **16.** false   **17.** true   **18.** true
19. false   **20.** true   **21.** true   **22.** true
23. Ø   **24.** Ø, {1}   **25.** Ø, {1}, {2}, {1, 2}
26. Ø, {1}, {2}, {3}, {1, 2}, {1, 3}, {2, 3}, {1, 2, 3}
27. {1, 2, 3, 4, 5, 7}   **28.** {3, 5}   **29.** {2, 3, 5, 6, 8}
30. B   **31.** A   **32.** A   **33.** A   **34.** Ø

Index

Prime Factored Form of Whole Numbers From 2 Through 100

$2 = 2$	$26 = 2 \cdot 13$	$51 = 3 \cdot 17$	$76 = 2^2 \cdot 19$
$3 = 3$	$27 = 3^3$	$52 = 2^2 \cdot 13$	$77 = 7 \cdot 11$
$4 = 2^2$	$28 = 2^2 \cdot 7$	$53 = 53$	$78 = 2 \cdot 3 \cdot 13$
$5 = 5$	$29 = 29$	$54 = 2 \cdot 3^3$	$79 = 79$
$6 = 2 \cdot 3$	$30 = 2 \cdot 3 \cdot 5$	$55 = 5 \cdot 11$	$80 = 2^4 \cdot 5$
$7 = 7$	$31 = 31$	$56 = 2^3 \cdot 7$	$81 = 3^4$
$8 = 2^3$	$32 = 2^5$	$57 = 3 \cdot 19$	$82 = 2 \cdot 41$
$9 = 3^2$	$33 = 3 \cdot 11$	$58 = 2 \cdot 29$	$83 = 83$
$10 = 2 \cdot 5$	$34 = 2 \cdot 17$	$59 = 59$	$84 = 2^2 \cdot 3 \cdot 7$
$11 = 11$	$35 = 5 \cdot 7$	$60 = 2^2 \cdot 3 \cdot 5$	$85 = 5 \cdot 17$
$12 = 2^2 \cdot 3$	$36 = 2^2 \cdot 3^2$	$61 = 61$	$86 = 2 \cdot 43$
$13 = 13$	$37 = 37$	$62 = 2 \cdot 31$	$87 = 3 \cdot 29$
$14 = 2 \cdot 7$	$38 = 2 \cdot 19$	$63 = 3^2 \cdot 7$	$88 = 2^3 \cdot 11$
$15 = 3 \cdot 5$	$39 = 3 \cdot 13$	$64 = 2^6$	$89 = 89$
$16 = 2^4$	$40 = 2^3 \cdot 5$	$65 = 5 \cdot 13$	$90 = 2 \cdot 3^2 \cdot 5$
$17 = 17$	$41 = 41$	$66 = 2 \cdot 3 \cdot 11$	$91 = 7 \cdot 13$
$18 = 2 \cdot 3^2$	$42 = 2 \cdot 3 \cdot 7$	$67 = 67$	$92 = 2^2 \cdot 23$
$19 = 19$	$43 = 43$	$68 = 2^2 \cdot 17$	$93 = 3 \cdot 31$
$20 = 2^2 \cdot 5$	$44 = 2^2 \cdot 11$	$69 = 3 \cdot 23$	$94 = 2 \cdot 47$
$21 = 3 \cdot 7$	$45 = 3^2 \cdot 5$	$70 = 2 \cdot 5 \cdot 7$	$95 = 5 \cdot 19$
$22 = 2 \cdot 11$	$46 = 2 \cdot 23$	$71 = 71$	$96 = 2^5 \cdot 3$
$23 = 23$	$47 = 47$	$72 = 2^3 \cdot 3^2$	$97 = 97$
$24 = 2^3 \cdot 3$	$48 = 2^4 \cdot 3$	$73 = 73$	$98 = 2 \cdot 7^2$
$25 = 5^2$	$49 = 7^2$	$74 = 2 \cdot 37$	$99 = 3^2 \cdot 11$
	$50 = 2 \cdot 5^2$	$75 = 3 \cdot 5^2$	$100 = 2^2 \cdot 5^2$